A History of Musgrove Military Hospital During World War II
and
The 67th General Hospital

Published by
The Rocket Publishing Co. Ltd.
Taunton, Somerset, England

ISBN 978-1-899995-29-5

Printed July 2010 in Great Britain by
Colourtone (Taunton) Ltd

Originally published - January 2008
in the United States of America
as

The Cactus and the Pine

By
Sidney A. Smith, M.D.

Lost Creek Publishing
2526 Pilgrim Estates Drive
Texas City
Texas 77590

The following pages are a copy of the original book published in the U.S.A. in 2008.
Consent has been obtained from the author for its reproduction.
Following the wish of the author all net profits will be donated to Musgrove Park Hospital via The Rotary Clubs of Taunton and Taunton Vale together with The League of Friends based at Musgrove Park Hospital

The Cactus and the Pine

A History of the 67th General Hospital
and
Musgrove Military Hospital
During World War II

By

Sidney A. Smith, M.D.

Edited by Ted Benedict, PhD

Lost Creek Publishing

The Cactus and the Pine

A History of the 67th General Hospital
And
Musgrove Military Hospital During World War II

Inquiries should be addressed to:
Lost Creek Publishing
2526 Pilgrim Estates Drive
Texas City, Texas 77590
WWW.LostCreekPublishing.com

ISBN 13 978-0-9814716-0-0
ISBN 10 0-9814716-0-9

Library of Congress Control Number: 2008920307

First Edition: January, 2008

The information in this book is true to the best of our knowledge. The author and publisher disclaim any liability in connection with the use of this material.

Printed in the United States of America
By
Instant Publisher

Dedication

I dedicate this book to my parents, Richard, who served his country as a member of the 67th General Hospital, and Bessie Smith, who both encouraged me in every way, my wife, Bonnie, whose encouragement, patience and optimism provided an impetus for continuing the project and the men and women of the 67th General Hospital, who gave a part of their life to perform such a critical function in the war effort.

Author's Note and Acknowledgement

Everything has a history, but when I began looking, I could not find anything written about the 67th General Hospital. My interest in the history of the 67th General Hospital began five or six years ago as I started to catalog some of my father's papers and found his draft notices and discharge papers, but nothing about his military unit. As a child I was fascinated by the postcards, photographs, English shillings and large English pence coins and various items which had come from a foreign place and were Dad's souvenirs of his time in England. Even the container holding these items seemed foreign-an x-ray film box. I occasionally would sneak a look at the V-mail letters my mother had collected from that time she and my father were apart for more than three years immediately following their marriage in January, 1942.

I knew that my father was a medic in a hospital in England, I knew that he was proficient in first aid and had a better than working knowledge of medical subjects, but his nature was to keep most things to himself and my knowledge of what he had done and experienced at the hospital was lacking. My mother always had a desire to see where my father had been stationed during that traumatic gap in her life. He was absent during the birth of their first child, which did not survive the labor, and she sat at home waiting for my Dad's uncertain return, looking forward to his letters. My father died in 1969, as I was starting my second year of medical school, closing the door to any opportunity that I might have had to learn more from him. I had the ability and took the time in 1980, to travel with Mom to tour England, and we visited the site of the hospital where Dad had been stationed in Taunton. An active hospital remained on the site and many of the old Nissen huts were still standing at that time. As we walked among them Mom was uncharacteristically quiet and after about fifteen minutes there, she stated "I've seen enough." My interest about the hospital was low at that time and I was ready to move on and see other parts of England.

As I organized the scattered records of my Father's life, I tried to find more information about the 67th General Hospital, and turned to the Internet. My first contact came about when I found a reference to Raymond Bungard, who was featured in his school's (Loma Linda) Alumni section on their web site. I obtained his address through the school with his permission and started a long-term correspondence with him. He in turn, gave me the name of Ted Benedict, a fellow soldier in the 67th. Both men were photographers for the Unit and after I had gained their confidence, they shared their experiences and thousands of photographs that they had taken. I owe a special thanks to Ted Benedict who volunteered to edit what I felt was a finished product and made many helpful suggestions.

A Red Cross web site directed me to Betsy Larson Crumrine, who had been a Red Cross worker at the 67th General Hospital and who has been an inspiration and a source of motivation as I have worked on the book, with almost biweekly telephone calls to inquire about "how I was coming along with the book." Through Betsy, I met Mildred Butler, RN, the Assistant Director of Nursing of the 67th General Hospital, and a former captain of the Army Nurse Corps (ANC). I had the privilege to meet and visit with both Betsy and Mildred in the summer of 2005, in Mildred Butler's home and enjoy its gorgeous setting along the shores of the Bay of Fundy in St. George, New Brunswick, Canada. Mildred referred me to a former nurse, now Mrs. Ruth Fairbanks Stewart and to Lt. Bob Walker, a former Quartermaster. After his death, his widow, Lucille Walker provided photographs which are included in the book.

Further internet searches turned up Doctor Eugene McManamy, a surgeon in the Unit. A link led me to Dr. Joe Braly, whose stepfather was a surgical technician in the operating room at the 67th General Hospital who deserves a special acknowledgement for his interest and enthusiasm about the history of the

67th General Hospital. Dr. Braly met me in San Angelo, Texas, and we spent two days visiting with and interviewing Joe Bullock, a First Sergeant of the 67th General Hospital. Dr. Braly and I traveled together in 2004, to visit Taunton and Musgrove Hospital where we toured the Administration Building of the 67th General Hospital, now called the "Old Building". We were only able to find one Nissen hut still standing.We visited with a current employee of the hospital, Jenni Clark and with one of the hospital volunteers, Ken White, who took us in their vehicles to tour some of the nearby countryside, a museum and old airport where Joe Kennedy took off on his final flight. While we were in Taunton, we had coffee with Betty Wells, a secretary for the Red Cross in the Unit, and with Bobbie Burns, a secretary in the kitchen at the unit. Mrs.Wells' name had been given to me by Betsy Crumrine, who had remained in contact with her since the war.

I was able to locate Carol Tettter, the daughter of a member of the 67th General Hospital, Vernard Dubois, a bunkmate of my father and whose name my father had written on his boarding pass, when he came home on the Queen Mary. Dr. Alvin H. Morrison, son of Alvin A. Morrison, M.D. was contacted, with the assistance of the Maine Medical Center Archives, and added some reminiscences of his father's service with the Unit. Dr. Braly and I have found numerous descendants of members of the 67th Hospital and all have helped this history in some fashion.

Mary Bird overheard our inquiries at the library at Taunton, and took time to give us a tour of Bishop's Lydeard, Whiskey Lane and the hospital site at Sandhill. Mac Hawkins, an author who lived in the Taunton area, took time to invite us to his home and shared helpful information, autographed and gave us one of his books, which proved relative to my research. The librarian and his assistant, David Bromwich and Christina at the Somerset Studies Library in Taunton, were most helpful, and provided relevant material found in their archives. Dr. John Morgan-Guy, an author of a book about another hospital in Taunton, provided me with information which assisted me in my research. Bill Keitch of Taunton, an English veteran of the Normandy invasion, provided me with blue prints of the original Musgrove Hospital and many colorful conversations.

The Archives at the Maine Medical Center, the Archives in Somerset and the National Archives in Washington, D.C. were all helpful in finding and sharing their materials for the book.

This book could have not been written without the help of the many people mentioned above, many of whom shared my passion and made it their own. The interest and help given me on the research for the book have spurred my own efforts. I fully believe that the drive to finish the book came in part from a desire not to disappoint the people who had believed in me enough to share a part of their lives. I have learned about the system of military medicine during World War II, the character of the people who made it work and about myself as well. History has no true beginning and has no real end. History continues as the residue of life, and truly the history of the 67th General Hospital, with its subtle effects on the people who came after it, cannot truly ever be finished. I simply had to draw a line in the sand. For many reasons, I am proud to say that the book is finished and I hope you enjoy it.

Sidney A. Smith, M.D.

The Cactus and the Pine

A History of the 67th General Hospital
And
Musgrove Military Hospital
During World War II

Table of Contents

From Left, Betsy Larson Crumrine, the Author, Mildred Butler on Mildred Butler's Home on the Bay of Fundy. The Tide Is Out. Photograph in Collection of Author.

From the Left: Dr. Joe Braly, the Author, Janice Bullock and Joe Bullock in San Angelo, Texas. Photograph in Collection of the Author

Chapter 1
How We Got Into This Mess

For much of 1941, the United States was officially neutral in the conflict that was raging in Europe, which became known as World War II. The men who would serve in the 67th General Hospital were, for the most part, living ordinary lives. The Depression still gripped the country and the conditions which inspired the *The Grapes of Wrath* were still real for most of these men. Richard Smith left his team of horses and small share-cropper farm in Oklahoma, and moved to Nazareth, Texas, where he drove a tractor and plowed long straight lines in the level land of the Texas plains where the towns of Levelland and Plainview are appropriately named. Before that, he rode the rails to California, where he obtained his Social Security card and joined the other Okies trying to survive the effects of the Oklahoma Dust Bowl. Ted Benedict was attending college in California, and Raymond Bungard was felling gigantic trees in the Pacific Northwest, as history marched on.

Few understood the events which were driving the United States to war. Many of the men and women who were to form the Detachment Medical of the 67th General Hospital most likely did not. The doctors and nurses, who would later be the professional component of the hospital, might have had more concerns since circumstances drove the renewal of an Affiliated Unit agreement with the Maine General Hospital and the War Department. It took a mere eleven months to draft, train and mobilize the Detachment Medical of the 67th General Hospital following the attack by the Japanese on Pearl Harbor and the entry of the United States into the war. The events leading up to this mobilization and the performance of the 67th General Hospital are the subject of this and subsequent chapters.

Walking the Neutrality Fence

Although the official position on the war was neutrality, the United States was not asleep. Discussions were held between British Prime Minister Winston Churchill and U.S. President Franklin D. Roosevelt. In 1940, the U.S. sent military advisors to their embassies in Europe. The advisors to Britain reported that the British would win the Battle of Britain against the Luftwaffe and recommended that the United States incorporate the tactics and equipment of the Royal Air Force into the U.S. Army Air Force. Talks were begun between American and British military officers about specifics of joint operations in case the United States should enter the war. One of the agreements was that in case of involvement of the United States in the war, the first priority would be the defeat of Germany, before concerted efforts would be made on other fronts. Military missions were exchanged between the two countries and a Special Observer Group was established in London.

The military mission was organized along military lines despite the fact that the participants wore civilian clothes and to outside observers appeared to be part of the U.S. Embassy in London. One of the first responsibilities was the preparation for the occupation of Iceland by

American troops in an agreement, made with President Roosevelt, to provide protection for that country.

Iceland had been occupied by Britain earlier in the war and the United States agreed to take over the responsibility of protecting Iceland after the British troops withdrew. Iceland was in a strategic location to control communication and protect North Atlantic shipping lanes. On 7 July 1941, a force of 4,000 marines from the 1st Provisional Brigade landed in Iceland, at Reykjavik. In August, 2,200 men of the 33rd Pursuit Squadron of the Air Force, along with their planes arrived. Army ground troops began to arrive in September, with 5,000 men of the 10th Infantry Regiment along with the 46th Field Artillery Battalion, which arrived as an advance attachment of the 5th Division. The Marine detachment departed in January of 1942, as more Army troops arrived.

As the American troops arrived, the British forces which had been defending the island, departed in staggered embarkation. American planes, including P-40's and flying boats, were flown from Iceland, and began to participate in the protection of convoys. American destroyers based in Iceland, also took part. (Some of the first patients treated at Musgrove Military Hospital by the 67th General Hospital were soldiers who were inherited when the 67th assumed control of the hospital. These soldiers had become infected with hepatitis while in Iceland.)

The agreements made during the combined talks between American and British military officers called for four separate forces to be established in the United Kingdom, prior to any American involvement. Firstly, a bomber force of 36,000 men, 7,500 men for the British Southeastern Command area, a Northern Ireland force of 30,000 and 13,500 men to be stationed in Scotland. Most of the men were to be utilized in the defense of naval and air bases to be used by American units. The American military mission in London, was given responsibility for the construction of naval bases in Northern Ireland and Scotland. Labor from the USA, and local unskilled labor were to do the construction and the first American technicians arrived in June of 1941, consisting of 350 men. To preserve the façade of neutrality, the British Foreign Office admitted that American workers were in Ulster, but stated that they had exercised their legal right to become employees of the British Government. Therefore, technically, American neutrality was maintained despite the fact that Americans were building bases using American money for eventual American use.

Eight airfields, under construction in the fall of 1941, were selected for the use of the first bomber units, and were located in the Huntingdon area, sixty-five miles north of London. On 1 July 1941, a B-17 arrived in the United Kingdom, by air. This was the first of many which would follow.

In 1941, an estimated 10,000 American volunteers were serving in British forces, primarily the RAF. In addition, the Americans assisted the British in their war effort by training English pilots in the United States.

The Neutrality Acts were changed on 4 November, by the United States, which permitted nations to purchase materials from companies in the United States, but required them to provide their own ships to transport the goods back to their countries. Only the British and the French were able to take advantage of this change in law due to their control of the high seas. Germany ordered that all ships flying the French or British flags were to be sunk and began the mining of British shipping lanes and ports.

Out in the Open: America Joins the War

The Japanese, using their Imperial Fleet and 184 carrier-based aircraft, launched a surprise attack on the naval base at Pearl Harbor, Island of Oahu, Hawaii, on 7 December 1941, at 0755 Hours. The sky over Pearl Harbor was clear and ships along Battleship Row were lined up and offered an inviting target for the attacking planes. A second wave of mostly torpedo bombers followed. After the fighters and torpedo planes had done their damage, 2,403 Americans were left dead and more than 1,100 were injured. The Battleship Oklahoma capsized and the Battleship Arizona took a bomb to its magazine which exploded and killed 1,177 of the total dead. Three other battleships were also sunk and the three remaining battleships were hit during the attack. Three carriers, which were not in port at the time of the attack, were the only operable major US ships remaining in the Pacific following the attack.

President Franklin Delano Roosevelt, in an address to Congress, 8 December 1941, asking for a declaration of war, made the following statement:

> "Yesterday, December 7, 1941 -- a date which will live in infamy -- the United States of America was suddenly and deliberately attacked by naval and air forces of the Empire of Japan…I believe I interpret the will of the Congress and of the people when I assert that we will not only defend ourselves to the uttermost but will make very certain that this form of treachery shall never endanger us again.
>
> Hostilities exist. There is no blinking at the fact that our people, our territory and our interests are in grave danger.
>
> With confidence in our armed forces -- with the unbounded determination of our people -- we will gain the inevitable triumph -- so help us God.
>
> I ask that the Congress declare that since the unprovoked and dastardly attack by Japan on Sunday, December seventh, a state of war has existed between the United States and the Japanese Empire."

Congress agreed and the United States was at that moment formally committed to a role in the Second World War. The declaration did not call for war on Germany, but on 11 December,

Hitler declared war on the United States, and the United States immediately declared war on Germany and Italy. The United States was firmly engaged in the conflict.

On 8 January 1942, the War Department authorized the activation of the United States Army Forces in the British Isles (USAFBI). Eventually USAFBI grew into the European Theater Operations United States Army (ETOUSA). The transformation occurred on 8 June 1942, and General Chaney was placed in command. The Commanding General was charged with the:

> "tactical, strategical, territorial, and administrative duties of a theatre Commander. He was to exercise planning and operational control over all U.S. forces assigned to the theater, including naval. He was given the mission 'to prepare for and carry on military operations in the European Theater against the Axis Powers and their allies, under strategical directives of the combined U.S.-British Chiefs of Staff…' "

At the time of the formation of ETOUSA, there were only 35,668 American troops in the British Isles of which 32,202 were the Northern Ireland contingent.

Bolero and Torch

General George Marshall and Harry L. Hopkins, confidential adviser to President Roosevelt, traveled to London, to meet with Prime Minister Churchill and the British Chiefs of Staff in April of 1942. This conference was held to discuss tentative plans for a cross-Channel invasion of Europe. At the time, the Russians were sustaining losses and retreating against the German assaults. The assault was intended to relieve pressure against the Russians and prevent their total defeat. The code name *Roundup* was given to a cross-Channel assault tentatively scheduled for the middle of 1943. Another operation, code name *Sledgehammer*, was planned as an emergency operation against the French coast in the fall of 1942, if the situation in the East worsened and the Russians were on the verge of capitulation.

At the meeting, a plan put forward by the American War Department was accepted and given the Code name *Bolero*. Bolero called for a build-up of American forces in Britain for the purpose of an eventual invasion across the English Channel into German-held Europe. The War Department, in a major reorganization, organized the forces in the United Kingdom to facilitate this operation. The U.S. forces were to be divided into three co-ordinate commands under the ETOUSA: the Army Ground Force, the Army Air Force and for services, the Services of Supply **(SOS)**. This was the command in which the 67th General Hospital was to serve, and they wore a unique shoulder patch to identify their command.

Patient Receiving Care from a Member of the 67th General Hospital. Notice Services of Supply Patch.
Photograph by and Courtesy of Raymond Bungard

This paralleled the organization in the War Department in the United States (to be known as the Zone of the Interior). The SOS was responsible primarily for the logistics of operations. Major General John C.H. Lee was placed in charge of the SOS in May of 1942. Doctors were not excited by this organization since it placed the Surgeon General under the Services of Supply and eliminated direct access to the Commander-in-Chief.

Marshall's plan for Bolero called for the build-up of U.S. forces to one million men for a proposed invasion of the Continent on 1 April 1943. Shortly after Bolero was proposed and accepted, Churchill began to voice doubts about the feasibility of an invasion of the continent at that time, and raised as an alternative an attack in North Africa. General Marshall felt that there was a need for an attack by the Allies to take pressure off the Russians. General Marshall and Admiral King lobbied for decisive action in the Pacific should the plans for Bolero be abandoned. The British took the position that they were not in a position to make a cross-Channel invasion in 1943, due to other commitments. President Roosevelt would not consider the plan to concentrate on the Pacific, and sided with Churchill for the Allied invasion of North Africa. The invasion of North Africa was given the code name of *Torch.*

Torch

On 11 June 1942, General Dwight D. Eisenhower was chosen as Commanding General, ETOUSA, and received orders on 17 June, relieving him of his responsibilities in the War Department. On 24 June 1942, he assumed command in England, and was placed in command of Torch.

Due to the preparation for Torch, buildup for Bolero came to a standstill. The Eighth Air Force, which had been deployed to fly against Germany, was diverted to the Mediterranean and previous plans to attack Europe were abandoned temporarily.

By June of 1942, U.S. troop strength in Britain stood at 54,845 men. In July, the decision was made to proceed with Operation Torch and the invasion of North Africa, putting the buildup of troops and supplies for Bolero on hold. There were some disasters occurring at that time which gave impetus to Torch. On 13 June, German tank forces under Rommel won a large tank battle. Additionally, on 29 June, Tobruk fell. Continued success by Rommel and his Afrika Korps could have meant a complete collapse in the Middle East, the loss of the Suez Canal and the loss of the oil supply in the vicinity of Abadan. (3) Good news came in the form of American victories in the Battle of the Coral Sea, Midway and the first 1,000 plane raid by the RAF on Cologne. Other disasters added to those in North Africa including the fall of Sevastopol to the Germans and other actions favoring the Germans in Russia. The heaviest losses of the war to Allied shipping occurred about that time, with 400,000 tons lost in one week alone.

With the decision to pursue Operation Torch, the emphasis at ETOUSA was transferred from operations against the Continent to an invasion of North Africa. This, everyone agreed, would further postpone Operation Roundup, as the proposed invasion of the European Continent was then termed, well beyond the planned date in 1943. By October, 1942, there were 228,000 American soldiers in Great Britain, and by the end of October, 1942, movement of troops to North Africa began.

Torch eventually necessitated the withdrawal of more than 150,000 American troops by the end of February, 1943, leaving only 104,510 in Great Britain. Most of this force earmarked for Torch consisted of the 1st Armored Division and the 1st and 34th Infantry Division, which were already in England. By the end of December, 1942, when the 67th General Hospital arrived, there were 134,808 American soldiers in Great Britain.

Torch called for:

> "landing in three areas on the North African coast. A Western Task Force, composed entirely of American ground, naval, and air forces and coming directly from the United States, was to land in the vicinity of Casablanca on the Atlantic coast of Morocco. A Center Task Force, also American, but sailing from the United Kingdom with British

naval support, was to land at Oran. An Eastern Assault Force, predominantly British but containing some American troops and escorted by the Royal Navy, was to land at Algiers."

Oran, the second largest port in Algeria, lies on the Mediterranean Sea about midway between Tangier (Morocco) and Algiers, at the point where Algeria is closest to Spain. Vichy France, which controlled Morocco and Algeria, anchored the major part of the French fleet at Mers el-Kebir, a city adjacent to Oran, following the armistice with Germany, in June of 1940. In July of 1940, a British naval force destroyed the majority of the Vichy French fleet to prevent its falling into German hands. (5) Negotiations were carried out and feelers were put out to Vichy French leaders in an effort to avoid French resistance against the invasion forces. These were not successful.

The initial landing occurred on 8 November 1942, at 0100 and met stiff resistance from the Vichy French who decided to resist the landing. French shore batteries caused significant damage to ships and landing troops until they were finally stilled. Many things went wrong either due to inexperience or to bad luck. Tanks which were landed became stuck in the sand. Landing craft which had not been used before were swamped by waves. There was a lack of co-ordination and amateurishness, but despite it all, the landing was eventually successful. On 10 November 1942, Oran was captured by American forces (3), and the major objectives, the ports in Northern Africa and the airfields, were under Allied hands in the first 48 hours of hostilities. (Some of the troops injured in this landing, including those of the British allies, were returned to England and the first combat patient treated by the 67th General Hospital came from the hostilities at Oran.)

Operation Torch proved to be a good decision. The Germans were forced to expend large amounts of materiel and men. The North African campaign accounted for 349,206 Italian and German troops killed or captured with 200,000 tons of materiel captured or destroyed. (3)

The experience from the North African invasion served the United States well. A serendipity of the diversion of forces to Torch and the postponement of the Continent invasion was that new doctrines, such as how to waterproof supplies, how to enter and leave assault boats and set up their stations to manage evacuations were learned in battle and the new ideas learned in battle were passed on to units in training. (4) Leaders were trained in the lessons learned in the invasion of North Africa. Mr. Hanson Baldwin, a New York Times military commentator, stated that North Africa was "a training and testing ground, a college on the conduct of war by the Allies, a dress rehearsal for the far larger and more difficult operations...that are still to come." (1)

Bolero Resumes

Following the invasion of North Africa, the American Chiefs of Staff wished to press on with the invasion of the Continent but the British Staff did not feel that the forces necessary to make a successful cross-Channel invasion would be available until 1944. These views were presented to President Roosevelt and Mr. Churchill meeting at Casablanca, in January, 1943, and the result was plans for the invasion of Sicily. Also decided at that meeting was the formation of

COSSAC (Chiefs of Staff Supreme Allied Commander) which was to begin planning for the cross-Channel invasion.

To carry out the Bolero plan, it had been estimated that approximately thirty U.S. Divisions would be needed, totaling one million men. To reach this goal in any reasonable amount of time it became necessary to begin moving U.S air and ground forces on every available ship to England. Committees were formed in Washington and London to co-ordinate the logistic nightmares that would be faced. These committees were called the Bolero Combined Committee. Detailed planning was underway in May of 1942, to receive the Bolero forces. To carry out Bolero, decisions regarding the number of troops needed, their composition, the priority in which units would be shipped to England, their shipping schedule and preparation for reception and accommodation facilities there, had to be made.

Planners, while working on troop composition, revealed that only 11.8 percent of U.S. troops in 1942, were service troops, which was inadequate based on previous experience in World War I when 34 percent were service troops. Planners allotted 25 percent of the troops for service. General priorities were established for movement of American units to the United Kingdom. Air units would be shipped first followed by essential SOS (Services of Supply) units, then ground forces and finally additional service units.

Shipping proved to be the biggest problem of all. U.S. shipping was limited and other needs had to be met including the need to move U.S. troops to the Southwest Pacific. The Bolero Combined Committee of Washington notified the London committee in May, 1942, that no more than 832,000 troops could be transported by 1 April 1943. This was 250,000 men short of the proposed target. The men were available but transport did not exist to move them in an expedient manner.

The British offered the use of the Queen Mary, the Queen Elizabeth and part-time use of other ships including the Aquitania, beginning in August. Due to their availability, scheduling was changed to allow the transport of 150,000 troops to the United Kingdom by 1 September 1942.

Planners on the Bolero Combined Committee decided that the Southern Command would house American troops by simultaneously withdrawing British troops and utilizing their facilities, thus reducing the amount of construction that would be needed. Combat areas would be organized into divisional areas of 25,000 men each and corps areas of 15,000 men with Services of Supply troops to be accommodated in depots, ports and in other major installations. A tentative selection was made to use Clifton College, Bristol, as the most suitable location for an Army headquarters, and Cheltenham, ninety miles northwest of London. The Southern Base section of the SOS was under the command of Colonel C.O. Thrasher, with headquarters at Wilton, near Salisbury. "The Southern Base Section eventually became the great concentration and marshaling area for the ground forces and was the springboard for the cross-Channel operation."(1)

Part of the function of the Services of Supply was the administration of hospitals. Hospital construction was planned in two phases. In the build-up phase, hospitals would have to keep up with normal incidence of sickness and would have to maintain a growth rate proportional to the number of new troops arriving. The number of beds in this phase was placed at 3 per cent of the total force. An additional allowance was made for colored troops due to a higher rate of illness. Bolero requirements were placed at 40,240 beds. Requirement for the invasion phase was estimated at ten per cent of the force or a total of 90,810 beds once operations began. This was 50,570 beds more than the Bolero phase required. One source stated that 94,000 beds would be needed. (3)

Troop flow to Great Britain slowed during the build-up in North Africa. The average flow of troops in the months of February, March and April of 1943 averaged less than 1600 monthly. The rebuilding of forces in Great Britain resumed in May.

By May of 1942, five hospitals with a capacity of 2,200 beds had been arranged from the British War Office and the Ministry of Health. Additionally, arrangements were made for the transfer to the Americans of certain British military hospitals, and several hospitals which had been constructed to prepare for the Nazi air blitz. New construction would be needed to meet the anticipated need for hospital beds and as a rough guide, it was planned to place one 750 bed hospital in each divisional area of 25,000 men. By July, 1942, orders had been given for the construction of two 1,000 bed Nissen hut hospitals and eleven 750 bed Nissen hospitals, as well as the expansion of some existing hospitals. Due to the need and high cost required, it was decided to convert military camps, abandoned when the invasion began, into hospital facilities with certain additions such as operating rooms, clinics and laboratories. Camps which had not yet been built were laid out with this conversion plan in mind. Thus, 1250 man camps would become 750 bed hospitals. To make up any deficit, ten 1,000 bed Nissen hut hospitals were planned.

By the end of 1942, American hospital facilities consisted of only 4 General Hospitals, 4 Station Hospitals and one Evacuation Hospital operating in Great Britain, with a total bed capacity of 5,000, which was of concern since the plan was to receive some of the casualties from North Africa and Operation Torch. The 67th General Hospital, organized and trained to be part of Bolero was in place in Musgrove Military Hospital, Taunton, Somerset, England to do their share and their story begins.

References

(1) *The United States Army and World War II.* The United States Army Center of Military History.

(2) Brown, Donald. *Somerset v Hitler: Secret Operations in the Mendips 1939-1945.* Newbury, Berkshire: Countryside Books. 2001.

(3) *Biennial Reports of the Chief of Staff of the United States Army to the Secretary of War 1 July 1939-30 June 1945.* Washington, D.C.: Center of Military History, United States Army, 1996.

(4) Cowdrey, Albert E. *Fighting for Life.* The Free Press, 1994.

(5) "Oran." *Encyclopedia Britannica Library.*

(6) "Organizational History of the 180th Station Hospital, U.S. Army, 18 March 1942 to 30 April 1944." National Archives.

(7) Personal Communication with Ted Benedict.

Chapter 2
Origins of the 67th General Hospital
The Doctors and Nurses

Maine General Hospital, now renamed Maine Medical Center, is located in Portland, Maine, and at the beginning of World War II, was an outstanding hospital with a proud reputation and history. It had numerous training programs and many of their graduates provided service to their country during World War II.

On 28 December 1923, a letter was received from the office of the Surgeon General addressed to the Superintendent of the Maine General Hospital, Portland, Maine, suggesting that the hospital sponsor an affiliated unit. (2) A committee was appointed for the purpose of addressing the "organization of a War Unit", and it met on 25 February 1924. Present were Doctors Milliken, Bradford, Tobie, Davis, Thompson, Robinson, Cragin, Moulton, Moore, Pudor, Swift, Mortimer Warren, Haney, Bickmore and Tibbetts. At that meeting, it was immediately suggested that a smaller ad hoc committee composed of ex-servicemen be named with Dr. Moore as the Chairman. Dr. Moore was selected because of his previous experience in "organizing similar bodies of men." (Doctor Roland Moore served in World War I, and for more than a year was Assistant Division Surgeon of the 76th Division and Adjutant of the Hospital Center at Commercy, France. After the Armistice, he was an officer of the American Military Commission to Berlin. (12))

The responsibility of this ad hoc committee was to study the matter, formulate opinions and transmit these to the Board of Directors of the hospital. Upon the recommendation of the larger committee, originally named to study the hospital's study of an affiliated unit, Dr. Roland B. Moore named four other doctors to the ad hoc committee, who had been recommended for the position by the larger committee--George A. Tibbetts, Charles H. Hunt, C.M. Robinson and Herbert E. Milliken. There is no indication that any of the doctors were ex-servicemen or had any previous military experience. (3)

On 24 April 1924, in response to the recommendation of the ad hoc committee chaired by Doctor Moore, the Board of Directors of the Maine General Hospital voted to approve "the formation by the hospital staff of a unit for service in case of a national emergency". On 25 April 1924, the hospital staff, at its regular meeting, voted to turn over organization of such a unit to Doctor Roland B. Moore as "Chairman of the Committee for the Organization of an Army Unit." (2, 4)

In May of 1925, an affiliated unit was authorized by the War Department and designated as the 67th General Hospital. At that time twenty-eight doctors of the hospital staff were commissioned in the Medical Reserve Corps to form the professional component of the Unit. Thomas J. Burrage was named the Commanding Officer and Dr. W. Bean Moulton the Adjutant. (11) This Unit was never activated and so far as is known none of those commissioned in it served any periods of active duty, and for the most part allowed their commissions to lapse at the end of the five year period. A few, including Colonel Thomas J. Burrage, who was designated as

Commanding Officer, retained their commissions in the Reserve Corps but never did any duty in connection with the hospital as an organization. The affiliation with the War Department was apparently dropped sometime about the year 1930, although no official notice to that effect is known to have been received.

Following the breakout of war in Europe, in 1939, the War Department drew up a plan of mobilization which included Reserve Army General Hospitals. The mobilization of numbered General Hospitals followed the realization of the need for available mobile hospitals that could follow the Army to the field of battle. To help meet this need, a policy from World War I was re-implemented which allowed hospitals and medical schools to sponsor an affiliated reserve unit.

This plan was approved in August of 1939, and many large general hospitals across the country formed their own units. For example, the 20th General Hospital was staffed by the University of Pennsylvania and the 21st General Hospital was staffed by the Washington University and Barnes Hospital of St. Louis, Missouri, Medical Staff. Non-numbered Army General Hospitals such as Walter Reed were fixed in location and served to provide a high level of medical care in the United States, or as it was known during WWII, the Zone of the Interior.

On 16 May 1940, a letter was received from the Surgeon General's Office, U.S. Army, addressed to the Maine General Hospital, suggesting renewal of affiliation and re-establishment of the unit. By vote of the Board of Directors of the Hospital and after consultation with the hospital staff, it was agreed that the formation of such a unit would be attempted and Doctor Roland B. Moore, at that time President of the Medical Staff, was authorized to assume charge of the preliminary work. On 15 August 1940, the Board of Directors of the Maine General Hospital made formal application to the Surgeon General for the formation of an affiliated hospital unit recommending Doctor Moore as "Unit Director" and as Commanding Officer in case of mobilization.

During a regular monthly meeting of the Executive Staff on 30 August 1940, a motion was voted to authorize the Medical Defense Committee to send a questionnaire to members of the Staff regarding the formation of a hospital unit and to call a meeting of the General Staff for consideration when the answers were received. (5) Doctor Roland B. Moore made a report of the military questionnaire sent out to the General Staff as a result of the Executive Staff meeting. Dr. Moore then introduced Colonel Lelard O.C. Moore of the U.S.A. Medical Corp who spoke on the foundation of a hospital unit and a discussion followed. (6) Twenty-three applications for commission were submitted, all dated 7 October 1940.

Reflecting the attitude of the day, the Executive Committee of the Attending Staff instructed their Secretary to:

> "write a letter of the Commanding Office in charge of the Local Defense Units, as well as Surgeon in charge of United States Marine Hospital, extending an invitation to all

the medical staff to attend ward rounds, operation, clinics and other hospital functions which might be of interest of instruction to them". (7)

At the same meeting, the possible depletion of staff by military service and a need for a list of doctors who would carry on the work of the hospital was requested. (7)

On 3 March 1941, the Board of Directors of the Maine General Hospital received a letter from the Adjutant General advising that sponsorship of a General Hospital Unit had been approved by the Secretary of War and ordered that this hospital be organized as the 67th General Hospital. During March and April, 1941, the first commissions were granted in the Medical Reserve Corps, and Doctor Roland Moore, was designated as the Unit Director. During the next year many applications for commission were submitted through the Unit Director until the authorized number of medical officers had been acquired--all members of the Maine General Hospital Staff. Organizational meetings were held but no definite training program was instituted. Dr. Elton Blaisdell was the only original member of the Unit which had been formed in 1925. (11) In the meantime, applications for enrollment in the Army Nurse Corps were being initiated by Miss Irene Zwisler, who had been chosen by the Unit Director as prospective Chief Nurse of the Unit--all of the applicants were graduates of the Maine General Hospital or residents of the State of Maine. (2)

The 67th General Hospital was authorized by the War Department on 3 March 1941, for the reception and treatment of all classes of patients. (1) The Reserve Affiliated Unit which had existed at the Maine General Hospital shortly after World War I was reborn for a more pressing purpose. What must be kept in mind is that these doctors were volunteers in the sense that there was no doctor draft as such. Able-bodied men less than 28 years old, who happened to be doctors, could be drafted as regular soldiers and thus there was some subtle pressure to volunteer. The American Medical Association took the attitude that doctors should be patriotic and volunteer and during the war, at least 56,000 of them did so. The loss of doctors from communities was not proportional and left many communities without physician service and others with too much. The nurses were all volunteers as well and held what the Army called "Relative Rank" meaning that they did not get the same compensation or position in the command structure as did the regular officers but did have the status and wore the insignias that accompanied their rank. They, unlike their male counterparts, could not be drafted and their participation was completely altruistic. (16)

Responding to a letter from the author written in 2003, Dr Eugene McManamy stated that he was motivated to join because of "a patriotic urge to serve my country". He had received his medical training at McGill University in Montreal, Canada, and was a general surgeon, having received his training at Montreal General Hospital and the Mayo Clinic in Rochester, Minnesota. Other doctors in the Unit had similarly outstanding credentials.

The physician staff and the nursing staff came from various areas. The doctors, for the most part, came from the hospital staffs of the Maine General Hospital, of Portland Maine, the Central Maine General Hospital of Lewiston, Maine, the St. Mary's Hospital of Lewiston, Maine, and the Eastern Maine General Hospital in Bangor, Maine.

Nurses were also recruited from various Maine facilities. Mildred Butler, R.N., who rose to the rank of Captain before her discharge from the Army, and Assistant Director of Nurses before she left England, received a call from Colonel Roland Moore, asking her to join the Unit. She had been working as a private nurse for a surgeon who received orders to go on active duty in the Navy. Therefore, she had no other plans at the moment. Dr. Moore encouraged her to get a physical exam and the next thing she knew she was in the Army.

The Medical Staff voted on 31 July 1942, to send a letter to the Board of Directors to inform them of the inability of the Staff of the Maine General Hospital to staff most of the clinics at the Dispensary after the Hospital left on 1 September. (8) In consideration of their personal sacrifice, Board of Directors and the Medical Staff acted to preserve the privileges of the doctors leaving for military service by granting them a leave of absence from the Medical Staff and by agreeing to provide Blue Cross protection for one year for the members of the immediate families of the Active Staff who were serving with the Armed Forces. (9, 10)

Last Supper--Going to Texas

> "The Board of Directors of the Maine General Hospital cordially invite you to attend the Reception and Dinner to be given to the Members of General Hospital, Number 67 of Maine General Hospital (to be activated September 1, 1942) on Friday evening, August twenty-eighth. Reception 7 o'clock--Gold Room, Lafayette Hotel Dinner 7:30 O'clock--Mayfair Room." (14)

This invitation was received by the doctors and nurses who were officers in the soon-to-be-activated 67th General Hospital. At the dinner were Robert Braun, who served as toastmaster and the Honorable Ralph O. Brewster, United States Senator who addressed the gathering and the honored guests. Sitting at the head table were Senator Brewster, other honored guests and Irene L. Zwisler, Lieutenant, U.S. Army, in charge of the nursing contingent of the 67th General Hospital. (15)

Senator Ralph O. Brewster

Lt. Colonel Roland Moore and Lt. Irene L. Zwisler. The Photograph Was Taken at Maine General Hospital
Photograph courtesy Maine Medical Center

The invitation mentioned the members of the Board of Directors as well as the President of the Board and the officers. The officers, members and honorary members of the Women's Visiting Board were listed as well. Members of the Staff of Maine General Hospital who were already in active service in other units were added to the program. (15)

The menu consisted of honeydew melon au citron, celery hearts, Spanish olives, cream of Maine corn with croutons, roast half milk-fed chicken, cream giblet gravy, rissolee potato, new peas in butter, iceberg hearts with Russian dressing, chocolate royale, blueberry cake and black coffee. (15)

Enjoying the meal, listening to selections by the Schubert Instrumental Quartet, and ultimately being honored for their impending role in the largest conflict in history were the doctors and nurses of Maine General Hospital including their Unit Commander Lieutenant Colonel Roland B. Moore, Lieutenant Colonels Elton R. Blaisdell and Stephen A. Cobb, 13 Majors, 22 Captains, 13 First Lieutenants and 89 Second Lieutenants, listed below: (15)

Medical Officers and Nurses of 67th General Hospital Taken at Maine General Hospital, Portland, Maine.
Photograph Courtesy of Maine Medical Center, Portland, Maine

Medical Officers of the 67th General Hospital 28 August 1942
Photograph Taken at Maine General Hospital, Portland, Maine. From left to right:

First row: Major Philip H. McCrum, Major Charles W. Steele, Major Eaton S. Lothrup, Major Jack Spencer, Major Milton S. Thompson, Major Alvin A. Morrison, Lt. Colonel Elton R. Blaisdall, Lt. Colonel Roland B. Moore, Lt. Colonel Stephen A. Cobb, Major Carl E. Richards, Major Merrill S.F. Greene, Major William B. Jordan, Major Edward A. Greco, Major Wilfrid J. Comeau, Major Henry M. Tabachnick.

Second Row: Captain E. Allan McLean, Captain Homer F. McDavitt, Captain George C. Poore, Captain J. Rogbert Feeley, Captain Gordon H. Johnson, Captain Paul C. Marston, Captain Edward W. Holland, Captain Henry H. Grant, Captain Otis B. Tibbetts, Captain Parker Mann, Captain Gerald H. Donahue, Captain Eugene P. McManamy, Captain Bertrand A. Beliveau, Captain Joseph A. Villa, Captain Paul R. Chevalier, Captain Ralph E. Williams, Captain Alvin E. Ottum.

Third Row: First Lt. Walter G. Dixon, First Lt. Howard H. Milliken, First Lt. Franklin R. Smith, First Lt. Samuel M. Cope, Captain Maynard B. Colley, Second Lt. Leon C. Pullen, Jr., First Lt. Joseph G. Ham, First Lt. James H. Cunningham, First Lt. Wilfred A. Houle, First Lt. Harry E. Christensen, First Lt. C. Lawrence Holt, First Lt. J. Robert Downing and Captain James W. Reed.
Photograph Courtesy of the Maine Medical Center, Portland, Maine.

Medical Officers of the 67th General Hospital

(Doctors and Nurses)
At Time of Activation
Date of Activation 1 September 1942

Lieutenant Colonel Roland B. Moore

Lieutenant Colonel Elton R. Blaisdell

Lieutenant Colonel Stephen A. Cobb

Major Wilfrid J. Comeau
Major William V. Cox
Major Edward A. Greco
Major Merrill S.F. Greene
Major William B. Jordan
Major Eaton S. Lothrop
Major Philip H. McCrum
Major Alvin A. Morrison
Major Carl E. Richards
Major Jack Spencer
Major Charles W. Steele
Major Henry M. Tabachnick
Major Milton S. Thompson

Captain Bertrand A. Beliveau
Captain Paul R. Chevalier
Captain Gilbert Clapperton
Captain Maynard B. Colley
Captain Gerald H. Donahue
Captain Charles W.Eastman
Captain J. Robert Feeley
Captain Henry H. Grant
Captain Edwin W. Holland
Captain Albert C. Johnson
Captain Gordon N. Johnson
Captain Frederick C. Lord, Jr.
Captain Parker Mann
Captain Paul C. Marston
Captain Homer F. McDavitt
Captain E. Allen McLean
Captain Eugene McManamy
Captain Alvin E. Ottum
Captain George C. Poore
Captain James W. Reed
Captain Otis B. Tibbetts
Captain Joseph A. Villa
Captain Ralph E. Williams

1st Lt. Harry Christensen
1st Lt. Samuel M. Cope
1st Lt. James H. Cunningham
1st Lt. Walter G. Dixon
1st Lt. J. Robert Downing
1st Lt. Joseph G. Ham
1st Lt. C. Lawrence Holt
1st Lt. Wilfred A. Houle
1st Lt. John R. Merrick
1st Lt. Howard H. Milliken
1st Lt. Rosario A. Page
1st Lt. Franklin R. Smith
1st Lt. Irene L. Zwisler

2nd Lt. Leon C. Pullen, Jr.
2nd Lt. Elizabeth Alexander
2nd Lt. Edith Austin *
2nd Lt. Goldie E. Barton
2nd Lt. Ina Mae Beane *
2nd Lt. Olga Berryman
2nd Lt. Florence Blair *
2nd Lt. Elizabeth Blake
2nd Lt. Arneta Blanchard
2nd Lt. Barbara A. Bragdon *
2nd Lt. Gladys M. Breen
2nd Lt. Dorothy Briggs
2nd Lt. Mary Ann Burke
2nd Lt. Virginia M. Burnham
2nd Lt. Frances Burtt
2nd Lt. Mildred K. Butler
2nd Lt. Elva Carpenter
2nd Lt. Bertha L. Carter *
2nd Lt. Agnes Chapados *
2nd Lt. Margaret Chapman
2nd Lt. Vera A. Chenoweth
2nd Lt. Hazel M. Churchill
2nd Lt. Barbara Coll *
2nd Lt. Oleva Corey
2nd Lt. Helen D. Currie *
2nd Lt. Etta M. Currier
2nd Lt. Madelyn Cyr
2nd Lt. Marion A. Davis *
2nd Lt. Irene Desmond
2nd Lt. Helen Dudley
2nd Lt. Mary A. Dunn
2nd Lt. Adelaide M. Emery *
2nd Lt. Ruth Fairbanks
2nd Lt. Geneva Faulkner
2nd Lt. Marjorie French
2nd Lt. Priscilla French

2nd Lt. Ruth Gifford
2nd Lt. Mary G. Gordon *
2nd Lt. Ruth P. Haskell *
2nd Lt. Myrtle Housel *
2nd Lt. Emily Kismonak
2nd Lt. Ethel Gilbert
2nd Lt. Delores M. Graham
2nd Lt. Ethel Hemphill
2nd Lt. Beryl Jones
2nd Lt. Elva J. Laverty
2nd Lt. Methyl Gilman
2nd Lt. Reba Jo Green
2nd Lt. Eleanor L. Henry
2nd Lt. Mildred A. Judkins
2nd Lt. Madeline Le Blanc

2nd Lt. Louise G. Libby
2nd Lt. Martha Martel *
2nd Lt. Ruth A. McDonald
2nd Lt. Marie A. Murphy *
2nd Lt. Genevieve S. Robinson
2nd Lt. Evelyn E. Small
2nd Lt. Pauline Smith
2nd Lt. Vivian C. Tarbell
2nd Lt. Beatrice Tracy
2nd Lt. Viola Van Ornum *
2nd Lt. Eleanor L. Walker
2nd Lt. Helen G. Williams
2nd Lt. Mary G. Woods
2nd Lt. Beulah Mack *
2nd Lt. Annie M. Martin
2nd Lt. Edna L. McFarland
2nd Lt. Marjorie Nash
2nd Lt. Phyllis Rogers
2nd Lt. Ruth Small
2nd Lt Ruth Smith *
2nd Lt. Marion G. Timmons *
2nd Lt. Ina Tranton
2nd Lt. Priscilla Veilleux *
2nd Lt. Betty Wallace *
2nd Lt. Dorothy Willis
2nd Lt. Julia Zelek
2nd Lt. Effie MacLoud *
2nd Lt. Ada W. McConnell
2nd Lt. Hilda B. Morrill
2nd Lt. Carolyn Norton
2nd Lt. Pearl H. Shepardson
2nd Lt. Almeda F. Smith
2nd Lt. Elizabeth Swain
2nd Lt. Madeleine A. Tolman
2nd Lt. Barbara Ulrich
2nd Lt. Vina L. Vosmus
2nd Lt. Harriette Ward
2nd Lt. Eleanor F. Wood

Names marked with an asterisk * are those of nurses identified by Mildred Butler, who became the Assistant Head Nurse while Marjorie French was Chief Nurse. Ms. Butler stated with certainty that despite the program recognizing the named nurses as members of the 67th General Hospital contingent, they were not among the nurses who left for Fort Bliss, Texas, and subsequently were not among the cadre of nurses shipped to England. Her impression was that the nurses identified with an asterisk above were some who were interested in serving in the 67th General Hospital or were connected in some fashion with the Army post at Camp Devon, Massachusetts. (17)

The Maine members of the 67th General Hospital boarded the train on 1 September 1942, in Portland, Maine, which would take them to El Paso, Texas, and further training for their new adventure. (1)

References

(1) "Annual Report of the 67th General Hospital to the Chief Surgeon, SOS, ETOUSA, APO 887, U.S. Army." Dated 31 January 1944. National Archives.

(2) "Annual Report of the 67th General Hospital to the Chief Surgeon, SOS, ETOUSA." Dated 15 January 1943. Signed by Lt. Colonel R.B. Moore, M.C., Commanding. National Archives.

(3) "Medical Staff Minutes of Maine General Hospital for 25 February 1924." Courtesy Maine Medical Center Archives.

(4) "Medical Staff Minutes of Maine General Hospital for 25 April 1924." Courtesy Maine Medical Center Archives.

(5) "Executive Staff Minutes of Maine General Hospital and Medical Staff Minutes of Maine General Hospital for 30 August 1940." Courtesy Maine Medical Center Archives.

(6) "Medical Staff Minutes of Maine General Hospital for 20 September 1940." Courtesy Maine Medical Center Archives.

(7) "Executive Committee of the Attending Staff Minutes of Maine General Hospital for 27 December 1940." Courtesy Maine Medical Center Archives.

(8) "Medical Staff Minutes of Maine General Hospital for 31 July 1942." Courtesy Maine Medical Center Archives.

(9) "Letter to Stephen S. Brown, Director, Maine General Hospital from John F. Dana Secretary, Board of Directors." Dated 5 August 1952. Courtesy Maine Medical Center Archives.

(10) "Medical Staff Minutes of Maine General Hospital for 28 August 1942." Courtesy Maine Medical Center Archives.

(11) "The 67th General Hospital." By Dr. Maynard B. Colley, September, 1980. This was a descriptive booklet regarding the film about the 67th General Hospital narrated by Dr. Colley. Courtesy Maine Medical Center Archives.

(12) *Lewiston Journal; Magazine Section.* Saturday, October 25, 1969. Courtesy Betsy Larson Crumrine.

(13) www.mmc.org. Web site of Maine Medical Center, Portland, Maine.

(14) "Invitation to Testimonial Reception and Dinner for Members of General Hospital Number 67 given by the Board of Directors of the Maine General Hospital on 28 August 1942." Courtesy Maine Medical Center Archives.

(15) "Program for Testimonial Reception and Dinner for Members of General Hospital Number 67 Given by the Board of Directors of the Maine General Hospital on 28 August 1942." Courtesy Maine Medical Center Archives.

(16) Cowdrey, Albert E. *Fighting For Life.* The Free Press, 1994.

(17) Communication with Mildred Butler, R.N., Captain, Army Nurses Corps.

Chapter 3
History of the 51st General Hospital
Men Who Formed the Detachment Medical of the 67th General Hospital

A Radiogram (wireless telegraph) from the Third Army headquarters in San Antonio, Texas, activated the 51st General Hospital at Ft. Bliss, El Paso, Texas, on 16 May 1942. (2) The activation was confirmed by General Order 52 from the Headquarters, Third Army, Smith-Young Tower, San Antonio, Texas, dated 18 May 1942. This order was by command of Lieutenant General Krueger and was signed by Brigadier General Alfred M. Gruenther, General Staff Corps, Chief of Staff. (8)

A cadre of 25 enlisted men from the William Beaumont General Hospital, commanded by Lieutenant Norman Mitchell, M.C., arrived at Fort Bliss on the same day as the activation. An additional 100 enlisted men were received from the Reception Center of Camp Wolters, 1840 Service Unit. (9) (Camp Wolters was located four miles east of Mineral Wells, Texas. (1)) The men were quartered in tents and on cots on the parade ground of the post. One of the original cadre, then Staff Sergeant Joe Bullock, assigned as clerk to the First Sergeant's office, recalled 61 years after the fact that the reveille cannon was very close to the parade ground and on the first morning spent in the tents, the cannon marked the beginning of the day with a roar which could be heard all over the post. This close, sudden explosion startled Sergeant Andrew Hatton, who jumped up in alarm, fell back and broke his cot in the process. (4) The men were temporarily assigned to the First Medical Squadron, for training and administration, with Colonel L.K. Patterson, Commanding Officer of the First Medical Squadron, temporarily in command. (7)

Living in tents was a nuisance for only a short time. On 20 May, four days after the 51st General Hospital was activated, the men of the 51st General Hospital were assigned to seven two-story barrack buildings. In addition, they were assigned three mess halls, three administrative buildings, and three day-rooms. Soon, enough men arrived to fill up the seven barracks. Fifty enlisted men were received from the Reception Center at Ft. Logan, Colorado, 125 enlisted men from the Reception Center at Fort Sam Houston, in San Antonio, Texas, 125 men from the Reception Center at Fort Bliss, 2 men from the First Medical Squadron, Fort Bliss, 6 men who were attached for duty from the Cadre Replacement Center and 100 enlisted men from the Reception Center at Fort Sill, Lawton, Oklahoma. These additions and transfers brought the number of men on 23 May, to 533 enlisted men. (7, 9) Among them was Richard F. Smith, who wrote his wife on Sunday, 24 May 1942:

> "I landed here Saturday evening (Ft. Bliss) about 6 O'clock (from Ft. Sill, Oklahoma). We came by Ft. Worth, went through Waurika about 85 miles from Burneyville. I have had more experience this past week than I thought I would ever have. The shots I have had haven't been so bad. I was sick Thursday but I have felt real well every since. I have also

drilled about half a day and you should see me salute those officers ha ha. One old boy saluted with his left hand which should have been his right. We have good eats and can keep clean---I signed up for motorized div. which will be ambulance driving so on.

I am not assigned to anything so far I will have to get about six weeks Basic training before I am assigned to anything. I am going to dinner now. Here I am again we had corn on the cob, stewed chicken, cherry pie, celery, butter and light Bread." (3)

It didn't take long to discover his fate:

"This is another day just a little tired not as tired as I would be if I was working at home. We have been introduced to lots of things such as talks and new drills pretty good. I try and stay in the back lines some times. I will be in the medical care for certain God knows what part and I know I will git some over sea service. You understand I won't be in combat--I got my big foot locker today and also got my knee all skint up. I got tripped doing doubletime. I will hafta report to the Dr. in the morning at 6:15. We hafta drill at 6:20. The Dr. said he would keep me in until after drill hrs. -- the only nice guy I have run across here. A fellow has to take a lot he wouldn't take in civilian life but so much for this army life. I understand we will be hiking about 25 miles a day by the last of next week or that will be some days. My feet haven't bothered any at all since I have been here."

It was all new to Richard as his letters to his wife, Bessie, indicate:

May 25: "I think we will get $42---I have got to take a bath and get my laundry ready for tomorrow. I won't have time then. I haven't had any K.P. or guard duty so far but everyone has their turn at it I have got to memorize a lot of G duty stuff."

Richard had been drafted through the Selective Service Office in Nazareth, Texas. At the time he was driving a tractor on a large farm in West Texas. He had only been married since 19 January 1942, and his honeymoon was cut short by the government's need for men to fight the Axis forces. Richard had been given notice of selection under the Selective Training and Service Act of 1940, on the fourth of May, and told to report on 18 May 1942.

The 51st General Hospital acquired its separate headquarters on the twenty-second of May and the administrative responsibility held by the First Medical Squadron passed to the First Cavalry Division. Plans for basic training of the men were made. On 24 May 1942, Colonel James H. Gambrell, M.C., a prominent physician and surgeon of El Paso, assumed command of the 51st General Hospital. (10) Lt. C.V. Beinfohr, Lieutenant F.L. Goodwin and Lt. Kuzell from the First Cavalry Division were attached for special duty. There were four officers on the staff (The three above plus Lt. Mitchell). (7)

Their work was cut out for them. The men had been sent from the processing centers without being fully processed or equipped and had been in the Army for an average of only five days. Some of the men had various infirmities with 28 marked for limited duty, and fifteen of the men were said to be unable to speak English, although Sergeant Joe Bullock stated that to his knowledge, all of the men were able to speak English. (4, 5, 7) While at the post, the men would have had initial and sequential injections which would have included smallpox (one injection only), tetanus, typhoid, and possibly yellow fever and typhus.

Scenes from Fort Bliss, El Paso, Texas
Three Photographs Above Courtesy of Betsy Crumrine

Regular post life continued for the men. Richard Smith reported this regularly in his letters home:

May 27: "I haven't been off this post only to drill. We went off on a hike -- there were nearly 500. Some were on guard and KP. I guess my turn is coming. I guess you have had another letter from me by now and what do you think about my job? The only weapon I will carry will be a .45 caliber automatic pistol. We get lectures every day and some drilling. A lot of boys complain with their feet more than I do. I have made up my mind to make a good soldier. It's not as bad as I thought. For speaking about rain it won't rain any here until next fall. It sure is dry and hot, the temperature in here now is 90 degrees and it is about sundown.---I got me a GI hair cut today but didn't get a real short one I told the barber just where I could get by with it."

May 31: "Well we have had it pretty easy the last three days I guess on account of the shots. Lots of the old boys had to be carried off of the field I thought I was puny. I don't feel so hot at that. We don't even have roll call on Sunday, but I went down to the bulletin board so I will have to be on guard duty starting 5:00 P.M. for 24 hours, two on and four off. I have found one boy that I like very well to chum with. We went to the show together. His name is Smith too, Hubert. There will be 12 Smiths on duty at once.

Men of the 51st General Hospital on Hike
Photograph Courtesy of First Sgt. Joe Bullock

Men on Hike--Taking a Break. Franklin Mountains in Background
Two Photographs Above Courtesy First Sgt. Joe Bullock

Our sergeant sure is a nice fellow. I went walking around over the Ft. I seen some beautiful places---I like this branch of service more everyday they say that we will be behind the firing line as much as 200 miles sometimes. That sure does sound good to me. Knowing that I have to go anyway I would like for this to be over with soon."

June 2: "---this bunch of us here had a chance to sign up for the infantry in a mountain country but they didn't get a volunteer out of the five hundred and twenty eight of us. Well, darling I got that guard duty I was telling you about. I walked about twenty miles and was I tired. Every one complains about it so much for army life."

June 5: "---On top of all that I got my last typhoid shot yesterday. Sweet, I don't remember whether I told you about a fellow going over the hill that was in this div. Or not but he was caught two days after he left and done sentenced for twenty five years in Prison. He was a married man at that darling." (The Roster of the 51st General Hospital was changed on 6 July 1942, with one man changed from AWOL to Absent "Desertion". (9))

June 6: "Well we had inspection this morning and everything was OK. As clean as a pin. I also got my shelter half, mosquito net and pack equipment to make a full pack. I don't have overshoes or gas mask or helmet yet.

---I am learning more about drilling everyday. I didn't have to drill this morning and was I glad. I was helping cleanup so the sergeant told me to stay in and finish up. It's sure nasty outside. The wind is blowing a little more than usual this old dry dirt sure does blow."

June 9: "Well believe it or not I went to Sunday School and Church Sunday. I do wish so much you could have been with me all afternoon. I went and seen Gone With the Wind and did I like it but did I get tired sitting although we sure did have good seats and it was air conditioned.

---I will be on kitchen duty until I have to go starting in the morning at 5:00 A.M. Yes we have been on another hike today, about ten miles. We were packed up to just half-packed. We also had to pitch our tents while on our hike. Yes seems like the U.S. is doing very well but Sweetheart you probably know more about what is going on than us boys although we have newspapers but they don't talk it much seems like. You was asking about how we were treated. Well a fellow can make it lazy on his self or he can make it tough so far I haven't had any trouble with anyone."

June 10: " I sure have been working today K.P, I have put in fourteen hrs. washing vessels and my hands sure are tender. I have two more days of it

---I suppose I won't get to write you any more until Sat. as I won't be off till late about ten oclock. Today was payday. I got paid for eleven days and after my laundry and insurance was taken out I had $1.45 left. That sure is something isn't it?

--- The first lieutenant said that one more case of gonorrhea showed up we would be confined here for thirty days but if we can get our basic training maybe I can come to see you for a few days or you can come. I don't know what to tell you.

---I haven't been to town any more and I don't have any business down there from all account there sure is a bunch of sorry women down there surely must be. We had a little scrap here but I missed it. A colored boy and a M.P. I would liked to of seen it.

---its every thing but cool in this desert sand. Bet my bed is covered in sand now. No Darling I just can't imagine a fellow deserting. I had rather be here all my life than do that. I have been studying about trying to be a cook. I don't know for sure yet."

June 13: "Well we all had a chance to sign up for what we thought we would be best in. I am still holding out for mechanic work though most of the boys have done signed up for nurse and all that sort but I will get to sign up for mine next week. They will try us out and if we can make it that's where we will be put.

---Well I worked two days on K.P. and the work I did was washing cooking vessels for baking. They use big deep bread pans and for soups and other things like that. They use things looks like pressure cookers, 10 and 20 gallons. After the cook found out I couldn't eat any supper he wouldn't let me work. He said I had done a good job and if the high up didn't like about me gitting they could romp on him. He sure was nice about it in fact all these fellows are nice if you take interest in things. I'll make a soldier yet, what do you think? I might get to go to Alaska yet from the looks of things. Say, hasn't the USA been going to town on those Japs? I guess that little raise in the pay helps some."

June 15: "I have just finished eating supper. We eat at 5:00 O'clock every evening. Gosh it sure is hot and dry. I hate this place more every day. They sure have been putting us through lately. Some of the boys are going to school over at the hospital. They signed up for that work but our lieutenant tells us we have got to know what the boys know that went over there. That means I will have to be a dock. I suppose even if I get a chance to do mechanic work anyway we are confined here for the rest of this week.

---Well, what did you do Sunday? I went to a show by myself beings you can't be with me. I like to be by myself and think things over. I sure do get tired of so much racket and bull. Oh yes honey what I was talking about was diseases which are caught from bad women you remember what I have told you and if a certain percent catches it the whole bunch is confined to the Post the rotten Devils."

Richard Smith and Part of His Unit at Ft. Bliss, El Paso, Texas.
Photograph in Author's Collection

Photo Collage from Scrapbook of Vernard Dubois
Courtesy of Carol Tetter, His Daughter.

On June 18, Richard wrote his wife again:

June 20: "Hun they sure have put us through lately or today in other words we got up at three O'clock ate breakfast and hiked ten miles by sun up this morning. It didn't bother me at all."

Richard Smith, Private
Collection of the Author

On June 25, twenty-four enlisted men were selected for technical training and sent to the Fitzsimmon General Hospital, Denver, Colorado. A similar group was also sent for special training to the William Beaumont General Hospital, Fort Bliss, Texas. (7)

On June 25, Lt. Thomas Brett, Chaplain's Corps, reported to duty and three days later Lt. Robert M. Powers, also of the Chaplain's Corps joined the unit. Lt. Robert L. Garmire, M.A.C. was transferred from the 64th Medical Regiment, Camp Bowie, Texas, and joined the 51st as adjutant. Captain Thomas B. Greer, M.A.C. was transferred from the 55th Medical Battalion, Fort Sam Houston, Texas, and joined the organization on July 9th as Detachment Commander. With the addition of these officers, those under temporary assignment from the First Cavalry Division returned to their own organizations. (7)

On July 2nd, the 51st General Hospital was relieved of its attachment to the First Cavalry Division, and released to the Commanding General of Services and Supply. The 51st General Hospital, and later the 67th General Hospital, remained under the command of the Services of Supply for the duration of the war. On July 9th, the 51st was attached to the Station Hospital, Ft. Bliss, for administration and training. (7)

In July, an outbreak of mumps occurred and along with it, one of the complications of mumps orchitis (inflammation of testicles). Many of those affected passed out during drilling and training and had to be hospitalized in the Ft. Bliss Station Hospital which was across from the old blimp hanger. (4)

On August 7th, orders were received from Headquarters, Fort Bliss, Texas, instructing the Commanding Officer of the 51st General Hospital, to select a cadre of thirty men and one officer to be transferred to Camp White, Oregon, where it was to become the nucleus for the 82nd General Hospital. On 11 August 1942, these men left camp at 0800 hours under the command of Lieutenant Norman Mitchell, M.C.. Lieutenant Mitchell had led the cadre that originally formed the 51st General Hospital. In the group were 6 of the original cadre of 25. Of the original cadre of 25, 14 became members of the 67th General Hospital. (7) At the time, the 51st was in its last week of basic training. The Morning Reports throughout the months of August for the 51st General Hospital reported "Usual Garrison Duty". (9) The letters of Richard Smith to his wife Bessie adequately reflected "usual garrison duty" from a soldier's standpoint.

Joe Bullock was one of the original cadre of 25 men who helped organize the 51st General Hospital. Prior to joining the Army, Joe was in college at Sam Houston State Teachers College for the Fall, 1940 and the Spring, 1941 semesters. He volunteered and signed up in Huntsville, Texas, on 19 June 1941, where he was going to school, took a bus to Houston, and a troop train from there to Midland, and on to El Paso. There, he received training initially on the medical wards, and then as a ward clerk. (Harold Chisum and Leon Hatton were in this unit with him, also.) He made a trip home to Milano, Texas, his home town, and on his return discovered that he had received a promotion from PFC to T5, and was assigned to the Orderly Room, where he stayed, through several other promotions until he became First Sergeant.

P.F.C. Joe Bullock
Photograph Courtesy of First Sgt. Joe Bullock

The men of the 51st General Hospital were to have a final major upheaval. Approximately one week after finishing their basic training, the headquarters of the 51st General Hospital issued Special Order Number 10 on 1 September 1942, as follows, "Pursuant to GO 43 Hq Fort Bliss, Texas, dated August 27, 1942 and instructions contained in letter WD, AGO dated 7-30-42, file, AG 320.2 (7-28-42) MR-M-GN, Subject:

> Ordering into Active Military Service Certain Numbered General Hospitals (affiliated units), the following named officers and enlisted men of the 51st General Hospital are hereby transferred in grade to the 67th General Hospital at Fort Bliss, Texas, and will report to the Commanding Officer of the 67th General Hospital for duty as of this date. This transfer does not necessitate change of station. No travel involved." (6)

This transfer included one Colonel, 1 Captain, 4 First Lieutenants, 2 Master Sergeants, 1 First Sergeant, 3 T-Sergeants, 2 Staff Sergeants, 2 T-3s, 5 Sergeants, 9 T-4s, 24 T-5s, 61 PFCs and 321 Privates for a total of 6 officers and 430 enlisted personnel. The roster of the 51st General Hospital as of 31 August 1942, showed 466 men. (9)

A cadre of one medical officer, Lieutenant R.S. Lander M.C., and 30 enlisted men were excluded from this transfer and were left to reorganize another General Hospital with the 51st General Hospital designation. (7) The 51st General Hospital was eventually assigned to the Pacific Theater of Operations at Hollandia, New Guinea, became one of two reception points for most Army Air Force patients in the theater SOS system (along with the 126th General Hospital) and in August 1944, was set aside for AAF patients. In July of 1945, it moved to Fort McKinley in Manila, the Philippines, FEAF headquarters. (13) The 67th General Hospital went in the opposite direction, to England and the European Theater of Operation.

Addendum

Cadre of 25 Men Who Activated the 51st General Hospital (11)

Name	Rank	Position Held in Cadre
Mitchell, Norman+	First Lieutenant	Officer in Charge
Freeman, Coy W.*	Master Sergeant	Sergeant Major
Wallace, Wilbur D.+	Master Sergeant	Sick and Wounded
Howell, Orville J.*	Technical Sergeant	Supply Sergeant
Caler, Harold R.*	Technical Sergeant	Mess Sergeant
Baldree, Charlie*	Staff Sergeant	X-ray
Morphew, Gordon K+.	Staff Sergeant	Laboratory
Krebs, Clois D.+	T4	Hospital Cook
Odell, William B., Jr.+	T3	Surgical Technician
Breedlove, Robert E.	T4	Hospital Cook

Allen, John B., Jr.+	Staff Sergeant	Clerk, Supply Office
Thrash, Rufus J.*	T4	Medical Technician
Hatton, Andrew L.*	Sergeant	Sick and Wounded
Cooper, William L.	Sergeant	Clerk, Admission and Disposition
Bullock, Joe C.*	Staff Sergeant	Clerk, 1st Sergeant's Office
Molyneaux, Harold G*	T3	Laboratory Technician
Martin, Frederick D.*	T4	Dental Technician
Warren, Robert M.+	T5	Dental Technician
Albrecht, Paul E.+	T3	Medical Technician
Chism, Harold B.*	T4	Medical Technician
Collier, Robert J.	T4	Medical Technician
Allen, Ronald G., Jr.*	T4	Surgical Technician
Escamilla, Leonelo E. +	T5	Surgical Technician
Van Valkenburgh, Dale B.+	T4	X-ray Technician
Kornegay, Thomas H.+	Sergeant	Pharmacy Technician
Lowe, John W.	T5	Pharmacy Technician

Those men with an asterisk after their names were transferred to the 67th General Hospital. Those with a plus mark after their names were transferred to Camp White, Oregon, 82nd General Hospital. It is not known where the men without an identifying symbol were assigned. (6, 12)

Addendum

Officers and Enlisted Men Transferred from the 51st General Hospital to the 67th General Hospital on 1 September 1942 (9)

Colonel James H. Gambrell, O152176
Captain Thomas B. Greer, O286647
1st Lt. Robert L. Garmire, O408664
1st Lt. Archie L. Faulk, Jr., O405483
1st Lt. Robert M. Powers, O477462
1st Lt. Thomas Brett, O477108

M/Sgt. Coy W. Freeman, 38060772
1st Sg. Earl A. Barton, 18020592
T/Sgt. Harold B. Chism, 38067597
S/Sgt. Charlie D. Baldree, 6296113
T/3 Ronald G. Allen, Jr., 38002500
Sgt. Sam Arisco, 38161754
Sgt. Harold Maner, 1032282
T/4 Angelo Biagi, 38161704
T/4 Samuel O. Hughen, R-2249008
T/4 Roy Pizolato, 38161849

M/Sgt. Charles L. Wittlif, 38035109
T/Sgt. Harold R. Caler, 6248631
T/Sgt. Orville J. Howell, 18014923
S/Sgt. Joe C. Bullock, Jr., 38057409
T/3 Harold G. Molyneaux, 38067825
Sgt. Wesley Carter, 38049356
T/4 Willie B. Barton, 18081780
T/4 Louis Frauman, 38049376
T/4 Frederick D. Martin, 39160924
T/4 Koly Novak, 18081757

T/4 Robert L. Shields, 38067346
T/4 Rufus J. Thrash, 6296561

T/5 James D. Ables, Jr., 38049348
T/5 Robert B. Booker, 38128405
T/5 Johnnie H. Canton, 38161692
T/5 Mangum H. Dawson, 38120475
T/5 Gabriel T. Gullota, 38161771
T/5 Richard C. Harvel, 38158187
T/5 Oscar A. Hinze, 38158179
T/5 Spencer J. McDaniel, 38152000
T/5 Thomas L. Miller, 38120908
T/5 Edward J. Pickard, 37328499
T/5 Joseph H. Rowe, 38138054
T/5 Hubert Smith, 38151638
T/5 Ralph W. Allred, 38137933
T/5 Wesley G. Bridges, 38137911
T/5 George D. Caviggia, 38014547
T/5 Joseph M. Driskill, 38132352
T/5 John M. Harbacheck, 38161777
T/5 Carl S. Heiman, 38132205
T/5 Kenneth C. Jennings, 37348285
T/5 Roy M. McFadden, 38161783
T/5 James B. Parker, 38161831
T/5 Clifford L. Robberson, 38152006
T/5 Paul V. Saxe, 37328252
T/5 R.V. Wilkerson, 38137810

PFC Jose Ballini, 38158268
PFC Jack Barnett, 18128659
PFC Fred Boozer, 38132212
PFC John H. Browder, 38161841
PFC Ricardo Bustamante, 38120814
PFC Dominic Collida, 38161775
PFC Bud H. Davis, 38014536
PFC Antonio C. Flores, 38158202
PFC Adan J. Gallaga, 38158193
PFC Roberto Guillen, 38158280
PFC James L. Hansen, 37348296
PFC Curtis T. Hawkins, 38049336
PFC Francisco Hernandez, 38158199
PFC J.D. Hicks, 38132278
PFC Vurnie A. Johnson, 38105278
PFC Jugh J. Lewis, 38120907
PFC Joe M. Luckey, 18115720
PFC Raymond Manygoats, 38014616
PFC Ira McGee, R-1489762
PFC Johnnie H. McVicker, 38137970
PFC Allen N. Muery, 38161709
PFC Albert W. Paxton, 37348251
PFC Woody R. Purcell, 38158140
PFC Forest E. Russell, 38152022
PFC Agapito P. Sarabia, 39847044
PFC Delma L. Smith, 38137945
PFC John W.T. Smith, 38049257
PFC Melvin C. Spradley, 38151679
PFC Joe W. Truitt, Jr., 38049383
PFC Alton Williams, 38161815
PFC Nash J. Wolf, 38158128
PFC Roy B. Barnard, 38105088
PFC Ray A. Bilyeu, 38161691
PFC Troy M. Burleson, 38120820
PFC Floyd R. Bryant, 38151928
PFC Juan F. Castelo, 38120821
PFC Carl E. Dale, 38161706
PFC Henry Dorsett, 38158275
PFC Marcelo O. Flores, 38158195
PFC Apolonio L. Garcia, 38120857
PFC Robert H. Graves, 39847014
PFC William H. Hanson, 38138025
PFC John D. Hendrix, 38161785
PFC Ignacio R. Hernandez, 38138006
PFC John C. Hughes, 38105407
PFC Runi Juan, 39847037
PFC Perry I. Lowber, 38151965
PFC Victor B. Mangini, 38014436
PFC James W. McConnell, 37077447
PFC William C. McGinnis, 38049157
PFC Charles G. Millett, 37328293
PFC Martin F. Murphy, 38137968
PFC Chester A. Petefish, 37348310
PFC John J. Pursell, 38132244
PFC Alvin W. Sapp, 37348286
PFC Charles E. Smith, 39847040
PFC Herman E. Smith, 38158224
PFC Raymond S. Smith, 38151834
PFC Hugh E. Stevens, 38049360
PFC William T. Weaver, 18115711
PFC Richard E. Wilbur, 37328329

Pvt. Albert Adams, 37348331
Pvt. Jack Ake, 38158254
Pvt. Pieto Alderigi, 38161765
Pvt. Fred Austin, 38049352
Pvt. Ralph E. Autrey, 38014290
Pvt. Robert G. Agee, 18105321
Pvt. Manuel Alcala, 38158272
Pvt. Edgar Angel, 38151909
Pvt. Kayo Attaiki, 39847022
Pvt. Albert E. Axe, 18075996

Pvt. James R. Baker, 38137988
Pvt. Gus T. Ballenger, 38138008
Pvt. Lee Barber, 38158261
Pvt. Johnnie F. Beavers, 38105335
Pvt. Jose S. Beltran, 38120592
Pvt. Ollie G. Bennett, 38158080
Pvt. William P. Billings, 38049260
Pvt. J.T. Bishop, 38152039
Pvt. Norman T. Bogan, 38049397
Pvt. James M. Boyd, 38105156
Pvt. Milburn F. Boyles, 38152007
Pvt. William W. Branham, Jr., 18081691
Pvt. Dick R. Brocato, 38161838
Pvt. Alva C. Brown, 37348303
Pvt. Thomas R. Buck, 38007907
Pvt. Grover L. Burns, 38049385
Pvt. Manuel N. Calderon, 38120848
Pvt. Clarence C. Callicoat, 38151338
Pvt. Evon Campbell, 38132263
Pvt. Richard Cantebury, 38137874
Pvt. Juan Carrasco, 38120851
Pvt. Felipe Castaneda, 38158250
Pvt. Jesus Cavazos, 18105313
Pvt. Gustave E. Chassanoil, Jr., 38161757
Pvt. Elevinio Chavez, 38014560
Pvt. Joe J. Chavez, 39847034
Pvt. Tony A. Chopito 38014541
Pvt. Claud R. Clark, 38152030
Pvt. Melvin F. Coffey, 38105415
Pvt. Virgil L. Collins, 38151357
Pvt. Walter J. Connor, 37348325
Pvt. James R. Cork, 17086271
Pvt. Joe G. Crowley, 38077889
Pvt. Pablo E. Cuellar, 38158270
Pvt. Dock Cunningham, 38120824
Pvt. Rafael M. de la Garza, 38158267
Pvt. Eugenio T. Diaz, 38120854
Pvt. Lee R. Dick, 38161758
Pvt. Jesus Dominguez, 18105319
Pvt. Eduardo Duarte, 38120841
Pvt. Ramon Duenes, 38158273
Pvt. Ralph E. Duncan, 37348279
Pvt. Earl F. Edson, 39847021
Pvt. Dominick Embesi, Jr., 38161247
Pvt. Thomas R. Farnsworth, 38120172
Pvt. Emmet N. Felps, 37348266
Pvt. Paul W. Flaming, 38014539
Pvt. Federico F. Flores, 38014483
Pvt. Lasaro Flores, 38161702
Pvt. Benserlado Fuentes, 38120826
Pvt. Anastacio M. Galindo, 38120827
Pvt. Leonardo G. Garcia, 38014380
Pvt. John E. Baker, 37348352
Pvt. Jose G. Balli, 38158189
Pvt. Piff F. Basaldua, 38158244
Pvt. Luther R. Bell, 38132356
Pvt. Dan Benally, 38014610
Pvt. Louis H. Berger, 37328558
Pvt. Jimmie O. Bishop, Sr., 38049369
Pvt. Homer C. Bloxsom, 18128797
Pvt. Nelson N. Boullion, 38161784
Pvt. Virgil C. Boyle, 37348148
Pvt. Lewis H. Bramlet, 37348173
Pvt. Ernesto Brionez, 38158245
Pvt. James C. Brooks, 18108245
Pvt. Frank Brown, 38014573
Pvt. Vincent Bugaj, 38161748
Pvt. Joseph E. Calam, 38105303
Pvt. Russell A. Caldwell, 37348105
Pvt. Arthur B. Campbell, 37348300
Pvt. J.D. Campbell, 38105401
Pvt. Francisco C. Cantu, 38158276
Pvt. Leonardo Carrasco, 38120849
Pvt. Antonio Castillo, 38158203
Pvt. Noel K. Chandler, 38105373
Pvt. Lawrence M. Chastain, 37348341
Pvt. Epifanio Chavez, 38014549
Pvt. Luis Chavez, Jr., 38120852
Pvt. Esequiel M. Cisneros, 38158264
Pvt. Ollie B. Clements, 38132261
Pvt. George Coffman, 38158238
Pvt. Dewey G. Conley, 38137978
Pvt. Stanley E. Cook, 38152025
Pvt. Victor Cortez, 38105383
Pvt. Manuel Cruz, 38014491
Pvt. Samuel R. Cummings, 39847047
Pvt. Conrado de la Cruz, 38158159
Pvt. Harry A. Devine, 38128561
Pvt. Delbert W. Dieter, 38105409
Pvt. Floyd E. Dodson, 38128555
Pvt. Emmett H. Drake, 38128523
Pvt. Vernard W. Dubois, 38151958
Pvt. Andrew M. Dugan, 38161833
Pvt. Roy J. Dunn, 38138037
Pvt. Robert W. Edwards, 38151982
Pvt. Ralph B. Farley, 38137974
Pvt. Jack L. Fell, 38128092
Pvt. William L. Figueroa, 39847019
Pvt. Daniel Flores, 38120842
Pvt. Gualterio A. Flores, 38161742
Pvt. Grady N. Forson, 38161855
Pvt. Clarence W. Fullerton, 38151883
Pvt. Juan C. Garcia, 38158198
Pvt. Nativad Garcia, 18016769

Pvt. Pedro G. Garcia, 38158177
Pvt. James C. Garrison, 38049294
Pvt. Paul E. Gensheer, 37348328
Pvt. Peter I. Giron, 37348322
Pvt. Otto W. Glona, 38158143
Pvt. Meliton S. Gonzales, 38014464
Pvt. James G. Gould, 38105358
Pvt. Homer T. Graham, 38138036
Pvt. Roy S. Graves, 38132355
Pvt. James P. Hagan, 38138011
Pvt. Paul Hale, 38137823
Pvt. Merl A. Hammel, 37328115
Pvt. Charles E. Hartsock, 38128503
Pvt. Jimmie H. Hawks, 38120507
Pvt. Edwin H. Henry, 37348290
Pvt. Roy H. Hodges, 38151562
Pvt. Fred F. Horvat, 37348314
Pvt. Virgil R. Houston, 38137957
Pvt. William E. Hughes, 38128212
Pvt. Roberto Jaso, 38158289
Pvt. Odell Jimerson, 38137967
Pvt. William F. Johnson, 38128368
Pvt. J.B. Jones, 38105293
Pvt. Roy Kimbrell, 38137976
Pvt. Victor C. King, 38049227
Pvt. Norman A. Lake, 37348288
Pvt. Gordon A. Langford, 39847045
Pvt. Martin H. Leal, 38158110
Pvt. Edward S. Lewis, 37348326
Pvt. Alexander H. Lipscomb, 38128496
Pvt. Johny B. Livingston, 38132264
Pvt. Cecilio G. Lopes, 38158281
Pvt. William Love, 37348099
Pvt. Fred W. Lueck, Jr., 38158213
Pvt. Eduardo Madrid, 38014489
Pvt. Jack Manuelito, Jr., 38014582
Pvt. John Martin, 38128326
Pvt. Diamond D. Martin, 38137909
Pvt. Flavio C. Martinez, 38014428
Pvt. Luciano Martinez, 38014479
Pvt. Raymond R. Mathews, 18081759
Pvt. Troy L. McDonald, 38137996
Pvt. Vincent P. McKenna, Jr., 18081767
Pvt. William E. McKnight, 38014558
Pvt. French McLemore, 38128324
Pvt. Edval N. Meyer, Jr., 38161835
Pvt. Edidoro C. Minjares, 38158235
Pvt. Ben Montez, Sr., 38161723
Pvt. Thomas Moore, 38161755
Pvt. Jerome C. Morey, 38105375
Pvt. Eddie Mosley, 38120895
Pvt. Byron C. Naron, 38132348
Pvt. O'Dire G. Gard, 38014564
Pvt. Salvador V. Garza, 18105311
Pvt. Finis E. Gibson, 38132347
Pvt. Lloyd G. Gist, 39847013
Pvt. John E. Gonzales, 38014437
Pvt. Roman Gonzalez, 38158277
Pvt. Benton E. Grace, 38151953
Pvt. Earl Graves, 38151854
Pvt. Deward Grissom, 34187366
Pvt. Donald M. Hakala, 38004408
Pvt. Robert L Hall, 38132266
Pvt. Henry Hannah, 38014584
Pvt. Elton C. Hatfield, 37348151
Pvt. Jess L. Hemphill, Jr., 38161689
Pvt. Noah L. Hines, 38049258
Pvt. William L. Horton, 38049358
Pvt. Lawson W. House, Jr., 38049394
Pvt. Robert L. Howard, 38105363
Pvt. John C. Jacobs, 38120888
Pvt. Earl Jepson, 38161795
Pvt. Norman T. Jones, 39847025
Pvt. William W. Johnston, 38161770
Pvt. Herman E. Kessel, 38158235
Pvt. Alfred A. King, 38158254
Pvt. Tony J. Lackey, 38151787
Pvt. James J. Lane, 38105378
Pvt. Kenneth D. Lankford, 38152033
Pvt. Glen D. Lechner, 38014532
Pvt. Thomas L. Levet, 38161788
Pvt. William M. Little, 38128251
Pvt. Joseph Locospino, 38014542
Pvt. Joe C. Lopez, 38014551
Pvt. Robert N. Lowe, 38105367
Pvt. George A. Lytle, 39847041
Pvt. August W. Maler, 38161699
Pvt. Gregorio V. Mares, 38158204
Pvt. Sidney E. Martin, 39847016
Pvt. Elonsio S. Martin, 38120559
Pvt. Jose E. Martinez, 38014496
Pvt. John W. Matula, 38158287
Pvt. J.H. McClung, 38137993
Pvt. Luke E. McDonald, 38138015
Pvt. Anthony W. McKinney, 38014507
Pvt. Lychtle V. McLean, 18075986
Pvt. Fernando C. Merris, 38132158
Pvt. John A. Miller, 38105393
Pvt. John H. Mitchell, Jr., 38138040
Pvt. Paul Montoya, 38014597
Pvt. Saragoza J. Moreno, Jr., 38089548
Pvt. Bicente P. Morin, 38158165
Pvt. Clem D. Myers, Jr., 38161852
Pvt. Tony Narvaiz, Jr., 38014615

Pvt. Horace H. Nations, 38120860
Pvt. Gilberto G. Ochoa, 38161807
Pvt. Pedro Ortiz, 38014621
Pvt. Martin E. Parr, 38049171
Pvt. N.P. Parks, 37348287
Pvt. William A. Parsons, 38132331
Pvt. Ray Peery, 38105371
Pvt. Guadalupe T. Pena, 38158173
Pvt. Joe Petranovich, 38014574
Pvt. Glendon F. Presson, 38105296
Pvt. Virgil T. Price, 37328446
Pvt. William R. Rasberry, 38138035
Pvt. Leroy Rhodes, 38158158
Pvt. Olen Rideout, 38049379
Pvt. Manuel A. Rivera, 38014440
Pvt. Frank Roche, 38161701
Pvt. Cre Rosales, 37348223
Pvt. Charles A. Rowan, 38060071
Pvt. Virgil R. Rust, 38151628
Pvt. Lupe Saldana, 38158100
Pvt. Joseph J. Sandoval, 38014593
Pvt. Charlie W. Scroggins, 38150189
Pvt. Giles E. Shilling, 37328425
Pvt. Jimmie Simon, 38158297
Pvt. Clarence O. Simpson, 38105246
Pvt. Bruce D. Smith, Jr., 37348152
Pvt. Jervis L. Smith, 38049374
Pvt. Joe L. Snow, 38049106
Pvt. Nasario S. Soto, 38158240
Pvt. Darwin J. Stacy, 38132349
Pvt. Cyril M. Stastny, 38161744
Pvt. Ernest M. Sterzinger, 38161761
Pvt. Alfred O. Stewart, 38158136
Pvt. Francisco Q. Subia, 38120866
Pvt. James W. Thompson, 38077996
Pvt. Andres Toscano, 38158181
Pvt. George Trujillo, 37348237
Pvt. Herman J. Truckenmiller, 38161736
Pvt. James R. Tyner, 38105357
Pvt. Rube D. Vaughn, 38128340
Pvt. Berto T. Villegas, 38120834
Pvt. T.M. Ward, 18075984
Pvt. G.P. Webb, 38137127
Pvt. George A. Whisenant, 38105397
Pvt. James C. Williams, 38105264
Pvt. Everett C. Williams, 38151760
Pvt. Dillard O. Willis, 38151923
Pvt. Calon H. Wisdom, 38158200
Pvt. Harold Wood, 38049153
Pvt. John A. Woods, 39847006
Pvt. Gerald J. Wright, 38161817
Pvt. Felisito R. Zavala, 38158266
Pvt. Bruno J. Nowak, 38161807
Pvt. Jose U. Ortega, Jr., 38014568
Pvt. John E. Osborne, 38161772
Pvt. Bennie Padron, 38161719
Pvt. Maurice Parmenter, 37348311
Pvt. Lawrence F. Patke, 38049175
Pvt. Charles V. Pelter, 38151918
Pvt. Joe A. Perkins, 38132293
Pvt. Judge W. Pierce, 38077893
Pvt. Joe Price, 38014576
Pvt. Fred R. Quintana, 37348293
Pvt. Rafael Reyes, 39847027
Pvt. Charlie C. Richardson, 38161799
Pvt. Jose R. Rios, 38120819
Pvt. Rommy Rizzo, 38161737
Pvt. Ben J. Rodriguez, 37348301
Pvt. Walter A. Ross, 38161823
Pvt. Ishmael L. Rowbotham, 38128334
Pvt. Francisco Salas, 38158279
Pvt. Adolph Z. Sanchez, 38158242
Pvt. Roy Sargent, 18128739
Pvt. Herman B. Sherman, 38161734
Pvt. Henry C. Shoemaker, 38138004
Pvt. Clifford C. Simpson, 38127454
Pvt. Benjamin F. Smith, Jr., 38049137
Pvt. Clarence W. Smith, 38138023
Pvt. Richard F. Smith, 38105411
Pvt. Guadalupe Soliz, 38158259
Pvt. Sam L. Sparks, 38105230
Pvt. Timothy J. Stanton, 39847043
Pvt. Henry Stearns, 38132257
Pvt. Victor J. Stevens, 38158295
Pvt. Wayne A. Stransky, 37348307
Pvt. Walter L. Tennison, 38138020
Pvt. Wayne Tolino, 38014579
Pvt. Alfonso F. Trevino, 38120836
Pvt. Jesus M. Trujillo, 38014527
Pvt. John B. Tubbs, 38161739
Pvt. Victor T. Van Noy, 39847010
Pvt. Adolfo Valencia, 38014559
Pvt. Arthur M. Wagerman, 37328385
Pvt. L.D. Waters, 38158195
Pvt. Glenn E. Weir, 38152040
Pvt. James A. Wilbanks, 38137918
Pvt. Lloyd R. Williams, 39847012
Pvt. James M. Williamson, 38152015
Pvt. Horace E. Witt, 38105370
Pvt. Henry L. Womack, 38151961
Pvt. James A. Wood, 38105355
Pvt. Richard D. Wood, 35286375
Pvt. Bruce C. Yoeman, 37348212

References

(1) Handbook of Texas Online.

(2) "History of the 51st General Hospital." National Archives.

(3) Letters from Richard Smith to wife Bessie, transcribed and partially edited by the author.

(4) Interview with First Sergeant Joe Bullock, June 20 and 21, 2003, in San Angelo, Texas.

(5) "History of the 51st General Hospital, Ft. Bliss, Texas." Dated 9 June 1942. National Archives.

(6) "Special Order #10, Headquarters, 51st General Hospital, Ft. Bliss, Texas, 1 September 1942." National Archives.

(7) "Annual Report, 51st General Hospital, Fort Bliss, Texas, 1942." National Archives.

(8) "General Order #52, Headquarters Third Army, San Antonio, Texas, 18 May 1942." National Archives.

(9) "Rosters Number 1 and 2 of the 51st General Hospital and General Order #2, Headquarters 51st General Hospital, Office of the Commanding Officer, Fort Bliss, Texas, 24 May 1942." Signed James H.Gambrell, Colonel, Med Corps, Commanding. National Archives.

(10) "Detail of Training Cadre, William Beaumont General Hospital, March 31, 1942." Signed by Lt. Colonel W.L. Richards, Executive Officer for Colonel Edwards. National Archives.

(11) "Notice of Transfer from Headquarters 51st General Hospital, Ft. Bliss, Texas, 12 August 1942."National Archives.

(12) http://www.usaaf.net/ww2/medical/mspg8.htm.

Chapter 4
The 67th General Hospital at Fort Bliss

In a telegram dated 14 July 1942, signed "Magee Washington, D.C." to the Unit Director, 67th General Hospital Portland Maine, the following was transmitted:

> "PLEASE NOTIFY AUTHORITIES INSTITUTION AND PERSONNEL ASSIGNED SIXTY SEVENTH GENERAL HOSPITAL THAT UNIT WILL BE ACTIVATED AUGUST FIFTEENTH AND PERSONNEL PLACED ON ACTIVE DUTY AT THEIR HOMES AND DIRECTED TO PROCEED TO UNDETERMINED STATION FOR UNIT TRAINING STOP IMPERATIVE THAT FINAL TYPE PHYSICAL EXAMINATIONS BE MADE SINCE MAY FIFTEENTH AND SENT IMMEDIATELY TO THIS OFFICE ATTENTION COLONEL FITTS ON ALL OFFICERS AND NURSES STOP NO ORDERS WILL BE ISSUED WITHOUT SUCH REPORTS STOP COMPLETE ROSTER LIST ESSENTIAL IMMEDIATELY INCLUDING ENTIRE PERSONNEL INCLUDING THOSE ON DUTY AND PENDING CASE STOP LETTER FOLLOWS STOP ACKNOWLEDGE END SPMCQ" (2)

This was followed on 16 July 1942, by another telegram from Magee:

> "DATE OF ACTIVATION OF YOUR UNIT CHANGED TO SEPTEMBER FIRST END SPMCQ" (2)

An order for Activation of Units was sent by Headquarters, Fort Bliss, Texas, dated 27 August 1942, which activated the 67th General Hospital at Fort Bliss, Texas, effective 1 September 1942. (5)

"Pursuant to instructions contained in letter WD, AGO, dated July 30, 1942, file AG320.2 (7-28-42) MR-N-GN, Subject, Ordering into Active Military Service Certain Numbered General Hospitals (Affiliated Units), and 1st Indorsement (sic) thereon, Hq 8th Serv Comd, dated August 3, 1942, file AG 320.2 (Med), the 67th General Hospital is activated at Fort Bliss, Texas, effective September 1, 1942, in accordance with T/O 8-550, April 1, 1942. By order of Colonel Taulbee: J.S. Money, Lt. Col, A.G.D., Adjutant." (5)

The doctors and nurses of the 67th General Hospital in Portland, Maine, were notified of their activation and the personnel at that time consisted of fifty medical and dental officers and sixty-one nurses. The doctors and nurses departed Portland, Maine, on 1 September 1942, arrived at Fort Bliss, Texas, on 4 September 1942, and were attached to the Station Hospital, Fort Bliss, Texas, for administration and training. (1) There, they joined the staff of 6 administrative officers and 430 enlisted personnel who had been transferred into the 67th General Hospital on 1 September 1942, from the 51st General Hospital at the time of activation. (9)

Most of the officers and men of the 51st General Hospital were ordered to report to Headquarters, 67th General Hospital, in compliance with Special Order number 10, dated 1 September 1942, Headquarters 51st General Hospital, effective 1 September 1942, with Colonel

James H. Gambrell in charge. (4) After they were transferred, a cadre of only 30 enlisted men and one officer remained to staff the 51st General Hospital. (3)

First Lieutenant Robert L. Garmire was assigned to duty as Adjutant to the 67th General Hospital, and appointed Class A Agent to the Finance Officer, United States Army, Fort Bliss, Texas. His responsibility was the preparation of monthly and furlough ration money payments to members of the 67th General Hospital. Captain Thomas Greer was assigned to duty as Detachment Commander, DMD, 67th General Hospital, and also assigned the duty of Recreation Officer. First Lieutenant Archie Faulk was assigned to be the Supply Officer for the 67th General Hospital as well as appointed Motor Officer, Summary Court Officer and Mess Officer. First Lieutenant Robert M. Powers was appointed Chaplain and Postal Officer. First Lieutenant Thomas Brett was also assigned to duty as Chaplain for the 67th General Hospital. (3) In addition to the officers, the transfer included 2 Master Sergeants, 1 First Sergeant, 3 T-Sergeants, 2 Staff Sergeants, 2 T-3s, 5 Sergeants, 9 T-4s, 24 T-5s, 61 Privates First Class and 321 Privates--a total of 430 enlisted men and 6 officers.

On 1 September 1942, James H. Gambrel, Colonel, M.C., assumed command of the 67th General Hospital. (10) Colonel Gambrell remained in command until 18 September 1942, when he was transferred, and Lieutenant Colonel Roland B. Moore, who had been acting as Executive Officer, assumed the command. (9, 11)

Officers assigned to the Medical Service were assigned as follows: (8)

Chief of Service	Lt. Colonel Elton R. Blaisdell
Assistant Chief of Service	Major Charles W. Steele
Chief of General Medical Section	Major Edward A. Greco
Chief of Cardiovascular Section	Major Wilfrid J. Comeau
Chief of Gastroenterology Section	Major Henry H. Tabachnick
Chief of Communicable Disease Section	Major Merrill S.F. Greene
Chief of Neuropsychiatry Section	Captain Charles W. Eastman

Ward Officers

Captain Bertrand A. Beliveau
Captain Paul R. Chevalier
Captain Gerald H. Donahue
Captain Joseph A. Villa
Captain Ralph E. Williams
First Lieutenant Harry E. Christensen
First Lieutenant Charles L. Holt

The officers who were to be on the Medical Service of the 67th General Hospital began work in the office and wards of the Medical Service in the Station Hospital where they trained under the direction of the Station Hospital's Chief of the Medical Service and his ward officers.

Paper work and the general routine of the wards were stressed, since it was so much different from the manner in which it was done in civilian medical practice and because the conformity of records was critical to the overall military medical system. The Chief of Service and Assistant Chief of Service were also trained by the Station Hospital Chief of Service on the military style of documentation and office management. Daily rounds were made by the doctors of the 67th General Hospital with the Chief of Service regarding their responsibility to their various sections, the responsibilities of the different Chiefs of Sections and those of their ward officers. (8)

After six weeks of intensive training the ward officers were put in charge of wards, the majors took over their sections and the Chief and Assistant Chief did a portion of the actual work in the medical office including final inspection of all charts, the supervision of patient examination, the completion of charts on medical clinic days and making ward rounds with the Station Hospital Chief of the Medical Service. (8)

In addition to the training at the Fort Bliss Station Hospital, the officers had calisthenics, close order drills and evening lectures. A typical day was as follows:

0645-0700	Calisthenics
0700-0800	Duty at Headquarters
0800-1200	Duty in Wards and Offices
1300-1600	Close Order Drill
1900-2000	Lecture on Courts Martial

In a letter to the President of the Maine Medical Association on 11 October 1942, Lieutenant Colonel Stephen A. Cobb, who was at that time President-elect of the Maine Medical Association, reported some of the activity of the 67th General Hospital at Ft. Bliss as follows:

> "As you know the 67th General Hospital sponsored by the Maine General Hospital, and composed of Maine doctors is attached to the Station Hospital here at Fort Bliss for instruction and intensive training. At the present time we have working at the Station Hospital, members of our unit, and sixty-six nurses from New England, most of them from Maine.
>
> We are all well and happy. Many of the Officers have their wives with them, so that we have many pleasant get-togethers. Lieutenant Colonel Moore (Roland B.) makes a great Commanding Officer and has the respect and admiration of all the men. Our enlisted personnel is made up of men mostly from the southwest. There are about five hundred of them. They are a fine lot of boys and soldiers. They had three months' training before we arrived.
>
> El Paso is really a beautiful spot. Fort Bliss is situated on the United States side of the Rio Grande River, and at the base of the Rocky Mountains, with some of the camps on the slopes. The sun has shone every day that we have been here. When it rains it is

generally in the night. This is probably due to the fact that we are at 4,000 feet elevation. The days are warm and the nights cool. We are still in khaki, and our shirt sleeves. The people of El Paso have really been more than hospitable. The Chamber of Commerce, Service Clubs, and Religious Organizations are continually having entertainments for everyone in the service. We are across the river from Juarez in old Mexico, a favorite retreat for the service men.

This is our daily schedule:

6:00 a.m.	Reveille
6:45-7:00	Calisthenics
7:00-7:30	Breakfast
7:30-8:30	Close Order Drill
8:30-12:00	Work in operating room and on the wards
12:00-13:00	Lunch
13:00-16:30	Work on the wards
17:00-18:00	Dinner
18:00-19:00	Lectures (Note the army time)
19:00-22:00	Free to write letters, play cards, or go to the movies
22:00	Taps

From Saturday noon until Monday at 6:00 a.m., those who are not on duty are free. There have been trips to the Carlsbad Caverns, and up and down the Rio Grande Valley. These in addition to being enjoyable are very instructive and educational.

I do want to say that we have as finely trained doctors in our unit (and all from the state of Maine) as there are in the Army. I am sure that wherever we go our bunch will not shirk and that some day when this holocaust is over the 67th General Hospital will have been a credit to the Army of the United States and the State of Maine." (12)

The medical officers destined for the Surgical Service were attached to the wards and the offices of the Station Hospital to familiarize themselves with the system of records and the routines of pre-operative, operative and post-operative care in all types of surgical cases along with their final disposition. The chief and assistant chief of the service made regular rounds and conferences with the corresponding officers at the Station Hospital. Surgical officers worked in the operating room and attended various meetings of boards including reclassification, section VIII, C.D.D. (Certificate of Disability for Discharge), and Line of Duty Boards. Evening lectures and demonstrations were held four times weekly from 1900 to 2000 hours by arrangement of the Commanding Officer of the Station Hospital. During this same period a course in war surgery was organized by Lieutenant Colonel Stephen A. Cobb, the Chief of Surgical Service, consisting of lectures by the officers of the 67th General Hospital on various types of war injuries including gas warfare. (7)

On 21 October 1942, the surgical officers were assigned to the actual management of one half of each surgical ward, making them responsible for the admission, care and discharge of those patients. This gave them practical experience for the complete management of the Surgical Service of a General Hospital. These duties continued until 13 November 1942, when the hospital unit left Fort Bliss. (7, 8)

The enlisted men of the Detachment Medical, who had already received about 3 ½ months of basic training, undertook a period of technical training. The annual report of the 51st General Hospital described the course that their men followed at Ft. Bliss, and it would be assumed that the men of the 67th General Hospital followed an identical curriculum. They were divided into three groups. Half of the men were further sub-divided into Group A or B and the other half went into Group C. They received the following courses:

Group A received two weeks didactic lectures in subjects such as Elementary Anatomy and Physiology, Hygiene and Sanitation, Nursing Methods, Elementary Mathematics including the Metric System, Essentials of Pharmacy, Minor Surgery and Medical Field Service. Group B received training in Bandaging, Treatment of Wounds, Treatment of Fractures, Application of Splints, and Bed Patient Nursing Care. Group C received one months training training in outside practical subjects such as Litter Drill, Ambulance Loading, Ward Tent Pitching, Chemical Warfare lectures and demonstrations, Emergency First Aid, Sanitation and Hygiene, Outdoor Military Courtesy, Shelter Tent Pitching, Organization and Function of Medical Field Units, and Close Order Drill. Group A and B exchanged places and when they were finished with their two didactic sessions, they began the month-long outside training which Group C had finished. The initial Group C divided into two groups and repeated the initial Group A and B courses. (1)

A Group of 67th GH Soldiers at Ft. Bliss. Note the Tan Faces and White Foreheads.
Photograph Courtesy Carol Tetter, Daughter of Vernard Dubois.

Payday at Ft. Bliss
Photograph Courtesy of Carol Tetter, Daughter of Vernard Dubois

In addition to the original members of the 51st General Hospital, soldiers were transferred in to fill needed positions. Some had received special training that the original members of the 51st General Hospital had not received. Raymond Bungard, who worked in the clinical laboratories, arrived at Fort Bliss slightly more than a week before he shipped out with the 67th General Hospital. Two of his friends (neither part of the original 51st General Hospital that became part of the 67th General Hospital upon its activation), Ted Benedict and Wayne Hixson were already there when he arrived. Benedict had finished his basic training and clerk's school at Camp Barkley, in Abilene, Texas, before shipping to Ft. Bliss, knowing that he would be a clerk in a medical unit, but not knowing the specific unit. (13) Lieutenant Bob Walker of the Quartermaster Corp, had been in the Army for a year before he drove to El Paso, in his own car, to join his new unit. He subsequently sold his automobile after arrival. (4)

The original census of the men transferred from the 51st General Hospital consisted of 430 enlisted men and 6 officers. The arrival of the Maine contingent added 50 additional officers and 61 nurses. Between the time of the organization of the Unit on 1 September 1942, and their departure in November, 1942, there were additions of 3 Officers, 12 nurses and a net change of 67 additional enlisted men. (The enlisted contingent lost 39 men in October, but gained 107 men in November.) The Red Cross workers arrived in the latter part of October. (16)

Ft. Bliss Theater
Photograph Courtesy Carol Tetter, Daughter of Vernard Dubois

Ted Benedict was a member of the Seventh-day Adventist Church, as were Raymond Bungard and Wayne Hixson, and because of their beliefs they were placed in a hospital unit. The Sabbath for them started at sunset on Friday and ended at sunset on Saturday. Ted Benedict provided a narrative of his experiences at Ft. Bliss which were a consequence of his beliefs:

> "The first weekend in El Paso was a little dramatic. As an Adventist, I wanted to go to church, and so I got a pass to go into town for the day that first Sabbath. I forgot to turn in my pass on my return that evening, and so was officially AWOL overnight. That earned me a week's restriction and extra duty, to be served on KP. When the next Friday rolled around I was in a bind, because sundown was certain to fall while I was working in the mess hall. I talked to the Mess Sergeant about it, advising him that I was going to be a problem for him when I quit work at sundown. He suggested that I just fade into the furniture, but I told him that I would be observed by the personnel officer, since the whole issue was my Sabbath observance. So I did quit work, and indeed was noticed doing so. I was put 'under guard' waiting for a decision about what to do with me. The next morning (Saturday) was payday. The 1st Sgt. came around and told me to go get paid and report immediately back to quarters and confinement. I replied that it would be O.K. to be redlined, since I didn't want to be paid on my Sabbath. He muttered something and left, returning in a bit with the C.O. He then repeated the order to go get paid, and again I refused. The C.O. responded by saying that 'I've seen a man who wouldn't work, but this is the first time I've ever seen one who wouldn't be paid.'
>
> The very next event in this little drama was my transfer to the 67th, along with four others whose 201 files indicated that they had some kind of conscientious objection in their history. I was told informally that the C.O. said that he didn't want any more of this kind of trouble in his outfit."

(Ted's mother and future wife were able to visit with him in El Paso, about two weeks before he shipped out with the 67th General Hospital. They crossed over into Juarez, Mexico, leaving Ted waiting at the bridge since he was not allowed to enter because of "some kind of discipline.") (17) Authors note: The 51st General Hospital had remained at Ft. Bliss as a cadre but soon was expanded with more men. Ted Benedict was probably one of these new additions before he was sent to the 67th General Hospital.

Ted Benedict had comments relating to the men from Texas and Oklahoma and those from other areas.

> "There was some adjusting between the Oklahoma / Texas men and the few of us who came from other areas (California, Washington, Iowa, Brooklyn). We weren't numerous, but initially we weren't readily accepted. The men referred to us as 'Yankees' and the officers and nurses as 'damned Yankees', a meaningful distinction in their language and culture."

He also had a story regarding some American Indian recruits.

> "About two o'clock this afternoon, a call came in for an Indian boy from his father, who had just come from New Mexico to see his son. Apparently the kid had written simply that he had been 'sent to the 51st General Hospital', for his dad had the impression that his boy was sick. The fellow had never used a phone before, didn't even know how to hold it up to his ear, but grinned when the ordeal was over (he shook visibly with fear) and said that he liked it very much. (NB: At induction, I saw Indians cry when the barbers removed their 'tribal hair' for a G.I. haircut.)" (17)

The Cactus and the Pine

The 67th General Hospital adopted a banner which bore the images of a pine tree and a cactus plant to symbolize the Maine contingent of doctors and nurses joined with the enlisted men who were mostly from Texas and Oklahoma. The cactus appears to be a Saguaro, which is native to Arizona. On the banner was the motto "Servimus Sanando," which translated from the Latin as "We Serve to Heal." (14) A truer, although less picturesque, cactus would have been the barrel cactus which is native to El Paso, but it was the effort to recognize the enlisted men that counted.

Fort Bliss

El Paso, Spanish words for "The Pass", was originally known as El Paso del Norte (the Pass of the North). The pass is a break through the Franklin Mountains on the north, or American side of the Rio Grande, and the Sierra Madre on the south, or Mexican side, of the river. The Franklin Mountains are three miles wide by twenty-three miles long and rise to an elevation of 7,192 feet above sea level. Typical Chihuahuan Desert plants are seen, including the large barrel cactus, which is found nowhere else in Texas. The Army created the First Calvary Division in 1921, at Ft. Bliss, and William Beaumont General Hospital opened that same year on 1 July. (22) The cavalry remained useful in an era of increased mechanization because of the difficulty of patrolling the rough and untamed Mexican border. After 1942, the patrols became unnecessary following Mexico's declaration of war on the Axis forces. The First Cavalry dismounted in 1943, became a mechanized infantry unit and served in the Pacific Theater.

When the men of the 67th General Hospital arrived, there were still cavalry units at Ft. Bliss. Ted Benedict recalled his first exposure to Ft. Bliss and to the cavalry:

> "As our train approached El Paso, we ran along side a cavalry outfit, complete with horses, raising a lot of dust. There was a medical caisson among them, with two horses pulling it with a medical cross painted on top, and two medics covered with dust on top of it. I wondered if that was to be my fate." (17)

After the departure of the First Cavalry, the post became primarily an artillery post. In 1940, it became an antiaircraft training center and during the 1940's, Ft. Bliss expanded from several thousand acres to more than one million, covering an area seventy-five miles long and fifty-four miles wide. (22)

Cavalry Barracks at Fort Bliss
Photograph Courtesy Betsy Larson Crumrine

The enlisted men, who initially were part of the 51st General Hospital and who became the enlisted component of the 67th General Hospital, arrived in El Paso, in May, 1942. The average high temperature in May is 87 degrees, with an average low of 56 degrees. This, combined with its low humidity must have been very pleasant for the Oklahoma and Texas soldiers accustomed to hot temperatures and higher humidity. June, July and August, are less pleasant with temperatures hovering in the mid-90's. The nights, however, remained pleasant. June, July, August and September, are the rainy months with average precipitation averaging one inch in June, and two inches respectively in July, August and September. When the doctors and nurses from Maine arrived in September, they were greeted with an average 87 degree daily temperatures with the temperature dropping to 62 degrees at night. (19) This might have been somewhat a shock since average temperatures for Portland, Maine, average 70 degrees as a high during the day and 47 degrees as a low at night during this same time period. (20)

The training for the 67th General Hospital ended 12 November 1942. Based on a report titled "History of Organization" signed by Lt. Colonel Roland B. Moore on 30 March 1943, there would have been 492 enlisted men, 59 officers and 73 nurses who left Ft. Bliss on 12 and 13 November 1942, and headed for the New York Port of Embarkation after receiving orders for overseas duty. They arrived at Camp Kilmer, New Jersey, on 16 November 1942. (1,9)

References

(1) "Annual Report, 51st General Hospital, Fort Bliss, Texas, 1942." National Archives.

(2) "Telegrams from Magee, Washington, D.C. to Unit Director, Maine General Hospital, Portland, Maine." National Archives.

(3) "Special Order #1, Headquarters, 67th General Hospital, Fort Bliss, Texas, 1 September 1942. National Archives.

(4) "General Order #1, Headquarters, 67th General Hospital, Fort Bliss, Texas, 1September 1942, Titled 'Assumption of Command'." Signed by James H. Gambrell, Colonel, M.C., Commanding. National Archives.

(5) "General Order #43, Headquarters Fort Bliss, Texas, Titled 'Activation of Units'." Dated 27 August 1942. By order of Colonel Taulbee and Signed J.S. Mooney, Lt. Col, A.G.D., Adjutant. National Archives.

(6) "Annual Report of the 67th General Hospital APO 511 for 1944, to the Surgeon General, United States Army." Signed by Colonel Roland Moore, M.C., Commanding Officer. National Archives.

(7) "Annual Report of the Surgical Service to Lt. Colonel Robert B. Moore, Commanding Officer of the 67th General Hospital." Dated 31 December 1942. Signed by William V. Cox, Major, M.C., Chief of Surgical Service. National Archives.

(8) "Annual Report of the Medical Service to Lt. Colonel R.B. Moore, Commanding Officer of the 67th General Hospital." Dated 30 December 1942. Signed by Lt. Colonel E.R. Blaisdell, M.C., Chief of Medical Service. National Archives.

(9) "Annual Report to the Chief Surgeon, SOS, ETOUSA of the 67th General Hospital." Dated 15 January 1943. Signed by Lt. Colonel R.B. Moore, M.C., Commanding. National Archives.

(10) "General Order 1, Headquarters 67th General Hospital." Issued at Ft. Bliss, Texas, on 1 September 1942. National Archives.

(11) "General Order 3, Headquarters 67th General Hospital." Issued at Ft. Bliss, Texas, on 18 September 1942. National Archives.

(12) Letter from Lt. Colonel Stephen A. Cobb, M.C. to Carl H. Stevens, M.D., President of the Maine Medical Association. The letter appeared in the Journal of the Maine Medical Association: Volume 33, No.11, November, 1942. Courtesy of Maine Medical Center Archives.

(13) Communication with Raymond Bungard, M.D.

(14) *Lewiston Journal: Magazine Section.* Saturday, October 25, 1969.

(15) Personal Communication with Lieutenant Bob Walker.

(16) "Reports to the Red Cross from the Red Cross Unit Assigned to the 67th General Hospital. Narrative and Recreation Report for August, 1943." National Archives.

(17) Communication with Ted Benedict.

(18) http://147.71.210.21/adamag/district/district.htm.

(19) http://www.underground.com/NORMS/DisplayNORMS.asp?AirportCode=KELP&SafeC...1/16/2003.

(20) National Weather Service.

(21) "Franklin Mountains." *The Handbook of Texas Online.*

(22) "Fort Bliss." *The Handbook of Texas Online.*

Chapter 5
Going to War

Following the activation of the 67th General Hospital on 1 September 1942, there was a continuous effort to prepare the men and women of the Unit to function as integral parts of a General Hospital. That point was reached during the first part of November, 1942. The majority of the enlisted men had been at Fort Bliss, El Paso, Texas, since 23 May 1942, and some had been there since 16 May 1942, receiving basic, technical and clinical training. It was time to use their training to help the war effort. The doctors and nurses had arrived shortly after the activation and had been receiving specialized training which adjusted their peacetime civilian skills to those of a military unit.

The Train

The enlisted men left Fort Bliss, at 6:35 p.m. Mountain Time, on 12 November 1942. (10) Lt. Colonel Stephen A. Cobb, in a memorandum to the Commanding Officer, 67th General Hospital, described the trip and the following itinerary is structurally based on his note. (1) I believe that the nurses and doctors departed on the following day, but have been unable to document this. The Detachment included 9 officers and 499 enlisted men. They had to wait in El Paso until a kitchen car was repaired, then shifted from the Southern Pacific Railroad to the Santa Fe Railroad, and finally left El Paso at 8:51 p.m. While they waited in El Paso, the men had supper. The schedule called for the men to eat breakfast at 7:30 am, dinner at 12:30 p.m., and supper at 5:30 p.m. It was noted by Lt. Colonel Cobb, that it took 30 minutes to feed the enlisted men.

Lt. Colonel Stephen A. Cobb : Portrait by Felix Weinberg
Photograph Courtesy Ted Benedict

The train containing the enlisted men of the 67th General Hospital moved west--out of El Paso, passed south of the Franklin Mountains, and after passing the mountains, turned north into New Mexico. They traveled north with the San Andres Mountains to the east on their right and the Rio Grande immediately to the west on their left. (The Rio Grande flows south out of New Mexico and turns east near El Paso.) At the time of their departure, the men did not know their ultimate destination. (3) Their first stop
was in Belen, New Mexico, about thirty miles south of Albuquerque. (by this time, it was **13 November 1942**) where they arrived at 2:50 a.m. Their direction changed to an eastward direction after Belen. They then stopped in Vaughn, New Mexico, arrived at 6:18 a.m. If they kept to schedule, they had breakfast on their way to Krider, New Mexico, where they arrived at 8:59 a.m. They arrived in Clovis, New Mexico, at 10:39 a.m., did calisthenics, marched for 30 minutes, and probably had lunch. They departed at 12:33 p.m. By this time they were traveling in a northeastern direction as they re-entered Texas, and the Central Time Zone, and arrived in the Panhandle town of Amarillo, Texas, at 2:35 p.m., and after a two minute stop, left for Waynoka, Oklahoma, in northwestern Oklahoma, at 2:37 p.m. arriving there at 7:32 p.m., and had supper on the way. In Waynoka, the men marched through the town for thirty minutes, and the train left at 8:37 p.m.

The train entered Kansas, and stopped at Wellington, just north of the Oklahoma-Kansas border, at 10:35 p.m. After a brief stop, they left at 10:58, arrived at Newton, Kansas, at 1:23 a.m. **14 November 1942**. They arrived in Kansas City, Kansas, at 5:10 a.m., left at 6:25 a.m., headed northward. Breakfast was scheduled at 7:30 a.m., and they arrived in St. Joseph, Missouri, at 9:01 a.m. While in St. Joseph, they did 10 minutes of calisthenics. They had lunch and supper on the train and arrived at Oelwein, in northeastern Iowa, at 6:15 p.m. While there, they did thirty minutes of platoon drill through the town and chocolate bars were purchased for the men. An order was sent ahead to Chicago, for meat, ice cream, paper plates, and chocolate bars to be picked up when they arrived. The train left Oelwein, at 7:15 p.m.

First Sergeant Joe Bullock recalled that the men looked like they were getting ready for a minstrel show. Their faces were blackened by the soot coming from the locomotives, particularly those who stuck their heads out the windows as the train moved down the track. (3)

The train traveled through the night, was held up by a train wreck for three hours, and finally arrived in Chicago, at 7:15 a.m., **15 November 1942**. The train transferred from the Chicago Great Western yards to the New York Central at 8:15 a.m., and left Chicago at 9:08 a.m. Breakfast was probably eaten during the transfer. They arrived in Elkhart, Indiana, at 11:30 a.m., did twenty minutes of calisthenics and exercise, and left at 11:52 a.m. They had lunch and arrived in Toledo, Ohio, at 3:32 p.m., where they again had thirty minutes of exercise. They left Toledo at 4:15 p.m., had lunch, and arrived in Cleveland, Ohio, at 6:20 p.m. and left at 7:00 p.m. The next stop was in Buffalo, N.Y., at 9:50 p.m., where they changed to Lehigh (Lehigh Valley Train Line), at 10:20 p.m., and left Buffalo at 11:26 p.m..

On **16 November 1942**, they arrived at Lehighton, Pennsylvania, at 6:53 a.m. and left at 7:29 a.m., and had breakfast shortly after leaving. The last stop was at Camp Kilmer, New Jersey, at 10:10 a.m., Eastern Time. (1) The trip had taken 4 days, 1 hour and 25 minutes, and crossed three time zones--Mountain, Central and Eastern.

The nurses and the doctors had a somewhat spirited trip. They possibly felt a sense of new-found freedom after escaping the confines of Fort Bliss, and this feeling of release, combined with the excitement of traveling over the country in a strange and exciting environment to a new and possibly dangerous destination may have released some inhibitions. During the journey, a plain-clothes security person was put on the train, possibly in Chicago, to control what can best be described as "activities", which involved some nurses and doctors with one of the other or both traveling between each others' cars, etc. for a "party". One of the nurses remembered serving as one of the "guards of surveillance" with three nurses "under guard" at Camp Kilmer. No one was known to have been punished or reprimanded in the MD group. There was some discussion of whether these particular high-spirited nurses would be going over-seas but ultimately they were shipped out with the Unit. (9)

Camp Kilmer, New Jersey

On the day of arrival, Richard Smith wrote a letter to his wife, Bessie. The envelope was postmarked New Brunswick, New Jersey, and the letter return address was Camp Kilmer, New Jersey. (2)

"November 16, 1942
Dear Wife

We arrived this morning about 10:00, I think. I don't think I will be here very long we haven't heard a thing so far. I hope you made it home OK. (Bessie was living and working in El Paso, while Richard was in basic training. She left El Paso about the same time as he shipped out with the 67th General Hospital on its way to Ft. Kilmer.) We left Bliss Wed. night about 7:00 P.M. I mean we have been over the country since then. We come by Lake Erie--some lake. I lost track from there on. We also come through Chicago. I sure don't like this eastern country at all but we had a grand time. Everyone was jolly.

Private Richard Smith

P.S. I just heard that we would leave in 5 days one bunch is leaving here tonight have been here 7."

Camp Kilmer, part of the New York Port of Entry, was two mile east of New Brunswick, New Jersey, and 30 miles south of New York City. It was activated in June, 1942, the first staging area to be built solely for that purpose in the United States, and at the time, was the largest staging area in the United States. It was named for Joyce Kilmer, a soldier-poet who wrote the poem, "Trees". (Kilmer, whose home was in New Brunswick, New Jersey, was killed during WWI). Camp Kilmer was an installation of the New York Port of Embarkation, a part of the Army Service Forces' Transportation Corps. (10) The camp was described as immense with new buildings--some still under construction, painted in camouflage colors of reds, yellows and greens. (15) There was another embarkation center in New Jersey, Fort Dix, not far away.

At Camp Kilmer, the Red Cross workers were billeted with the nurses. While there, they contacted the Red Cross Field Director who was able to arrange some emergency loans for those who had been added to the group without adequate advance warning to make financial arrangements prior to departure from Fort Bliss. (13)

When the men of the 67th General Hospital arrived in Camp Kilmer, they found it to be crowded, as Richard Smith reported in his letter which follows. Sergeant Joe Bullock remembered that they did close-order drill to stay busy. (3) A history of the 2nd Evacuation Hospital which staged out of Camp Kilmer recalled numerous clothing and equipment checks, physical inspections, and "gang plank" exercises. The history also recalled the men being roused from sleep to have their ID photographs taken. (15) The facility was so large that men were urged to remember their billet and needed to travel across the camp on buses. The 67th General Hospital waited for their turn, along with thousands of other soldiers in other units, to board a ship to take them to their final destination.

"November 18, 1942

Well Sweetheart, we still haven't left yet this is Wed. Tomorrow, I guess. I haven't done a thing but line up and sign my name. We hafta stay right in the Barracks we eat out of of mess kits. It's getting old and this soon. What will it be later? I have never seen so many men in all my time. I rather like the climate here. It sprinkled a little this morning. My long wools are a little too warm but decided that I had better keep them on.--- one good thing a fellow can't think much for all the racket going on.

P.S. one of our barrack's boys are leaving in the morning."

There was no leave available at Camp Kilmer and preparations were made to depart for travel to the ship. They were instructed to pack six cans of army rations in their mussett bag. (13) The men of the 2nd Evacuation Hospital, which also left from Camp Kilmer, marched to the train in full kit, departed on a train which arrived at the Jersey City terminal 1 hour and 45 minutes later, and then marched to the Brooklyn ferry and taken to board the ship. The men of the 67th General Hospital followed a similar route. (15)

The Queen Elizabeth

When the order was given to leave, the enlisted men of the Detachment Medical of the 67th General Hospital were transported to the New York City wharf and the Cunard Pier, on the night of 23 November 1942. They unloaded, formed up and marched into the Cunard Liner Queen Elizabeth, by units, through a door in the ship which was at pier level. The enlisted men boarded prior to the nurses, to their quarters deep in the bowels of the ship.

In his diary, Ted Benedict recalled his trip from Kilmer to an unknown destination:

"It must have been near nine in the evening, because it was almost completely dark. And it was raining; a long lazily slanting drizzle that made the tramping column of men ahead of me visible by the reflection of nearly blacked out streetlights from the tops of the men's helmets and their shoes, nodding and swinging in cadence. If it hadn't been for the heavy barracks bags I was trying to keep on my shoulders and head, I guess I would have felt pretty bad then, for that came as near to being the actual time of departure as any.

A wet mile hike and we were packed into trains and shuttled into New York, then sent across the North River on a ferry and emptied out into a long shed like building on the opposite side. Our line didn't once stop moving, but wound through and into the side of the Queen in carefully controlled order, where we were put into our staterooms by the stewards.

Unless you've counted on a three or four weeks trip in a slow, dangerous convoy you wouldn't know the surprise and relief we felt when it was confirmed that we actually boarded the Queen Elizabeth. None of us knew beforehand where or exactly how we were going, and this possibility hadn't even entered our heads. So it was a real thrill to find that we were going to make a dash for Scotland in the world's biggest, fastest luxury liner, totally without armed escort." (18)

Sergeant Joe Bullock recalls his trip into the Queen Elizabeth:

"We went by train from Camp Kilmer to New York Harbor. We unloaded directly from the troop train into a giant warehouse and then a short distance into what I thought was another warehouse, but it was the Queen. Having never seen anything larger than a row boat, I could not believe anything that large would float. Old country boy!" (3)

The Queen Elizabeth was at berth on the west side of Manhattan Island, at the New York Passenger Terminal, along the East River. These piers were between West 44th Street and West 52nd Street and included piers 84 through 94. The Queen Elizabeth was probably berthed at Pier 90. Raymond Bungard recalls seeing the capsized French liner Normandie in the water at Pier 88.

"Adjacent to the docked Queen E could be seen the half-submerged French luxury liner Normandie which had caught fire during preparation as a troop ship." (19) (Note: The Normandie had been seized by the U.S. Government after the attack on Pearl Harbor and the declaration of war and renamed the U.S.S. Lafayette. While being refitted as a troop ship, sparks from a welder's torch caught the ship afire and attempts to put the fire out involved pumping huge amount of water into the ship. This put a large weight of water into the top portions of the ship due to the watertight compartments of the lower parts of the ship and the top-heavy liner broke its moorings and capsized. She was salvaged, but the expense to restore her would have been excessive and ultimately, she was sold for scrap in 1946.)

One nurse recalls leaving Camp Kilmer at midnight, taking six trucks to the port with the nurses, then taking a wet, dirty, barge-like conveyance across the Hudson River to dock on the New York side. Somewhere along the line, they picked up 33 "pool" nurses to combine with the Maine nurse contingent of 72 nurses to make up their General Hospital quota of 105 nurses. (The Table of Organization regulated the numbers of various personnel for a General Hospital.) With the nurses were two physiotherapists from Portland, Maine, and two dieticians who had been obtained from the pool. They were met at the Port of New York by the Port Army Nurse who checked their roster. (9) Roll call was done and the nurses walked onto the ship at ship deck level. The Red Cross contingent reported a "very hard trip" and "what seemed like miles in the rain" before reaching the ship. (13) The Queen Elizabeth steamed out in the early morning of 24 November 1942, under escort. (10) One internet source reports a sailing of the Queen Elizabeth on 22 November 1942, with 15,000 troops which included the 78th Fighter Group on its manifest. Probably the manifest included the 67th General Hospital, and it is likely that the author entered the sailing date incorrectly.

The Queen Elizabeth
Clipping in Collection of Author

Postcard of Queen Elizabeth
Courtesy Raymond Bungard

Most of the men had nothing with which to compare this experience. Most had never traveled on a ship, or even seen the ocean. Their experience had no resemblance to the one enjoyed by the paying passengers who cruised on the Queen Elizabeth after the war was over.

When the men entered the ship, they were assigned to either a Red, White or Blue section and issued a button of corresponding color which they were required to wear as designation of their assigned section. The Red, White and Blue areas extended from fore to aft with the sections comprising vertical sections of the ship. For example, the Blue area comprised the stern area of the ship from the bottom ship's area to the deck, the White composed the middle, etc. The men assigned to KP or other duties wore buttons which documented their need to be out of their assigned area. In the berthing area, selection of a top bunk was the wisest choice, since any men above might get sea sick with unpleasant results for the men below them. (12)

The Queen Elizabeth was one of the largest ships ever build, possibly the largest in the world, when the 67th General Hospital was transported to Scotland. The ship was 1,031 feet long, 118.5 feet wide and had a draft of 38 feet and a gross tonnage of 83,673 tons. (11) She had been fitted and certified to carry 15,000 soldiers across the Atlantic with the trip taking an average of

five days. Normally, she would have carried 3,174 passengers and crew when serving as a luxury liner. The additional weight of the men was enough to increase the draught from twenty-nine feet and six inches to forty-four feet.
There was a justifiable concern that this extra draught might cause the Queen Elizabeth to strike the Holland Tunnel in New York, over which it must pass, resulting in damage to the ship and catastrophe in the tunnel. Departures were timed to catch the maximum high tide to alleviate some of the concern about hitting the tunnel.

Additionally, a list of five degrees would be disastrous to the trim causing the ship to capsize which might happen if a mass of the soldiers crowded to one side, or another, for example, to view the Statue of Liberty. The soldiers were ordered to stand in place on deck until they were past the tunnel and the Statue of Liberty. (12)

When the captain gave the sign, the passengers were allowed to leave their berthing area, but the movement was difficult with the halls full of men, often carrying their rifles. Traffic was one-way with military policemen controlling the movement. For example, starboard passages were used for forward movement and port-side passages for aft movement. The captain was not given the time of the ship's departure until 24 hours prior and was not informed as to the course or zig-zag pattern until they were out of New York Harbor, past the Ambrose lightship. He then was allowed to open the sealed orders at this time--obtained prior to departure from the shipping office, and set the course and the zig-zag pattern.

The zig-zag pattern was not random. The most commonly used pattern was designated as "Number 8", which:

> "began with the ship steaming along her base course for four minutes, then altering course twenty-five degrees to port and maintaining that new course for eight minutes. Then she swung to starboard fifty degrees, held that for eight minutes, and turned twenty-five degrees to port again, which would bring her back on her base course, holding that for four minutes. She then made another twenty-five-degree turn, this time to starboard, followed eight minutes later by a fifty-degree turn to port, and eight minutes after that a twenty-five-degree turn to starboard, which brought her back on her base course again. This cycle was repeated every forty minutes, all the way across the Atlantic. A special clock in the wheelhouse chimed whenever the time arrived for another course change." (12)

One soldier remarked on the rough ride encountered with the frequent course changes as he was thrown about and unable to get a good sleep.

The sleeping quarters consisted of 3 tiers of 4 bunks each for the enlisted men, eighteen inches apart in each room. They slept on Standee bunks which consisted of a rectangular frame the size of the bed mounted on hinges and bolted to the bulkhead. A chain on each end of the frame allowed it to lie horizontally when fully extended to the length of the chain. Heavy canvas was then laced tautly to the frame, upon which the soldiers slept. (12) Some soldiers had hammocks, and Joe Bullock was one of those.

The Queen Elizabeth only had 12,500 Standee bunks and in the summer time, if there were 15,000 troops aboard, 2,500 would be allowed to sleep on deck for two nights. This was a coveted arrangement due to a chance to breathe fresher air, have more space and in some cases, it was felt, a higher degree of safety should the ship be torpedoed. During the winter months, sleeping on the deck was not an option because of the extremely cold temperatures on deck. (12)

The nurses had similar accommodations, as did the other women of the 67th contingent. The quarters were crowded to maximize space. The nurses' staterooms were filled with as many bunks as possible and were so crowded that some would lie in their bunks to allow others sufficient space to dress or undress. (9) Five Red Cross workers, two dieticians, and 2 physiotherapists shared a small stateroom about nine by twelve feet in dimension, which had three three-tiered bunks, a standard arrangement. Seven of the nine ladies became seasick.

Standee Bunks.
Photograph in Collection of the Author

Mildred Butler, ANC in Her Bunk
Photograph Courtesy of Betsy Crumrine.

There were no chairs and no places to sit except on their bunk. Sitting on the bunk required a bit of contortion, with the limited space between the bunks necessitating a knee-chest position to sit. The mattress was described as having the thickness of two blankets which were laid over strips of wood, rather than springs (or stretched canvas which the enlisted men enjoyed). (13) They left the room for fire drills which were held twice daily and for their meals. Two meals were served daily. Breakfast was served in the morning from 6:00 A.M. until 11:00 A.M. Dinner was from 3:00 P.M. to 7:30 P.M. (12) Enlisted men took their meals in the First Class Dining Room which had been converted into a cafeteria seating 2500. They ate in shifts, and each section was allowed forty-five minutes to get their meal, eat it and clean their mess kits. All ship's company were required to wear life preservers except when they were in their staterooms or bunks.

More than likely the noncommissioned officers and enlisted men of the 67th General Hospital had the same mess, eating at 9:30 and 6:30. (6) Each soldier was issued two lengths of wire. One was threaded through holes in his knife, fork and spoon and the other through the D-rings of his mess kit. First, he would dip and swirl them into a vat of soapy water, next in one full of boiling fresh water, and the third with boiling disinfectant and lastly a saltwater rinse. When the soldiers left the mess, they passed tables full of ham and cheese and roast-beef sandwiches which they could take to tide them over till the next meal. (12)

The Officers' Mess was in the Tourist Class lounge. There, they had tables and stewards who served their meals at their table, and received a tip for this service. (12) They also had fewer men in each stateroom, often only one, two or three, whereas the enlisted men often had as many as twenty soldiers to a room. Mildred Butler, a nurse, recalls the meat on the way over being rather salty. (9)

Ted Benedict was issued a card for his sleeping quarters which assigned him to Room R75A and a messing card assigning him to Section 4, "A" Mess Hall with his first meal at 9:30 a.m. and his second at 6:30 p.m. Both of these were issued after he boarded the Queen Elizabeth. (18) Sergeant Joe Bullock also received an assignment to the "A" Mess Hall.

MESSING CARD

"A" MESS HALL

4
SECTION

FIRST MEAL 9-30 a.m.
SECOND MEAL 6-30 p.m.

Messing Card from Queen Elizabeth
Courtesy of First Sgt. Joe Bullock

Very few made the dining room trip due to motion sickness from the rocking of the ship as it made its way through the waves. (7) The mess crew was British and boiled mutton was a perennial menu item. The soldiers were so tired of mutton, that they were ready consumers of loaves of bread that the British crew would briskly and illegally auction in the passageways at night. (18) The stench of the mutton, along with the body odor of thousands of men, combined with the pervasive smell of vomit was almost more than one could stand. The ventilation system was originally designed for three thousand people, not 15,000, and there were no showers for the enlisted men. (12) On the way over, they had some bad weather but no storms. (3) One officer remembered the trip as being "an over-crowded ship and rough sea trip". (5)

In reality, the most danger to the ship was as it was leaving from and as it was arriving to the next port. As a consequence, the Queen Elizabeth was accompanied by the escort ships to a distance of about 150 miles from shore and then by airplanes which followed it until their gasoline became low and by this time the liner was well away from New York. When they neared the coast of Ireland, they were met by escorts of airplanes and escort vessels which served to safeguard them in this vulnerable time until they arrived safely in Scotland. Some men thought they saw several submarine periscopes and on one occasion one soldier stated the ship threw out ash can explosives to deter submarine attack. (3) One noise that Sergeant Bullock might have heard could well have been gunnery practice with the extensive arsenal, including six inch guns, that the Queen Elizabeth carried. Ted Benedict recalled that at about 11:00 hours, garbage crates were thrown off the rear of the ship and used for target practice, creating rumors of U-boats being fired upon. (18) A documented encounter by the Queen Elizabeth with a submarine is discussed later.

Doing touch-up painting, scrubbing decks and cleaning common areas and other work details kept some of the men busy and was an opportunity to get a little fresh air. Sergeant Joe Bullock volunteered frequently for these details for this reason. While at sea there were fire drills at 10:00 A.M. and again at 6:00 P.M. (9) There were boat and air-raid drills also. Some of the men would do impromptu comedy routines or concerts to entertain each other. A small number of movies were available for viewing. Additionally, lectures on various subjects were given for interest and information. Daily Orders were published by the Permanent Staff every morning and posted through out the ship. The Daily Orders announced work assignments, religious services, entertainment available and general news. Betsy Larson played bridge to help pass the time. The biggest source of entertainment--gambling, was also illegal. The MPs tried to shut the gambling games down only to see them re-open somewhere else. It did help pass the time. Regulations required that the men always wear their life preservers and to wear their steel helmets if on deck. This made it difficult to do calisthenics, but some officers persisted and had their men do them. (12) There was a black-out in effect on the ship as well. The men were forbidden from throwing things overboard, because a trail of trash might alert U-boats to the presence of a target.

This is how First Sergeant Joe Bullock remembers the trip:

> "The trip over to England on the Queen Elizabeth was about as good as could be had in those days...convoys were much slower, often involved in torpedoes by German submarines, and the ship was so large that it took the waves with only a gentle rolling motion...I think nothing much to induce sea sickness...yet there were many of us who did get seasick. One corporal, Delmar Smith (called "Hog Eye" for reasons unknown) started getting seasick while still in New York harbor...and he spent the entire trip sitting on the floor in front of the commode, although after a day or two there wasn't anything to come up!
>
> Most of the enlisted men were right off the farm, and had not seen a body of water larger than a stock tank.
>
> The ship had quite a bit of ammunition on it and the crew were always asking for volunteers to shift the ammo around from one magazine to another, and I volunteered for that duty every day...I think they actually did the moving around just to give some of the troops something to do on the top side.

The plush staterooms of the original configuration had been chopped up into many small rooms with cots & hammocks for the enlisted men. I'm not sure of the sizes, but to the best of my recollection, I think they were about 10 feet X 10 feet. I had one of the hammocks.

There was much left to be desired in these arrangements…if some one vomited on the floor...we had to clean it up...but after making many trips back & forth and many troops being housed in the rooms...it constantly smelled like something you will have to imagine.

Everyone ate in one of the large dining rooms (mess halls). The meals were provided by the British crew...and I think every day was mutton day...which really did not help the weak stomachs. Incidentally, I never did get to that point...my seasickness consisted only of a slight dizziness and, again, this would wear off when I was out on the deck with the clean cold air.

Unfortunately, there were so many troops on the ship, and nothing to do to occupy the time for most of them, it simply meant they were confined to the small rooms day & night...and about the only action was crap games, etc." (3)

Ted Benedict recalls that his quarters were in a very small room clearly marked, "These quarters are certified to accommodate two able-bodied seamen." The reality was that his room housed six with two three-tiered bunks. He also recalls missing meals because he was so tired of mutton. On 25 November, he celebrated his 23rd birthday while at sea on the Queen Elizabeth. (18)

Raymond Bungard had some very graphic recollections:

"I don't remember my bunkmates coming or going but they were probably 67th. They had periodic lifeboat drills topside (that's a joke--only enough lifeboats for maybe 2000). I did not attend these drills as I knew if we were torpedoed it was the end. One feature of the Queens were huge steel sliding doors in the hold which at the touch of a button could be slammed shut in the event of an attack isolating a portion of the ship. As I wandered about the hold I thought of being trapped. These could also be used in the event of the striking an iceberg.

'Man overboard' would have meant nothing to the QE captain. The ship would stop for nothing on the Queens. The enlisted men ate in the 'hold' (about waterline). Food was supplied by the British who had plenty of mutton and dumped it on the Queens. I have had an aversion to lamb-mutton (whatever) for the past 60 years. At the end of each table was a 55 gallon drum for those who had to 'toss their cookies'. The commissioned officers, I observed topside ate from white table cloths. (Rank has its priviledge.)" (19)

The Queen Elizabeth and the men of the 67th General Hospital were placed in considerable danger while at sea. The Queen Elizabeth was so fast that other ships could not keep up with her and she depended on her speed and alteration of her course to keep her safe from U-Boats. There was no escort vessel which could keep up with her and protect her and therefore she traveled alone. The situation of 15,000 men sheltered below decks with little chance of escaping , inadequate numbers of lifeboats and little chance of surviving the cold waters of the North Atlantic in winter, made any attack on the Queen Elizabeth potentially more deadly. Some had been told at Camp Kilmer that the RN's and MD's stood some chance of getting off the ship in case of emergency, but that the enlisted men who were billeted in a lower section of the ship would not be able to get out in time. (9)

In an interview by National Geographic, a retired West German business executive and former U-Boat commander, Horst Kessler, described an incident which could have significantly altered the course
of the war. (4) Kessler, then the commander of U-Boat U-704, described a narrow escape in November, 1942, by a ship which Kessler and National Geographic felt was most certainly the Queen Elizabeth. Kessler stated in the interview:

> "We had already spent 1 ½ months on the Atlantic and had seen action several times. At the end of November, we were heading for our home port in France. The sea was very rough as you would expect that time of the year, and we had very strong winds from the west--Force 10. There were as usual 4 men on the bridge as lookout. They were all strapped in their positions so that they would not be washed overboard by the high seas."

The National Geographic video continues to state that his lookouts cited what they described simply as a very big ship. While preparing his attack Kessler reached his conclusion that the target could only be the liner Queen Elizabeth. Kessler continued to state:

> "When truly by accident you have an enemy ship of that size in front of your torpedo tubes you must understand it is the absolute situation in the life of a U-Boat captain. At that moment you put everything else in the background and you have only one thought. What can I do to take maximum advantage of this lucky situation?" *The narration continues to describe how Kessler fired 4 torpedoes.* "An explosion was heard but the Queen Elizabeth was not hit--probably Kessler's torpedoes detonated short of their target. In any case, a fateful moment had passed which could have significantly altered the course of the war"

Kessler continued:

> "A few minutes went by and then came a report from the sound technician that we didn't like at all. The Queen Elizabeth's engines could be heard, the noise from the screws of the ship, and it became fainter and fainter and of course that meant that she was continuing on her course, getting further away and naturally it was hopeless to try to follow her."

Following this encounter, Germany's Information Minister, Joseph Goebbels, announced that the Queen Elizabeth had been sunk on November 9. This, of course, was only propaganda, but the sinking would have had numerous consequences. On the ship was Alan Turing, the cryptographer who was responsible for breaking the Enigma cipher system of the Germans. Turing played a pivotal role in breaking the U-boat ciphers which allowed the Allies to understand the communications between German headquarters and the U-boats, thereby knowing their movements and plans and thus helped to defeat the Germans in the Battle of the Atlantic. The battle might not have been won without Turing's contribution. (12)

This event occurred while the Queen Elizabeth was on its westbound (outbound) voyage, about two hundred miles west of Ireland, carrying a few hundred British government officials and army officers, along with Turing, who were on their way to an Allied strategy conference, as well as several thousand women and children who were being evacuated from the British Isles. An explosion which occurred when a torpedo hit a wave, was heard but no one saw the torpedo or the submarine. (12) The next voyage of the Queen Elizabeth was inbound to Britain and carried the men of the 67th General Hospital. The loss of one of the Queens would have been catastrophic to the war effort. Churchill estimated that the use of the Queen Mary and Queen Elizabeth to transport troops to England shortened the war by one year.

One trick the Germans used was to announce that the Queen Elizabeth had been sunk, in one step demoralizing the Allies and also hoping that she would break radio silence to deny the allegation and in the process, give away her position. This trick was tried as the Queen traveled east carrying the 67th General Hospital and other thousands of troops. The announcement of this attempt gave everyone a nervous laugh. (7)

England
The End of the Line

Five days after departing the New York dock, the Queen Elizabeth and the 67th General Hospital landed in Gourock, on the River Clyde, in Scotland, on 29 November 1942. This was the site of the shipyards where the Queens had been built. Their landing was preceded by sea birds flying far from shore and British patrol planes which met them and insured a safer trip to the docks. (3) Ted Benedict recalled the arrival in his diary.

> "So we got to feeling pretty much alone with the seagulls and fish before we rounded Ireland. For an hour or so before sighting Rhinn's Point in the rain Monday afternoon we passed several small fishing craft, and the first sign of an escort was the appearance of two Spitfires skimming the water in circles around our ship at the Sound of Jura. We sailed alone up the Firth of Clyde and dropped anchor after dark. We unloaded the next morning." (18) The men actually remained on the ship until sundown the next day. (18)

Gourock had the only dock complex in the United Kingdom that could berth the Queens safely. The harbor in Southampton was at risk from Luftwaffe bombers, but only the longest range bombers could reach the Clyde. (12) When they arrived in Gourock, they noted the harbor entrance to be narrow, opening to a large round harbor. Barrage balloons reached up into the sky above the white and red houses along the shoreline. A lighter, which is similar to a ferry, carried the men to shore and was used because the dock was not yet finished and would not be finished until mid-1943. (12)

They made a cold trip to the railway station, in the midst of a wet, snowy drizzle. When they arrived, they were greeted by Red Cross canteen workers who fed them hot tea and buns. Betsy Larson, a Red Cross worker attached to the 67th, remembers being taken from the ship by a tender and having to wait aboard the tender for five hours because the train was late. She recalled being cold and damp but especially remembered the gallant gesture of Dr. Christensen when he laid his rain coat over her shoulders while they were waiting for the train. (7) That night they dined on army canned rations. On their train trip south, the men would parade through some of the towns (She said the Brits liked parades.) on some of their stops. Also on their stops, they were met by the British Red Cross who served biscuits (scones) and hot tea which were appreciated by the soldiers newly exposed to the cold weather. As they made their way south to Somerset, they were often side-railed by supply trains which had priority over the troop train. (3) Ted Benedict recalls that the engine pulling the troop cars was a steam engine which would scoop up water between the rails as it sped down the track at a high rate of speed. (18)

When the 67th General Hospital left Camp Kilmer, and departed on the Queen Elizabeth, the gossip and opinion of most of the Unit was that they had orders to go to Africa. There must have been some consideration of the brass for North Africa as a destination, since the baggage of the unit contained mosquito netting which was later used to decorate their theater, and preparations were underway in the United States and England for Operation Torch. Imagine their surprise, and probable delight, to discover their ultimate destination did not involve an amphibious landing, bullets whizzing over their heads, sand or sea.

The 67th General Hospital left Scotland on the very evening they left the ship, rode the train all night, passed through Bristol near sunrise the following morning and arrived in Taunton, Somerset, England, around noon, on 1 December 1942. (18) The hospital was not ready for occupancy since work was still being done to complete the construction. Trucks transported the RNs, officers, dieticians, physiotherapists and Red Cross workers to Norton Manor Park, a military camp nearby, for billeting.
The enlisted men were housed at Norton Manor also. (Today, Norton Manor provides billeting for the 40 Commando Royal Marines) Some stayed in the Old Manor House. Betsy Larson (Crumrine) recalled a large "horse barn" where she stayed before arriving in the Taunton facility. (7, 21) Mildred Butler recalls three level biscuit beds-- 3 section iron beds which folded into one unit. She recalls "dirty old blankets, rocks and soil thrown in, not very cozy." (9) To compound the discomfort, there was no hot water.

The officers were also stationed in the same general area, but the Commanding Officer and a few other officers continued on to London Headquarters. Upon their return, an advance party of 20 to 30 was taken to Musgrove Park. The stay at Norton Manor lasted about two weeks, while they waited for workers to finish the needed construction at the hospital in Taunton, and for the total removal of the Evacuation Hospital which had been stationed there before the arrival of the 67th General Hospital. Ted Benedict remembers feeling a sense of history when he was" barracked in a Roman army camp with chariot wheel tracks leading across rocks into the camp."

but does not specifically remember if this was Norton Manor. (18) The hospital was taken over by the 67th General Hospital on 5 December, at 0001 Hours. (8, 10)

When the 67th General Hospital assumed command of Musgrove Military Hospital, a hospital originally built for the British military, they took over from the 2nd Evacuation Hospital. The hospital had been occupied by an American hospital since the latter part of July, or first part of August, 1942, when one officer and forty enlisted men of the 298th General Hospital assumed charge. This was an affiliated hospital with the University of Michigan. (14) The majority of the 298th General Hospital was stationed at Frenchay Emergency Hospital, Frenchay Park, Bristol, taking over that hospital in November, 1942. Thus, the unit at Musgrove may have only been a detachment of the 298th. No records were available to confirm these facts at the time the Annual Report of 1942 for the 67th General Hospital was submitted, and no exact dates were given. It was understood that this unit remained there for only a brief period and was succeeded on 20 August 1942, by the 180th Station Hospital. (On 9 November, the 180th Station Hospital which had recently occupied Musgrove Park Military Hospital, departed Taunton and arrived at Liverpool, the next morning. They boarded the H.M.T. Andes at 1300 Hours, 10 November 1942, and sailed to Mers-el-Kebir, Oran, Algeria, where they debarked at 1300 Hours, 22 November 1942.) (16) The 180th Station Hospital was relieved on 10 September by the 38th Evacuation Hospital and on 23 October by the 2nd Evacuation Hospital. (10).

The 2nd Evacuation Hospital was originally affiliated with St. Luke's Hospital, New York City, New York, with the enlisted men originally coming from Camp Barkley in Abilene, Texas. A detachment of the 2nd Evacuation Hospital consisting of eight officers, 12 nurses and 40 enlisted men had been sent to Musgrove Military Hospital, under the command of Major Charles L. Munson, from Ballymena, to relieve the 180th General Hospital which was sailing for North Africa. (After being stationed in several locations in Great Britain, following their stay at Musgrove Military Hospital, in Taunton, the 2nd Evacuation Hospital sailed for France arriving at D-Day + 17. (15))

The officers and nurses of the 67th General Hospital found central heat (wartime style) hot water and English woven blankets. The enlisted men had adequate, if not quite as comfortable, accommodations in Nissen Huts where they remained until they were moved to eighty 6-man tents prior to D-Day. This move was to make room for the anticipated larger numbers of patients which were expected to increase following the invasion of the Continent.

Richard Smith shared his experiences and impression of the camp and the trip to Taunton with his wife, Bessie:

> "3 December 1942
>
> I'll try writing a few lines today we landed without any trouble at all this sure is a nice place it isn't so cold just wet and be glad when we get lined up every thing is much better than I expected to find it such as our quarters, etc.. I guessed I was fortunate not being sea sick while coming over although some of the others did. We sure have been treated nice by the people here. We were met at some of the stations and was treated with tea and cookies. We are allowed to go into town every 3rd night. Your Husband. Richard F. Smith" (2)

The number of officers and nurses and enlisted men in the 67th General Hospital was determined in advance by military bureaucrats. A Table of Organization (T/O 8-550) put out by the War Department on 1 April 1942, specified the number and rank of officers (1 Colonel, 6 Lt. Colonels, 14 Majors, 19 Captains, 13 First Lieutenants, and 3 Second Lieutenants and specified into which medical departments these various ranks would be placed. One hundred and five nurses were allowed and 500 enlisted men were allowed or needed, depending on how one interprets the document.) As time went by these T/Os would be modified to reflect current thinking on organization or to reflect manpower availability. (17)

Even before the Unit left the United States, there were rumors that they were to be shipped to Africa, as mentioned earlier. The arrival in Taunton did not still these speculations. There were many rumors about the disposition of the various units, particularly about whether they would be moved to another station, remain in their same station or follow the soldiers to the front. Ted Benedict made a diary entry in August of 1943, which illustrated the wild ruminations of men who had too much time on their hands and too much imagination:

> "Now that it's over and can be put down, here's something of what has been going on for the last two weeks. Rumors began flying around that we were being moved to another station a few miles away which is not occupied, but only being guarded by our men. No one knew why, but lots of people were guessing. The most persistent story was that it was to be a temporary staging area, that we would be sent to Africa, from there along with an infantry division. Less reasonable ones were that the supplies being taken there were field type, that we would all be retrained as company aid men and that we would be paid off next week in American money. The reason for that last one was that week we're headed for Panama. A special order was posted Monday canceling days off, ordering no passes before 5 pm and no furloughs. Thursday, our men and supplies began coming back, pass and day-off restrictions rescinded, and for the time being there is quiet again." (18)

Reality became truth as time passed and the 67th General Hospital remained in place in Taunton.

Aerial View of Musgrove Military Hospital
Collection of Author

References

(1) "Memorandum from Lieutenant Colonel Stephen A. Cobb of the 67th General Hospital to Commanding Officer, 67th General Hospital, Camp Kilmer, New Jersey, Subject: Travel Trip." National Archives.

(2) Letters from Richard Smith, to His Wife, Bessie, Transcribed and Partially Edited by the Author.

(3) Interview with First Sergeant Joe Bullock, 20 and 21 June, 2003, at His Home in San Angelo, Texas, as Well as On-going E-mail and Postal Communication.

(4) National Geographic Video, "The Superliners: Twilight of an Era." Program Copyright 1980.

(5) Communication with E.P. McManamy, M.C., Captain. August, 2003.

(6) Messing Card from Queen Elizabeth Obtained from First Sergeant Joe Bullock, June, 2003.

(7) Communication with Betsy Larson Crumrine.

(8) "Annual Report to the Chief Surgeon, SOS, ETOUSA, APO 887, U.S. Army." Dated 31 January 1944. National Archives.

(9) Communication with Captain Mildred Butler, ANC.

(10) "Annual Report of the Medical Service to Lt. Colonel R.B. Moore, Commanding Officer of the 67th General Hospital." Signed 30 December 1942, by Lt. Colonel E.R. Blaisdell, MC., Chief of Medical Service. National Archives.

(11) Encyclopedia Brittanica CD 98.

(12) Butler, Daniel Allen. *Warrior Queens--The Queen Mary and Queen Elizabeth in World War II* . Stackpole Books, 2002.

(13) "Reports to the Red Cross from the Red Cross Unit Assigned to the 67th General Hospital. Narrative Report for 31 December 1942." National Archives.

(14) " Records of the 298th General Hospital." National Archives.

(15) "Records of the Second Evacuation Hospital." National Archives.

(16) "Organizational History of the 180th Station Hospital, U.S. Army 18 March 1942 to 40 April 1944." National Archives.

(17) "Table of Organization No. 8-550 for General Hospital, War Department, 1 April 1942." National Archives.

(18) Communication with Ted Benedict.

(19) Communication with Raymond Bungard.

Chapter 6
Musgrove Military Hospital

On 5 December 1941, at 0001 Hours, the 67th General Hospital took over facilities northwest of the town of Taunton, Somerset, England, known as Musgrove Military Hospital. The hospital was new, originally built as a British naval hospital, on land turned over by the Musgrove family (27), but was never occupied by British forces. The hospital was originally designed for 700 patients and consisted of a complex of some 30 one-story buildings. (22) The building complex was only 80% complete at the time of the arrival of the 67th General Hospital.

Dr. John R. Guy, in his book *Malachi's Monument*, a history about The Taunton and Somerset Hospital at East Reach, briefly discussed Musgrove, and wrote that the hospital was built as the "British Army's Venereal Disease Centre". A set of original blueprints of the hospital indicated that a number of beds were set aside for treatment of venereal diseases but there was no indication that the hospital was built to treat this class of patient exclusively. No source was found which mentioned Musgrove Military Hospital's future as a venereal disease center. The co-ordinates for the hospital were VT6646 on the Ordinance Map of Great Britain. The Musgrove family presented Colonel Roland B. Moore, the Commanding Officer of the 67th General Hospital, with a regimental mascot, a Springer Spaniel, named "Musgrove Trooper 3rd". (27)

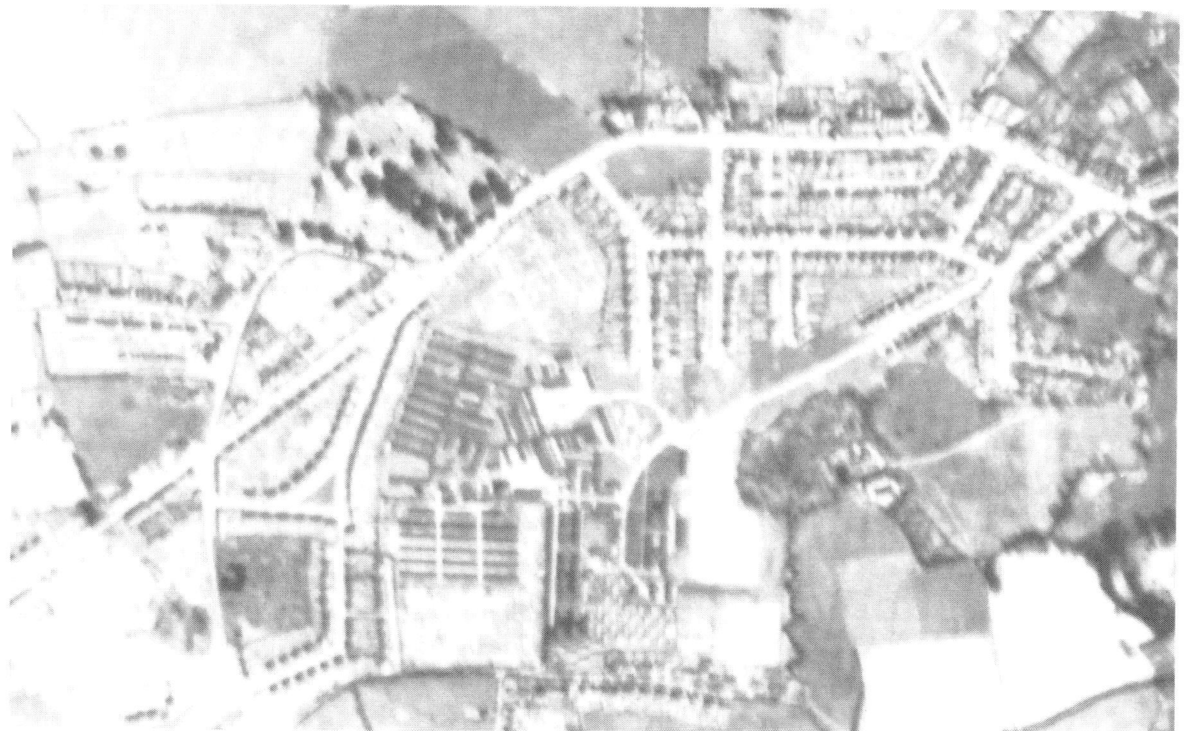

Detail from theGerman Reconnaissance Photograph on Following Page, Showing Musgrove Military Hospital
(Seen on lower part of photograph to the left of the midline on This and Following Photographs)
Photograph Copied from Original, Courtesy of Somerset Studies Library, by Author

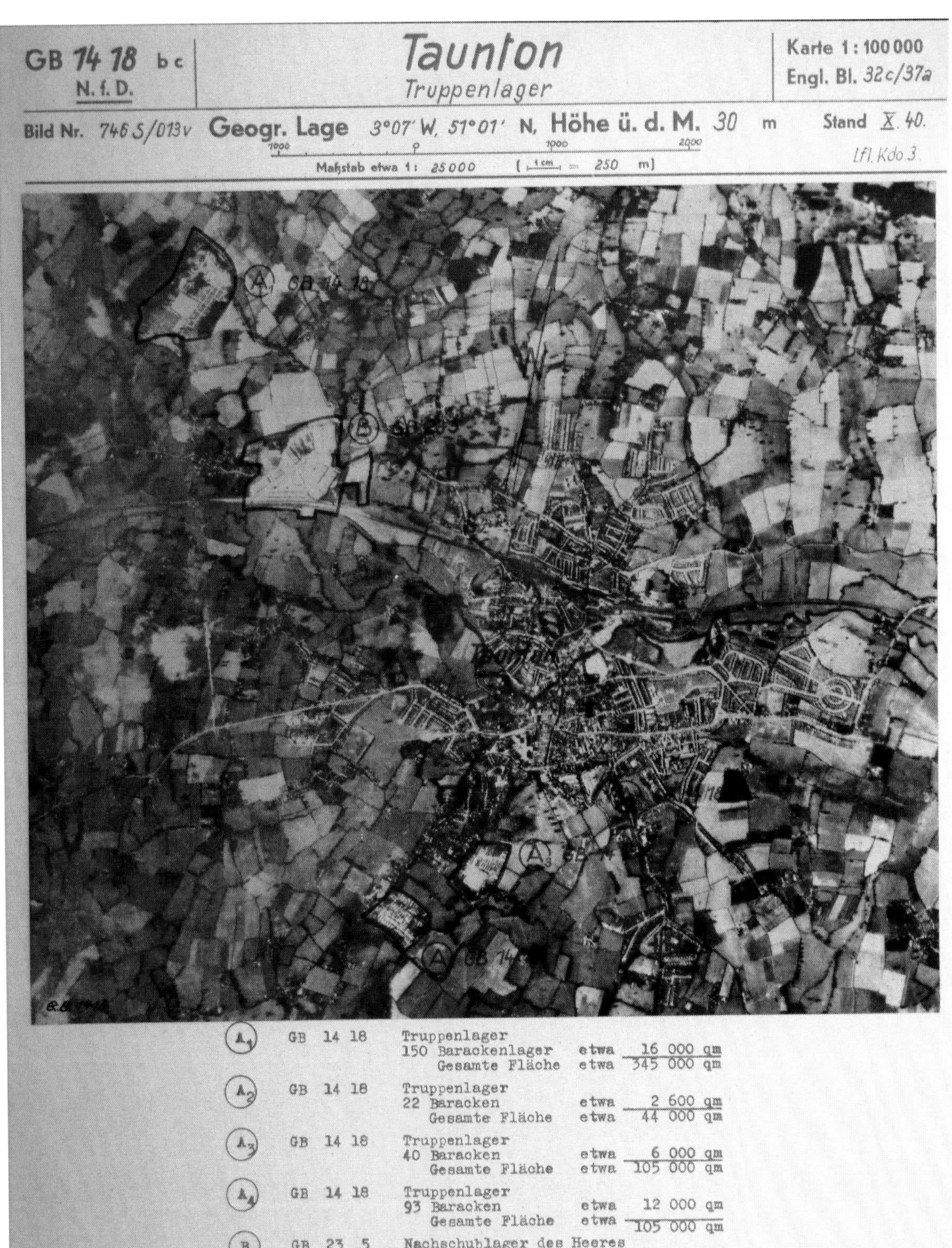

German Reconnaissance Photograph of Taunton, Somerset, England
Courtesy of Somerset Studies Library, Taunton, Somerset, England

The Camp
1 January 1944

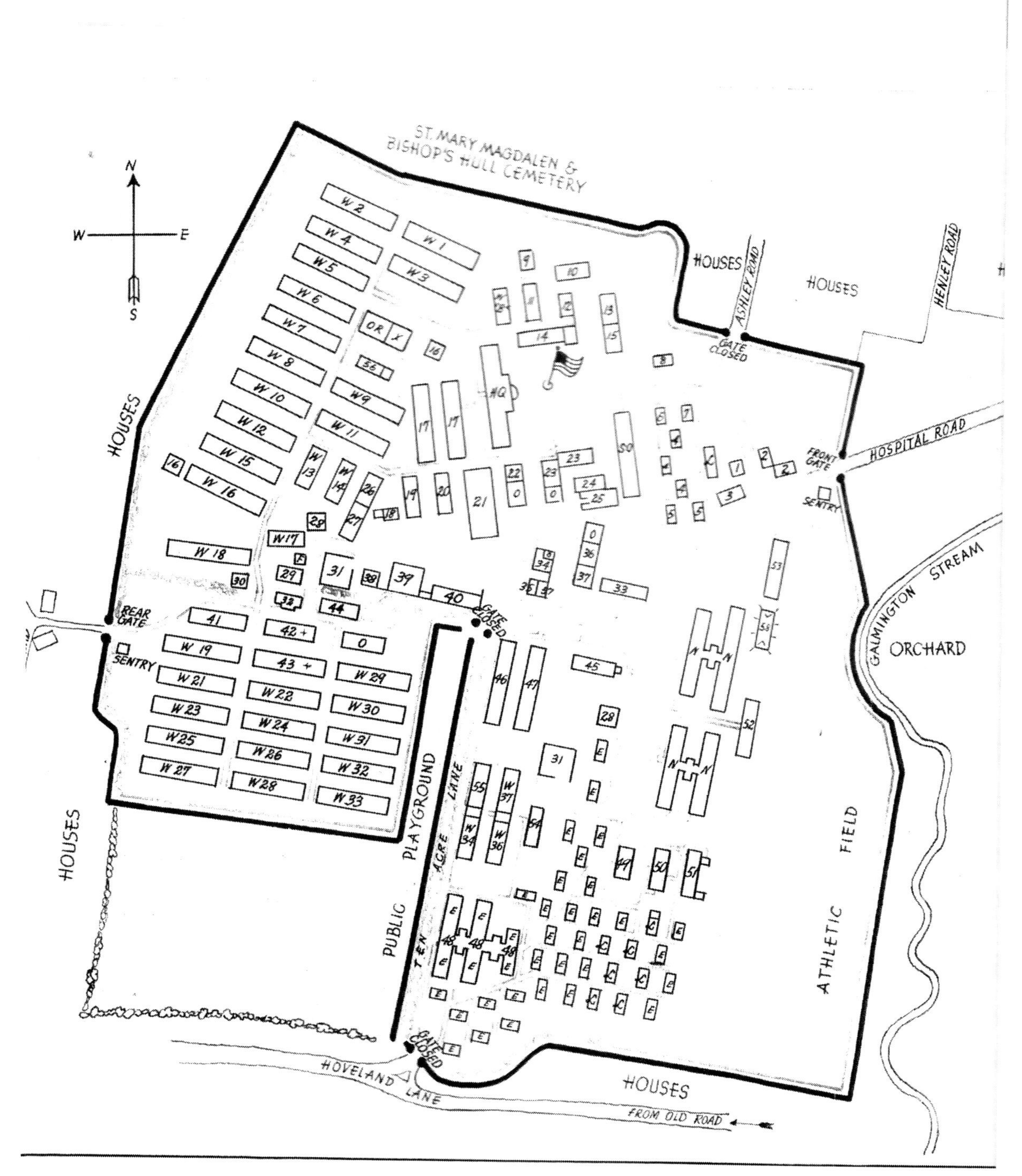

National Archives

Legend of the Camp
1 January 1944

LEGEND

W - Wards
OR - Main Operating Room
X - X-Ray
HQ - Administration Bldg.
SO - Senior Officers' Quarters
O - Officers' Quarters
N - Nurses' Quarters
E - Enlisted Mens' Quarters
F - Fire Station
L - Latrines and Baths

1 - Sgt. of the Guard
2 - Guard Houses (Jails)
3 - Prophylaxis Station
4 - Guards' Quarters
5 - Equipment Storage
6 - American Registrar
7 - British Registrar
8 - Post Office
9 - Emergency Operating Room
10 - Out-Patient Clinic
11 - E.E.N.T. Clinic
12 - Dental Clinic
13 - Detachment of Patients' Office
14 - A & D Office
15 - Baggage Room (Det. Pats).
16 - Equipment Storage (O.R. and X-Ray).
17 - Pat. Mess Halls.
18 - Detachment Supply
19 - Linen Supply
20 - Medical Supply
21 - Main Kitchen
22 - Photo. Lab.
23 - Officers' Mess
24 - Emerg. Kitchen
25 - Air Raid Shelter
26 - Laboratory
27 - Pharmacy
28 - Static Water Tanks
29 - Small Boiler House
30 - Water Tower
31 - Fuel Dumps
32 - Patients' Post Exchange
33 - Personnel Post Exchange
34 - Post Quartermaster
35 - Barber Shop
36 - Officers' Club
37 - Nurses' Mess
38 - Mortuary
39 - Main Boiler House
40 - Vehicle Storage
41 - Post Theatre
42 - Red Cross Arts & Crafts Shop
43 - Red Cross Service
44 - Utilities Shop
45 - Post Chapel
46 - Physiotherapy
47 - E.M.Recreation
48 - N.C.O.Quarters
49 - Orderly Room
50 - Det. Kitchen
51 - Det. Mess Hall
52 - Nurses' Recreation
53 - Vehicle Repair Shop
54 - G.U.Mess Hall
55 - G.U.Clinic
56 - Central Supply
57 - Motor Vehicle Dispatcher
58 - Bicycle Storage Tent.

Taunton Town

Taunton proved to be the final destination of the 67th General Hospital, and at the time of their arrival in 1942, was a town with a population of 30 to 40 thousand people. Taunton, the County Seat of Somerset County, in the Administrative District of Taunton Deane, was a quiet agricultural town when World War II began. It was built beside the Tone River which provided the origin of its name--Tone Town, or town along the Tone.

The town of Taunton was idyllic as viewed by the men of the 67th General Hospital. Swans swam on the River Tone, sheep and cattle were herded through the town on the way to market. Tales were relayed to the men of bonfires set on the frozen Tone river during celebrations or holidays. They never experienced such a sight but did have snow on several occasions during their stay.

Swan on the River Tone
Photograph Courtesy of Raymond Bungard

The men of the 67th General Hospital became accustomed to such scenes as cattle and sheep being driven down the middle of town. They visited the local produce and livestock markets which dated prior to 1066 and the Norman Conquest. Some soldiers visited sites in Somerset

County such as the town of Cheddar, in the Mendip Hills which gave its name to Cheddar Cheese. They also visited Bath, Bristol, Glastonbury and Weston-super-Mare, which were nearby.

Cattle in Streets of Taunton, Somerset, England
Photograph Courtesy of Raymond Bungard

Sheep Market, Taunton, Somerset, England
Photograph Courtesy of Ted Benedict

Buildings and Grounds

The hospital was built on 35.37 irregularly shaped acres, approximately 1400 by 1100 feet, sloping gently from the back to the front, facing east, about 1/3 mile from Taunton. There were 133 recently constructed buildings: 56 permanent brick buildings one story high and 77 Nissen huts with concrete floors and brick or tile side walls. Nissen huts had been developed by a Canadian engineering officer in World War I. (The Quonset hut was a more deluxe and larger American derivative.)

In 1942, there was an administration building, post office, storehouses, supply buildings, hospital mess, officer's and nurses' quarters, post exchange, officer's and nurses' mess, Red Cross building, physiotherapy building, morgue, detachment office, senior NCO quarters, operating room and 26 ward building of permanent brick construction. The X-ray department was housed in one end of the operating room building with the principal entrance through the operating suite. In addition there was a fire station, two guard houses, Registrar's office, five guards' quarters, dental operating room, three kitchens, detachment mess, chapel, twenty-nine barracks for enlisted men, theater, supply building, twelve enlisted men's latrines and wash houses, two utilities shops and a garage, as well as sixteen wards in the convalescent area, which were of Nissen type construction.

Administration Building (Now Called the Old Building)
Photograph Courtesy of Lucille Walker

Administration Building
Photograph Courtesy of Raymond Bungard

Covered walks connected the administration building, receiving ward and eighteen wards of the main hospital, while in the convalescent area, uncovered walks of tarmac connected the various buildings. In the area reserved for housing of the Detachment Medical, there were gravel walks with plans made for sidewalk construction and drainage. Landscaping and beautification of the hospital grounds were needed when the Unit arrived and application for assignment of civilian help in gardening was made to level and fill the grounds and plant trees, shrubs and lawn throughout the hospital area. Adequate quarters for junior officers and a recreation building for the enlisted men were needed at this time, also. (21)

The permanent brick buildings, in 1943, accommodated the Administration Building, post office, store houses, supply, hospital mess, officers and nurses' quarters, officers and nurses' messes, Detachment day room, physiotherapy, morgue, senior N.C.O.'s quarters, operating room, A and D Office, Detachment of Patients, Dental Clinic, E.E.N.T. Clinic, boiler house, main kitchen, patients' messes, laboratory and pharmacy, darkroom and studio, V.D. Clinic and 21 wards. (14)

In 1943, fifteen wards were used mainly for convalescent patients and housed in Nissen type buildings. Twenty-nine modified Nissen huts, with tiled walls were used as living quarters for the Detachment Medical Department. Twelve of the permanent brick wards were heated by stoves, and the remainder by central heating facilities. All of the Nissen type buildings were heated by stoves. The Administrative and Clinic Building had central heat. Covered cement walks connected the Administrative Building, receiving ward, clinics, operating room, x-ray, and 18 wards of the main hospital, as well as the main kitchen and patients' mess halls. Wards in the convalescent area had uncovered walks of tarmac. There were immediate plans to cover them using unit labor, since materials for the purpose had just been received at the time of the annual report. (14) Mildred Butler recalled:

> "There were 18 wards with number 18 being for sick nurses only. Beyond ward 18 were Nissen huts, each numbered--open ramp. 30 or 31 was last ramp. I worked out my captaincy on night duty last 5 Nissen huts. 1 corpsman each hut. I was only R.N. 30+ patients each hut. Only heat was electric stove in kitchen--base board in office, plus 2 private rooms for critically ill. Open ward--3 small iron stoves, no grates to control fire. Either hot or out. Patients able to be up and about took turns keeping fires going--coke was fuel." (26)

Ward 17 in Foreground
Photograph Courtesy of Lucille Walker

Nissen Wards from the Tower
Photograph Courtesy of Ted Benedict

In 1943, hard tarmac surface roads provided access to all essential parts of the hospital. Progress was made in landscaping and ground beautification and two civilian gardeners were employed to supervise this work. (14) The junior officers were distributed among permanent brick buildings correcting a housing problem which had been reported earlier. (14) Also, during 1943, a wooden building was added which housed a post exchange, barber shop and tailoring shop in an area reserved for convalescent patients.

As D-Day neared, the building formerly used as the non-commissioned officer's quarters was converted into 5 wards with a total of 112 patient beds and the Nissen huts formerly occupied by enlisted personnel were converted into 12-bed wards for convalescent patients who required no active medical care. This allowed an additional 252 convalescent beds.

Richard Smith Standing on Far Left, in Front of His Nissen Hut Prior to Being Moved to the Tents.
Photograph in Author's Collection

Convalescent Wards
Photograph Courtesy of Lucille Walker

The enlisted men were housed in 108 six-man pyramidal tents, in the field adjacent to their previous quarters. They utilized the same latrine facilities as before the move and were within easy distance of the Detachment mess. These tents were fully winterized by January, 1945. (2)

Tent Area and Game of Horseshoes
Photograph Courtesy of Ted Benedict

Water was obtained from the surrounding lakes and hills 7 miles away, In the hospital, there were two large storage tanks each with a capacity of 25,000 gallons. Additionally, there were 36 tanks mounted on various buildings with a capacity of 2,500 gallons each, serving as an auxiliary supply, in case of fire or damage to the main system. During 1944, a well was driven near the western end of the post, which could supply an additional flow of water to the available supply if needed. (8)

One of the challenges was the electrical system. Electricity was supplied as a 230 Volt current while the equipment made in the U.S. and supplied for the hospital operated on a 110 Volt current. There were difficulties in obtaining transformers or resistance units to convert the current. This was a problem particularly in surgery, the laboratory, the kitchen and in most departments throughout the hospital which required electrical equipment. This shortage caused a delay in installation and use for much of their electrical equipment. (24)

Food was obtained through the General Supply Depot, the G-50, located 4 miles from the post, with the exception of vegetables grown on the post.

Remaining Buildings of the G-50
Photograpy by and Courtesy of Dr. Joe Braly, Taken in 2004

In April, 1943, a tractor plowed eight acres of ground for the vegetable garden destined to supplement the supply of fresh vegetables making it less necessary to purchase food on the open market. (23) The food was prepared in two kitchens: The main kitchen prepared food for all patients--bed and ambulatory and for the officers' and nurses' mess. This food was distributed in insulated containers to the various wards and messes, where warming ovens were used to maintain it at proper temperature prior to being served. A second kitchen was maintained in the Detachment area for the mess of the Detachment Medical Department.

Kitchen at Musgrove Military Hospital
Photograph Courtesy of Ted Benedict

Chowline
Photograph Courtesy Ted Benedict

The ambulatory patients and Detachment Medical ate cafeteria style. Each ward had a diet kitchen where dishes and eating utensils were kept, washed, rinsed in boiling water and air dried. Food containers were kept in the wards, and carts were carried to the main kitchen by ward attendants immediately before meal time. Using a system of one way traffic through the kitchen, it was possible to serve all wards and messes in less than 20 minutes. In 1943, there was a shortage of food-serving carts to deliver food to the bed patients on the wards. (14) By 1944, two messes were needed for the use of ambulatory patients with a capacity of approximately 800 for each mess. The messes had dish washing machinery and used metal trays. Food waste was collected daily by a civilian under contract which required him to keep the cans clean.

The eight acres of land which were planted to vegetables in 1943, were later converted into an "obstacle course" for the training of convalescent patients. (2) During 1944, additional covered walks were constructed to connect all new wards to the original buildings. (8) Between two and three acres of land were leveled and landscaped with lawn, shrubs and flowers and by June, 1945, a total of five acres had been landscaped. (5) Two civilian painters were kept busy throughout the year of 1943. and two civilian painters, one civilian carpenter, and one civilian electrician were employed for the maintenance of Musgrove Hospital according to a June, 1945 report. (2)

Organization

The management of the hospital was divided into two main sections, Administrative and Professional, as follows:

Administrative Section

Headquarters Group determined the policies involved, assigned the personnel, issued necessary orders, bulletins and memoranda and conduct correspondence.
Note: This Group is covered in more detail in Chapter 10.

Commanding Officer
Executive Officer
Adjutant
Chief Nurse

Colonel Roland Moore, Commanding Officer of the 67th General Hospital
Photograph By and Courtesy of Ted Benedict

Executive Group carried out the policies and orders of the Headquarters group.

Registrar
Receiving and Evacuation Officer
C.O. Detachment of Patients
C.O. Detachment Medical Department
Medical Supply Officer
Mess Officer
General Supply Officer
Utilities Officer
Chaplains

The Detachment Medical Department consisted of the enlisted medical personnel and their Commanding Officer was involved in their day-to-day management and discipline. The Detachment Medical is discussed further in Chapter 10.

The **Professional Section** was concerned only with the care of the sick and wounded and the professional instruction of personnel. It was divided into five Services with supplementary Departments of Dietetics and Physiotherapy, administered by female civilian officers of the Medical Service. (They served without rank or commission.)

"All services and sections are closely related by numerous inspections conducted by the Commanding Officer or Executive Officer, and by frequent consultations among the various professional services, as well by weekly staff meetings which all officers are required to attend." (14)

"Consultation outside their respective service, to another service in the hospital, had to be cleared through the office of their Chief of Service." (30)

Colonel Moore, Commanding Officer of the 67th General Hospital, (in front of left door), at Merryfield, Prior to Loading of Patients Through Cargo Doors for Transfer
Photograph by and Courtesy of Ted Benedict

Medical Service

The Medical Service was organized under a **Chief of Medical Service** who coordinated the various functions of the service. It was divided into five **Sections** as follow:

Gastroenterology
Neuropsychiatry
Cardiovascular
General Medicine
Communicable Diseases

Each of these sections was commanded by a **Chief of Section** who was responsible to the **Chief of Service**. In addition, each ward in the Medical Service was under the direct supervision of a **Ward Officer**. The Chief of Service or a Chief of one of the Sections served as a consultant if their experience was requested elsewhere.

In 1943, three deaths were reported from the Medical Service. The patients died of the following causes :

(1) Acute encephalitis with cause unknown

(2) Purulent meningitis, fracture, compound, comminuted supra-orbital notch and fracture, compound, comminuted of nose.

(3) Glioma, of right parieto-occipital area, type undetermined. (13)

A total of 319 patients appeared before the Disposition Board in 1943. The recommendations of the board regarding these patients were not noted. (13)

A total of 750 patients appeared before the Disposition Board in 1944, with the recommendation that they be returned to the Zone of the Interior. (7)

There were 9 deaths on the Medical Service in 1944 with the following diagnoses. (7)

(1) Leukemia, lymphocytic
(2) Subacute bacterial endocarditis caused by *Streptococcus viridans*
(3) Head injury resulting from a soldier stepping in the front of an automobile on 2 February 1944, on road known as Road A-30, in Middle Street, near junction of Wyndam Street, Yeovil, England.
(4) Atypical pneumonia with acute myocarditis
(5) Acute meningococcemia
(6) Suicide
(7) Tuberculosis, miliary
(8) Acute aleukemic leukemia
(9) Anterior myocardial infarction.

<u>Roster of the Medical Service at Ft. Bliss and Upon Arrival at Musgrove Hospital on 5 December 1942</u> (20)

Chief of Service	Lt. Colonel Elton R. Blaisdell
Assistant Chief of Service	Major Charles W. Steele
Chief of General Medical Section	Major Edward A. Greco
Chief of Cardiovascular Section	Major Wilfrid J. Comeau
Chief of Gastroenterology Section	Major Henry H. Tabachnick
Chief of Communicable Disease Section	Major Merrill S.F. Greene
Chief of Neuropsychiatry Section	Captain Charles W. Eastman

Ward Officers

Captain Bertrand A. Beliveau
Captain Paul R. Chevalier
Captain Gerald H. Donahue
Captain Joseph A. Villa
Captain Ralph E. Williams
First Lieutenant Harry E. Christensen
First Lieutenant Charles L. Holt

Roster of The Medical Service, 1943 (13)

Chief of Medical Service	Lt. Colonel E.R. Blaisdell
Assistant Chief of Medical Service	Major Edward A. Greco
Chief of General Medical Section	Major Merrill S.F. Greene
Chief of Communicable Diseases Section	Major Paul W. Marston
Chief of Neuropsychiatric Section	Major Charles W. Eastman
Chief of Cardiovascular Section	Major Wilfrid J. Comeau
Chief of Gastroenterology Section	Major Henry H. Tabachnick
Ward Officer	Captain Harry E. Christensen
Ward Officer	Captain Howard E. Milliken
Ward Officer	Captain Charles L. Holt

Activities of Officers on the Medical Service in 1943 (13)

Major Charles W. Steele, former Assistant Chief of Medical Service, was transferred to the 121st Station Hospital as Assistant Chief of Medical Services.

Captain Bertram A. Beliveau was boarded to the Zone of the Interior with a diagnosis of active duodenal ulcer.

Captain Paul R. Chevalier was returned to the States due to illness of his family.

Major Paul Marston, Captain Maynard B. Colley and Captain Howard H. Milliken were assigned to the Medical Service.

Major Edward A. Greco was made Assistant Chief of Service.

Captain Charles W. Eastman was advanced to the rank of Major. First Lieutenants Harry E. Christensen, Charles L. Holt and Howard H. Milliken were advanced to the rank of Captain.

Roster of The Medical Service, 1944 (7)

Chief of Medical Service	Lt. Colonel E.R. Blaisdell
Assistant Chief of Medical Service	Major Henry M. Tabachnick
Chief of General Medical Section	Major Paul C. Marston

Chief of Communicable Diseases Section	Major Merrill S.F. Greene
Chief of Neuropsychiatric Section	Major Charles W. Eastman
Chief of Cardiovascular Section	Captain Maynard B. Colley
Chief of Gastroenterology Section	Captain Gilbert Clapperton
Ward Officer	Captain Harry E. Christensen
Ward Officer	Captain Howard E. Milliken
Ward Officer	Captain Charles L. Holt
Ward Officer	Lt. William V. Flynn

Activities of Officers on the Medical Service in 1944

Major Greco transferred on 13 August 1944.

Major Comeau transferred on 17 July 1944.

Captain Donahue was transferred on 28 January 1944.

Captain Villa, who had been on the Medical Service at the beginning of 1944, was transferred to the Admitting Office on 1 March 1944, where he remained until 1 May 1944. At this time he was transferred back to the Medical Service, and on 25 June 1944, he was transferred to the X-Ray Department.

Captain Williams was sent home on 1 April 1944, as a result of illness.

Captain Berman, who was assigned to this hospital on 6 June 1944, was transferred to another hospital on 8 December 1944.

Major Jacobs was assigned to the 67th General Hospital on 1 June 1944, and on 30 June was transferred to the A. and D. Office.

Lt. Hamel was assigned to the 67th General Hospital on 13 August 1944, and was transferred to another hospital on 12 December 1944.

Lt. Flynn was assigned to the 67th General Hospital on 19 July 1944, and was on the Medical Service until 16 October 1944, at which time he was assigned to the Surgical Service. On 29 December 1944, he was transferred back to the Medical Service.

Captain Clapperton was transferred from Surgical Service to the Medical Service on 14 August 1944.

The 1943 Report noted that weekly conferences were held, often in conjunction with the X-ray Service with discussions of associated medical problems. Every other week, a general staff meeting of the hospital was turned over to the Medical Service at which time interesting cases were presented and discussed.

The 1944 Report goes on to state that weekly conferences had been held whenever possible and always whenever it was necessary to bring up important matters. The officers of the Medical

Service took part and discussed cases of interest in the weekly General Staff Meetings of the hospital. As battles raged, the case load increased and the officers took on the extra work.

Venereal Disease Control in 1943--Regular instruction by lectures and training films were conducted throughout the year. The Prophylaxis Station near the main gate, and a second Station in the down-town area of Taunton, were furnished with personnel from the 67th General Hospital. All enlisted men of the command received instruction on sex hygiene and the prevention and control of venereal disease. Prophylaxis materials were on sale at the Prophylaxis Stations and were available without cost at the Orderly Room. There were five cases of syphilis and five cases of gonorrhea reported in the command during the year. Prophylaxis was used or administered in three instances. (14) It was reported that the new drug, penicillin, was used regularly in the treatment of sulfa-resistant gonorrhea, and in a few cases of serious surgical infection, with good results. (14)

Penicillin was given for treatment of sulfa-drug-resistant cases of gonorrhea with 51 cases treated under the direction of Major George Poore, Chief of the Urological Section. The treatment of syphilis which had been carried on by the Urological Section until September, 1943, became the responsibility of the Medical Service.

Surgical Service

The Surgical Service was organized under a **Chief of Surgical Service** who coordinated the various functions of the Service. It was divided into five **Sections** as follow:

Orthopedic
Urologic
Eye, Ear, Nose and Throat
Septic Surgery
General Surgery

Each of these sections was commanded by a **Chief of Section** who was responsible to the Chief of Service. In addition, each ward in the Surgical Service was under the direct supervision of a **Ward Officer**. The Urological Section operated as a separate unit in three wards assigned to it under the command of the Urological Chief of Section. The E.E.N.T. Section conducted a clinic in a separate building and had a separate building for the treatment of eye, ear, nose and throat infirmities.

The Physiotherapy Department had its own building operated by trained physiotherapy aides under the control of the Chief of the Orthopedic Section. One officer in the Surgical Service was assigned as anesthesiologist and was in charge of all anesthesia given in the hospital, as well as supervision and responsibility for the operating room. During the days in 1944, prior to D-Day, The Anesthesia Section, under Captain Clapperton, trained personnel on temporary duty from other units in the administration of anesthesia. Additionally, two officers and two nurses of the 67th General Hospital were trained to administer anesthesia for possible use in other units. (6)

A constant problem was severe loss of well-trained personnel, both officers and enlisted men, partially through personnel being boarded to the ZI (Zone of the Interior--i.e. USA) for physical disability but to a much greater degree because of their transfers to other hospital installations. Replacements, in most cases, were not as well-trained, and would need time to gain adequate experience. (6)

Upon arrival in 1942, an emergency shock team was set up consisting of eight officers and the necessary numbers of nurses and enlisted men. Under their supervision, two shock wards were set up and equipped for the care of a potentially large number of acutely wounded patients who might be in shock at the time of admission. Four emergency operating teams were set up for emergencies within the hospital with an equivalent number available in the hospital for further emergencies. Surgical officers took part in courses in specialized fields at various locations in England, and in 1942, six officers were given detached duty for one week periods for special training. (18)

In 1943, there were 3215 admissions to the Surgical Service with three deaths--none post-operative. Two deaths were the result of severe basilar fractures of the skull in patients who lived less than six hours after injury and the third was a patient with severe basilar fracture of the skull who died from complications of pneumonia. All diagnoses were confirmed by autopsy.

Post-operative complications listed included 2 patients who had venous thrombosis following pentothal sodium injection, six with post-operative atelectasis, 8 with postoperative bronchopneumonia, one who had cardiovascular collapse in the O.R., one with respiratory arrest under pentothal sodium, seven with wound infections with serous collections and 5 others who suffered from wound infections.

Section Chiefs supervised the performance of junior officers in 1943, in pre and post-operative care and performance of operative procedures. In the early parts of 1943, many of the surgical officers took short courses in various branches of surgery, offered through the Chief Surgeon's Office. The ward officers and nurses trained the enlisted personnel about such procedures as preparation of operative sites, hypodermic injections, administration of intravenous fluids and catheterization, to enable these soldiers to perform these tasks if the census became large enough to warrant their assistance in those duties. Officers from other units were assigned for temporary duty for periods of 30-60 days on the general service. Ten medical officers were assigned to periods of 30-60 days for instruction in anesthesia under the supervision of Captain Clapperton, the Chief Anesthetist. After 25 October 1943, 4 medical officers were attached for three days of each week for instruction in cast application under the direction of Major Thompson,

Chief of Orthopedic Section. Several of the medical officers from the 67th General Hospital were given temporary duty in either English or American hospitals. During December, enlisted men in groups of four were attached to the Surgical Service for instruction in the operating room to enable them to work in surgery if needed. (12)

A Central Supply depot was located near the operating room to supply sterile goods and supplies for both the surgical and medical wards. An auxiliary operating room was set up some distance from the main operating room in reserve in the event the main operating room became damaged and was incapable of carrying the surgical load. During the early months of 1943, a rehabilitation program for convalescents was begun and managed by Captain Holland and Captain Gordon Johnson. Captain Gordon Johnson continued to direct the rehabilitation program in operation during 1944. Good results were obtained in chest injury cases with the use of chest exercises. (6) This program was gradually discontinued as convalescent hospitals were later established in the ETO. (12)

Roster of Surgical Service 1942 (18)

Chief of Surgical Service and Chief of Neurosurgical Section	Major William V. Cox
Assistant Chief of Surgical Service	Major Philip H. McCrum
Chief of Orthopedic Section	Major Milton S. Thompson
Chief of Septic Surgical Section	Major Eaton S. Lothrop
Chief of E.E.N.T. Section	Major Carl E. Richards
Chief of Genitourinary Section	Captain George C. Poore
Chief of Anesthesia Section	Lt. Gilbert Clapperton

Ward Officers:
Captain John R. Feeley
Captain Edward W. Holland
Captain Albert C. Johnson
Captain Gordon N. Johnson
Captain Emory C. McLean
Captain Eugene P. McManamy
Captain Alvin E. Ottum
Captain Otis B. Tibbetts
Lieutenant Joseph G. Ham
Lieutenant John R. Merrick
Lieutenant Walter G. Dixon
Lieutenant Rosario A. Page

Roster of Surgical Service 1943 (12)

Chief of Surgical Service	Lt. Colonel William V. Cox
Assistant Chief of Surgical Service	Major Philip H. McCrum

Orthopedic Section

Chief of Section	Major Milton Thompson
Ward Officer	Captain Gordon Johnson
Ward Officer	Captain Walter G. Dixon
Ward Officer	Captain Alvin Ottum
Ward Officer	Captain Rosario Page

Septic Surgery Section

Chief of Section	Major Eaton Lothrop
Ward Officer	Captain Joseph Ham
Ward Officer	Captain Eugene McManamy

General Surgery Section

Chief of Section	Major Alvin A. Morrison
Ward Officer	Captain E.A. McLean

Urological Section

Chief of Section	Major George C. Poore
Ward Officer	Captain A.A. Brin (Detached Service from 1st Aux. Group)

EENT Section

Chief of Section	Major Carl E. Richards
Ward Officer	Captain A.C. Johnson
Ward Officer	Captain Otis B. Tibbetts

Anesthesia Section

Chief of Section	Captain Gilbert Clapperton

Detached Service

Ward Officer	Captain Edward Holland
Ward Officer	Captain John Feeley

In 1944, there were 9462 admissions to the Surgical Service--5390 of those after D-Day. In 1944, there were 39 deaths on the Surgical Service, a mortality rate of 0.41% which did not represent an operative mortality since most of the patients had received their surgeries prior to arriving at the 67th General Hospital. Additionally, there were 4220 surgical consultations by the Surgical Service in 1944. (6)

The 67th General Hospital at Musgrove Military Hospital was designated as one of the Neuro-surgical Centers in the UK. There was a large volume of work from 27 July 1944, to 8 December 1944, and two members of the 1st Auxiliary Surgical Group, Captain Donaghy and Captain Wallman, were on detached service to the 67th General Hospital to help with the neurosurgical work. It was the policy to suture nerves as early as possible and the tantalum wire suture and tantalum cuff techniques were carried out in the majority of the cases. (6) As a result of this Neurosurgical Center designation, most of the nerve injuries were repaired at the 67th General Hospital before the patients were boarded to the Zone of the Interior (U.S.A.). (8)

Almost all battle casualties were treated with sulfa drugs and penicillin, and both drugs were started in the forward areas before evacuation to the Communication Zone. The clinical opinion of the doctors was that penicillin and sulfa drug systemically, and penicillin locally, were a distinct help in combating infections. However, no control series of patients treated using this protocol were done. Secondary closures of wounds proved to be a safe, time-saving procedure and also yielded a better cosmetic and functional result. The sooner secondary closure could be carried out the better, and those closed within ten days following the injury did much better than those closed after the ten day period. In the last four months of 1944, this was the treatment of choice for compound fractures, with wounds closed by secondary suture or combined with a skin graft, to make a closed fracture out of a compound fracture. In the last few months of 1944, all fractures of long bones were treated by traction until the fracture sufficiently healed and then the patient was sent to the Zone of the Interior (the U.S.) in a supporting cast. (6)

A Consultant Service for the 1st Hospital Group (Prov), 801st Medical Service Detachment (Hospital Center) was augmented by members of the 67th General Hospital Surgical Staff. The eight consultants visited hospitals within the group and made suggestions to the Commanding Officer of the individual hospitals and the Commanding Officer of the Hospital Group. Consultants named from the 67th General Hospital Surgical Staff included: (6)

Consultant in General Surgery	Lieutenant Colonel William V. Cox
Consultant in Neurosurgery	Lieutenant Colonel William V. Cox
Consultant in Orthopedic Surgery	Major Irvine M. Flinn
Consultant in Urological Surgery	Major George C. Poore
Consultant in ENT Surgery	Major Carl E. Richards
Consultant in Opthalmologic Surgery	Captain Otis B. Tibbetts
Consultant in Anesthesia	Captain Gilbert Clapperton

In addition to those named above, the 67th General Hospital provided consultants in roentgenology as well as general medicine. The responsibility of being a consultant took a large portion of their time which was spent on inspections, consultations, etc. (5)

Roster of Surgical Service 1944

Chief of Surgical Service	Lt. Colonel William V. Cox
Assistant Chief of Surgical Service	Major Philip H. McCrum

Orthopedic Section

Chief of Section	Major Irvine M. Flinn
Ward Officer	Captain Walter G. Dixon
Ward Officer	Captain John R. Feeley
Ward Officer	Captain E Allan McLean
Ward Officer	First Lieutenant Stanley A. Isenberg

Septic Surgery Section

Chief of Section	Captain Gordon N. Johnson
Ward Officer	Captain John R. Merrick

General Surgery

Chief of Section	Major Alvin A. Morrison
Neurosurgery	Captain Averill Stowell
Anesthesia	Captain Gilbert Clapperton
Ward Officer	Captain Joseph G. Ham
Ward Officer	Captain Eugene P. McManamy

Urological Section

Chief of Section	Major George C. Poore

EENT Section

Chief of Section	Major Carl E. Richards
Opthalmology	Captain Otis B. Tibbetts

Dental Service

The Dental Service was organized under a **Chief of Dental Service** who was directly responsible to the Commanding Officer. It comprised three Sections as follows:

Oral Surgery
Prosthetics
General Operating

A Dental Clinic was conducted in a separate building with a dental laboratory and separate operating theater for dental surgery, which could be used in emergency as an additional general surgical operating room. (8) In September, 1944, space across the ramp from the entrance to the clinic was acquired and used as a waiting room and office for the chief clerk. (5) Another building behind the Dental Clinic contained another small laboratory, x-ray room and guard room, as well as storage for dental supplies. (5, 8)

The Annual Dental Report of 1942, related that the Dental Clinic was established specifically for the personnel of the hospital, but that emergency treatment was given to the personnel of surrounding units when no other dental treatment was available. The report noted that the lack of equipment prevented the clinic from operating at its full capacity and that prosthetic treatment was considerably handicapped due to the lack of a gold supply. (17)

Dental personnel, in the 1943 Annual Dental Report, included six dental officers from 1 January 1943 to 25 June 1943, and then five dental officers for the rest of the year. Twelve enlisted men were included in the report as assigned to the Dental Service. (11) According to the Annual Dental Report dated 4 January 1945, personnel at the end of 1944, consisted of five dental officers who were there throughout the year. Lt. Colonel Roy O. Perkins became Chief of the Dental Service on 6 September 1944, replacing Lt. Colonel William B. Jordan who transferred to the 154th General Hospital. Private James M. Williamson was sent on detached service in May of 1944, and had not returned by the end of 1944. In July of 1944, T/5 Charlie Lacy, a trained chair assistant and dental x-ray technician, was sent on detached service to the local military police organization for two months and by the end of 1944, had not returned or been replaced. In November, 1944, T/5 Paul W. Flaming went back to the States on detached service and by the end of 1944, had not returned. Private First Class Adam Melkonian was assigned to duty in the Dental Clinic in November of 1944. It was reported that the dental officers from surrounding units continued to have the facilities of the Dental Clinic at the 67th General Hospital available to them as the need dictated. (5)

The Annual Report of 1944, further classified the military personnel as of 31 December 1944 as:

Colonel Jordan	President of General Court
Captain Grant	Member of Special Court and Summary Court Officer
Captain Mann	Member of General Court and Summary Court Officer

Captain Cope	Summary Court Officer
Captain Smith	Summary Court Officer

Captains Grant, Mann and Cope were trained in the administration of pentothal sodium anesthesia after reporting to the operating room for half a day for a period of two weeks. Captain Franklin Smith received anesthesia training and also went on detached service at the 30th General Hospital, for two weeks in February. There he took a course of instruction in the making of plastic eyes--made of the same plastic from which dental plates were fashioned. (5,22)

Laboratory Service

The Laboratory Service was organized under a **Chief of Service** who had commissioned assistants and several well-trained enlisted men working with him. The laboratory was housed in a separate building which was fully equipped to do all types of medical analysis, bacteriological, pathological and serological examinations.

Laboratory Service: Shown on Left in White Standing: Richard Wood. Seated in White from Left to Right are Unidentified, Richard Callicot, Robert Siverling, Robert Bell. Behind Bell, Sam Cummings, Continuing on Left to Right, Raymond Bungard and Deward Grissom. Behind Grissom in White is Harold Zucker. In Olive Drab, from Left to Right in Back Row are Edwin McArthur, Unidentified, Wayne Hixson, Mac Innis, Major Jere Downing (Chief of Service), Harold Mullinex (NCO in Charge of the Lab), John Rodney and Diamond Martin. Not Pictured Are Lt. Harry Harper and Ted Benedict.
Photograph Courtesy Raymond Bungard.

The laboratory was organized into six major Departments: Serology, Hematology, Pathology, Bacteriology, Chemistry and Urinalysis. The Morgue was apart from, but staffed by the laboratory personnel. A commissioned officer was responsible for supervision, matters of general policy and use and care of departmental equipment. Lt. Harry Harper, M.A.C., was transferred into the 67th General Hospital in March, 1944, to perform this function.

Second Lt. Harry Harper (on left) and Major Jere Robert Downing, Chief of the Laboratory (on the right) Performing Autopsy
Photograph Courtesy of Ted Benedict

Second Lt. Harry Harper
Photograph Courtesy Ted Benedict

The Chief of Laboratory Service, Major Jere Downing, selected a sufficient number of donors for blood and kept that list in his office. The donors were given physical examinations and serological examinations. When a request for donation was made, the patient's blood was typed and a suitable donor selected, and at the proper time, both donor and expected recipient were sent to a designated location for the transfusion. (30) Ted Benedict added some color to the blood bank story:

> "I was asked to care for inventory and collection of blood for our blood bank. This job required that volunteers be recruited, and so I had to find an incentive other than money. I found it by using Scotch whiskey as payment, one ounce per liter. No problems with that, except that we had to be careful to cite an appropriate medical justification for using such precious stuff, still on the official list of medicines just in case of snakebite.
>
> Our blood bank arranged for direct transfusions as needed, but usually the blood had been inventoried after typing and checking for disease (malaria, syphilis, mostly), and some prepared as plasma, in both cases being citrated. Major Downing would not let me, or Bungard, or Hixson donate, saying that he wanted to keep us in reserve for emergency direct (untested) transfusion.
>
> When we ran out of vacuum syringes, and, very briefly, regular syringes, we drew blood specimens by needle, letting the blood drip directly into the test tube. For transfusions we collected blood by improvising a Venturi-vacuum system connected to the water faucet." (35)

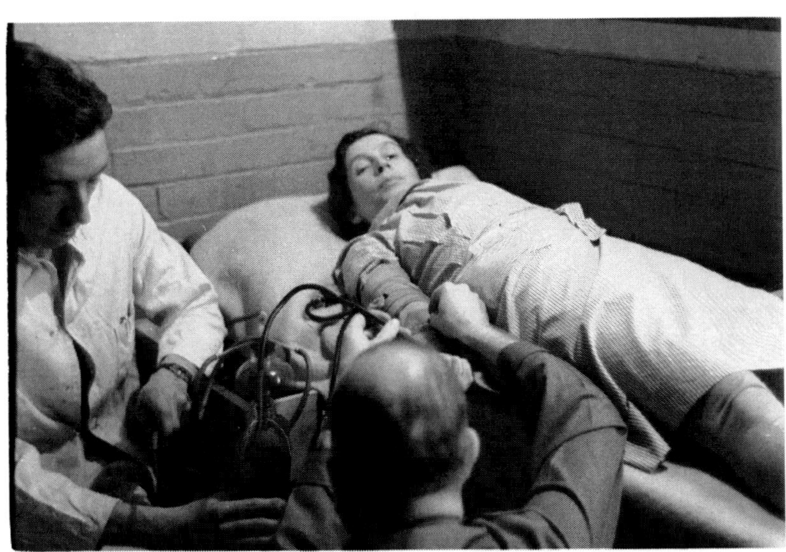

Miss Clancy volunteer Blood Donor, Has Needle Inserted by Major Downing, with Wayne Hixson Assisting.
Photograph Courtesy of Ted Benedict

The 1942 report lists two officers and twelve enlisted men in the laboratory. The officers were both medical graduates with civilian experience in medical practice. Four of the enlisted men had received training in Army hospitals other than the 67th General Hospital, and four had completed the laboratory course offered in the Army School for Medical Technicians. (16)

During the calendar year of 1943 and 1944, there were fourteen regularly assigned, trained enlisted men in the department until September, when two full duty men were transferred out and one replacement assigned for training. The two junior Medical Corps officers were reassigned to other departments in the hospital and the vacancies filled by two Lieutenants, Sn.C. On several occasions, extra enlisted personnel were temporarily assigned for purposes of training. (4, 9)

Raymond Bungard, who worked in the laboratory, went to medical school after the war and trained as a surgeon, had some recollections:

> "We had a well-equipped laboratory (for the time). Soldiers lined up by the dozens for blood tests. Blood drawing was primitive by today's standards. The technician would hold the needle by the hub putting his thumb over the opening and do a venipuncture letting the blood run into a tube all in a standing position. Predictably some would faint and did. On occasions an overzealous lab tech would straddle the fallen GI and finish the blood draw. The army had its share of alcoholics. One alcoholic lab tech could always find the unlabeled bottle of 95% ethyl alcohol in spite of my attempts to hide it. Many autopsies were performed as an assistant, it was my job to saw off the skull with a hand saw. On one particular odious occasion an autopsy was performed on an officer who had been floating in the Bristol Channel for two weeks. It was a good introduction to medical school.

Ted Benedict recalled the autopsy of the officer pulled from Bristol Bay.

> "When we autopsied the officer found floating in Bristol Bay, we said that we couldn't fingerprint him because of deterioration. We were ordered to get the prints in whatever way necessary. So I removed the finger skins and pickled them, dried them, and then made the prints." (35)

Raymond Bungard continues:

> "One of my other duties was running the photo lab. You mention a sciatic nerve injury. I was called to the operating room to document photographically that the neurosurgeon was unable to approximate the cut ends of the nerve due to a loss of segment of the nerve." (36)

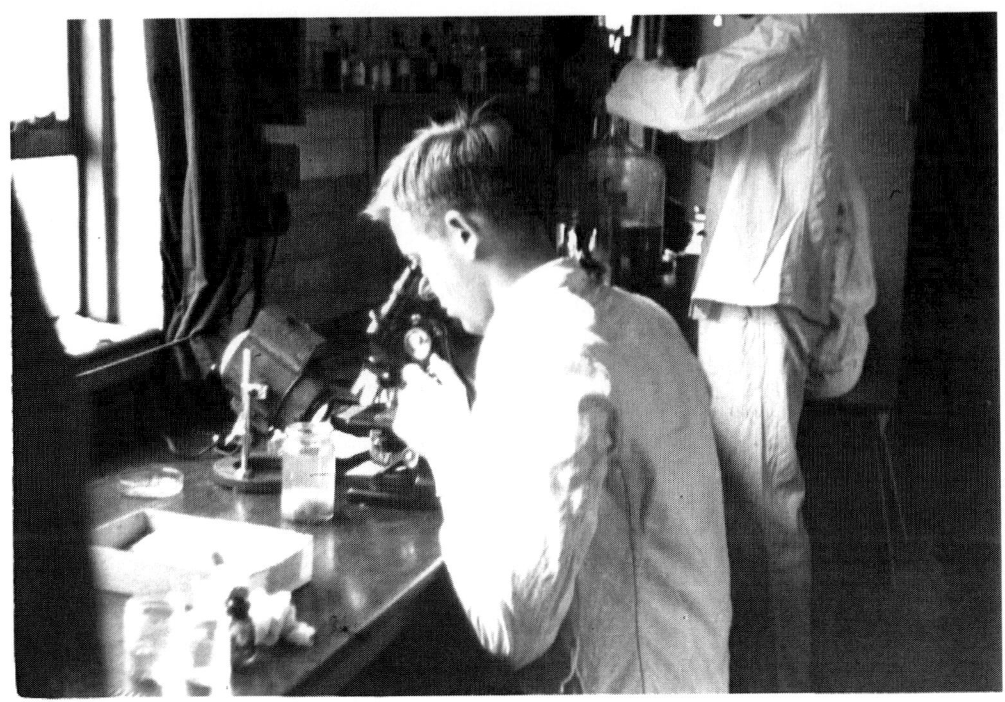

Raymond Bungard on Microscope
Photograph Courtesy of Ted Benedict

Another function performed by laboratory personnel was that of photographer, although possibly not designated by government regulations, the function fell to them in the following manner as described by Ted Benedict:

> "In addition to my duties in the clinical lab, I assisted Ray Bungard in operating the photography services. This happened when the unit photographer hit an officer and was removed. Col. Moore had seen me, Bungard, and Hixson leaving the hospital each Saturday on our way to church, usually with cameras hanging from our shoulders. When the Executive Officer asked him for authorization to requisition a replacement photographer, the CO said that it wouldn't be needed, because 'we have three of them'. Not knowing for sure who we were, he intercepted us the next Saturday and so we were named for the job." (35)

Ted Benedict mentioned some of his other duties in the laboratory:

> "I was transferred to the lab (from the Registrar's Office) where I was chief clerk. I had been to clerk school during my basic training in Abilene, Texas, so I was qualified. Both jobs were excellent educations for me, letting me get to know the wards, doctors and nurses and so I was qualified. In addition to this, I took dictation notes for some eighty autopsies while in the lab."

Ted Benedict on Typewriter
Photograph Courtesy of Ted Benedict

Roentgenological Service

The Roentgenological Service was organized with a Chief of Service and one commissioned assistant. The building housing the department had its entrance located at the rear of the operating suite, and a separate building was used for storage of films. (8)

The 1942 Annual Report enumerates nine men of the Service. (15) In the 1943 Annual Report, Jack Spencer, Lt. Colonel, M.C., Chief of X-Ray Service, reported that a captain was transferred and First Lieutenant Benjamin Allen was assigned to their Service. Regular X-ray conferences were held with medical officers and weekly X-ray conferences were planned with the 127th General Hospital. (10)

In the 1944 Annual Report, Lieutenant Colonel Jack Spencer submitted the report as Chief of Service and listed changes in personnel for 1944. He listed Major Tyler and First Lieutenant Benjamin S. Brown who had been assigned to the Service for temporary duty as well as First Lieutenant Benjamin Allen, Captain Rosario Page and Captain Joseph A. Villa who had been assigned to the Roentgenological Service and had subsequently been transferred. He notes that Captain John F. Henderson was assigned to the Service 31 July 1944. Two enlisted men who were serving on the Roentgenological Service were transferred to general services during this period also. (3)

In 1944, after several consultations with the senior consultant, a system was worked out whereby all radiographs were placed on the wards with a radiologist's report attached to the preserver, allowing each Ward Officer to review the films on each of his cases with a minimum delay. (3) When the patient transferred, the films went along with the patient to his next post. An additional room was assigned to the roentgenologist in 1944. (8)

Also noted was that weekly conferences were held with radiologists in the vicinity during 1944. (3)

Radiology Service
Photograph Courtesy of Betsy Crumrine

Operations of the Hospital

In the third quarter report of 1944, Colonel Roland Moore discussed that a major challenge was that the 67th General Hospital had been required to set up to function as a "transit" hospital and care for large numbers of patients who had come in from the battles in Europe. This extra work was accomplished by using officers of the Medical Service to function as surgeons--by scrubbing in the operating room, giving penicillin and other medicines, doing post-operative care such as changing bandages, etc. Also, more operations required more anesthesia personnel and two officers from the Medical Corps and one from the Dental Service were instructed in the administration of anesthesia. Twenty-five nurses were obtained from the 95th General Hospital, the 40th General Hospital and the 313th General Hospital. The enlisted men from the administrative staff functioned to handle the admission and disposition of patients.

Another problem was that the hospital had been designated as a "holding" hospital as well and patients who had been designated to return to the Zone of the Interior had not been moved out and they tied up a large number of beds that were sorely needed by the Surgical Service. Their presence also brought a morale problem to the other patients, due to the presence of seriously injured men and an attempt was made to segregate them from the other patients but this did not prove practical. (31)

During the last quarter of 1944, the designation of the 67th as a holding hospital was lifted. However, the bed capacity of the hospital was increased from 1463 to 1700. This put a strain on the mess facilities, latrines and bathing facilities and increased the work of the doctors, nursing service and ward personnel. Additional bed space was found by increasing the number of beds on each ward and by using 6 additional Nissen huts for convalescent patients. (32)

The building of 544 feet of covered ramp ways was finished in the last quarter of 1944, by engineers furnished by the Southern District. Also, an additional 327 feet was partially completed. In the last three months of 1944, 3,080 patients were admitted and 3,038 were discharged--638 back to duty, 2,071 to the Zone of the Interior and 329 to other dispositions. (32)

The rehabilitation policy underwent changes also, with more emphasis placed on an ongoing rehabilitation of the patient during their hospitalization. When the medical officer determined that the patient had sufficient recuperative capacity to return to duty and when he was ambulatory, he was placed into one of four groups--A through D. A and B groups were sent to the rehabilitation area and C and D groups remained on the wards. The patients in the rehabilitation area were organized into companies with a training program consisting of calisthenics, remedial exercises, lectures, army talk, etc. For those not returning to duty, but returning to the Zone of the Interior, some needed extra assistance on their journey home and for this purpose, 1 officer, 11 nurses and 10 enlisted men were temporarily returned to the Zone of the Interior to accompany patients. (32)

By the next quarterly report, it had become evident that the new rehabilitation system was paying off by allowing the men to either return to duty quicker or go to a convalescent hospital in a more expedient manner. On 8 January 1944, the patient census reached 1634, and on 5 February, it again rose to 1616. The shortage of personnel continued and the solution continued to be met by moving non-critical personnel from other departments and using them to help ease the shortage in the Surgical Service and wards. In the first four months of 1945, 1335 patients were returned to duty, 703 were sent to other hospitals, 1950 were sent to the Zone of the Interior and 8 had other means of disposition. Admissions totaled 3668 and discharges totaled 4016, with an average daily patient census in the hospital of 1136.

Reflecting the number of casualties at that time, the Unit awarded 697 Purple Hearts and 129 Oak-Leaf Clusters to patients. The Unit began using German prisoners for outside police and landscaping duties and in the mess hall and kitchens. They were guarded by personnel from the 67th. This served to increase the manpower which was sorely needed. The Table of Organization 8-550 dated 1 April 1942, was replaced and the hospital reorganized by TO 8-550 dated 3 July 1944. An inspection was given on 17 February, by Lt. General John C.H. Lee, Commanding General, and again on 21 February, by Colonel Banchfield, ANC from the Surgeon General's Office, Washington, D.C. (33)

Nursing Service

The Army Nurse Corps was under the command of a Chief Nurse, ANC. Each ward was headed by a commissioned officer in the Army Nurse Corps who supervised ward management and housekeeping and was assisted by qualified members of the Medical Detachment. (21) The first Chief Nurse was Irene Zwisler who was reassigned to organize nursing schools in Europe. She was succeeded by Marjorie French (seen in the photo below).

Mildred Butler, ANC, as the Assistant to the Head Nurse, Marjorie French, was required to have her report to the mess hall by 12:00, and the time spent preparing the report was the only time she was off her feet. She was in charge of 5 wards which constituted about 300 patients. These included two psychiatric wards, one post-neurosurgical surgery ward, one luetic (syphilitic) ward and a frost-bite ward. She recalled the peak patient census being 1779, with only 79 nurses available to care for them. She also

recalled that the nurses went over to England in their blue uniform but changed to olive drab in the next year.

Nurses from the 67th General Hospital Hear News From Home
From Left to Rght are: *All 2nd Lt's.* Hazel Churchhill, West Farmington, Maine, Marjorie French, Augusta, Maine, Louise Libby, Portland, Maine, Hilda Morrile, South Brewer, Maine, Dolores Graham, Myllinocket, Maine, Arneta Blanchard, Thorndike, Maine. (3 Mar 43) Signal Corps Photo: ETO-HQ-43-1819 (Pearson) Photograph Obtained from the National Archives.

Religious Activities

One of the first installations to be completed on the post was the Chapel, converted from an ordinary Nissen hut. Church services were held by Catholic and Protestant chaplains assigned to the 67th General Hospital. During the two and one half years at Musgrove, the 67th had four Catholic and 4 Protestant chaplains rotate through the unit. They held two baptisms, seventeen marriages and three funerals. Twenty-two marriage investigations were made and approximately 300 letters of welfare, sympathy and condolence were sent. (2)

In 1944, there was a marked increase in chapel attendance after D-Day, partly because of the increased number of patients and also apparently because of increased tendency to seek religious consolation. Eight marriages were performed. Chaplains who served at the 67th General Hospital included: Charles M. Bacon, Thomas Brett, Robert J. Curtis, Everett E. Denlinger, William Donaghey, Williiam T. Hoffmeyer, Arnold Horner, Homer B. Massie, Robert M. Powers and Rodney Taylor.

Mildred Butler, ANC related a human interest story to liven these statistics. She tells of a man named Gabriel, an assistant to the priest, who would sell the sacramental wine to willing buyers. (26)

Chaplain Wm Donaghy

Chaplain William Donaghy
Photograph Courtesy of Betsy Crumrine

Medical Supplies

When the 67th General Hospital took command of Musgrove Military Hospital, the equipment was meager and insufficient for the care of large numbers of patients. It was difficult at first to acquire the basic allowance of initial equipment particularly X-ray apparatus, surgical instruments, dental equipment, laboratory equipment and supplies. The supply situation continued to improve through the end of the year, and by the end of 1942, the operating room was capable of caring for at least four major surgical operations at one time. The laboratory still lacked necessary equipment such as Kahn Antigen, pneumonia typing serum, incubating apparatus and dark field apparatus. (21)

There was an initial scarcity of supplies during the first few months of 1943. (1) A comment in the 1943 Annual Report stated, "that recent allotments under T/BA and later T/E have necessitated the return of a considerable amount of supplies, some of which are considered almost essential for the efficient functioning of the hospital." (1) (T/BA refers to the Table of Basic Allowances which was replaced by the T/O&E which refers to the Table of Organization and Equipment. T/O&E are still used in the Armed Services today.)

Ted Benedict related a story about Folin-Wu tubes (which were used to determine fasting blood glucose using whole blood, rather that serum, which was the usual technique:

> "We did find some supplies hard to find or to substitute. I remember that I had requisitioned some extra Folin-Wu tubes just in case we broke the one we had, and subsequently I got a direct communication from the ETO Surgeon General telling me that we then had the total supply of Folin-Wu tubes for the entire theater. Would I return all but one? Well, of course…" (35)

Ted Benedict in Field Equipment and Ambulance
Photograph Courtesy Ted Benedict

In 1944, a Central Supply was established for sterilization and issue of all items used in ward dressings which improved efficiency and saved time, personnel and materials. The largest single function of the supply section at the end of 1944, was the issue of clothing and equipment to patients leaving the hospital--4,608 patients were fully clothed and equipped, 4,512 patients partially clothed, making a total of 9,120 patients served, of which 8,163 were outfitted after June, 1944. To compare, during the entire year of 1943, only 386 patients were outfitted. To accomplish this increase, warehouses were expanded and a model stock of 300 items of individual clothing and equipment had to be kept on hand at all times. The building formerly allotted to the British Registrar, and no longer needed, was converted to accommodate bulk storage of patients' clothing and equipment. (8)

An immense amount of supplies were used during the 2½ years spent at Musgrove. Pharmacy reported:

> "...the filling of 33,712 general prescriptions, 9,222 narcotic prescriptions--a total of 42,954. The amount of penicillin dispensed was 11,152 ampules of 100,000 units each; 287,000 aspirin tablets; 310,000 sulfadiazine tablets; 105,000 sulfathiazole tablets; 107 pounds sulfadiazine ointment; 118 pounds sulfathiazole ointment; 33,100 A and D vitamin capsules; 70,900 multivitamin capsules; 160,000 APC capsules and 460 pounds of various ointments." (2)

Transportation

In the 1943 Annual Report, eight minor driving accidents were reported for the year and in none of these was a driver from the 67th General Hospital responsible. The report goes on to state that the total number of trips made during the year was 8,761, covering a total of 131,306 miles. (1)

In 1944, gasoline consumption was 27,794 gallons, with the vehicles averaging 8.4 miles per gallon. There were seven minor accidents with no claims against the government and no action against the drivers, who were considered blameless. Five complete motor assemblies were installed by Unit personnel. At the end of 1944, the personnel, functioning under the Post Quartermaster, consisted of one staff sergeant, two mechanics, and nineteen drivers. Seventeen additional men were trained as extra or emergency drivers, and fifteen others were in the process of being trained. (8)

The final report, made 15 June 1945, prior to departing Musgrove Hospital, noted that the greatest problem which faced the Transportation Department was loss of trained drivers due to redeployment. Statistically, there were 27,131 trips made in the previous two and one-half years with a total mileage of 483,528. The vehicles consumed 55,354 gallons of gasoline, 348 gallons of oil and 314 pounds of grease. Fifteen minor accidents were reported with the drivers found blameless. Due to excellent maintenance, only four vehicles had to have heavy maintenance during this period and all vehicles had been painted annually. (2)

Motor Pool Photographs ShowingTrucks
Photographs Courtesy of Lucille Walker

Laundry

The hospital laundry was handled on on a contractual basis with the British, and the work was done by the County Laundry, Gloucester Street, Taunton.

In 1944, all ward linen was handled under contract by the Southwestern Cooperative Laundry, Gloucester Street, Taunton, and the Convent Laundry, Minehead. Blankets were cleaned by a civilian laundry at Wellington, and by a Quartermaster Mobile Laundry Unit at Chard, with each locale about sixteen miles away.

Uniforms, aprons and barbers' towels were handled by the Southwestern Cooperative Laundry, and personal laundry of officers, nurses and enlisted men were done by a Quartermaster Mobile Laundry Unit. The quality of work done by civilian laundries was far superior to that done by the Mobile Laundry Units, and the amount of loss and damage was far less. This was proven by the fact that personal bundles were only about one-third the number of the previous year as the men preferred to make arrangements for laundry work at their own expense rather than submit to the damage, shrinkage and loss by the Mobile Laundry Units.

Dry cleaning (spot) was done in the tailor shop of the Post.

A Big Operation Takes a Lot of Laundry

Conservation of Material and Man Power

A Salvage Section, composed of three privates, was under the direct supervision of a commissioned officer. (14) In 1943, they collected:

78,000 pounds of paper--an average of 1,500 pounds per week.
143,480 pounds of ferrous and non-ferrous metals--an average of 2,500 pounds per week.
1,300 gallons of fats--an average of 25 gallons per week.

Fats were used to make soap, when a shortage existed in the Unit, and practically all soap used for scrubbing purposes was obtained in this manner. Suitable containers for different kinds of salvage were placed about the Post, and served all wards and departments, in addition to three main salvage centers. (14)

Conservation of food and reduction of food waste was a big problem in 1943, due to the difficulty of procurement, transport and distribution of food. Efforts were made in 1943, to reduce waste to the minimum, and while this was not a problem with the personnel or ambulatory patients, the problem came with bed patients who thought that they had big appetites only to find that they are unable to eat, particularly if heavily medicated with sulfa drugs. Strict attention was given the amount of food served to these patients in an effort to reduce wasted food. In spite of this and the fact that the amount of unused food in wards was reduced during the year (1943) by 80%, it was felt that there would always be some unavoidable wastage by the patients. All unused food which had not been handled or served was returned to the kitchen in the food containers, and in most cases was used again in the preparation of meals during the next 24 hours. (14)

Recycling
Photograph by and Courtesy of Raymond Bungard

Post Exchange

The Post Exchange was opened 11 December 1942, and was located in a separate building, planned to expedite flow of traffic. Patients, nurses, officers and enlisted men were all customers. The supply of merchandise was scanty and most articles sold out almost immediately upon their receipt.

Soldiers Handling Concession at Post Exchange
Left to Right: P.F.C. B. Wade, Unknown Soldier, P.F.C. G. Wells, and Possibly Meliken
Photograph Courtesy of Lucille Walker

References

(1) "Annual Report to the Chief Surgeon, SOS, ETOUSA, APO 887, U.S. Army." Dated 31 January 1944. National Archives.

(2) "Period Report, 67th General Hospital, Medical Department Activities to the Surgeon General, Washington D.C." Dated 15 June 1945. National Archives.

(3) "Annual Report of the Roentgenological Service for 1944." Dated 8 January 1945. Submitted to the Commanding Officer, 67th General Hospital, by Lieutenant Colonel Jack Spencer, M.C., Chief of X-Ray Service. National Archives.

(4) "Annual Laboratory Service Report for 1944." Dated 2 January 1945. Signed by Major Jere R. Downing, Major, M.C., Chief of Laboratory Service. National Archives.

(5) "Annual Dental Report for 1944, to the Commanding Officer, 67th General Hospital, APO 511." Dated 4 January 1945. Signed by Chief of Dental Service. National Archives.

(6) "Annual Report of the Office of the Chief of Surgical Service to the Commanding Officer, 67th General Hospital." Dated 8 January 1945. Signed by William V. Cox, Lieutenant Colonel, M.C., Chief of Surgical Services. National Archives.

(7) "Annual Report of the Office of the Chief of the Medical Service to the Commanding Officer, 67th General Hospital, APO 511." Dated 9 January 1945. Signed by E.R.Blaisdell, Lt. Colonel, Medical Corps, Chief of the Medical Service. National Archives.

(8) "Annual Report of the 67th General Hospital to the Surgeon General, United States Army, for 1944." Dated 31 January 1945. Signed by Roland B. Moore, Colonel, Medical Corps, Commanding Officer. National Archives.

(9) "Annual Report of the Laboratory Service to the Commanding Officer, 67th General Hospital, APO 511." Dated 31 January 1944. Signed by Jere R. Downing, Captain, M.C., Chief of Laboratory Service. National Archives.

(10) "Annual Report of the X-Ray Service to the Commanding Officer, 67th General Hospital, APO 511." Dated 30 January 1944. Signed by Jack Spencer, Lt. Colonel, M.C., Chief of X-Ray Service. National Archives.

(11) "Annual Dental Report for the period 1 January 1943 to 31 December 1943." Signed 4 January 1944, by William B. Jordan, Lt. Colonel, D.C., Chief of Service. National Archives.

(12) "Annual Report of the Surgical Service to the Commanding Officer, 67th General Hospital, APO 511, U.S. Army." Dated 1 January 1944. Signed by William V. Cox, Lieutenant Colonel, M.C., Chief of Surgical Service. National Archives.

(13) "Annual Report of the Medical Service to the Commanding Officer, 67th General Hospital, APO 511, U.S. Army." Dated 12 January 1944. Signed by E.R. Blaisdell, Lieutenant Colonel, M.C., Chief of Surgical Service. National Archives.

(14) "Historical Report of 1943, to the Chief Surgeon, SOS, ETOUSA." From R.B. Moore, Colonel, Medical Corps, Commanding Officer, 67th General Hospital, APO 511. Dated 31 January 1944. National Archives.

(15) "Annual Report of the Roentgenological Services for 1942, to the Commanding Officer, 67th General Hospital." Dated 3 January 1943. Signed by Jack Spencer, Major, M.C., Chief of Roentgenological Service. National Archives.
(16) "Organization and Activities of the Laboratory, Report to the Commanding Officer, 67th General Hospital." Dated 2 January 1943. Signed by Jere R. Downing , M.C. Chief of Laboratory Service. National Archives.

(17) "Annual Dental Report for 1942, to the Commanding Officer, 67th General Hospital." Dated 16 January 1943. Signed by William B. Jordan, Major D.C., Chief of Service. National Archives.

(18) "Annual Report for the Surgical Service for 1942, to Lieutenant Colonel Roland B. Moore, Commanding Officer of the 67th General Hospital." Dated 31 December 1942. Signed by William V. Cox, Major, M.C., Chief of Surgical Service. National Archives.

(19) "Monthly Sanitation Report to the Commanding Officer, 67th General Hospital, APO 511, U.S. Army." Dated 2 January 1943. Signed by Merrill S.F. Greene, Major, Medical Corps, Medical Inspector. National Archives.

(20) "Annual Report of the Medical Service to Lt. Colonel R.B. Moore, Commanding Officer of the 67th General Hospital." Dated 30 December 1942. Signed by Lt. Colonel E.R. Blaisdell, M.C., Chief of Medical Service. National Archives.

(21) "Annual Report of the 67th General Hospital to the Chief Surgeon, SOS, ETOUSA." Dated 15 January 1943. Signed by Lieutenant Colonel R.B. Moore, M.C., Commanding. National Archives.

(22) *Lewiston Journal; Magazine Section.* Saturday, October 25, 1969.

(23) "Reports to the Red Cross from the Red Cross Unit Assigned to the 67th General Hospital. Narrative and Recreation Report for March, 1943." National Archives.

(24) "Records of the 2nd Evacuation Hospital." National Archives, Washington, D.C.

(25) Personal Communication with First Sergeant Joe Bullock.

(26) Personal Communication with Mildred Butler, ANC.

(27) Information from Alvin Hamblen Morrison PhD, son of Alvin Alward Morrison MD, a surgeon in the 67th General Hospital.

(28) Bush, Robin. *A Taunton Diary 1787-1987. Two Centuries of Gossip, Scandal, Success and Calamity in Darkest Somerset.* Buckingham, England: Barracuda Books Limited, 1988.

(29) http://www.somerset-health.org.uk/tst/.

(30) "Hospital Regulations, 67th General Hospital, U.S. Army Medical Corp." Somerset Record Office in Taunton, Somerset, England.

(31) "Historical Data of 67th General Hospital for Third Period Quarter 1944--July, August, September 1944." Dated 14 October 1944. National Archives.

(32) "Historical Data of 67th General Hospital for Fourth Period Quarter 1944--October, November and December 1944." Dated 15 January 1945. National Archives.

(33) "Historical Data of 67th General Hospital for First Quarter 1945--January, February, March, April to 8th May, 1945." National Archives.

(34) "Historical Data of 67th General Hospital for Period May 8 to September 22, 1945." National Archives.

(35) Personal Communication with Ted Benedict.

(36) Personal Communication with Raymond Bungard.

(37) Brown, Donald. *Somerset v Hitler: Secret Operations in the Mendips 1939-1945.* Newbury, Berkshire: Countryside Books, 2001.

Chapter 7
D-Day

On the morning of 6 June 1944, German sentries on the Atlantic Wall of Normandy rubbed their eyes in disbelief as the sight of almost 4000 ships of all sizes and shapes filled the horizon, apparently all headed for them. Naval bombardment from battleships, destroyers and other ships with armament preceded the landing of wave upon wave of soldiers onto the beach who, minutes before, had been packed shoulder-to-shoulder in hundreds of landing craft. The battle, which had just begun at 0630, was to become the most dramatic and decisive battle of the Second World War and possibly of all recorded history.

D-Day, in the military sense, refers to the day on which a particular operation will occur. The staging of the operation can be based on such a designation without attaching a particular action to a specific day, or deciding in advance when this D-Day will be. For the Normandy Invasion, code-named **Operation Overlord**, D-Day was initially set as 5 June 1944, but inclement weather forced General Eisenhower to change it to 6 June 1944, a day which has proven to be so important in history, that the invasion of Normandy is synonymous with the expression "D-Day".

Preparation and Build-Up

Plans for a cross-Channel invasion had begun even before the official involvement of the United States in what was to be known as World War II. Shortly after the attack on Pearl Harbor, American and British leaders confirmed their agreement that Germany should be defeated before Japan, and that their resources should be primarily directed toward this end. The buildup of supplies and men, earmarked for the invasion of the Continent, and code-named **Bolero**, began shortly after this conference and was briefly slowed by the need for men and supplies to invade North Africa, in Operation **Torch**. In January of 1943, President Roosevelt and Prime Minister Churchill, along with the Combined Chiefs of Staff, met in Casablanca, and decided that the next invasion after North Africa, was to be Sicily, but they also resolved to continue the build-up of forces in England for the invasion of Europe. By July of 1943, supplies from the United States to England, had reached 753,000 tons per month which later increased to 1,900,000 tons per month by May of 1944.

Assault craft totaling 3,780 and 142 cargo ships were accumulated for the landing. Strategic bombardment had begun to reduce the power of the German Army long before D-Day, with priority targets of "submarine construction yards, the aircraft industries, transportation, oil plants and other critical enemy war industries." (10) To meet the needs of convoys with invasion supplies moving to the south of England, fuel dumps were placed at strategic locations along the road. Gasoline was placed in 5 gallon cans, and when a convoy would pass through a fuel area, they would be topped up by eight stations placed 100 feet apart all along the route. The empty cans would be picked up by trucks moving along the same road and replaced with full cans. The empties would then be refilled from tank cars located at railroad sidings. The convoys would be timed to come by every 15 minutes. There were 1,250 men trained for this purpose from the Quartermaster Corps, and this 24-hour fueling service continued from the start of operations until past D-Day. Additionally, all trucks and vehicles were topped off with fuel when they reached their designated port and caps of the gas tanks were waterproofed. (14)

This mobilization of sufficient forces to effect the invasion required 1,200,000 men, most of whom had to be transported across the Atlantic from the United States. Their anticipated medical care required 94,000 beds in fixed accommodations, later augmented by 30,000 beds using tent accommodations. (10) Living quarters for these men had to be furnished. Eventually, American troops occupied more than 100,000 buildings, ranging from small Nissen huts and cottages to hangers, workshops and assembly plants in more than 1,100 cities and villages. (9)

G.I.'s Being Billeted in Taunton
Photograph Courtesy of Ted Benedict

"Storage and shop space required 20,000,000 square feet, with 44,000,000 square feet of open storage and parking areas also needed. Parks for 50,000 military vehicles were also needed. To accommodate the extra railroad usage, 270 miles of railroad line had to be constructed. More than 20,000 railroad cars and 1000 locomotives had to be shipped from the United States. In addition to the needs above, the Air Force needed 163 airfields, seven centers for combat crews and replacements, accommodations for 450,000 men and 8,500,000 square feet of storage and shop space." (10)

The presence of the 67th General Hospital in England was part of the **Operation Bolero** D-Day build-up and Musgrove Military Hospital was used as a hospital to care for other patients prior to D-Day. The beds of the 67th were a small part of the more than 100,000 beds provided by 100 or more major American hospitals to accommodate the anticipated need. (12)

In 1944, the Transportation Department of the 67th General Hospital made 13,179 trips, with a total mileage of 235,033, which was 50% greater than had been documented in 1943. A large part of the extra mileage was for the transport of troops and supplies from marshalling areas to ports during the build-up prior to D-Day. Vehicles of the 67th General Hospital were loaned to other units for this purpose. (6) This build-up of troops became heavy in Mid-March, 1944, and was accompanied by a ban on travel by civilians to the coastal areas. (Residents in critical areas had been previously evacuated and the area sealed off.) The transmission or receipt of uncensored communications by the foreign diplomatic corps was banned after 17 April 1944. General Eisenhower gave the order in mid-May to move the assault forces toward the ports on the southeast coast of England, where the invasion was to embark. Munitions and supplies were moved by non-ending convoys to the coastal areas and supplies were stacked alongside roadways and covered with camouflage, due to the lack of warehouse space. (9)

Prior to D-Day, taxi lanes of airports in England were full of aircraft, nose to tail and wing-tip to wing-tip, ready to participate in their part of the invasion. C-47 aircraft, designated to carry paratroopers over Normandy, as well as other aircraft, had been painted with three white stripes over the fuselage and wings to allow identification by their own forces. Painting of the aircraft started two days prior to D-Day and exhausted the supply of white paint in England. (5)

Glider Showing Invasion Stripes
Photograph Courtesy Ted Benedict

Betsy Larson Crumrine recalled 5000 gliders and their towing aircraft going over the hospital one day and remarked about the tremendous noise their engines made. Mildred Butler, ANC, recalled a nightly steady rumble of equipment traveling from the central part of England, above them to the coast. She described the atmosphere as very tense, with everyone knowing that a change was ahead. She also recalled a few injured enlisted men who were brought into the hospital for treatment and assigned to a closed ward, ostensibly for security, and then a few days later, D-Day began. Men were moved into tents in open fields in counties adjoining the coastal areas near the ports to be used for embarkation. (9)

Tugs and Gliders Over the Hospital
Photograph Courtesy Ted Benedict

Careful study had shown that the ideal combination of tides, phases of the moon, hours of daylight and weather would occur on June 5, 6 and 7. The initial plan called for D-Day to be on June 5. Ship loading began on June 1, and the men were briefed about their mission, issued French phrase books, extra K and D rations and munitions, seasick tablets and vomit bags, cigarettes, lifebelts, toothbrushes, extra socks and Invasion money. Tension built among the men as they realized that this was not a drill but rather the real thing. One thing that might have given the invasion away was the delivery of whole blood to the LSTs. Whole blood would only last for fourteen days. (12)

Tension was present in the Office of the Supreme Commander. The great unpredictable element was the weather and the realization that the operation could not be stopped and restarted without a loss of secrecy, not to mention the effect postponement would have on the morale of the men. Some of the ships were ordered to sail toward a rendezvous point on June 3. On the morning of June 4, it was obvious that the weather would not allow the air portion of the assault. There were divided opinions by the advisors as to whether the invasion should be postponed for the next optimal window. The decision rested on General Eisenhower, the Supreme Commander of **Overlord** and his decision was, "Go", stating that it was the danger of not going which was "too chancy". (9) The orders went out to the fleet to begin the attack on the morning of 6 June 1944, and the English Channel was churned by the propellers of 4,000 ships.

The Paratroopers

The takeoff routine of an aircraft involved taxiing to the runway, locking the breaks, revving up the engines and then releasing the brakes with a subsequent acceleration down the runway. The next plane in line would follow, repeating the process every ten seconds. (5) The 441st Troop Carrier Group, a squadron of the 50th Wing of the United States Ninth Troop Carrier Command, flying Douglas C-47 (Dakota) aircraft was stationed at Merryfield Airport, at Ilton, not far from Taunton. They had been "practicing quick assemblies and close quarter formations in readiness for their part on the D-Day missions." (8) They were equipped with Hadrian gliders (15) and the hospital personnel recalled the skies full of Dakotas and gliders prior to D-Day, as they were practicing and recalled the thunderous clamor the night before D-Day, as the planes with their gliders passed by forming an aerial Armada as they joined with other aircraft on the way to rendezvous for the strike against Normandy.

On 5 June 1944, the 501st Parachute Infantry Regiment, attached to the 101st Airborne, took off from Merryfield Airport, near Ilton, at 2245 hours, when the daylight had mostly faded. A total of 90 planes took off from Merryfield that evening. (8) The 3rd Battalion, also part of the 501st Parachute Infantry Regiment departed at the same time from Welford. Their mission was to fly across the English Channel and parachute into Normandy. Their assigned drop zones were north and east of the town of Carentan. Two battalions were to seize key canal locks at La Barquette, and destroy the bridges over the Douve River, while the third battalion was held in division reserve. (1)

Men of the 506th Parachute Infantry Regiment, also attached to the 101st Airborne, stationed in Wiltshire County, with units in such villages as Aldbourne, Ramsbury, Froxfield, and Chilton-Foliat had been taking part in invasion exercises and on 5 June 1944, found themselves near the aircraft, in a field at Upottery, which would deliver them to their first combat mission. (18) At 0100, 6 June 1944, they took off on their first combat jump. Due to cloud cover and their plane's evasive action from anti-aircraft fire, their drop was, in many cases, short of the Drop Zone. (2) Easy Company of this unit was to be immortalized in print and film as the "Band of Brothers". A total of 13,000 American paratroopers left England to participate in this portion of the D-Day invasion. (8)

First Casualty of D-Day Treated in England

Some of the men on these planes did not make the jump. The C-47's had to descend to 600 feet to allow the jumps but this lower altitude also made them better targets for spot lights and ground fire. The flak which plagued the accurate delivery of the men to their Drop Zone penetrated some of the planes and wounded several of the paratroopers before they had a chance to jump. The wounded men remained on their planes, returned to their base and were sent immediately to hospitals for treatment. The 67th General Hospital is thought to be the first hospital in England to receive D-Day wounded. (9) At 0430 in the morning of 6 June 1944, prior to the actual landing of troops on the beaches of Normandy, three paratroopers, who had been hit by flak before they had had a chance to jump, were checked in and treated at the 67th General Hospital. (3) Three men were awarded Purple Hearts on 8 June 1944. These men were: Lawrence J. Wiltgen, Serial Number 39022229, Staff Sergeant, Company B, 501st Parachute Infantry, (for injury received due to enemy action on 6 June 1944, over enemy occupied area), John P. Androsky, Serial Number 32461611, Private, Company G and Roy W. Cobb, Serial Number 6663183, Private First Class, Company E, both with the 506th Parachute Infantry. (4)

When one looks at the times of departure of the planes carrying the paratroopers, it seems certain that Staff Sergeant Lawrence J.Wiltgen, mentioned above, was the first casualty from enemy fire on D-Day to be returned for treatment in a hospital in England. It would be logical that he was transferred back to Merryfield, where his transport plane had taken off, then sent to the 67th General Hospital, which was the nearest medical facility to the airfield, with the drama of taking off, being wounded and admitted to a hospital occurring in a period of just 6 hours. A Station Hospital was built at Merryfield, but not until July of 1944. (15) Therefore, he would have been transported directly to Musgrove Military Hospital and the care of the 67th General Hospital. A published report of another Parachute Infantry Soldier who was wounded by flak and returned to be treated by a hospital in England, gave his arrival at his hospital at 0600. (5)

At least one other mission against the Normandy beaches involving the 441st Troop Carrier Group took off from Merryfield Airport on 7 June1942, and involved gliders and about fifty planes. The gliders were released at about the same area which was the site of the mission the day before. The squadron continued in evacuation and re-supply missions as needed for some time after D-Day. (8)

Some of the doctors of the 67th General Hospital had been assigned duties outside the hospital to assist in the operations of D-Day. Major Merrill S.F. Greene was given the assignment of "checking each assigned service man to see if he was physically fit for the coming test." One has to assume that this meant that he gave pre-operational physical examinations. Captain John R. Feeley was assigned to an LST (also referred to by the soldiers as Large Slow Targets) with the duty to immediately treat any who had been wounded in the water or near shore and return them to a safe location for treatment. The LSTs had special brackets built into their side which would hold 140 stretchers with casualties. DUKWs carrying 11 litters (stretchers) would drive up to the ramp of the LST and unload.

(DUKWs got their name from D for GM model code for the year 1942, U for Utility Truck, K for front-wheel drive and W for dual rear-driving axles. Not surprisingly, the drivers of these vehicles became known as the "Quack Corps" by Marines in the Pacific. The DUKWs alone carried 18 million tons of supplies and munitions to the beaches of Normandy and then transported the wounded on their trip back to the ships offshore.) (16)

Rhino ferries, which were only barges linked together and powered by a small outboard engine to drive them to shore, also traveled from shore to the LST. LCTs (Landing Craft Tank) which drew only 18 inches of water were driven onto the beach, loaded with casualties and then taken to the LSTs where they would join ramp to ramp and unload. In some of these, blood transfusions were given and operating rooms were set up under tarpaulins as the LST fought waves, weather and air attacks to bring the wounded back to England. Hospital ships were also present off the beach and received many of the wounded and gave them the necessary urgent care. (13) Both officers were "struck with the spirit of the American serviceman in this ordeal". (3) Days after D-Day, planes from the 439th Troop Carrier Group, based at Upottery Field, near Smeatharpe, and others began landing behind the beaches of Normandy on grass strips and ferrying injured troops back to England and the care of the 67th General Hospital and other hospitals in the Communication Zone. (8)

As the war expanded onto the continent, the Communication Zone expanded along with it to include support facilities needed such as communication, evacuation, supplies, and medical care flowed from England. A medical evacuation system, referred to as the "Chain of Evacuation" moved the injured troops from the front lines back home to the United States. Field Hospitals were able to come ashore within one or two days of D-Day, closely followed by Evacuation Hospitals. Within three weeks there were fourteen Evacuation Hospitals ashore to handle the massive casualties of the Battle of Normandy and the push into France, which followed. (12) This "Chain of Evacuation" is discussed in more detail in Chapter 8.

Of the 55,674 casualties from D-Day, 18,415 or 33 per cent of the total, were flown to England by air with the remainder arriving by boat. This evacuation was carried out by medical units of the Ninth Air Force. Many times, supplies might be unloaded at one airfield and then the plane would be directed to another field to pick up patients. The planes had collapsible racks mounted on the wall which would hold a stretcher. On August 30, General Hawley, the chief surgeon in Europe, won approval for flights designated as separate missions, not just a part of a cargo flight. The General, however, was not able to send empty cargo planes to Europe with the sole purpose of picking up patient because other needs of the Army had to be addressed simultaneously. Lower-level commanders, however, found ways, often involving subterfuge, to make planes available for air evacuation when needed. (11) Of all the men evacuated, less than one percent died of their injuries after reaching England. (12)

As the battles continued, many more casualties resulted. The hospital had been operating prior to D-Day, but at a relatively low volume. The census dramatically increased at this time. Images of two stretchers across the front of a jeep and two stretchers across the back driving into the water to unload the patients onto an LST can be seen in footage shot on the day of battle. The soldiers were lined up four or five abreast in the LSTs and taken to ships waiting off-shore for them, eventually making their way to General Hospitals. The 67th General Hospital had a daily census of 1,000 men prior to the D-Day invasion, but this number rose to 1,600 after D-Day, and reached a maximum census of 1,700 following the Battle of the Bulge. During a four month period it never dropped below 1,600. (3)

Ted Benedict reported that his brother-in-law, an anesthesiologist in a General Hospital in Circencester, didn't get out of the operating room for several weeks, even sleeping in a corner when he could. Most likely, the 67th General Hospital's experiences were similar. The hospital was swamped with work--especially work in surgery. They were busy. (17)

Back at Musgrove Military Hospital, life went on, although at an accelerated rate. As battles raged and casualties came into the hospital, it was obvious that things of historical importance were occurring. The Red Cross made their monthly report to their headquarters on 31 August 1944, and the following observation made:

> "At this particular time it seems of small significance to put into writing the account of our activities here during the past month. Each broadcast one misses and each edition of the newspaper that one neglects to read immediately upon its arrival contributes to the general feeling of being passed by in the onrush of events so important that even making every effort to be informed, we cannot fully appreciate the far-reaching effects of the things that happen today. Sometimes it is rather difficult to convince oneself and one another that doing whatever task the day presents and doing it well, regardless of how monotonous and unimportant it may seem by comparison, is the best contribution we can make to the whole picture and is the only part we can play." (7)

References

(1) Unit History Provided to 1st Battalion, 501st Parachute Infantry Regiment Currently Stationed at Fort Richardson, Alaska, by Their Honorary Regimental Colonel, LTG (Ret) Harry W.O. Kinnard. Obtained at http://thedropzone.org/units/501history.html.

(2) The 101st Airborne from www.ww2-airborne.us/units/506/506.html.

(3) Skinner, Ralph B. *"World War II's 67th General Hospital Reunion."* Lewiston Journal: Magazine Section; Lewiston-Auburn Maine. Saturday, October 25, 1969. Courtesy Betsy Larson Crumrine.

(4) "General Order Number 10, Headquarters, 67th General Hospital, 8 June 1944." National Archives, Washington, D.C.

(5) Ambrose, Stephen B. *D-Day June 6, 1944: The Climactic Battle of World War II.* New York: Simon & Schuster, 1994.

(6) "Annual Report of the 67th General Hospital to the Surgeon General, United States Army, for 1944." Dated 31 January 1945. Signed by Roland B. Moore, Colonel, Medical Corps, Commanding Officer. National Archives.

(7) "Narrative Report of the Assistant Field Director of the Red Cross." Submitted 31 August 1944, by Wanda Morgenthaler. National Archives.

(8) *Devon Dawn of Peace 60th Anniversary of VJ-Day and the end of World War II, Commemorative Souvenir of the Three Blackdown Hills World War II Air-Fields.* South West Airfields Heritage Trust, B-24 Marcus Road, Dunkeswell, Devon.

(9) *Chapter IX: Final Preparation for the Invasion. The United States Army and World War II. European-Mediterranean-Middle East Theaters of Operations.* The United States Army Center of Military History.

(10) *Biennial Reports of the Chief of Staff of the United States Army to the Secretary of War 1 July 1939-30 June 1945.* Center of Military History; United States Army, Washington, D.C. 1996.

(11) Nanney, James S. *Army Air Forces Medical Services in World War II.* Air Force History and Museums Program. 1998.

(12) Cowdrey, Albert E. *Fighting For Life--American Military Medicine in World War II.* The Free Press 1994.

(13) "That Men Might Live!" from Stars and Stripes. One of a Series of G.I. Stories of the Ground, Air and Service Forces in the European Theater of Operations, Issued by the Orientation Branch, Information and Education Division, ETOUSA.

(14) http://www.qmfound.com/fueling_up_for_d-day.htm.
Quartermaster Museum--Quartermaster Foundation. *"Fueling Up for D-Day."* WWII Gasoline Supply in England in Support of the Invasion of France, June 6, 1944; Quartermaster Technical Bulletin 26 October 1944. Based on an Article by Warren C. Platt in the 30 August 1944, Issue of "National Petroleum News."

(15) Hawkins, Mac. *Somerset at War.* The Dovecote Press, 1996.

(16) Allen, Thomas B. "Odd DUKW." Smithsonian Magazine, August, 2002.

(17) Personal Communication with Ted Benedict.

(18) Ambrose, Stephen B. *Band of Brothers.* New York. Simon and Schuster, 1992.

Chapter 8

The Care of the Military Patient

The most stirring moment of a medical school graduation ceremony is the recitation of the Hippocratic Oath by the newly-trained young doctors. The oath states in a paraphrased form that the new doctors will to the best of their ability and judgment, keep their patients from harm and injustice. This attitude will always protect the patient regardless of any action a physician might consider and when used as the standard of practice insures a better outcome for the patient.

Military medicine has a slightly different objective for its doctors who care for the soldier-patient. In the military setting, the care of patient is still considered important, but the primary goal is preparing him for return to combat. The welfare of the individual becomes somewhat subrogated to that of the military service. The doctor who has practiced in a civilian setting may have some conflicts while trying to accommodate these two attitudes, but it is doubtful that any serious conflicts arose in the 67th General Hospital over these conflicting goals. Most doctors who had practiced as a civilian looked upon their situation in the military as temporary and imagined themselves as civilian doctors in military clothes. Medical care in the private practice of medicine is given to patients who have chosen to visit a particular doctor and are able to establish a doctor-patient relationship. In the military, the relationship is involuntary and not as personal. The patient may see many different doctors during his stay in the Armed Services.

Patients seen in private practice run the gamut from the very young to the very old with varying stages of health. The patient seen by the military physician would be a younger, healthier specimen than the typical patient seen in a private practice. Good food, healthy environment, regular exercise and the strength of youth combined to make a healthier patient who almost always would be cured of his problems.

Each war has brought many casualties, more with the progressive development of mechanized warfare, but there has been a concurrent evolution of medical care with each subsequent conflict. One such injury might be an injury resulting from the impact of a high-velocity weapon. The best care occurs when the soldier can be cared for immediately after his injury. The French devised a system of treating the patient at the battle front and this system has been copied since that time. The French use a similar system to stabilize and treat accident victims at the site of accidents today. They were criticized for their care of Princess Diana when one of their mobile units, complete with doctors but lacking sophisticated imaging equipment, failed to diagnose serious injuries which ultimately caused her death. Some felt that the outcome would have been different had she been more promptly transferred to a major hospital, which was equipped for more sophisticated forms of treatment. Every good idea has its detractors.

At the beginning of World War II, there were five General Hospitals--Walter Reed, Army and Navy, Fitzsimmons, Letterman and William Beaumont in the United States, one in Hawaii and one in the Philippines. The fixed hospitals as named above were to be operated in the Zone of the Interior, i.e., within the boundaries of the United States. Many General Hospitals were formed in response to the threat of war and were often affiliated with a medical school or large hospital and staffed with their doctors. Numbered General Hospitals such as the 67th General Hospital were to be established in the Communication Zone, the area behind the lines away from the battle which supported the battle troops with supplies, evacuation, communication and medical care. As the battle surged toward the enemy, the Communication Zone would enlarge and General Hospitals would follow and provide care.

The Army defined the General Hospital:

"The General Hospital is designed to serve general and special rather than local and ordinary needs…to--

a. Afford better facilities than can be provided at the ordinary station or other hospitals for the study, observation, and treatment of serious, complicated, or obscure cases. For this reason, general hospitals are equipped with the most modern apparatus and assigned especially qualified personnel.

b. Afford opportunities for the performance of the more difficult or formidable surgical operations, facilities for which may be lacking at station or mobile hospitals.

c. Study and finally dispose of cases that may have long resisted treatment elsewhere, and to determine questions of the existence, cause, extent and permanence of mental and physical disabilities of long-standing or unusual obscurity.

d. Instruct and train junior Medical Department officers in general professional and administrative duties.

e. Form the nucleus for the initial hospitalization needs of the Zone of the Interior in time of War.

f. Receive and give definitive treatment to patients from other hospitals in the theater of operations, particularly mobile units in the combat area."

It mentions that the General Hospital is designed to have a normal capacity of 1,000 beds but in emergencies and "by crisis expansion under tentage care for 2,000 patients if the period of stress is not too prolonged." (3)

The amount of equipment needed for a General Hospital was staggering with the following approximate figures: "Net weight 220,983 pounds; shipping weight, 324 tons; volume, 13,000 cubic feet; freight cars required, 7.3; trucks, 1 ½ tons , 73.3. The number of separate packages required to pack the initial supplies for a general hospital is 2,474, but if the individual items are counted the total runs up to 100,000." (3)

From Left, T5 Richard Smith, with Sgt. Smith, a Patient
Photograph in Author's Collection

Richard Smith with Patient
Photograph in Author's Collection

A number of advancements in medicine made survival more certain for the wounded soldier. The most important improvement was prompt treatment in a **first aid station or by a medic** and then rapid transportation behind the lines to receive more definitive and advanced treatment. This was termed "The Chain of Evacuation". The first level of care was at the line of fire where medics would bandage wounds, apply splints and compressions and administer morphine. From there it was usually a short ride by jeep or stretcher to a **Collecting Station** which was set up on a regimental level. At the Collection Station, the wounded were triaged with the less-severely-wounded sent back to their unit and the more-seriously-wounded among them given plasma or blood transfusions and other immediate care if needed, and then moving to a **Clearing Station** where even more sophisticated care was administered including wound, airway and fracture management, antibiotic and pain medicine administration.

From the Clearing Station, he would pass to a **Field Hospital**, designed to treat 400 patients, where any needed surgery was performed and bandages were changed. Bandages placed by a corpsman or aid station were left on until the patient arrived at the Field Hospital, except in the face of hemorrhage under the bandage. Patients with abdominal wounds were explored and sewn closed except for a loop colostomy (an operation in which a loop of bowel was pulled through an incision in the abdominal wall which served to keep the contents of the bowels drained to allow healing of injured bowel distal to the colostomy.). Those who survived were given penicillin every four hours. The Field Hospital was composed of 223 men divided into four units--one headquarters unit and three hospitalization units. The hospitalization units could operate independently and sometimes one unit might be left behind as the Field Hospital went forward or even go forward toward the front before the remainder of the Field Hospital caught up with them.

From the Field Hospital the patient, when he had recovered sufficiently, might be sent on to an **Evacuation Hospital** which would be further behind the battlefield near a form of transportation such as a major roadway, railroad or airport. Here, even more surgery might be done, and here the patient was stabilized. At the forward hospitals, the patients categorized as "non-transportables" received care. There, men with shock or having massive injuries such as disembowelment, were treated with emergency surgery. The death rate for this class of patient was about 11 to 14 percent. (1)

If more complex care was needed, or if he was unfit to return to his unit, the soldier might be transferred to the Communication Zone by air evacuation or ship, to a **Station Hospital** or a **numbered General Hospital** such as the 67th General Hospital, for further care. Following care at the General Hospital, they would be sent to a **Convalescent Hospital** or to a **General Hospital in the Zone of the Interior (USA).** Sometimes, this "Chain of Evacuation" was short-circuited and patients were flown directly from the battlefront to the major facilities in the Communication Zone. The men going into combat were educated about the high level of medical care that they would receive and this must have been reassuring to them as they went into battle.

Loading Patient onto Plane
Photographs, This and Following Page, By and Courtesy of Ted Benedict

Flight Nurse Checking Patient onto Plane and Then "They're Off"

The larger hospitals were sometimes specialized hospitals for such things as orthopedics or neurosurgery and had specialized staff and equipment. (The 67th General Hospital was a designated Special Hospital for neurosurgery.) Here, reconstruction surgery took place and repairs were made that time and condition of the patient might not have allowed at the Field Hospital. Regulations covered every type of surgery and how it should best be done and the regulations were enforceable under the Code of Military Justice. Because of this finely honed system of medical care, the hospital death rate was kept around 3 percent (from injury to the last phase of medical care in the system.) (1) One source gave 3.9% of ETO casualties for death rate.

As the Zone of Communication enlarged with the Army's advances toward Germany, General Hospitals began to advance across the Channel to follow the Army. Soldiers passed through the medical evacuation system were routed through the port of Cherbourg, shipped by hospital ship to Southampton, and then to a General Hospital in England. (1)

Air evacuation became routine as planes moved seriously wounded patients from the front line to hospitals thus increasing their chances of survival. Light planes would move patients to larger airfields where larger planes such as the C-47, the C-54 or the C-54A would carry them to the Communication Zone and the larger hospitals. Hospital ships and hospital trains were used to move patients to and within the Communication Zone.

Patients for the 67th General Hospital arrived by hospital train to the nearby train station in Taunton, from transfer by ambulance from nearby hospitals or units or by air transport which would land at Merryfield, an airfield north of Ilton, and about six miles south of Taunton. Merryfield was transferred to the United States Army Air Force on April of 1943, from the RAF. During the invasion of Normandy on D-Day, it served as a glider base and later it received patients by air transport and sent supplies back out on the same planes when they returned to the front. In July of 1944, an American Field Hospital was established there to serve as a triage center for casualties returned to the Zone of Communication.

Once a patient was treated in the Communicaton Zone (CZ), he was either sent back to the United States (Zone of the Interior), transferred to a Convalescent Hospital or transferred to a Replacement Depot "repple depple" (RD) for reassignment to a unit--usually not the one he had belonged to, at the time of his injury. Men with neurological problems or burns who needed more extended care might be sent by train from the 67th General Hospital to the nearby burn hospital at Bishops Lydeard. (4)

The ferocity of the war on the continent expressed itself in the number of casualties who needed to be treated. The Chain of Evacuation extended itself in the Zone of Communication as the front widened and deepened. As previously mentioned the military looked at the value of the medical system as its ability to return a soldier to the front in fighting condition. Thus, the number of patients in hospitals was, in itself, a potential pool for replacements. The Chief Surgeon, General Hawley, elected to keep wounded men in the European Theater of Operations as long as there was potential to return them to combat. Thus, transfer to the United States was postponed. This policy backed up the system at all levels resulting in hospitals which were full and their staff overworked. To meet the needs of the more recently injured soldier, General Hawley made efforts to move the men to England, but weather and transportation limitations often stranded the movable men in Europe. Men were stranded in hospital trains parked on sidings or even put up in hotels in Paris. (1)

Ambulances at Merryfield Near Taunton
Photograph By and Courtesy of Ted Benedict

Research was done to develop treatments for burns and trauma. Blood and serum was further perfected and used more extensively on the battlefield than ever before. A typhus vaccine developed by Herald R. Cox, an American scientist, as the war was beginning, prevented American troops from contacting this devastating disease. A liberal use of DDT contributed to the prevention in the non-vaccinated.

An approach to surgery was perfected. Wounds were debrided, meaning that the dead tissue was excised and the wound was probed and left open. The wound was allowed to heal by delayed closure, which meant allowing the wound to drain, heal from within and thus avoid severe infection from germs retained in a closed wound. This common-sense approach to wound care is still the gold standard in today's treatment of infected wounds. Soldiers who had compound fractures (defined as a fracture in which the integrity of the skin is compromised, e.g. the bone might be sticking out) would arrive with their limbs in cast to await reconstruction. Mildred Butler, ANC, a nurse at the 67th General Hospital, recalls some of these soldiers arriving and when their cast were opened, maggots would fall to the floor. (7) This wasn't a bad thing, despite the visceral reaction generated by the description, because the maggots served to remove the dead flesh and facilitated healing and are deliberately used today for this purpose.

Consultants in the various theaters traveled from hospital to hospital instructing the surgeons on the proper technique and introducing new techniques as they were proven. Multiple injuries required multiple specialists. (1, 6) The chief responsibility of the consultants (who for the most part were professors from major medical schools in the United States) was to originate and implement the surgical policies of the theater and this responsibility extended to the transportation of the wounded as well as the selection and allocation of medical equipment. Surgical procedures and results of surgery were followed in all the hospitals in England. When a unit would arrive in the ETO, it would be visited by the consultants and personnel would be evaluated as to the most beneficial function that they might serve, depending on their qualifications. Special treatment facilities were set up in various hospitals for specialized treatment involving cold injury, burns, and neurosurgical, urological or plastic procedures. For example, the 67th General Hospital was known for its treatment of the neurosurgical patient. To maintain the standards of care which had been established by the consultants, a manual, "The European Theater Manual of Therapy" was prepared by the consultants of the Chief Surgeon's office published before D-Day, and made available to all the medical officers of the ETO. (6)

New research and experience provided the basis for the treatment of shock which had been recognized in the past but had not been investigated in a thorough enough manner to explain its mechanism of action, let alone allow its rational treatment. The introduction of plasma to patients in shock allowed their recovery and became available after the later 1930's. The concept of the anesthesiologist and surgeon working together to treat a patient in shock with the anesthesiologist treating the patient with plasma and or whole blood and the surgeon performing the necessary surgery to stop the bleeding was first seen in World War II. Blood services were organized for the first time and the timely delivery of this life-sustaining ingredient saved many thousands of lives. Prior to World War II, orthopedic surgeons were minimally involved with fractures and as a result most of the fractures were handled by general surgeons. Since most of the injuries involved fractures of some sort, their treatment necessitated a huge orthopedic department and slowly, orthopedic surgeons became more involved and evolved to the type of care we see them do today.

Antibiotic therapy came into its own during World War II. Soldiers were issued sulfanilamide, which was first used clinically in 1936, and instructed to sprinkle the powder over open wounds in order to discourage infection. Most importantly, the use of penicillin was begun after Pfizer discovered a process in the fall of 1942, to make large amounts of penicillin and then agreed to share the process at no charge with its competitors for large-scale production to supply the needs of the wounded soldiers. At one time, 19 companies were manufacturing penicillin using Pfizer's process for the war effort. (2)

Raymond Bungard, one of the laboratory technicians, and later a surgeon, had some anecdotes regarding the use of penicillin in the 67th General Hospital:

> "I recall the advent of penicillin. The first patient at the 67th to receive penicillin was an officer who had contracted gonorrhea. Unfortunately he was not the only one. All others were enlisted. The 67th was also the laboratory facility for a huge area of southwest England. Suspected VD cases were referred for diagnosis. As the pathology lab tech I

prepared the dark-field apparatus for Treponema pallidum--it was my first introduction to the 'Queenly gait' of the spirochete." (8)

References

(1) Cowdrey, Albert E. *Fighting for Life.* The Free Press, 1994.

(2) Http://home.attnet/~steinert/wwii.htm.

(3) "History of the 51st General Hospital Annual Report for 1942." National Archives.

(4) Hinton, David J. *An Illustrated Social History of Bishops Lydeard and Cothelston.* Published by the Rocket Publishing Co., Ltd., and Printed by Taunton Printing Company in Great Britain.

(5) http://webappl.somerset.gov.uk/her/details.asp?prn=55403.

(6) http://history.amedd.army.mil/booksdocs/wwii/actvssurgeonvol2/chapter1.htm.

(7) Communication with Mildred Butler, ANC.

(8) Communication with Raymond Bungard.

Chapter 9
The Red Cross

Imagine a Nissen hut, colorfully and cheerfully decorated with pictures and posters, filled with soldiers far from home, in various stages of dress--some in uniform, other in fatigues, some in pajamas over which were worn blue or burgundy corduroy robes emblazoned with "MHD". In one corner of the room men are sitting around a table covered with magazines, books and newspapers. Around another table, men are chatting convivially. Some have slings on their arms, others various bandages, while even others have casts on arms or legs. Some are ambulatory, some hobble in on crutches and others are pushed in by wheelchair, or in some cases, on stretchers.

Red Cross Building with Many Activities in Progress
The Three Photograph Above Courtesy Raymond Bungard

Many activities are going on at once. One soldier throws darts while several others stand around a loom as a pattern becomes a beautiful work of art. One man rests his foot on a stool while another canes the top of another stool which resembles the stool in use. Cabinets and shelves line the back of the hut and hold various craft materials. Young women cheerfully make their rounds through the hut, chatting and encouraging the soldiers while another enjoys a game of checkers with a soldier.

Betsy Crumrine Playing Checkers with Patient Photograph Courtesy Raymond Bungard

The atmosphere is of cheer, and the purpose of this Red Cross building and the Red Cross workers is to help make these men whole--both mentally and physically. The young women assisting these wounded soldiers are workers for the Red Cross and this Red Cross Unit was assigned to the 67th General Hospital. They departed Ft. Bliss with the officers of the 67th General Hospital by train, on 12 November 1942, crossed the Atlantic on the Cunard Liner Queen Elizabeth, and proceeded by train to Taunton, Somerset, England.

To be in the Red Cross required a voluntary effort. The workers involved in the war were not drafted and were in harm's way while crossing the North Atlantic and braving the U-Boats, by their own volition--a conscious choice and decision. Betsy Larson, one of the youngest of the group, had been an instructor in a Red Cross swimming and life saving course during her second year of college. This native of New Ulm, Minnesota, and the daughter of its Police Chief Ed L. Larson, was told that "the Red Cross needed people like her" so she sent in her application and was accepted. Betsy Larson wrote about her experiences after joining:

> "Prior to Ft. Bliss August, 1942, I spent two weeks in Washington, D.C. headquarters of the American Red Cross being briefed on my work assignment to be. Then assigned to Ft. Bragg, North Carolina Red Cross Unit attached to the Military Hospital. Then on to Kessler Field Red Cross Unit (Mississippi). Called back to Washington Headquarters to be assigned to a unit of 5 Red Cross workers, Margaret Hahn, Assistant Field Director and Social Worker, Ginnie (Virginia) Lytle, Social Worker, Floy "Mississippi" Kellum, Senior Recreation Worker and Betsy Larson, Junior Recreation Worker and Pat Murphy, secretary. Sent to Ft. Bliss to join the 67th Unit." (5)

Personnel Changes

At the end of December, 1943, Margaret Hahn, Assistant Field Director was transferred and was succeeded by Wanda Morganthaler. Virginia Lytle was transferred from the 67th General Hospital in November, 1943. Shirley Smith, who had been stationed previously at the 32nd General Hospital, replaced her in April, 1943, and Cornelia (Connie) Lowe joined the Unit with an assignment for an indefinite period as a recreation worker. At the same time, a temporary case worker, Mildred Minchew, arrived to help carry the increasingly heavy patient load. Floy (Mississippi) Kellum and Connie Lowe (who left to be Ms. Kellum's assistant) departed the 67th General Hospital on 31 May 1944. Some other workers came later. Margery Hird, a recreational worker, joined the Unit but transferred out in September of 1944. Dorothy Drake, the professional librarian who repaired Betsy's tartan book (mentioned later in this chapter) with new binding, transferred in during June, 1944. Selma Herr, a craft worker, came to the Unit in late 1944.

From Left to Right: Margaret Hahn, Assistant Field Director; Pat Murphy, Secretary; Ginnie Lytle, Social Worker; Floy Kellum, Recreational Worker and Betsy Larson, Recreational Worker. Photograph Courtesy of Betsy Larson Crumrine.

Left to Right: Floy Kellum, Margie Hird and Connie Lowe
Photograph Courtesy of Betsy Larson Crumrine.

The Red Cross at the 67th General Hospital had two English secretaries--Dorothy Ozzard and Betty Wells. (See photograph below.) Mrs. Wells, in an interview in 2004, at age 95, recalled that when she first started working for the Unit, she could not understand the Americans because of their accents, and it took her some time to become accustomed to it. One of her duties was balancing the books at the end of each month. The Red Cross made temporary loans to the patients, and their individual loan accounts had to be balanced at the end of each month. She recalled that Sergeant Harold Maner assisted her to make sure the books balanced. She described her work as being secretarial and her duties included that of an office receptionist. A letter of recommendation from Margaret H. Hahn, ARC written 15 June 1945, stated:

> "Mrs. Betty Wells was employed by the American Red Cross as secretary…She did an outstanding job of handling the books, secretarial work, and acting as office receptionist. Besides being a skilled secretary, she met the great number of complex problems coming through our office with tact and understanding. She was well liked by the staff, patients and hospital personnel and I felt that at any time I was out of the office she could handle any matter coming up during my absence in an efficient manner." (7)

Left to Right: Betty Wells, Margaret Hahn--Assistant Field Director of Red Cross and Dorothy Ozzard. Photograph Courtesy of Betsy Larson Crumrine.

When the Red Cross arrived in Taunton, they were located in a brick building next to the chapel. They were moved later to a Nissen hut with a "temperamental coal burning stove which scattered soot everywhere", requiring constant cleaning. Their brick building became a recreation room for the enlisted men who had been moved from their Nissen huts to tents, thus making room for the rush of patients expected after D-Day. The Red Cross moved to a Nissen hut.

The Red Cross workers were housed with the nurses. Although they were not in the military, and were paid by the Red Cross, they were nevertheless, accorded the treatment and privileges of an officer. They also shared meals and various activities and became friends with many of the nurses and doctors.

The Red Cross was involved in improving the morale of the patients. This took many forms, as initially discussed, such as providing social activities, providing them books, making sure that they had basic things such as toilet articles, providing temporary loans, helping them to communicate with family back home, and teaching and providing materials for crafts. Typical activities included:

> "social recreation ranging from dancing to small informal gatherings. Patients and others may share in the committee work. Quiet games, including card and table games; semi-active games including shuffleboard and ping-pong, all forms of recreation dramatics, emphasizing those staged by the patients themselves, informal musical programs, including both choral and instrumental types. Varied craft activities, solely for diversion

and recreation, individual pursuits such as reading, writing and conversation; development of interest in hobbies." (8)

In a letter home, on 24 December 1942, Betsy Larson wrote:

"Red Cross gave a dance for the enlisted men in our Red Cross Building." (2)

Her letter of 11 July 1943, reported:

"We were fixing curtains in our Nissen Hut Theater. We now have three curtains and on the back curtain we put 67th G.H. painted Red, White and Blue. The stars were mounted on mosquito cloth (the stuff we got when we were supposed to go to Africa). We also used the stuff in making scrapbooks in the craft shop. The curtains had to be ready for tomorrow for a U.S.O. show. Next week is Bob Hope show and then the "Let's Be Buddies" Show from the 10th Repl. Depot. Shows in the afternoon patients and hospital personnel in the evening. A very busy time!!" (2)

4 November 1943

"This last Sunday nite we had a Halloween Party (a masquerade) complete with orchestra (from Special Services) masks and lots of girls. The patients had a marvelous time and what fun we had. As each person came in they were given a mask. We made all the decorations at the craft shop out of old x-ray paper and Sho Card Colors.

Our craft shop has been growing and yesterday we had it full of patients making rings from cylinders of wrecked planes and using wing tips for silhouettes of planes, metal picture frames, caneing foot stools, weaving scarfs, square knotting dog tag chains, purses and cigarette cases. I got pieces of alabaster from the sea shore." (2)

Betsy scrounged the countryside for materials for her crafts. She visited junkyards of junked or downed aircraft and picked up material for crafts. She recalled that the soldiers were very talented and were able to make use of most things she was able to find, such as German propellers and broken plexiglass from downed planes, government supplied leather, aluminum etc. She wrote her parents asking for:

"some small files for fine work, like needle files, three-cornered files, and the like I surely would appreciate it. We are making silhouette plane models from the wing tips of wrecked airplanes and we need so many files with a group of boys working on the projects." (She was able to procure a number of things from home.)

News about her activities and job was a frequent topic when writing home:

"Paramount news men, Red Cross public relations men, and a war correspondent were here to take pictures of our recreational hall, of the wards, and in the craft shop. Now you will be able to see first hand the craft shop that I have been trying to tell you about. I think it will be released just before the March Red Cross Campaign.

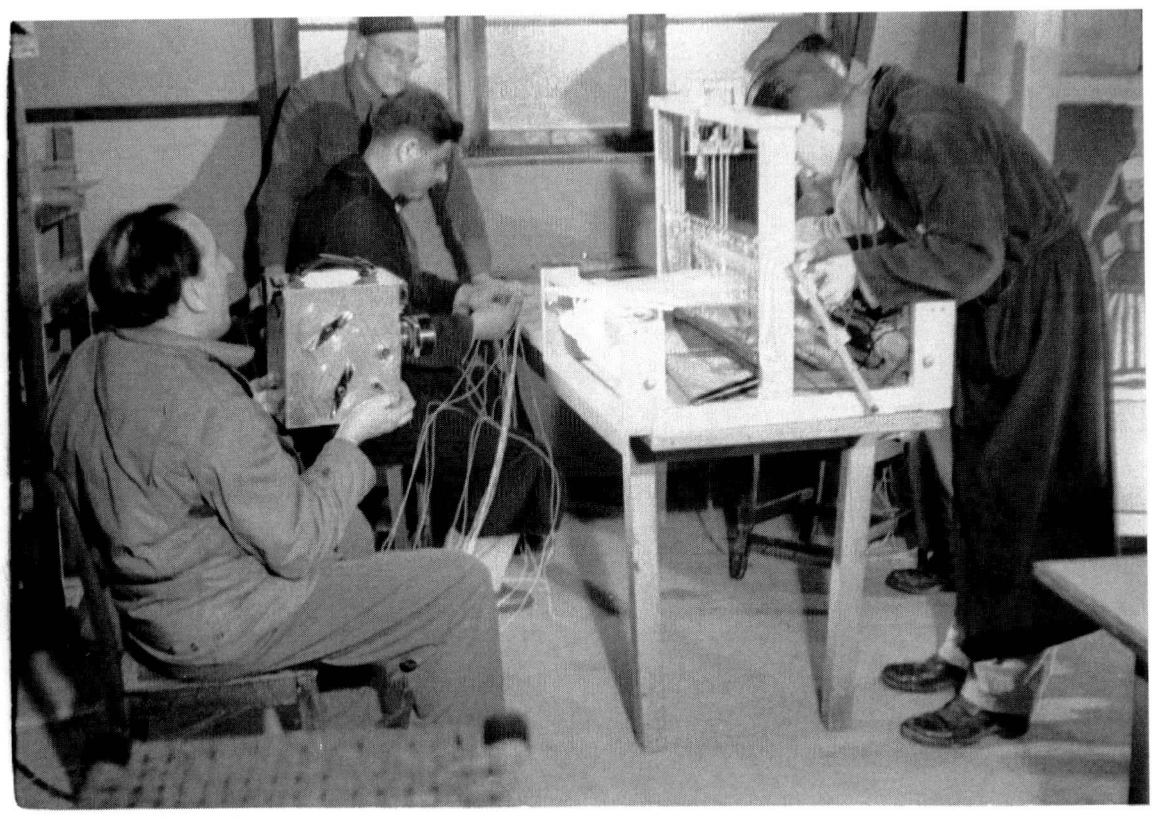

Cameraman in Red Cross Building with Men on Loom
Photograph Courtesy of Raymond Bungard

One of the patients, Felix Weinberg, a professional sculptor by trade, made a pencil drawing of me and they took a picture of the drawing, with him working and me as the model. He has done sketches for a lot of high ranking officers but I'm the second woman in the ETO that he has done. The other lady was Mrs. Eleanor Roosevelt, so I felt quite honored. She was able to get the Motor Pool to make tools for her boys to do their crafts."

Felix Weinberg Shows Betsy Larson His Portrait of Her
Photograph By and Courtesy of Raymond Bungard

Dorothy Drake, a former librarian from Sacramento, California, became the Red Cross Librarian when she arrived. The 67th General Hospital had a library of over 5000 books, and the Red Cross was entrusted with them. Before Ms Drake came to the 67th General Hospital, Corporal Avery Oaks served as an assistant in the library and was helpful in many ways, including help with the housekeeping.

Corporal Avery Oakes with Traveling Library (Book Cart)
Photograph Courtesy Ted Benedict

Ms. Drake would take the book cart round to the patients and got to know their literary likes and dislikes and was able to make suggestions as to what they might be interested in reading. Two social workers were assigned to assist the soldiers to write letters home. Betsy Larson's relationship with the men was such that she considered them her brothers.

Several of her miscellaneous responsibilities included taking a bus load of patients ready to be discharged on a trip to Dunster Yarn Market. While in Dunster, the patients and Betsy were invited to the estate of Lady Herbert, a friend of Margaret Hahn. The men enjoyed games and the peace of an English estate as her guest. On another occasion, Betsy made a trip with a car and driver to Salisbury to pick up two orphan children for a Christmas dinner and gifts for Christmas, 1944.

Dunster Yarn Market in Center with Dunster Castle in Background on Hill
Postcard Courtesy Betsy Crumrine

The Red Cross at the 67th General Hospital became the recipient of a quantity of Botany yarn in many beautiful colors from the main Red Cross headquarters in London. Six or eight looms were included in the shipment, but since Ms Larson had no experience with them, she proceeded to go to the Taunton Art School for instruction. She felt that tartans would provide a colorful pattern and searched for examples to use on the looms. After searching in vain for books, she found that they were not available due to the war. On a train trip back from London, accompanied by Margery Hird, their First Class compartment for which they held reservations, was usurped by four British officers. The other compartments were full and they were relegated to the Goods Wagon, sitting on pigeon crates. This proved to be a serendipity and provided the solution to her dilemma. While making the best of their situation, she had a conversation with a man on the train and brought up the difficulty she had experienced in not being able to find books for patterns of tartans. He asked for her name and address, which she reluctantly provided since he was a total stranger, but after a short time later found a book on tartans in the mail, inscribed by the donor, Forbes Morgan, from Aberdeen, Scotland, and dated April 5, 1943. This book provided the patterns for many scarves which were made by the patients on the looms. The soldiers on the wards would play a game with her by hiding the book and pretending that they did not know where it was.

One of the highlights of their service in England, was the visit of Basil O'Connor, (Chairman of the American Red Cross from 1944 to 1947, and later its President), to Taunton, and the 67th General Hospital's Red Cross Unit. Betsy Larson recalls that his visit came before the March, 1944, Red Cross campaign and that photographs of the visit were to be used in that campaign. (5)

The Red Cross organized or coordinated visits from Special Services bands, U.S.O. visits, such as Bob Hope and Francis Langford who entertained in the outdoor motor pool on 16 July1943, and visits from Irving Berlin (who came to the 67th to visit a patient who was a pilot, and was cajoled to play the piano and sing for the patients), and Jimmy Cagney. After Bob Hope performed, Floy Kellum arranged to have Bob Hope visit the bed patients who had been unable to travel to the performance. This kindness and consideration raised morale in the wards. Jimmy Cagney paid a visit to the 67th General Hospital primarily to visit a friend of his who was a patient. He graciously gave of his time while he was there.

Local talent provided considerable entertainment as well. One performer was Jenny Stockman, a young English girl who entertained the patients many times and enjoyed their attention and applause. She sang and danced and everyone looked forward to a sign announcing, "Little Jenny Tonight" being hung on the door of the auditorium.

"Little Jenny" Stockman
Photograph Courtesy Betsy Crumrine

Left to Right: Betsy Larson, Jimmie Cagney, Floy Kellum and Margery Hird.
Photo Courtesy of Betsy Larson Crumrine

In his Annual Report, Colonel Roland Moore, Commanding Officer of the 67th General Hospital, reported in 1944:

> "The American Red Cross has assigned to this Unit an Assistant Field Director and a Social Worker and three Recreational Workers, of whom one is an excellent instructor in arts and crafts. The welfare work of the organization naturally falls to this competent group

and has increased steadily throughout the year. It is impossible to exaggerate the importance of the Red Cross as an adjunct to hospital treatment…

Their contribution to the happiness and morale of patients cannot be over-estimated. The musical entertainments, amateur shows, birthday parties, dances and holiday celebrations sponsored by the Red Cross would alone justify its existence. The distribution of library books to wards, the mending of clothing for patients, the writing of letters, the arousing of their interest in handicraft in the wards, and finally the skillful and understanding adaptation of Arts and Crafts work both to the interest of the individual and the needs of the hospital, are all things which enhance the recovery of the patients." (12)

By the time the Red Cross and the 67th General Hospital left Musgrove Hospital, there were two metal and wood lathes, and there was a daily book distribution to each ward by a traveling library. (11)

Several of the Red Cross Workers were married while in England. Betsy Larson married Rob Roy Crumrine, of Ohio, in 1944, in Taunton, Somerset, England. They had initially met at Ft. Bliss, where he was in charge of the Ft. Bliss Hospital Medical Library. Their wedding was written up in the London Times as being unusual--an American marrying another American. She was given away at the ceremony by Colonel Roland Moore, the Commanding Officer of the 67th General Hospital. At the wedding, Rob, who had passed the audition for the Metropolitan Opera in New York, just before he joined the army, sang Carrie Jacobs-Bond's "I Love You Truly", and from that moment on, did not sing that song again since he intended it only for Betsy.

Betsy and Rob Crumrine
Photograph Courtesy Betty Wells

Betsy Larson (Crumrine) left the 67th General Hospital on 26 December 1944, returned to the United States on the Queen Elizabeth in January, 1945, before the 67th General Hospital departed. Dorothy M. Drake and Wanda W. Morgenthaler were passengers on the Queen Mary with the rest of the 67th General Hospital, departing 23 September from Southampton, England, and arriving in New York City, on 28 September 1945. Mrs. Betsy Larson Crumrine settled on her husband's Ohio farm after the war, where she lives today and continues to be a Red Cross volunteer in Ohio. Betty Wells lives in Taunton, Somerset, England. She received a Red Cross Ribbon in honor of her service.

Betty Well's Red Cross Pin
Photographed by the Author in 2004

The best way to describe the attitude of the Red Cross workers is to quote a portion of their monthly report made at the end of July, 1943:

> "It's no picnic at times, but every member of this unit loves the work, and we are glad to have a part in helping the men who have been to the battle front, and those who are fighting. The men have a grand morale, and the way they bear their hardships and the smiles on their faces, help our morale, too. This spirit makes us feel as though we can keep on and on, and never do enough for them." (13)

In turn, the attitude of the patient to the Red Cross mirrored this attitude,

> "In an address Mr. Beinecke once gave, stated, 'the Red Cross, through the American people, was trying to give to the soldier a little piece of America in a foreign land.' One patient said one day, 'You know, this recreation hall reminds me of my own home, as my mother is always changing the furniture to make it seem different, just like you folks do.' ". (13)

References

(1) Interview with Betty Wells, in Taunton, June, 2004, by Sidney A. Smith, M.D.

(2) Excerpts from Letters to Home from Betsy Larson (Crumrine).

(3) "The Federal Charter of the American Red Cross." www.Americanredcross.org. 2004.

(4) "World War II Accomplishments of the American Red Cross." www.Americanredcross.org. 2004.

(5) Personal Communications with Betsy Larson Crumrine.

(6) ARC 430 Rev. Oct. 1941.

(7) Letter of Recommendation Dated 15 June 1945, for Mrs. Betty Wells, Written by Margaret Hahn, Field Director, ARC. Courtesy Betty Wells.

(8) "General Guide for Selecting Recreation Workers for Service in Hospitals of the Army and Navy; Domestic and Overseas Guide 11." ARC 843, June 1943. Courtesy Betsy Larson Crumrine.

(9) "Unit Recapitulation Passenger List for Unit Service Number RE 7355-KK, the 67th (US) General Hospital." Courtesy First Sergeant Joe Bullock.

(10) "Historical Report for 1 January to 31 December 1943, for the 67th General Hospital." Dated 31 January 1944. Signed by Roland Moore, Colonel. National Archives.

(11) "Historical Report for 1 January to 31 December 1943, for the 67th General Hospital." Dated 31 January 1944. Signed by Roland Moore, Colonel. National Archives.

(12) "Annual Report of the 67th General Hospital to the Surgeon General, United States Army, for 1944." Dated 31 January 1945. Signed by Roland B. Moore, Colonel, Medical Corps, Commanding Officer. National Archives.

(13) "Reports to the Red Cross from the Red Cross Unit Assigned to the 67th General Hospital. Narrative and Recreation Report for July, 1943." National Archives.

(14) "Reports to the Red Cross from the Red Cross Unit Assigned to the 67th General Hospital. Narrative and Recreation Report for August, 1943." National Archives.

(15) http://library.uncg.edu/depts/archives/veterans/wv_0318.html.

Chapter 10
The Rules and Regulations of the 67th General Hospital

As apple pie is to mother-hood, regulations are to the Army. As covered previously, the management of the hospital was divided into two Sections: Administrative and Professional. The Professional Group was covered in Chapter 6. The Administrative Section was composed of the Headquarters Group and the Executive Group. This chapter is intended to show the workings of the hospital as they applied to these Groups and to the doctors, nurses and enlisted men of the 67th General Hospital as they worked in different departments. After reading these, you will realize that the 67th General Hospital was indeed a part of the Army, although the modern private general hospital has developed equally Byzantine procedures, rules and regulations.

Headquarters Group

Commanding Officer
Executive Officer
Adjutant
Chief Nurse

Executive Group

Registrar
Receiving and Evacuation Officer
C.O. Detachment of Patients
C.O. Detachment Medical Department
Medical Supply Officer
Mess Officer
General Supply Officer
Utilities Officer
Chaplains

Adjutant

The **Adjutant's Office** had the responsibility for arranging the appointments of the men for interviews with the Commanding Officer on matters of official business. It maintained the Message Center under the supervision of the Sergeant Major. Each department was required to call twice daily for their messages--once at 1100 hours and again at 1600 hours, with the calls usually made by one of the enlisted men. All reports and communications were turned into the Sergeant Major for distribution. (1) The Information and Visitors Pass Desk in the Adjutant's Office maintained a file with names and ward assignments of each patient in the hospital. This information included the name, rank, organization, serial number, the ward where the patient was located, name and address of person to be notified in case of emergency, date of patients' admission and discharge from the hospital and disposition made. Once the patient was discharged from the 67th General Hospital, the card was placed in an out-file, kept there for three months and discarded. (1) Correspondence regarding patients was routed through the adjutant's office for approval and transmission.

Visiting hours on non-contagious wards was from 1400 to 1600 hours daily. Permission to visit at other times could be granted by the Officer of the Day or the appropriate ward officer. Patients on venereal disease wards or in prison wards were not allowed to receive visitors on their respective ward, but if the visitor was a direct relative, the Adjutant might arrange for a visit in the reception hall of headquarters depending on the medical condition of the patient. If the adjutant was unavailable, the CO Detachment of Patients would assume the responsibility of handing out passes. (1)

The Personnel Section operated under the Assistant Adjutant and was "responsible for the preparation of payroll and vouchers, personnel reports, returns, rosters and all correspondence regarding personnel on duty at this hospital."(1)

An officer of the 67th General Hospital was designated as a Class A Agent Finance Officer with duties set forth in AR 35-320. The Agent Finance Officer had to notify the Adjutant 24 hours in advance of pay day, the Adjutant would then announce the date and hour payment was to be made to the men and provide the men necessary for the clerical duties of making the payment. The CO Detachment of Patients would furnish an appropriate guard for this. An armed guard would accompany the Agent Finance Officer to receive the payroll and stay with him until the payroll was paid. (1) Officers' and nurses' pay vouchers were prepared for signature in the Adjutant's Office.

The 67th General Hospital was a hospital facility which fell under the rules of the Geneva Convention. Thus, by definition, it was not allowed to possess firearms or weapons of any kind. The First Sergeant, Joe Bullock, claims that an old 1918 semi-automatic pistol was used to escort the payroll to the 67th--a pistol without ammunition. (2)

Going Through the Adjutant to Leave Town

> "When officers, nurses and noncommissioned officers of the first three grades will obtain and deliver to the Adjutant a clearance sheet showing clearance of indebtedness and proper responsibility before departing from this station for duty elsewhere, for extended leave, or upon resignation, retirement or discharge from the Army. Proper blank form will be furnished upon request to the Adjutant." (1)

Officers leaving the Post on leave of absence or returning from leave of absence were required to sign the Leave Book at the Information Desk. Passes were handled in the same manner, not to exceed 48 hours. (1)

Disposition of property belonging to deceased patients or patients who were AWOL was handled in channels through the Adjutant's Office. (10)

The Chief Nurse

The Chief Nurse was appointed by the Commanding Officer and was under his direct command with the responsibilities of the Nursing Service of the hospital and the nurses' quarters. She served in a capacity similar to a Company Commander over his troops and was responsible for their continuing education and instruction regarding the regulations that they were supposed to follow. This was in addition to being responsible for setting their hours and maintaining their discipline. (1)

All nurses, either coming into the 67th General Hospital or leaving it were required to meet with the Commanding Officer in company with the Chief Nurse. (1) The first Chief Nurse of the 67th General Hospital was Irene Zwisler, who helped organize the nursing component of the Unit, and was succeeded by Marjorie French after about a year. Ms French stayed with the Unit until it disbanded. Mildred Butler served as Ms French's assistant in the office.

The Registrar

When asked to comment on the Registrar's Office and on the Receiving and Evacuation Office, Ted Benedict had this to say:

> "I worked in the Registrar's Office for about a year before being transferred to the clinical labs. My duties there involved typing the 'morning report' and then editing the patient's charts upon transfer out--and building the fire in the coal stove before doing the morning report." (9) Ted also compared the Registrar's Office to that of Medical Records Department in a hospital today. Ted Benedict worked in the Registrar's Office for a year before he transferred to the laboratory. His responsibility was to type up reports which required "eleven copies, using carbon paper in two passes."

When a patient was to be discharged, the process centered around the Registrar's Office. Records of the discharged patients were maintained there until the end of the month, unless they were being transferred, in which case records were sent with the patient.

Registrar's Office. From Left to Right: Niilo J. Jacobson, Edwin J. Whitner, Ted Benedict, Thought to be Harold Zucker and Gordon D. Richmond (Identified by Ted Benedict)
Photograph Courtesy Raymond Bungard

Admitting and Disposition Officer

The Admitting and Disposition Officer was director of the Admitting and Disposition Office. This office was similar to the Admitting Office found in hospitals today. All patients, with the exception of emergency and contagious cases reported to that office. The office responded when it was informed by the nurse on duty that an emergency or contagious case had arrived and took appropriate steps to formally admit them to the hospital. The office was never unattended.

When the patient was taken to the ward, he was taken in pajamas, and shoes and his personal hat and socks. The ward gave the attendant a clean set of pajamas to return to the A and D Office. The Ward officer would see the patient as soon as possible after admission. Baggage, after it had been claimed, was tagged with the patient's name, organization and ward number and then stored in the Patients' Clothing Storeroom in the Detachment of Patients Office because baggage was not allowed on the wards.

Admitting Office. Note the Doors Which Could Be Opened Wide to Accommodate a Stretcher
Photograph Courtesy Raymond Bungard

Patients' Fund and Effects

The Admitting Officer informed the patients that the hospital would care for their money and valuables "if they were checked into the Custodian of the Patients' Fund Account for safekeeping".

The Detachment Patient Commanding Officer supervised the Patient's Fund Account.

Receiving and Evacuation Office

The Receiving and Evacuation Office held an infirmary for the men of the 67th General Hospital. Here, the men were seen and either returned to duty or admitted to the hospital.

Detachment Medical

The Detachment Medical Department consisted of the enlisted medical personnel and was involved in their day-to-day management and discipline. The Detachment Office Orderly Room housed the Commanding Officer of the Detachment Medical Department, the First Sergeant and Detachment support personnel. Here, a morning report was generated usually by the T5 on duty (by John Herbacheck most of the time), passed up through the First Sergeant and then to the Commanding Officer. (25)

John Herbacheck, right, and Joe Snow in Doorway of Orderly Room at Ft. Bliss
Photograph Courtesy First Sergeant Joe Bullock

Orderly Room with Bulletin Board Containing Daily Orders in Front
Photograph by and Courtesy of Raymond Bungard

The Commander of the Detachment Medical was referred to as Detachment Commander to avoid any confusion with the Commanding Officer of the 67th General Hospital, Colonel Moore. His duties and responsibilities were those of a company commander. (1) Most of the Detachment Medical Commanding Officers were lieutenants of the Regular Army, usually a Medical Administrative Officer (M.A.C.). The successive Detachment Medical Commanding Officers were Captain Thomas Greer, who did not accompany the Unit to England, Captain Wilmer H. Funk, Lt. Aronson, Archie Faulk and Lt. William Albreight. The office of the Detachment Medical also included the First Sergeant. The initial First Sergeant of the 67th General Hospital was Earl Barton, who later went to Officer Training School and was succeeded as First Sergeant by Joe Bullock. (2)

Standing from Left: First Sergeant Earl Barton, Captain Thomas Greer, Detachment Commander
Seated from Left: John Herbichek, Joe Bullock, Joe Snow. Photograph Taken at Ft. Bliss
Photograph Courtesy First Sergeant Joe Bullock

Lt. Aronson, Detachment Commander
Photograph Courtesy Betsy Larson Crumrine

From Left: First Sergeant Earl Barton and Captain Wilmer H. Funk, Detachment Commander "Reading the Riot Act" to Misbehaver at Administrative Hearing at Fort Bliss.
Photograph Courtesy First Sergeant Joe Bullock

Left to Right: Sergeant Major Mangum H. Dawson, Lieutenant William Albreight, Detachment Commander, First Sergeant Joe Bullock
Photograph Courtesy First Sergeant Joe Bullock

Captain A.L. Faulk, Detachment Commander and Lt. E.H. Weitzen, Utility and Motor Pool Officer
Photograph Courtesy of Mrs. Lucille Walker

The Detachment Commander was responsible for assigning men either to a Professional or Administrative Service on the basis of strength tables prescribed by headquarters (Table of Organization), and once the man was assigned, he was not allowed to reassign him except for reason. He set up prophylactic stations on base and in adjacent civilian communities and men who had had sexual intercourse had to report to the nearest prophylactic station for cleaning and "prophylaxis as may be prescribed by the War Department." Self administration of sulfanilamide by the personnel was prohibited. (1) The Orderly Room at the 67th General Hospital had a box filled with condoms which were free for the taking. (2)

Sick Call was at 0830 hours daily and the sick report was sent to the attending surgeon by the Detachment Commander.

Passes for the enlisted men were handled through the Detachment Commander. When off-duty, the men could stray no more than ten miles from the hospital. Men were allowed a pass for twenty-four hours each week, but not more than 7% of the strength of the unit could be on pass at one time. The pass had to specify the locale that was to be visited. Men with a one-day pass could visit areas 125 miles distant, those with a two-day pass could venture out 250 miles while those with a three-day pass could travel 375 miles. All passes had to be approved by the Chief of Service or department before it could be presented to the Detachment Commander. (1)

Parliament from Westminster Bridge
Photograph Taken by Ted Benedict While on Furlough in London

The enlisted men were not allowed to have any financial dealings at all with the patients, unless approval was given by the CO. Lending money to other enlisted men or patients was also prohibited. (1) If necessary, the enlisted men and the patients could borrow money from the Red Cross for short term purposes.

Regular duty for enlisted men on ward duty was 0700 to 1900 Hours for day duty. Regular duty hours for other enlisted personnel in the "operating rooms, clinics, receiving office, laboratory, kitchens, mess halls, post exchange, guard and administrative offices will be such as are prescribed by the officers in charge."(1) A list of enlisted men not on duty was sent by the heads of departments prior to noon of the day before the day the enlisted man was to be excused for the day or any part of the day. (2)

Men for night duty were requested by the Chiefs of Service and detailed by the Detachment Commander. The hours were from 1900 to 0700 hours. Tours on night duty usually were for one month, but the enlisted man could request a two month tour or be assigned for up to an additional month. In any event, no soldier could be kept on night duty for longer than two months. (1)

Sergeant Joe Bullock recalled several of his duties while serving as First Sergeant of the Detachment Medical in the Orderly Room:

> "Re German prisoners...we had about 30 of them, most of whom were assigned to outside yard work. They would come over every day from the camp where they were

located...one soldier would come with them, which didn't pose any threat because they were not the least bit interested in going back to Germany and getting back into the war. A few of them could speak English and were quite interesting to be around. One of them gave me a box full of photos of his army career...and another made a ring from monel steel (whatever that is) and I still have it although my fingers are too fat & lumpy to wear it now. My only involvement with them was in setting up the jobs they were to do in the yard. I was in the orderly room and that's where they came every day to get assignments.

After we arrived in Taunton the hospital work required someone on duty around the clock, which meant there were more important things than close order drill. By that time, I was a Technical Sergeant, assigned to the orderly room, where all of the administrative work for the 500 enlisted men was done. The British people loved parades, so we were often invited to parade through the streets of Taunton for some celebration or another. That was interesting because the bands were always British Army, and their cadence was a bit slower than ours and we had trouble in keeping in step and looking just right. But it was fun and that's about the only time I had to fall back on my ability as drill instructor." (2)

Joe Bullock also recalled traveling with the Payroll Officer to the G50 Depot to pick up the payroll. The payroll was always in cash--Pounds Sterling. Two men, one of whom had to carry a firearm, were required on the detail. The only one weapon he recalled was an old .45 caliber pistol for which he had no bullets. Sometimes, Sergeant Kennedy would take the responsibility of collecting the payroll. (2)

Other Regulations Pertinent to the Detachment Medical

Smoking was not permitted while on duty and designated smoking areas were set aside by officers in charge of the various departments. Gambling and drinking were not permitted on base. (1)

Each man was to consider himself "always on duty for the correction of disorders and irregularities as pertain to this hospital, regardless of when or where observed. When any action is taken under the foregoing provision, report thereof will be made informally to the Commanding Officer, or the Chief of Service, or the Officer in charge of the department concerned." (1)

Medical Inspector

The **Medical Inspector** was a medical officer whose duties included the supervision of the sanitation of the post. He made recommendations to the Commanding Officer regarding steps that needed to be taken to prevent and control infectious disease, and conducted periodic inspections of the hospital in areas where sanitation was important.

Medical Supply Officer

The Medical Supply Officer was responsible for the acquisition, storage and issuance of medical supplies needed for the hospital. In addition, he was responsible for the hospital linen exchange. Certain supplies not included on the T/O and E and considered as non-standard could be ordered through a special small fund at the 67th General Hospital which had been set up for this purpose by the Surgeon General. The request would have to specify the patient, and statements would have to be made as to whether another item which would be as effective was available and why this standard item was unacceptable in this particular case. (1) Detachment Supply was under the administration of Lt. Bob Walker of the Quartermaster Corps.

Lt. Bob Walker, Quartermaster Corps, Left, with Lt. Harry Harper of the Laboratory
Photograph Courtesy Lucille Walker

Professional Officer of the Day

The Professional Officer of the Day was designated daily by the Commanding Officer from the medical officers on duty and was responsible for a 24 hours tour of duty. After regular duty hours, the Professional Officer of the Day was responsible for the professional care of all patients in the hospital and at 1630 hours would visit all patients on the seriously ill list and familiarize himself with their condition. (This is similar to the resident and intern on call in a major hospital or a doctor on call for a particular medical service in current practice.) Additionally, he was to act as the Receiving Officer and admit all patients to the hospital, make the ward assignments depending on the nature and severity of the patient's problem, and institute proper medical care until the regular ward doctor came on duty. (1)

Administrative Officer of the Day

The Administrative Officer of the Day was selected from a list maintained by the Adjutant from a roster of dental officers, Medical Administrative officers and other officers and they provided a pool who might be assigned to this duty by the Commanding Officer. He was on duty for 24 hours and as the Administrative Officer of the Day, was the representative of the Commanding Officer.

Signal Officer

The Signal Officer was designated by the Commanding Officer and had charge of the telephone system on the post and was responsible for its maintenance and functioning, including any alterations and repairs. Personal telephone use was restricted to the officer's quarters, Officer's Club, Nurses' Recreation Club and Detachment Medical Departmental offices. The plan was to keep the lines open for incoming and emergency calls. The telephone number of the Unit could only be given out over the telephone to authorized military personnel. When answering the telephone, the name of the organization was not given and the telephone number was used for identification when the telephone was answered by the operator. (1)

Calls were disconnected after six minutes. Direct lines through G-50 (the supply depot) were used, if possible, because they were charged to the U.S. through the Lend-Lease Program to be compensated for in materials and supplies. The numbers of the direct lines were kept secret by the operators. One trunk line was reserved as an emergency line to be used only for emergency calls with the number kept secret and known only by the Taunton operator, the Signal Officer and the operators on the board. Individual personal calls had to be placed through the pay station located in the Administration Building. Enlisted men could take incoming calls only if placed to the Detachment Medical Departmental Office. (1)

Post Exchange Officer

The Post Exchange Officer was in charge of the Post Exchange and with the approval of the Post Exchange Council, could ration sales items to insure a more equitable distribution, due to the shortage of many items. He supervised the concessionaires for service and prices and reports were made to the Commanding Officer by the 10th of the month regarding operations. (1)

Patients at the Post Exchange (PX)
Photograph Courtesy Ted Benedict

Utilities Officer

The Utilities Officer was in charge of the maintenance of grounds and buildings. The senior officer in charge of each building was responsible for its care and it was his duty to report any damage or needed repairs, accompanied by a Request for Repairs Form, to the Utilities Officer so that repairs could be done. Any request for work to involve construction or changes to existing structures had to be submitted to the Commanding Officer for approval before going to the Utilities Officer. (1)

Regulating the temperature of the buildings during the wintertime was done by turning off the radiators. Cooling the building was done by opening the windows which rationally was not allowed while the radiators were on, since it wasted energy.

Transportation Officer or Motor Officer

The Transportation Officer or Motor Officer was responsible for the operation and maintenance of vehicles belonging to the 67th General Hospital. He regulated the official use of the vehicles, their operation, the training of the drivers and their familiarization with the rules, traffic regulations, etc. Lt. Edward H. Weitzen was a Motor Pool Officers at one time. (Photograph page 156)

Ambulances required authorization to leave the garage. Each driver had the responsibility of keeping their ambulance clean and neat, maintaining the equipment and driving by traffic regulations.

The speed limit could not be exceeded, even in an emergency, except by order of an officer. The ambulances carried one emergency kit, 3 blankets, and one pillow per litter. Each trip required that an emergency kit be picked up at the Receiving Office and the trip made with a medical officer. It was the responsibility of the driver to find out if his patient was contagious and take appropriate precautions. (1)

If a vehicle was damaged in an accident, an officer was appointed to investigate the accident to determine the responsible person. (1)

A record of daily usage of oil and gasoline was maintained for the vehicles. (1)

Melvin Spradley, Motor Pool
Photograph Courtesy First Sergeant Joe Bullock

Motor Pool From the Tower
Photograph From and Courtesy Ted Benedict

Library Officer

The Library Officer was in charge of the medical library issued to the station as well as journals purchased or received from other sources. It did not include non-professional books and magazines circulated by the Special Service Officer or Red Cross. These books could be checked out and maintained in separate parts of the hospital which might better benefit from a book dealing with a particular subject with permission of the Commanding Officer, such as a book on a surgical topic placed on a surgical ward, etc. Monthly inventory was required. (1)

Mess Officer

The Mess Officer was designated by the Commanding Officer and was responsible for the messes of the hospital, the menus in each mess and the selection, purchase, care, issue, preparation and serving of all food supplies. Inventory of food supplies was made on a weekly basis. (1)

Captain Pullen, Officer in Charge of the Kitchen and Messes
Photograph Courtesy Bobby Burns

The Mess Officer had the responsibility for seeing that all food handlers were examined before assigning them to duty. The examination and certification was done by the Examining Medical Officer, and a list of the certified handlers along with their dates of examination was posted.

The dieticians mirrored to some extent the function of the Mess Officer and were under his supervision. They planned the menus for all special diets, kept the cost of the meals within the budget and supervised the preparation and service of all meals to the wards, dining room and cafeteria patients. The Head Dietician ordered the food and assisted the Mess Officer in ordering new kitchen equipment.

Diet cards were prepared for each patient, (M.D. Form 73) and submitted to the Head Dietician by the Head Nurse of each ward by 0800 Hours each morning to cover meals in a 24 hour period from the noon meal of that day through breakfast the next day.

The following types of diets were prepared in the Patient's Mess:

1. Regular diet
2. Light diet
3. Soft diet
4. Liquid diet
5. Special diets (to consist of such articles of food as are specifically ordered)

Food for the wards for non-ambulatory patients was prepared by the cook on duty in the Patient's Mess, placed in the food container or special carts and then picked up by ward personnel. The actual serving of the trays fell to a nurse on duty on each ward. This allowed the nurse to check that the meals were prepared correctly, were served in an appetizing fashion, conformed with the menu advertised or specified and was either hot or cold as specified. Ward attendants, nurses and doctors were not allowed to eat in the wards and had to eat at their respective messes. (1)

The enlisted men used their mess kits when eating and their components were hooked together after eating and dunked in three separate 55 gallon drums. The first drum was filled with hot soapy water and the other two drums were filled with hot water. (3)

Richard Smith on the Right with Unidentified Corporal Holding Their Mess Kits. The Apparatus in Front Appears to be a Stirrup Pump Used for Fighting Fires. In the Background Are Tents Occupied by the Enlisted Men.
Photograph in Collection of the Author

Post Chaplain

The Post Chaplain had the responsibility of coordinating the other chaplains at the Post as they held religious services. He was the custodian of the Chaplain's Fund which was used "for the promotion of religious and spiritual comfort of the personnel of the command, not available by regular requisition".

As expected, he was to act as a contact between the seriously ill and their family and to make hospital rounds daily visiting particularly the seriously ill, the new patients and also making routine ward visits. He integrated the services of the Red Cross, U.S.O., neighboring churches and civilian organizations as it related to the religious activities of the personnel of the command. (1)

Pharmacy Officer

The Pharmacy Officer was a commissioned officer responsible for supervision of the pharmacy and the running of an efficient operation. All prescriptions were required to be written in the metric system of weights and measures. All personnel in the pharmacy wore the white uniform worn with a gown while on duty.

Gas Officer

The Gas Officer coordinated training and drills regarding the use of equipment and the procedures to follow during a gas attack.

Special Service Officer

The Special Service Officer was in charge of providing entertainment for the men of the 67th General Hospital, utilizing outside sources and well as the assets, facilities and personnel of the hospital while coordinating this with the Red Cross. Dr. Eugene McManamy served as the Special Service Officer while the 67th General Hospital was in Taunton, and was well-liked by all who knew him.

Captain McManamy, Special Services Officer
Photograph Courtesy Ted Benedict

Post Intelligence Officer

The Post Intelligence Officer:

> "is charged with the duties of rendering professional aid to his commander in all military intelligence matters, and with the execution and supervision of approved policies pertaining to domestic intelligence activities within the Post, and liaison with appropriate United States and British authorities." (1) No reference regarding the Post Intelligence Officer was found during research on the 67th.

Planning and Training Officer

Programs of continuing education were maintained under the direction of a Planning and Training Officer. He coordinated all instruction and provided literature, training aids and educational films. Particular emphasis was placed, in 1943, upon training in gas defense and individual treatment of gas casualties. (5)

> "A regular training program has been carried on throughout the year, with all personnel participating. This has included everything from a review of basic training to advanced courses in physical training, gas defense, recognition of enemy aircraft, treatment of gas injuries and fire fighting. Lectures, group discussions and showing of films have been utilized in this work, which has been under the direction of the Plans and Training Officer. Professional officers have been rotated in different departments, so that each is prepared to fill two or more positions in case of need. Staff meetings have been held weekly at which scientific papers are read and cases of general interest are presented and discussed. Practically every officer has been assigned to temporary duty for several days or weeks at various schools of instruction, or has attended medical meetings at other hospitals. Each officer so assigned is required to present to the entire staff a report upon the instruction received, within 48 hours after his return to this organization." (7)

Training activities continued through 1944. (6) Professional officers held compulsory meetings weekly where scientific papers were read and cases of interest were presented and discussed. Officers of the Dental Service also held weekly meetings apart from those of the Medical Officers, and in addition, frequently attended the Meetings of the Medical Officers. (5)

Members of the Administrative Staff held meetings weekly which were similar to the meetings held by the Professional Staff. In these meetings, problems relating to their departments were discussed. An "Officers' Call" was held daily at which all officers were present, and immediate and urgent questions were presented. (5)

> "The Army Nurse Corps received instructions from Medical Officers, each of whom is assigned to lecture upon a definite subject in which he is qualified; in addition to

this a regular course of instruction is conducted by the Chief Nurse and her assistants on such subjects as general nursing, ward management, dietetics, etc.

Enlisted personnel, in addition to the usual military instruction, calisthenics and close order drill, receive lectures from Administrative and Medical officers, and those assigned to hospital wards are required to attend classes conducted by lecturers from the medical staff, the Army Nurse Corps, and qualified Non-commissioned officers." (7)

Those doing ward duty received lectures, demonstrations and practical examinations, from three to six times a week from the officers, supervisors and ward nurses, which they were required to attend. (4, 5)

In addition to medico-military instructions, there were lectures on historical subjects and neighboring points of interest by civilians and British military personnel from the vicinity.

Regulations Regarding the Operation of the Wards

Ward Officers

Ward Officers were assigned by the Chiefs of Services and had charge of the ward to which they were assigned. They were responsible for the patients and their assigned nurses, enlisted men and other attendants, for the equipment of the ward, its care, and the proper use of supplies and material used on the ward. The medical record, the cleanliness and sanitation of the ward and grounds and general discipline and conduct were his responsibility. (1) When he assumed the duties of the ward doctor, he obtained a list of all non-expendable property from the Medical Supply Officer, checked the list against the property and signed a receipt for it.

"All non-expendable property in wards will be checked at least once each month between the 15th and 20th day and a report showing overages and shortages discovered made to the Commanding Officer. Suitable blank forms for the purpose will be furnished by the Medical Supply Officer. In conformity with paragraph 8, AR 35-6640, responsible officers concerned will initiate Form 15 AGO (Report of Survey), to cover any damage to or shortage of property for which they are responsible and for which adjustment cannot be made." (1)

The **Ward Nurse in Charge** was in charge of the ward, nurses, enlisted personnel and any who assisted with the care of her patients. Her responsibilities included nursing care of all patients, making rounds with the ward surgeon, receiving doctor's orders and recording them for the other nurses in the patient's record. Also, when possible, she gave all medication and injections. A Wardmaster, the senior enlisted man on the ward, was in charge of the other enlisted men on the ward, the "Ward Boys".

Convalescent patients were expected to do light work in and around the ward, depending on their health. Their help was to maintain cleanliness and generally help prepare the ward for inspection which was done at least once daily by the Ward Officer.

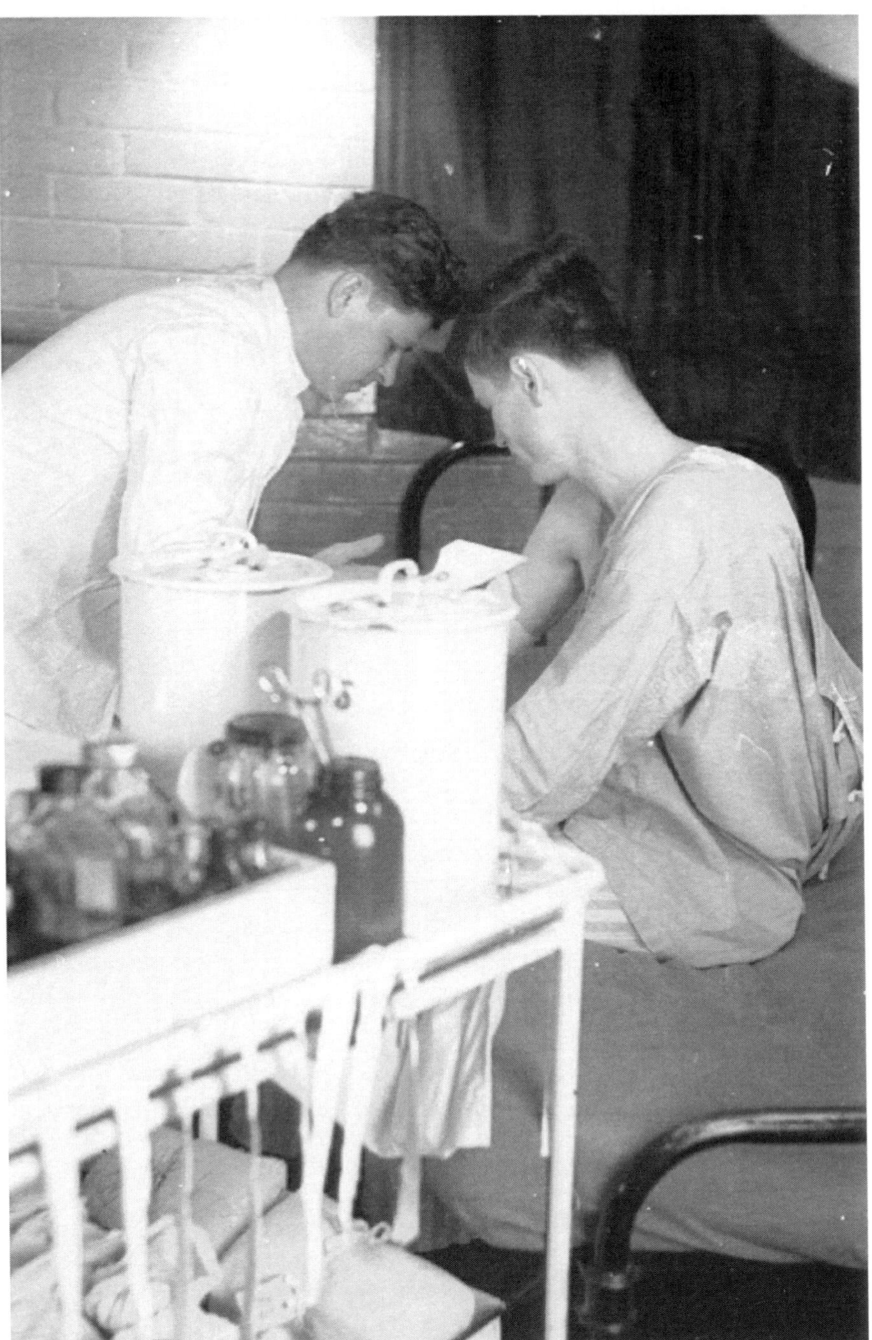

Ward Boy Changing Dressing
Photograph By and Courtesy of Ted Benedict

Patients Policing Their Area
Photograph Courtesy Ted Benedict

Messing of Patients: The ambulatory patients were required to eat at the mess hall. Those who required a special diet were served on the ward as were those who could not serve themselves in the mess hall because of their injuries. Bed patients were served on trays on the wards. All food containers, bottles, custard cups and food boxes were washed in the diet kitchen before return to the mess.

Regulation for the patients, referred to as the "Rules for Patients" were as follows:

"(1) Patients are under the direct command of the ward officer; in his absence the nurse; in her absence, the wardmaster.

(2) Gambling, the use or possession of intoxicating beverages, and abusive, obscene or profane language are forbidden.

(3) Valuables, and money in excess of one Pound, should be deposited with nurse or wardmaster for transfer to the Commanding Officer of Detachment of Patients, who will give a receipt for same.

(4) Ambulatory patients are to be out of bed at 0630 hours. Morning mess is at 0700 hours. All patients must remain in the ward after breakfast until excused by the Ward Officer. All patients must be in the ward by 2100 hours. There will be no unnecessary noise in wards after 'Lights Out'.

(5) There will be no visiting from ward to ward.

(6) Passes will be issued to visit clinics, Red Cross Building, occupational therapy, etc. Patients will notify the wardmaster when leaving the ward, and will hand their passes to him upon returning to the ward.

(7) If uniforms are issued to patients, they will be turned in to the wardmaster at 1700 hours, each day, without exception.

(8) Patients are not permitted on hospital roads, or in quarters or barracks or other messes than their own, and will not engage in conversation with guards either on post or at the gates.

Violation of these or other hospital regulations are punishable by disciplinary action under the 104th A.W. (Articles of War) trial by court-martial in the case of soldiers."

Patients were not permitted to make excessive noise and were required to control loud talk, whistling, laughter and boisterous behavior. They were not allowed to loiter in the hallways or in the offices of the ward officer or nurse. Radios were not permitted after "Lights Out" or during quiet hours which were designated by the Ward Officers. The nurses would check the presence of patients using the ward book at 2100 hours each evening and at other times if indicated. The bed book showed the name and bed number of each patient. Patients who were absent without leave were reported on the next morning's ward report.

Passes might be granted to patients through the Detachment Medical Commanding Officer if the patient was in adequate physical condition. Patients who were enlisted were not allowed to wear personal clothing on the ward except for their hat and shoes. When the patient went on pass, he would pick up his clothing at the clothing room at the Detachment of Patients office, and return them on return to the hospital. Women and officer patients had no such restrictions on the wearing of their own clothing.

Patients in Formation in Front of the Theater
Photograph Courtesy Ted Benedict

Passes for relatives or visitors were obtained from the Detachment of Patients Commanding Officer. The pass was issued subject to the approval of the ward officer who could deny the pass, particularly if he felt that a certain patient should not receive visitors. A list of patients who were not allowed to receive visitors was kept in the Detachment of Patients' office. Unruly or boisterous visitors or those intoxicated were asked to leave the post and a guard would be called to escort them to the front gate if necessary. (1)

Passes for patients to visit other patients on other wards were generally not given. Passes were not given to visit venereal patients, prisoners, the patients in isolation or for children to visit tuberculous patients. Should patients in these locations be critically ill, instructions for precautions (e.g. to prevent infection or prevent harm from the mentally excited patient) were given. If the venereal patient was ambulatory, arrangements were made for the visitor to see the patient in the recreation building or the lawn. (1)

Mail for patients was to be delivered by the mail orderly to the Head Nurse of each ward, who in turn, personally delivered the mail to the patient. All mail for prisoners or the insane, both incoming and outgoing was opened and checked by the Ward Officer. Any money which came in was deposited in their behalf by the Ward Officer in the Patient's Fund. All outgoing mail, except for officers, was to be censored.

Discharge of the Patient
(No one gets out without paperwork.)

The discharge of the **enlisted patient** was handled primarily through the Registrar's Office, and is covered in that section in this chapter.

When **officers or warrant officers** were discharged:

> "Upon completion of treatment and records required, officers and warrant officers will be returned to duty as soon as possible and without regard to the hour of departure. When travel orders are required, advance notice will be given the Adjutant to permit their preparation and in some cases secure transportation requests from the Quartermaster. Proceedings of disposition boards will be completed and submitted to the Commanding Officer, for consideration before actual departure in all cases in which the disposition is other than a return to duty. All officers and nurses *(who were patients)* will report to Commanding Officer, Detachment of Patients before being discharged." (11)

In case of death, the "following action will be taken:

> 1. Effects of deceased patients; The Ward Officer will secure all personal effects of the patient and deliver them promptly to the Summary Court in the cases of military personnel. Effects of deceased patients other than those mentioned above may be turned over to near relatives, if present, obtaining receipt for same. Rings will be removed from fingers, and bed and clothing will be searched for other valuables.
>
> 2. Disposition of Remains:
>
> (a.) Tags bearing the name, rank, and organization of the patient will be attached, one to the right great toe and one to the left thumb. The remains, after cavities have been plugged, will then be sent to the morgue, securely wrapped in a sheet so that no exposure of the body will occur enroute.

(b) Every effort will be made by all concerned to avoid delay in the shipment of remains to burial place.

(c) The Chief of the Laboratory or his assistant will inspect the remains at the undertaking establishment as the representative of the Commanding Officer of the hospital and as representative of the Quartermaster who let the government contract for undertaking services. He will arrange for his inspection at such time as will not delay shipment of remains to destination." (1)

Disposition of Bodies

"Bodies of deceased persons are prepared properly and removed to the morgue as required by paragraph 103, TM 8-260, 16 July 1941. Bodies of deceased persons committed to the morgue are placed in the correct posture. Care is exercised to prevent turning of the head, extreme flexion or extension of the neck, or malposition of extremities. Undue pressure by winding sheets, especially about the face, is avoided. During routine duty hours this is the duty of the Chief of Laboratory Service. Outside routine duty hours the responsibility rests upon the officer who determines the fact of death. The Chief of Laboratory Service or his representative is responsible for the care of bodies held in the morgue, and turns them over to the undertaker only on the written authority of the Registrar or the Administrative Officer of the Day." (1)

References

(1) "Regulations of the 67th General Hospital." Somerset Archives, Taunton, Somerset, England.

(2) Communication with Joe Bullock, First Sergeant.

(3) Communication with Raymond Bungard.

(4) "Annual Report of the 67th General Hospital to the Chief Surgeon, SOS, ETOUSA." Dated 15 January 1943. Signed by Lieutenant Colonel R.B. Moore, M.C., Commanding. National Archives.

(5) "Historical Report of 1943, to the Chief Surgeon, SOS, ETOUSA from R.B. Moore, Colonel, Medical Corps, Commanding Officer, 67th General Hospital, APO 511." Dated 31 January 1944. National Archives.

(6) "Annual Report of the 67th General Hospital to the Surgeon General, United States Army, for 1944." Dated 31 January 1945. Signed by Roland B. Moore, Colonel, Medical Corps, Commanding Officer. National Archives.

(7) "Annual Report to the Chief Surgeon, SOS, ETOUSA, APO 887, U.S. Army." Dated 31 January 1944. National Archives.

(8) "Monthly Sanitation Report to the Commanding Officer, 67th General Hospital, APO 511, U.S. Army." Dated 2 January 1943. Signed by Merrill S.F. Greene, Major, Medical Corps, Medical Inspector. National Archives.

(9) Communication with Ted Benedict.

Chapter 11
The Patients

When the 67th General Hospital first arrived in Taunton, it took over Musgrove Military Hospital, a hospital originally built by the British, for 700 patients. Some of the patients inherited from the 2nd Evacuation Hospital which had occupied the facilities prior to the arrival of the 67th General Hospital were afflicted with hepatitis contacted while serving in the Army in Iceland. Before the war was over, the hospital had expanded to 1000 beds and at one point was caring for almost 1700 patients. Initially, patients were transported in by ship and railroad and later many were brought by airplane. The 67th General Hospital informed headquarters daily about available bed space since it was a "transit hospital" named thusly because it conditioned patients from field hospital to base hospitals. In the setting of the General Hospital, proper care could be given and the soldier returned to combat. (9)

The first patients with war injuries to be treated were from the Battle of Oran, an amphibious operation carried out during the initial assault in Operation Torch.

The hospital treated about 500 casualties from this assault and the patients were a mix of British as well as American patients. For a time, the British maintained a Registrar to deal with British patients at the Musgrove Military Hospital. Ted Benedict, who was working in the Registrar's office at the time recalled his introduction to the treatment of battle casualties in a diary notation dated 20 December 1942.

> "Started the real thing today. After dinner a small shipment of casualties came in ambulances and the S and W office went over to H and D to help out there. The Colonel stood on the roof taking snapshots of the procedure, while nurses fluttered.
>
> Most of the patients came in on litters, a few walked. Some had no feet to walk on, a few are still carrying shrapnel. A week by boat from North Africa--no wonder they are sick.
>
> While I was filling out cards on the ones in ward 5, I found the core of a good story. On one side of the room was a fellow with only one leg, from an infantry outfit. Working around to the other side of the room, I saw a boy with no feet He was from the MD (Medical Detachment) of that same infantry outfit; in fact he lost his feet bringing the other boy in from the field. Machine gunned.
>
> They sounded pretty cheerful--especially as they were warm, in bed and eating warm supper within a half hour of the time they arrived. Hot coffee, all the butter they wanted, and good food. Sick, seven days in a hospital ship, eating ship rations--can't blame them for being happy.

One of them, told to wait for a wheel chair to take him to his ward, said testily, 'I walked all over North Africa. I guess I can walk out to the ward.' And he hobbled out of the room." (29)

Casualties from Operation Torch and the Invasion at Oran Having Party in the Red Cross Building
Photograph Courtesy Betsy Crumrine.

On 25 December 1942, a Red Cross worker wrote:

"Pat, Ginnie, Margaret Floy and Betsy took Ditty Bags and cakes and cookies to the patients on wards. The 500 patients were from Africa, our first wounded."(1) The ditty bags provided comfort items which most of the wounded soldiers didn't have when they arrived.

On 1 January 1943, 21 Purple Hearts were handed out on the wards of the 67th General Hospital, by the Commanding Officer, Lt. Colonel Roland Moore, to men injured in the landings at Oran and Algiers, and for other action in and around the invasion beaches of North Africa. Purple Hearts were received by soldiers from Battery A, 106th Coast Artillery (AA); 701st Tank Destroyer Battalion; 1st Armored Regiment; 135th Infantry Regiment; 503rd Parachute Infantry; 13th Armored Regiment; 6th Armored Infantry; 26th Infantry and the 36th Engineers; The men injured at Oran were in the 6th Armored Infantry. (28) Ted Benedict recalled the awarding of the Purple Hearts to the casualties from Operation Torch.

> "In the middle of the afternoon, I was in one of the wards when Colonel Moore, the Adjutant, a Lieutenant Colonel and two other officers came in and passed out the Purple Heart awards to the wounded fellows in the ward. Standing at the head of the ward, the officers stayed at attention while the Adjutant read the special orders and then they all trooped around while the Colonel passed out the ribbons, saluting and shaking hands with each patient who received one.
>
> After the offices had one the fellows jokingly complained that they weren't given out by a General." (29)

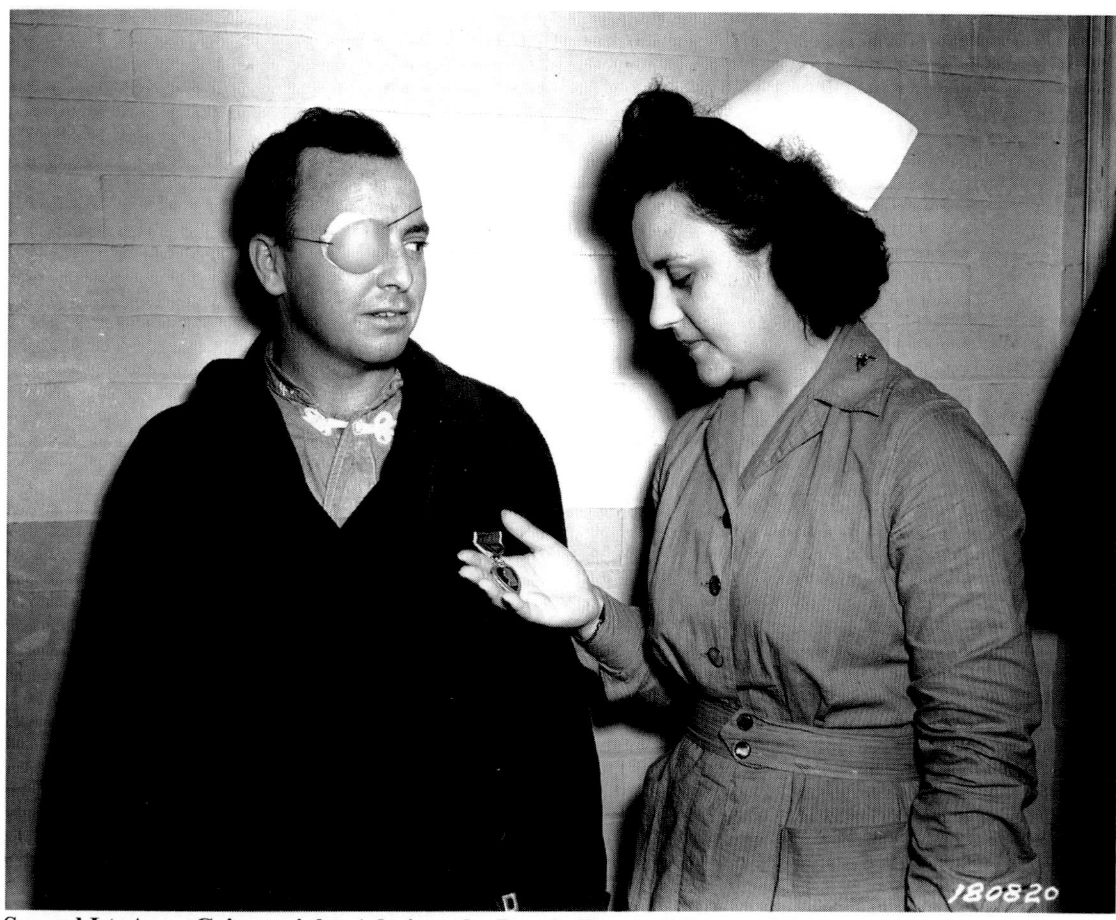

Second Lt. Anne Griner, right, Admires the Purple Heart of Corporal John M. Moore. The Action Where He Received His Wounds Is Not Specified.
National Archives

There were constant arrivals of hospital planes and it became a routine. Corpsmen would go to Merryfield in ambulances, unload their two-wheeled litter carriers and transfer the wounded servicemen from the plane, usually a DC-3, also known as a C-47, by passing them out the side door, under the watchful eye of the flight nurse in her coveralls (See photo on Page 114.). Then it would be away to the hospital for admission and care. (9) Their record would be stamped and imprinted with their dog tag information upon arrival to the hospital.

Patients were received from the XIX District, Southern Base Section, either directly by command or by transfer from other hospitals. For example the 2nd Evacuation Hospital used the 67th General Hospital to receive patients when they needed to clear up bed space. During the month of December, 1942, they transferred 42 patients to Musgrove Military Hospital. (25) Other hospitals did the same. The men of the 67th General Hospital occasionally became patients, themselves. Soldiers from the Unit who became ill would go on sick call, with an infirmary held in the Receiving and Evacuation Office, but no patients were treated as "quarters" cases, and were either returned to duty or admitted to the hospital as a patient. (2)

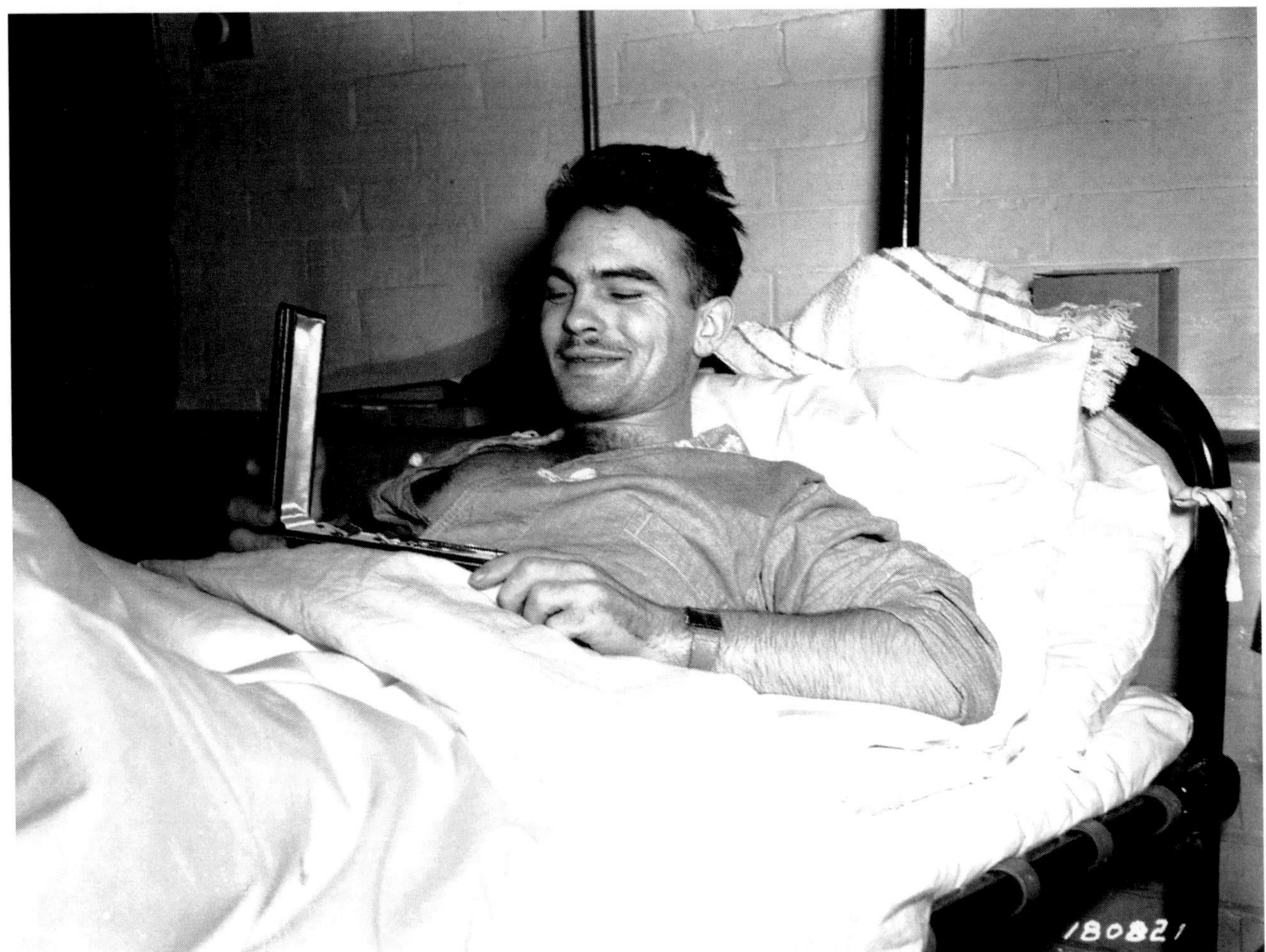

Corporal Harry Wilkenson Holding His Purple Heart Earned from Action on the African Front.
National Archives

An outpatient clinic was conducted by the Orthopedic Section of the Surgical Service on three days of each week. Outpatients were also treated in the Dental and E.E. N.T. Clinic. (2) In 1944, the out-patient clinic operated six afternoons each week--two days each for medical, surgical and orthopedic patients. Outpatients continued to be treated in the E.E.N.T. clinic and the Dental Clinic. (4) The outpatient department was extremely busy during the early days of 1944, but after D-Day, there was a sharp drop of patients and the census never reached the level seen prior to that time. (2) Five days prior to D-Day, the average daily attendance was 200 out-patients, but at the end of 1944, it had dropped to 40.

During 1942, the number of inpatients varied from 147 to 223, with an average daily census being 183. The total number of patients treated from 5 December 1942, to 31 December 1942, was 398 of which 282 were medical and 116 surgical. (5)

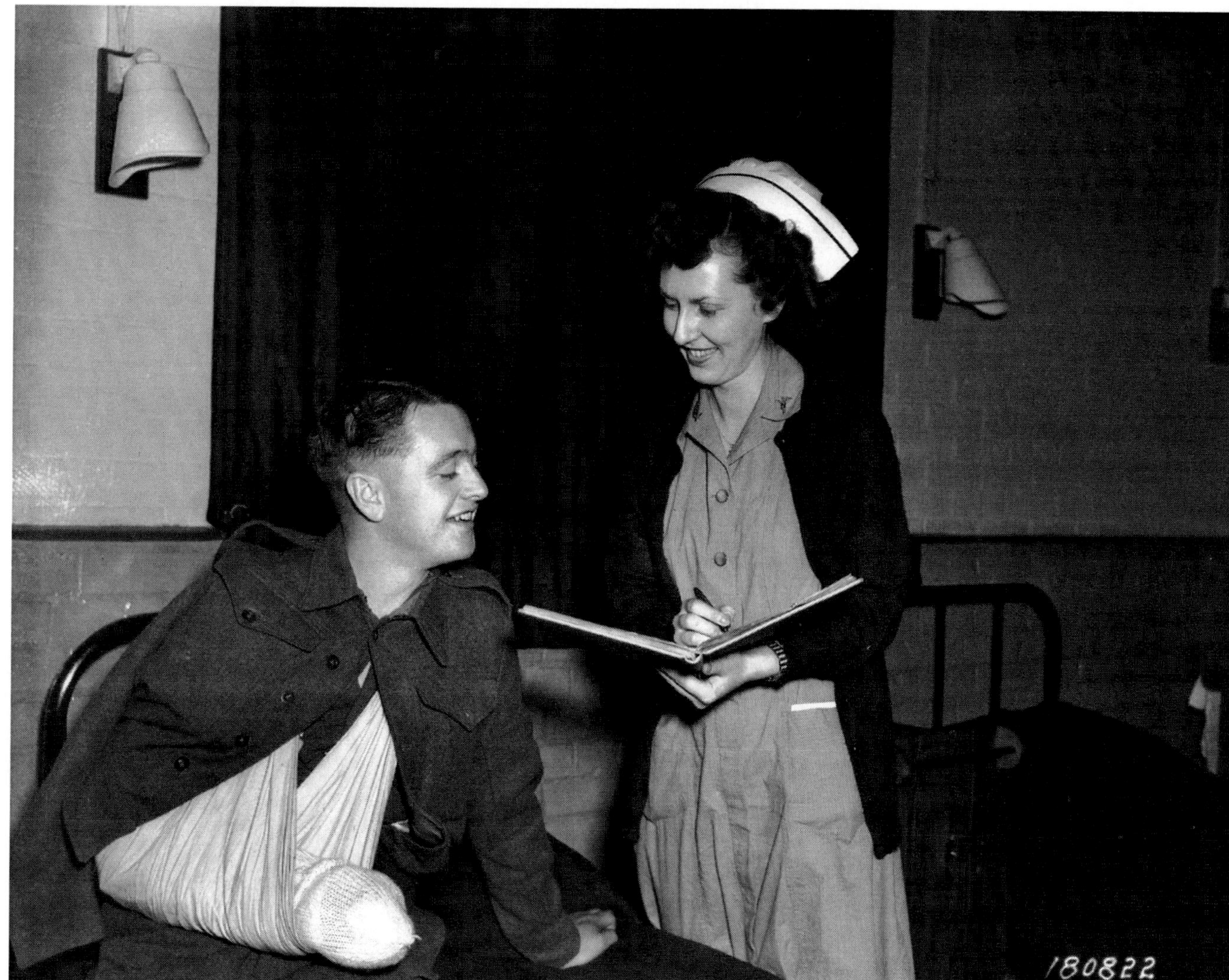

British Patient Injured in Operation Torch and Treated by the 67th General Hospital
National Archives

In January of 1943, there were fifteen wards which were open and operational: five orthopedic wards, one detention ward, two G.U.wards, three contagion wards for very ill patients, two wards for nurses and one ward for officers. (10) By November, 1943, all available wards and convalescent huts were open and operating.

Following D-Day, the patient census more than doubled and the bed capacity was twice increased to meet this demand. The bed capacity of 1700 was probably the maximum number which could be accommodated because of limited sanitary and heating facilities. The character of the professional work changed also, with battle casualties comprising more than 50% of the total number of patients. (4)

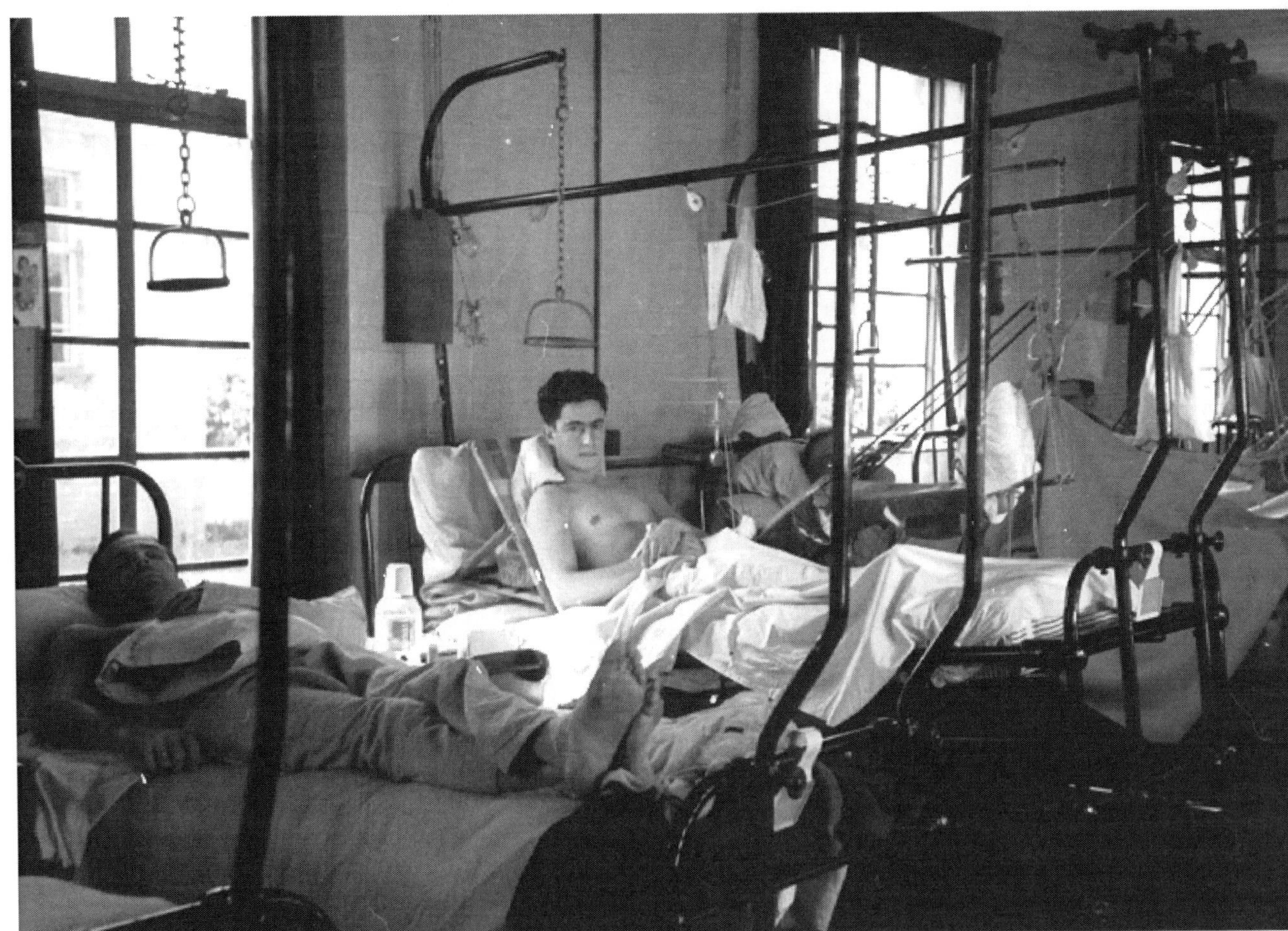

Orthopedic Patient Photograph by and Courtesy of Ted Benedict

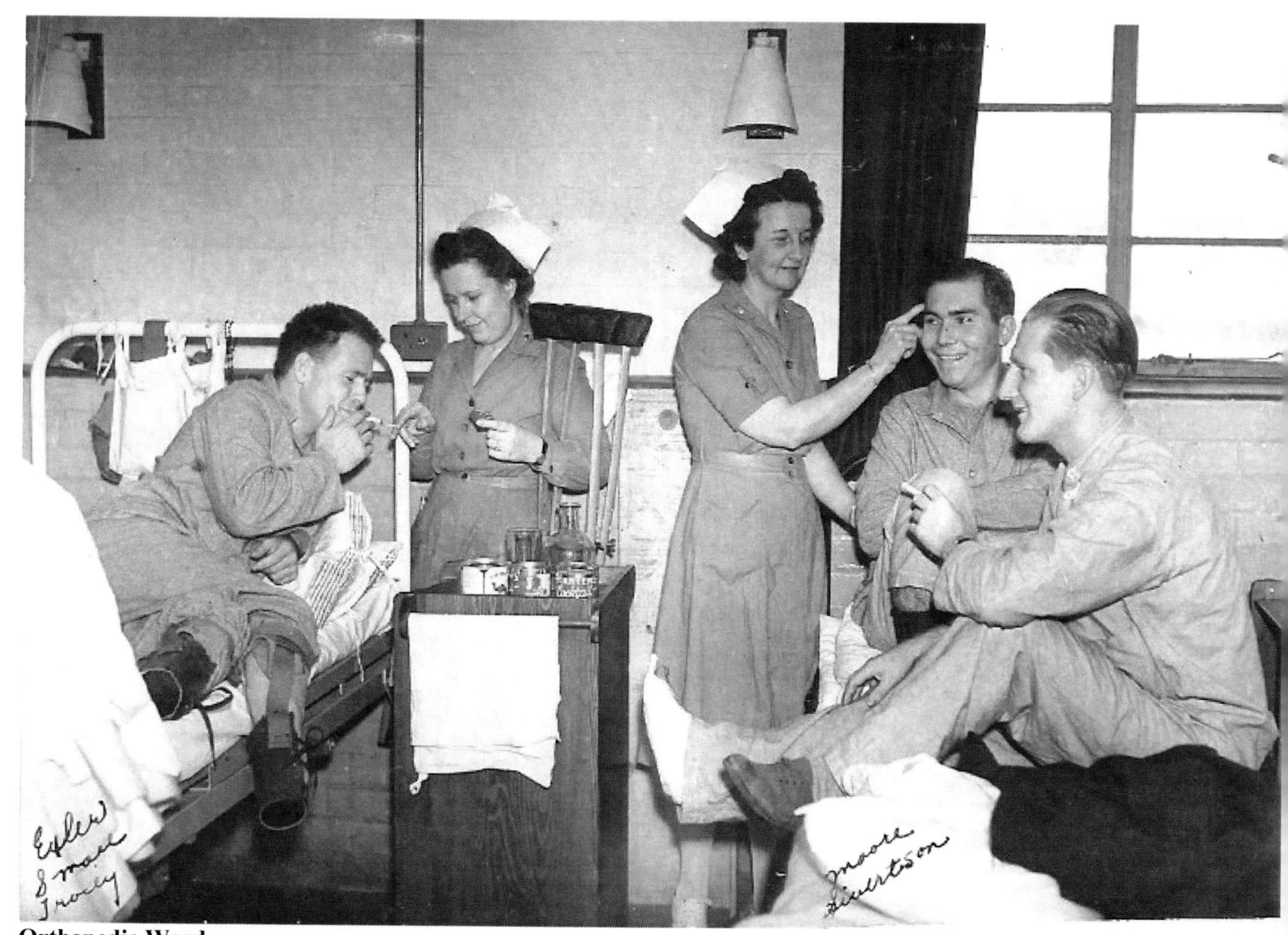

Orthopedic Ward
Photograph Courtesy Betsy Larson Crumrine

Following D-Day, the number of patients in the hospital varied from 311 on 6 June 1944, to 1484 on 12 December 1944. The average daily number for the period 1 January 1944, to 31 December 1944, inclusive being 938.9. There were 343,641 patient days for the period, 31 December 1943, to 31 December 1944, of which 225,936 were surgical and 117,705 were medical. The average hospitalization time was 25.61 days. When evaluating these statistics, keep in mind that many patients who were boarded to the Zone of the Interior remained from 50 to 100 more days at the 67th General Hospital awaiting evacuation. (4)

The patient census of the 67th General Hospital while it was in the European Theater of Operations, varied from a low of 147 to a peak of 1,686 on 8 January 1945. There were 850,618 patient days during this two and one half year period, with an average hospital stay of 36.46 days. Some patients were kept in the hospital past the needed time awaiting transfer to the Zone of the Interior, which increased the average hospital stay statistics. The largest number of patients received in one admission was 385 on 23 July 1944. They were all received by air from the continent, admitted and settled in bed two hours and twenty minutes after the first plane landed at the airport. On another occasion, 268 patients were received by train with their admission, from arrival of the train at Taunton Station to their being settled in bed, taking a total of one hour and ten minutes. A total of 2686 patients was admitted by air and 8729 received by train. Additionally, 7 German prisoners of war were admitted. (2) Betsy Larson (Crumrine) recalled that following the Battle of the Bulge, there were considerable numbers of frostbite patients. As the war progressed and the soldiers fought their way across Europe, a map of the theaters of operation showing the locale where each soldier was injured could demonstrate graphically the front lines of the conflict at any one time.

Mildred Butler,ANC, assistant to the Chief Nurse, recalled:

> "Patient wardrobe changed with improvement in health--bathrobe, uniform, etc. They were encouraged to dress and be active as soon as condition permitted. The 67th General Hospital was 'Back to Duty' or shipment back to USA--some on stretchers, some ambulatory." (27)

A total of $556,027.28 in salary was paid to patients through the Detachment of Patients during the two and one half years at Musgrove Military Hospital. The number of pieces of baggage handled during this time, other than hand luggage, came to 24,284. (3)

The most famous patients treated at the 67th General Hospital were General Dwight David Eisenhower, later to become President of the United States, and Bob Hope. Both were treated by Doctor Otis B. Tibbetts, an opthalmologist. Their visits are discussed in more detail in Chapter 12.

The patients wore maroon robes with the label M.D. U.S.A. which meant Medical Department, United States Army, but the standing joke was that it meant "Many Died, You Shall Also". A cemetery, the St. Mary Magdalen and Bishop's Hull Cemetery, was located at the north end of the hospital and probably added to the grim humor.

Convalescent Patients Marching Photograph by and Courtesy of Ted Benedict

Patients. Note the "MD USA" on the Robe of the Patient on the Left.
Photo in Author's Collection.

British Patients

The British Red Cross worked in close cooperation with the American Red Cross contingent of the 67th General Hospital. Part of their responsibility was to send "searchers" into the hospital to interview patients to assist the tracing of missing soldiers. Telegrams were sent to families and all efforts were made to bring them together. Problems which could occur included destruction of the family's home by bombing making it difficult or impossible to deliver the mail. The desire of a patient's families to visit them at the hospital created logistic nightmares because of the shortage of housing all over England, and the inability to find adequate housing near Taunton. On one occasion, upon request of the British Red Cross, the 67th Red Cross contingent was able to provide housing for a wife visiting her British husband. (11) The British Army had a welfare officer on the premises, who worked very closely with British Red Cross for patient care, along with the British Registrar, stationed at the hospital.

Sergeant Brian Brayson of the British Army was attached to Musgrove Military Hospital and worked in the Registrar's Office alongside Ted Benedict. His responsibility was the care of the records of the British military patients. Ted related a story which reflected the mentality of the British soldier.

Brian Brayson on the left with Ted Benedict
Photograph Courtesy of Ted Benedict

"He made out his records with a steel pen and an inkwell. We became friends, and I offered to buy him a Shaeffer Lifetime Pen (the one with the white dot on the cap), and he was appropriately grateful, because he didn't have access to our PX. The next morning he was making out his report, still using the steel pen and ink bottle. I expressed regret that he found the new pen defective, but he said it worked perfectly, and pulled it from his shirt pocket to show me. When I asked him why he didn't use it for his morning report, he said matter-of-factly, 'In the British Army we use a steel pen.' This respect for tradition, often seen in the British, always amazed and amused me." (29)

On at least one occasion, a local English woman was treated at the Musgrove Military Hospital following an accident, and there were likely other patients who were brought to the hospital on an emergency basis for care.

German Patients

When German airplanes were shot down or had to crash-land, invariably the crew had some injury that would require medical attention. When a list of questions was sent to Dr. Eugene McManamy, one of the questions asked was whether he had taken care of German prisoners and he answered in the affirmative, but did not elaborate. (26) When I questioned some of the men in the 67th, they had no recollection at all of German prisoners being treated at Musgrove Hospital. Mildred Butler, ANC recalls a nasty and uncooperative group of German airmen who were brought to the hospital for a 48 hour stay before they were turned over to the British. (27) The Annual Report of 1943, mentions the treatment of 7 German prisoners. (2) Several pilots who crashed near Taunton, were taken to the 67th General Hospital for care and died there.

Social Worker Functions of the Red Cross with Patients

When an injured soldier arrived at the hospital, in most cases, there were complicating factors. He was separated from his unit and his life lacked normalcy. This was often accompanied by a physical or mental disability which rendered him even more helpless. When wounded, the soldier was evacuated from his regular unit, passed through a series of hospitals and finally admitted to a General Hospital. Because of this constant moving, his paycheck usually did not arrive on time, since it was delayed passing through the same channels, trying to catch up with him. The normal communication channel was broken when he was wounded and receiving mail took an even longer time than usual. He was upset since he was not receiving mail from his family. His family was worried and upset because they were not hearing from him, especially if they heard he had been wounded, but did not know the details of the severity of the injury. Additionally, after being wounded, the soldier's gear might not be forwarded and he was left without personal items such as shoes, socks, toothbrush, razors, etc.

The Red Cross handled requests for locations of mail, wrote the patient's family, bought gifts for the patients to send to their families, did errands for them, sent cables, etc. Many times, the thing that was most helpful was to lend an ear to the patients' problems, discuss what had happened to them and what experiences they had experienced and attempt to allay their anxiety and apprehension. (11)

The census of patients in May 1943 was low which allowed the social workers to catch up on some of their work. The Red Cross dealt with many communication problems by contacting

Home Chapters of the Red Cross who would contact the families or girlfriends and get the real story and relay it back to the patient. (19) The report of the Red Cross in July, 1944, related stories of problems which were addressed:

> "One of the older enlisted men attached to the 67th who has grown children, received a letter from his brother-in-law stating 'that it was such a shame Mary's (the soldier's wife) crippled conditions made it impossible for her to do certain things.' The soldier was frantic, because he did not know that she was crippled. Correspondence to the States disclosed that she had sprained her ankle two years ago and this bothered her at times.
>
> Letters coming from 'well-meaning' relatives telling of seeing soldier's wives and sweethearts with some other man. They say only: 'I saw Jennie the other night at a dance with some soldier, or civilian'. They do not tell why Jenny is at the dance, or feel that she needs the same amount of recreation as the soldier. If he has not received any mail from Jennie for several weeks he suspects the worse.
>
> One of our Medical Detachment came into the office the other day and sat down saying, 'I want a divorce from my wife'. Questioning brought out the fact that he hadn't heard from her for what he first said was two months, and in pinning him down to dates was only three weeks. His brother had written him that his wife had moved to another town and did not come for her allotment check. He has finally agreed to wait until he can get mail from the States before seeing the judge advocate or writing an attorney.
>
> One patient had a five year old son left with his mother, grandfather and grandmother. The entire family was his responsibility and his allotment was made to his mother. She has since been hospitalized in an insane hospital, and the allotment checks could not be cashed. The family were without funds, and needless to say the patient could not sleep from worry. Contacts were immediately made with Home Chapter, and the patient assured they would be cared for." (13) During July of 1943, the Red Cross reported performing services ranging from shopping for gifts, postal cards, taking snapshots, writing letters, getting mending done, etc. The staff wrote friends in the States for film and despite the scarcity of film at home, they were able to receive a few rolls for use in taking pictures of the patients to send home." (13)

Evaluations were made each Monday, by the Red Cross, of the number of bed patients on each ward, and their condition. Those seriously ill would not benefit from recreation and this would become a ward to be covered by a social worker. There were frequent consultations with the medical officer on each ward as to particular needs of patients which needed to be addressed. When any recreation was done, a diary was kept by the recreation worker of activities performed or attended by particular patients and this was useful in these consultations to assist in planning future activities. (15)

One of the activities of the Red Cross in March of 1944, was to help send out Easter cards and Mother's Day cards. It was also noted in the report that the social worker, while trying to serve what seemed to be a trivial need or solve a minor problem, the patient would often discover in the process of the discussion the true purpose of the patient's visit. A report by Shirley Smith of the Red Cross, illustrated a story:

"2-25-44 Patient in office requesting loan of 10 Pounds.0.0. He said that the loan was for a personal situation about which he could not talk. We explained to Pvt. X why we had to have full information as to the reason and need for this loan. He said he understood our reasons for requiring the explanation and said he guessed, after all, he could tell us his story. We advised him that whatever information he divulged to us would be considered confidential and that we should be glad to help him in anyway we could. The soldier gave us a letter from a Mrs. S and asked that we read it. The letter indicated that the writer was very much in love with Pvt. X and that she hoped to hear from him soon regarding some plan for her care during her expected confinement in August.

Pvt. X paced the floor of the office and appeared to be extremely nervous and worried. We asked the patient why he was in the hospital and he advised us that he has a sinus and asthmatic
condition from which he has suffered for a number of years. He has been with an Engineering outfit here in England for over a year. During this time he slept outside on the ground and was told by the doctors here that the frequent bivouacs on the moors where it was cold and damp had tended to intensify his condition. At this time, according to the soldier, he is taking 'shots' and believes he will eventually be reclassified to a 'limited duty' classification. He said that the medical officer advised him that cases of his kind are usually returned to the Z. of I. but because of the soldier's desire to remain overseas, the officer agreed to recommend reclassification. The patient further stated that since his hospitalization he has improved and he believes he will not have a recurring attack of such severity if he is quartered inside and is not living in a cold damp environment as he has in the past.

Pvt. X went on to tell us about his relationship to Mrs. S. He stated that he is in love with Mrs. S and we concluded that he is quite devoted to her. He averred that Mrs. S married when she was very young--17 years and that the marriage was arranged by the families of both individuals who live in B. She has a young child for whom she received an allotment from her husband, K, who is in the British Army. This is to be discontinued this week. Pvt. X said that he has been going with Mrs. S since last September. He was accepted as part of the family and he found them a most hospitable group. He spent his furloughs and passes there. However, inasmuch as B is a small community, the parents of Mrs. S' husband wrote to him the fact that his wife was keeping company with a U.S. soldier. At that point, Mrs. S's husband instigated divorce proceedings thru the British governmental agency handling such legal procedure. The soldier said that the divorce would be effective in a few months and he intends to marry Mrs. S as soon as he can. He stated further that he has been married and divorced. He has a three year old child in the States who receives an allotment for his support. The patient said too, that he was recently 'busted' from Sgt. to Pvt. And now his income is too small to be able to allow him to do a great deal financially for Mrs. S. He lost his rating through being A.W.O.L. but was not given any fine. He felt that he was justified in receiving the loss of rating although he claims he will undoubtedly get his rating back in a very short time, if he is returned to his old organization. He is concerned, however, about his reduced pay and as a result, his inability to help Mrs. S as he wanted.

We asked the patient what, if any plans he had in mind. He said that he knows a family in the Midlands to whom he plans to write. He believes they may be willing to take Mrs. S into their home now and allow her to remain with them until after her confinement. He has written to Mrs. S about this place for her approval. She does not know the family, but, apparently, any plan made by the soldier will be satisfactory with her. He stated that he needed the money to bring Mrs. S to the neighbouring (note the English spelling, explained by the fact that the secretaries doing the typing were British.) town here so that she could be near him and could visit him at the hospital. She will leave the child in the home of her mother, Mrs. G. Mrs. G is a defense factory worker but her other married daughter and children are in the home. The other daughter receives an allotment from her husband who is in the R.A.F. The income has just been enough to maintain the group on a subsistence level, according to the patient, and he knows now that Mrs. S will no longer receive an allotment they will be unable to manage financially. The soldier said that he would be willing and would like to get a pass to get down to see Mrs. S if her coming here would not be practical.

We advised the patient that we would talk to the medical officer in an effort to learn what disposition might be made of the patient and whether or not he will leave the hospital soon. The soldier stated that he would return to the ward and write a letter to his friends regarding Mrs. S' care. We suggested that it would not be wise to have Mrs. S come to this community now as his continued hospitalization here is not certain and finding a suitable place for her to stay also constitutes a problem. He agreed to wait until we talked to the medical officer.

The patient, when he left the office, seemed to have been relieved and a great deal more calm than when he first came into the office. He said 'Just having someone to talk it over with has helped. I've kept it all to myself for so long. I haven't even been able to see Mrs. S and we've been trying to work everything out through correspondence.'

2-26-44 Spoke to medical officer on ward. We explained to him that Pvt. had come to us with a personal problem which had been the source of a great deal of anxiety and worry. The officer said he realized Private was worried about something but he had never been able to discuss it with him or to discover what it was. We told the officer that it involved a British girl and that the patient had hopes of eventually marrying her. The officer said that the patient has 'chronic asthma' and that he had had an exceptionally severe attack which resulted in his hospitalization for treatment. He has been given shots of Adrenalin and has responded to treatment satisfactorily. He reiterated information he had given the patient--that he will be reclassified to a 'limited duty' status, will remain in England and will probably get along satisfactorily if he does not have to sleep outside on the ground; however, the possibility of recurring attacks can be expected and hospitalization <u>may</u> be necessary again. The officer stated he felt the patient had been discouraged about himself and that he has attempted to reassure him. The patient, according to the medical officer, has had rather conflicting reactions to his situation. He feels his health will continue to be poor and that he will have to continue having treatment while he is in England, but he apparently wants to remain here. This is, no doubt, because of his situation with Mrs. S. We discussed with the officer the possibility of the soldier securing a pass to go to B and the <u>need</u> of the loan. The officer stated that he would gladly approve a loan of five Pounds.0.0 for the girl to come here but the pass to B for the soldier would be impossible as the patients are only allowed passes to neighbouring community unless there is an extreme emergency. The officer stated further that the patient would be dispositioned to a Replacement Pool within a few days.

Later: We advised Pvt. X that the medical officer had said that a pass to B would be impossible but that he would approve loan so that Mrs. S could come here or so that the soldier could go to see her if he can secure a pass at the Replacement Pool to which he will be sent. We suggested to patient that we want to hear what his friends in the Midlands have to say in reply to his request. This was agreed on.

2-29-44 Patient in office requesting loan of 1 Pound Sterling.0.0 for rations and P.X. supplies. We suggested he stop in in the morning as building was being closed for the day. Patient has been frequenting the Red Cross building and has assisted in the library. He is well liked by patients and nurses and Red Cross staff. He seems to be more at ease than when we first met him and has been taking part in activities in the Red Cross building.

3-1-44 Loan of 1 Pound.0.0 approved by Capt. Colley and made to Private.

3-3-44 We learned from patient today that he talked to his friends in the Midlands on the telephone and found they will not be able to accept Mrs. S in their home at this time. Advised patient we shall learn what facilities may be available for her in this County. It would seem preferable to have her work as a domestic in one of the homes until her confinement and in this way she would be self-maintaining. During this time the soldier could save some money to be used for her care at time of confinement. Mrs. S' mother will be able to take care of the other child, patient said he felt that would be perfectly agreeable. He stated that Mrs. S did not know about his previous marriage and obligations to his own child.

3-5-44 Patient in office. He is being dispositioned to the 10th Replacement Depot tomorrow morning. A loan of 5 Pounds.0.0 was made to soldier so that in the event he can get a pass he can go to see Mrs. S or he will be able to send for her. We discussed situation with medical officer and it was agreed that it is almost essential that the couple be able to see one another and personally work out their difficulties. We advised the soldier of the fact that we were unable to secure the information regarding the confinement and pre-natal care for Mrs. S but that we shall contact the Red Cross at 10th Replacement Depot and ask them to relay the information to him. Patient was quite happy that he is being released from the hospital. He said that he feels 100% now and knowing that he will not have to return to a combat outfit he feels he will be able to get along all right physically. He is also happy that he will soon be able to get a pass and that he and Mrs. S can see one another. He indicated that she is very disturbed over the whole situation and he feels that his being able to discuss everything with her personally will alleviate her worries. Soldier thanked us for our help. He asked us not to contact the F.D. (Field Director) at 10th Replacement Depot as he did not want his situation gone into by anyone else. He said that he will contact as soon as he can.

3-8-44 Contacted D. Davidson, County Medical Officer of Health. He advised that because of residence requirements it would be advisable to have Mrs. S make an application for work and future confinement at the Devonshire County Hall in Exeter, Dr. Davies, County Medical Officer. The soldier had wanted originally to have Mrs. S brought to neighbouring town to the hospital because his old unit is not stationed too far from here. However, because of the frequent changes in locations of units and the fact that the soldier does not know if he will return to his old unit or not, we feel it would be more satisfactory to have Mrs. S remain near enough to her home so that her mother might visit her and she would be able to see her other child occasionally.

3-13-44 Soldier in office. He has a 48 hour pass plus a 6 hour pass and is on his way to see Mrs. S. We told him of the information learned about Maternity Homes. He has to go through Exeter and plans to get Mrs. S and take her to Exeter with him so they will be able to make application and plans together. He still has sufficient money to make the trip and expects he may be paid at the 10th Replacement Depot soon. He said too, that he had written worker a letter but we have not yet received it. The soldier states that he has been feeling fine--that he is in a warm barracks and believes he will be transferred to S.O.S. He feels too that he can prove his worth in any job they put him in and that he will do his utmost to get another rating. He seemed happy and confident that things were going to work them selves out before long." (16)

One of the many problems presented by some of the patients was that of a soldier who had been treated and was due to be shipped back home, but who had a wife in England and really preferred to stay at the hospital and near the wife. In this situation, most soldiers were sent home, with the wife hopefully to follow as soon as circumstances permitted.

The month of April, 1944, saw a lot of loans which were for recreation, P.X. supplies and rations. The loans were made when soldiers were transferred from combat areas to Station

Hospitals and then to a General Hospital such as the 67th. Records had to be secured by the Detachment of Patients to allow the soldier to be paid, involving a considerable amount of time, and triggering the need for loans to tide them over. Other things done for the patients were: "securing money orders, cabling money home, buying gifts in town, calling other stationary units about personal effects, contacting R.T.O. for schedules, securing accommodations for guests, tracing money from unit to hospital and many other services." (17)

Following the invasion of Europe, on 6 June 1944, activities kicked into a much higher gear. When the patients arrived, they had little or nothing with them--no toilet articles, shoes or slippers and no money. When the Army Sales Store did not have these personal items, attempts were made to buy them through the local stores. Some razor blades received for the razors would not fit any ordinary razor. (19) Those who could walk to mess hall or clinic appointments had to walk barefoot, if not supplied with slippers. The craft shop got to work and did its best to manufacture these and other needed items. Those who had no slippers wore socks instead, but there were no socks available for months. Stationery was not universally available, and for a while there was much less correspondence than usual. (18) Another problem was money. Some patients arrived with French francs which could not be immediately converted into Pounds Sterling. Therefore, to obtain money to purchase personal items, it was necessary to get a loan from the Red Cross. The Red Cross was informed that the items needed were not available because of priority--they had been sent to emergency hospitals in combat zones. The thought was that these hospitals had not received them, because none of the patients coming from these areas had them. (19)

The family at home found out about their soldier's injuries in many ways. The best way to tell them would be to have the soldier write home and inform the family directly that he had been wounded. However, he was not allowed to give specific information about his condition due to censorship regarding casualties and when a letter arrived home from a General Hospital with his status and severity of his injury couched in vague terms, a considerable amount of anxiety was generated. Official notification might have already been sent from the War Department and occasionally, the Purple Heart arrived home before any other type of communication. The Red Cross worked to communicate with the family at home through the local chapters and encouraged the soldier to write, even though the soldier was afraid that a letter from the hospital would worry the folks back home. Handling social problems became difficult because the patients were transferred in and out quickly, sometimes without adequate time to solve the problems and sometimes leaving it be be solved by the next facility. (19)

The lack of personal articles following the D-Day invasion did not last. The items were almost universally available in about a month. Combs were in short supply for a while and were scarce everywhere. Most of the men obtained shoes through the regular supply channel but there was still some need for slippers made in the craft shop.

The need for better communication with the folks back home was illustrated by a situation reported by the Red Cross in August of 1944,

"We encourage all patients to write home if they can do so. This does prove to be a doubtful benefit, sometimes, as evidenced by the letters we receive constantly from the Red Cross Chapter workers at home. It would seem that many families are inclined to believe the worst of any situation about which they do not have detailed information. For example, one of our patients who had been boarded and knew he would be returning home, did not tell his family anything about his injury except that his leg had been broken, then in a letter written after he was boarded he told his mother that he had a nice surprise for her. This, no doubt, was as close as he thought he could come to announcing his return, and by no stretch of his imagination could he have foreseen that she would assume that he had had his leg amputated. That, however, is what she interpreted his letter to say, and she was extremely worried and anxious to have the Chapter find out exactly what had happened to him. Of course he had been discharged from this hospital, and perhaps had reached home by the time the letter of inquiry got here. There seems to be no sure way to avoid making relatives anxious, because many letters say the serviceman has not written; others say he has written and said he was all right, but the family concluded he is not since he writes from a hospital." (20)

The social workers expected a much different response from men who had amputations or other injuries that would have placed a mental burden on patients at home. Their comment is as follows:

"Social service to those with permanent disabilities hasn't been of the sort one might have expected. Generally, one anticipates having certain definite types of cases on which some help and encouragement, some interpretation and adjustment to disability may be expected. We are finding this by no means true in all cases. Most medical social workers found in civilian hospital work that amputation cases called for considerable social service as a rule. Circumstances here bring about different attitudes, and our own observations on this point have been confirmed by the comments of other patients as well as by officers and personnel of the hospital. There may be something in the fact that most of the men who have had these serious injuries have been seeing so many others lose their lives or suffer even worse wounds than theirs; at any rate, most of them are in remarkably good spirits, do not become self-centered, and give no indication of having become seriously worried about their future adjustments to civilian life. One patient not long over from the States remarked that he thought coming to the hospital for what he now considers very minor surgery had done more for him than anything that had ever happened to him. He would never have believed that men so seriously and permanently injured could have such cheerful associations on the ward. He summed up his observations by saying that his acquaintance with them had been a really vital spiritual experience to him, and no one had mentioned religion, but he had found that other 'guys like me can really take it, and if they can, I guess I could too, if I had to, and that's done a whole lot for me.' " (20)

A report in a more comic tone followed in the October-November, 1944, report:

“One patient who has since been returned to the States because of impaired hearing, asked to have a call made to his brother at a distant air field. We managed to get in contact with the brother, then allowed the patient to take the line, after explaining that the object was to arrange a visit, if possible. Our patient carried on for a few minutes with many happy remarks in the vein of, ‘You old so-and-so, why don’t your write? And ‘It was pretty tough over there, but here I am, ain’t I?’ and ‘What do you hear from home?’ All this with the most delighted smile on his face. He expressed such pleasure and gratitude afterwards that we refrained from asking if he could hear. Shortly before he was to leave he came in again to see if a message could be got to his brother not to try to come. To the sitters-around-the-stove he remarked happily, ‘You know, I ain’t seen hide nor hair of him for over three years, but I sure gave him hell when I had him on the ‘phone.’ Then he added, almost as if it made no difference, ‘Couldn’t make hide nor tail o’ what he was saying’ but I talked to him on the ‘phone.’”(21)

When the patients were posted for the Zone of the Interior, the Red Cross wished them a “bon voyage” and made up a packet to take with them containing cigarettes and matches. The cigarettes were supplied through the Medical Supply Office with one of the sources being the “Smokes for Yanks”. (22)

Patient Loaded Into Ambulance for the Trip Home by Either Air or Sea. Note the Two-Wheeled Cart.
Photograph Courtesy Lucille Walker

Nurses and Red Cross Worker Seeing Patients Off.
Photograph Courtesy of Betsy Crumrine.

By the end of March, 1945, a British Red Cross "Searcher", who would visit the hospitals to identify the British patients announced that for the first time, Musgrove Hospital had not a single British patient in the hospital. When the hospital first opened, there were enough to warrant their own Registrar. The American presence was now such that American needs were primarily met by American resources. (23)

After VE Day had passed, many comments from the patients such as "A guy can afford to get well now. Going back to duty doesn't mean the front line in two or three weeks." were heard. The patients became more interested in what ultimately would be their destiny and there was a general lifting of spirits. The number of patients coming from anywhere except other hospitals decreased markedly. The announcement of the discharge plan by the point system caused unlimited discussion among the men and everyone calculated their chance as well as their friend's chances of going home early.

During the two and one-half years that the 67th General Hospital cared for the sick and wounded from the European Theater of Operations, it handled a total of 24,000 patients with only 71 deaths--3 of those from medical disease. (9)

References

(1) Personal Communication with Betsy Crumrine.

(2) "Annual Report to the Chief Surgeon, SOS, ETOUSA, APO 887, U.S. Army." Dated 31 January 1944. National Archives.

(3) "Semi-annual Report, Medical Department Activities, 67th General Hospital to the Surgeon General, Washington, D.C." Dated 15 June 1945. National Archives.

(4) "Annual Report of the 67th General Hospital to the Surgeon General, United States Army, for 1944." Dated 31 January 1945. Signed by Roland B. Moore, Colonel, Medical Corps, Commanding Officer. National Archives.

(5) "Annual Report of the 67th General Hospital to the Chief Surgeon, SOS, ETOUSA." Dated 15 January 1943. Signed by Lieutenant Colonel R.B. Moore, M.C., Commanding. National Archives.

(6) Morgan-Guy, John, Dr. *Malachi's Monument.*

(7) Communication with Mildred Butler, ANC.

(8) Communication with Dr. John Morgan-Guy.

(9) "Lewiston Journal; Magazine Section." Saturday, October 25, 1969.

(10) "Reports to the Red Cross from the Red Cross Unit Assigned to the 67th General Hospital. Narrative and Recreation Report for January 1943." National Archives.

(11) "Reports to the Red Cross from the Red Cross Unit Assigned to the 67th General Hospital. Narrative and Recreation Report for March, 1943." National Archives.

(12) "Reports to the Red Cross from the Red Cross Unit Assigned to the 67th General Hospital. Narrative and Recreation Report for May, 1943." National Archives.

(13) "Reports to the Red Cross from the Red Cross Unit Assigned to the 67th General Hospital. Narrative and Recreation Report for July, 1943." National Archives.

(14) "Reports to the Red Cross from the Red Cross Unit Assigned to the 67th General Hospital. Narrative and Recreation Report for August, 1943." National Archives.

(15) "Reports to the Red Cross from the Red Cross Unit Assigned to the 67th General Hospital. Narrative and Recreation Report for September, 1943." National Archives.

(16) "Reports to the Red Cross from the Red Cross Unit Assigned to the 67th General Hospital. Narrative and Recreation Report for March, 1944." National Archives.

(17) "Reports to the Red Cross from the Red Cross Unit Assigned to the 67th General Hospital. Narrative and Recreation Report for April, 1944." National Archives.

(18) "Reports to the Red Cross from the Red Cross Unit Assigned to the 67th General Hospital. Narrative and Recreation Report for June, 1944." National Archives.

(19) "Reports to the Red Cross from the Red Cross Unit Assigned to the 67th General Hospital. Narrative and Recreation Report for July, 1944." National Archives.

(20) "Reports to the Red Cross from the Red Cross Unit Assigned to the 67th General Hospital. Narrative and Recreation Report for August, 1944." National Archives.

(21) "Reports to the Red Cross from the Red Cross Unit Assigned to the 67th General Hospital. Narrative and Recreation Report for October-November, 1944." National Archives.

(22) "Reports to the Red Cross from the Red Cross Unit Assigned to the 67th General Hospital. Narrative and Recreation Report for December, 1944 and January, 1945." National Archives.

(23) "Reports to the Red Cross from the Red Cross Unit Assigned to the 67th General Hospital. Narrative and Recreation Report for February and March, 1945." National Archives.

(24) "Reports to the Red Cross from the Red Cross Unit Assigned to the 67th General Hospital. Narrative and Recreation Report for April and May, 1945." National Archives.

(25) "Records of the 2nd Evacuation Hospital." National Archives. Washington, D.C.

(26) Personal Communication with Eugene P. McManamy, M.D.

(27) Personal Communication with Mildred Butler, ANC.

(28) "General Order 1, Headquarters, 67th General Hospital, 1 January 1943." National Archives.

(29) Personal Communication with Ted Benedict.

Chapter 12
Every Day Life

Life for the men and women of the 67th General Hospital was what happened to them while they were waiting to return home. There was drudgery, there was danger, excitement and fulfillment, but seldom was there boredom. Sprinkled among the patients and men of the 67th General Hospital were glittering reminders of the life they left at home thanks to the efforts exerted by all, including the patients, the Medical Detachment, the nurses, the doctors and other officers, the Red Cross and the community as a whole.

Fraternization

Fraternization was a natural turn of events when lonely young men and women were brought together in foreign places and was initially seen on the train ride from Fort Bliss to Camp Kilmer. Several RNs and MDs had steady relationships while they were in England, which was accepted. "But when those so situated returned to Maine, one would never know." (1)

The proof of fraternization lay in the fact that 52 men of the 67th General Hospital married English girls. (2) The usual saying was, "Over-sexed, over-paid and over-here", when referring to the American soldiers. The men were mostly young, away from home and had relatively more money to spend than their British counterparts. There is an interesting story dealing with an American soldier-patient who had problems born of a relationship with a married British woman which is told with more elaboration in the chapter entitled "The Patients". The Americans wore smarter, better-tailored uniforms than those of the British, seemed to be more open to doing things and were more exciting to the young British ladies. This combination of factors made competition for the English girls more intense for the young British men. Sadly, several children were born from dalliances between soldiers and nurses and between soldiers and the local English women who were never to met their fathers.

Fraternization of another type occurred, probably with more frequency than was admitted. A newspaper recorded the closing down of a House of Pleasure at Roman Road in Taunton, in 1944. (3) Such activity was certainly not condoned by the Army, but was not unexpected, and the Orderly Room of the Detachment Medical of the 67th General Hospital handed out free condoms to those who asked for them. First Sergeant Joe Bullock recalled the condoms:

> "On the counter in the orderly room there was a cardboard box about 12 by 18 inches by 12 inches deep which contained individually wrapped condoms, free for the taking, no questions asked. I don't know who ordained this practice but all of a sudden one day, there they were. Today this would not cause any eyebrows to raise but back then it was somewhat indiscrete." (4)

The War

There were constant reminders that a war was in progress and it involved every aspect of their lives. From the time of their arrival to VE day, Black-out orders were in effect and heavy curtains were placed over windows or paint was used to obscure the window panes. Two Black-out clocks were on some of the buildings--one to show when to black out the lights and the other to show when they need not be blacked out. (2)

Raymond Bungard in Front of Theatre Building (Nissodrome) Looking at Blackout Clocks
Photograph Courtesy of Ted Benedict

Captain Parker Mann recalled his introductory experience with Nazi bombing raids upon his arrival in England. His roommate who had arrived earlier, said, “I’ve been running downstairs every night the raid alarm sounded, I’m tired and I’m going to sleep. You can do what you want to.” Doctor Mann stayed in bed and luckily, the bombs hit somewhere else. (2)

Captain John R. Feeley had an experience in London, in the early days of the robot (V series rockets) bombing. While on leave in London, he had just departed the hotel and turned to see it hit by a bomb. He returned to find everything in his room in turmoil with debris scattered all about. He looked around, but could not see his traveling bag or any of his things which he had left in the room. On the way out, he encountered Major Milton S. Thompson, a fellow officer in the 67th. The Major had also rushed into the hotel, knowing Captain Feeley was there and wanting to see if he was all right, had gone to his room and finding him not there, had put his things in a closet. (2)

London Bridge Opening
Photograph by and Courtesy of Ted Benedict

The Musgrove Military Hospital was never an intended target for German Junkkers, The nearest potential target to the hospital was their supply depot, G-50, several miles away. There was always the fear of stray cannon fire or the risk of receiving a left-over bomb that the Germans decided to ditch, particularly if they were being pursued hotly by the Royal Air Force. (2) One such bomb crater on a farmer's property attracted people who came from miles around to see it. The farmer placed a box near the crater to receive donations to the Red Cross. (5) Many ponds in England which are admired today were once fresh bomb craters. The nearest crash of a German aircraft to the hospital was three miles away. (1)

Bomb Crater with Raymond Bungard Standing on Far Side.
Photograph by and Courtesy of Ted Benedict

Raymond Bungard, who worked in the laboratory, served as one of the unit photographers and had some observations and recollections:

> "We were not very busy at the hospital until the invasion, then I recall the wounded came by the trainload. On the day of the invasion cargo planes pulling gliders flew directly over the hospital. Later not so many planes returned and damage such as non-functioning propellers was noted. (Anti-aircraft fire). The hospital was never bombed but German bombers carrying block-buster bombs were sometimes chased by English fighters. To lighten the load the Germans dropped the bombs on the countryside causing huge craters. I believe I have a black and white negative of one of the craters." (6)

The Americans (or British in at least one case) would return from missions and often swoop low over the hospital letting their friends or girl friends know that they were back. (2) Pilots and Army nurses seemed to be attracted to each other. This practice of flying low over the hospital would often send the psychiatric patients under their beds seeking cover. (7) It also caused concern for the patients in traction who were obliged to remain in bed when the flyovers occurred. After complaints were made to the proper people, this practice ceased. One such low approach created a suction which pulled the blackout curtains out of the room windows of Dr. Gilbert Clapperton. Dr. Clapperton, the Officer of the Day at the time, thought it might be a crash landing and as he ran for cover, he stumbled at a doorway and scraped both knees. (2)

B-17 Flying Low Over the Hospital
Photograph Courtesy of Betsy Crumrine

B-17 Buzzing Hospital
Photograph Courtesy Raymond Bungard

Evidence of the war was everywhere. When visiting coastal resorts. glider obstacles, tank barriers or barbed wire near reinforced areas were recorded in many photographs. Men on leave were required to be in uniform at all times and popular tourist destinations were crowded with young Americans in uniform.

Tank Traps in Front of Pavilion, Bournemouth
Photograph by and Courtesy of Ted Benedict

Obstacles to Deter Glider Landings on Minehead Beach
Photograph by and Courtesy of Ted Benedict

Burial of German Flyers

Two German flyers, Obergefreiter F. Sagemuller and Leutnant A. Hahn were shot down near the hospital and are said to have died while under the care of the 67th General Hospital, although there is no formal notice found of their death or treatment in the documents obtained from the National Archives. Their burial took place in a cemetery immediately adjacent to the Musgrove Military Hospital, the St. Mary Magdalen and Bishop's Hull Cemetery. Betsy Larson recalls closing the curtains on Ward 1 over the windows overlooking the cemetery to prevent the patients from seeing the burial ceremony.

Their coffins were covered with the Nazi German flags with its Swastika and they were afforded honors from an Royal Air Force (RAF) squad which fired a volley over their coffins. The flags were gathered after the ceremony to use on future burials. Their tombstones carried the date 10-5-43. When Ted Benedict visited the cemetery years later, he was told by the groundskeeper that most German soldiers who had been buried around England had been moved to a single cemetery for the convenience of their visiting families and for that reason, they were no longer buried there. (8) Another consideration might be that some of the bodies, following their disinternment, were returned to Germany.

Funeral Ceremony for Two German Fliers
Photograph Courtesy Betsy Crumrine

RAF Honor Guard Firing Salute During Funeral for German Fliers
Photograph Courtesy Betsy Crumrine

Priest Picking Up Nazi Flag to be Saved for Future Burials
Photograph Courtesy Betsy Crumrine

Grave Markers of German Airmen
Photograph Courtesy of Lucille Walker

Making Things Homey

One of the things done to remind everyone of home was the planting of a State of Maine pine tree along with roses and asters in the oval plot in front of the Administration Building and to the left of its entrance. This was done in 1944. (2) In 2004, when this author visited the site of the old Musgrove Military Hospital, the Administration Building was still found to be intact, now called the Old Building, and the 60-year-old pine tree was thriving. A number of people have insisted that General Eisenhower was involved in a tree-planting ceremony, but a poll of members of the 67th General Hospital and a search of the National Archives material which includes diaries of General Eisenhower's associates failed to confirm this. (9) Considering the depth of the reports from the 67th General Hospital to Headquarters and the in-depth reporting in the Red Cross reports, it is extremely unlikely that Eisenhower was present for the planting of the pine.

Pine Tree to Right of Flagpole. Note the White Cross Around Flagpole Which Would Be Visible from the Air, Denoting a Medical Facility
Photograph by and Courtesy of Ted Benedict

Sixty Year-Old Maine Pine Tree in Front of Administration Building, Now Called the Old Building, Musgrove Hospital
Photograph Taken by the Author in June, 2004

Making It Feel Like Home

Some of the nurses planted a small garden, with familiar crops such as potatoes, in front of their quarters. They were hungry for Maine potatoes and any type of fresh vegetable that they might be able to raise. (2) There were a number of dogs that belonged to members of the 67th. One of the owners ordered a fire hydrant shipped from the United States so that the dog would feel at home. The 67th was the only facility that had laundry starch because it had been sent to the hospital Dental Service in error, instead of dental plaster, which had been ordered. Nurses from all around would try to get some of the starch for their laundry. (1, 9)

The 67th was the only post with ice cream and many high ranking officers, including general officers, made it a necessary stop if they were in the area. Mildred Butler, ANC had the key to the ice cream locker. She also recalled that flour from the depot was brown as was most of the English flour, and luckily, an air base nearby had a source of white flour and they "often shared a biscuit which was nice." (1)

The Quarters

Nurses slept on cots in brick, heated buildings as did the officers. The enlisted men slept on cots in 6 man tents which had been erected shortly before D-Day. Before that, their quarters were in Nissen huts (The Americans later constructed a similar, more elaborate, metal building which they termed a Quonset hut named after the Iroquois Indian's hut). Their cots were covered with mattresses which were stuffed
with straw. Sergeant Bullock recalled that his feet got cold at night and his girlfriend sent him foot covers to wear to keep them warm. He also recalled that the paths between the tents were covered with gravel. To make his tent homier, he found brick to line the floor of the tent. (4) Each tent was fitted with a small heating stove. Richard Smith complained about how the soot from the stoves made his clothing dirty. (10)

Raymond Bungard also had recollections of the tents:

> "Quonset huts--initially the enlisted men were billeted in Quonset huts with a coal stove in the middle. Quite comfortable quarters. As the hospital filled to overflowing, patients were moved to the huts for rehabilitation. Enlisted personnel *(from the Detachment Medical)* were then transferred to 6 man tents with a coal stove. Straw mattress ticks were provided. (Stuff your own ticks.) It was cold with 6 inches snow on the ground but we kept warm. None of us had any ill feelings and we were happy to give up the Quonset huts for the wounded GI's." (6)

"The Last Nissen"
Photographed by the Author in 2004.

Snow and Tents
Photograph by and Courtesy of Ted Benedict

Ted Benedict recalled that his tent had a wood platform floor, a central wood pole to support it, and a coal or coke stove which sat near the pole. The pole in his tent became charred to the point of near collapse. Outside the tent, the path to the Nissen latrine was filled with cinders, cleaned from the stoves and dumped in the paths. (8)

Sergeant Joe Bullock had comments about the tents and the winterization:

> "When we originally arrived at the hospital, the enlisted men did live in the Nissen huts for a while, but had to move out so the huts could be used for ambulatory patients. The tents usually housed 6 soldiers...sleeping on cots with blankets to cover. Some of the tents only had dirt (mud) floors, but some had concrete blocks (about 12 inches square) for flooring. You can well imagine we didn't spend any time in the huts other than to sleep, especially during the winters. 'Winterizing' consisted of some kind of treatment to the canvas, I suppose it was wax, which would at least shed water. My tent had the concrete blocks, and one day we were being inspected by a high officer from some headquarters, and when he got into my tent, he stepped on the corner of one of the blocks which caused it to sink into the mud and squirt muddy water up onto the leg of his trousers. He didn't penalize us on the inspection." (4)

Mud in the Tent Area
Photograph by and Courtesy of Ted Benedict

Straw was stuffed into mattress covers for the cots. The straw was furnished by a local farmer and delivered by farm wagon. In about a week, the straw, which had been stuffed until the cover was full, settled down to a comfortable size, and balanced on top of the cot. There was no further need to add straw after this. (8)

Stuffing Tick with Straw
Photograph by and Courtesy of Ted Benedict

The Chapel

The 67th had a Nissen hut which had been converted to a chapel. The carvings of the chapel's altar were done by Major Eaton S. Lothrop, a Portland doctor. (2) Services of various denominations were held regularly by the chaplains assigned to the Unit. Some weddings of the personnel and officers of the 67th General Hospital were performed at the chapel with the Commanding Officer, Colonel Moore, often standing in to give the bride away, if the bride happened to be a member of the Unit.

The Chapel in the Snow
Photograph by and Courtesy of Ted Benedict

Chapel Interior
Photograph Courtesy of Lucille Walker

The Censor and the Mail

"Loose lips sink ships" went the slogan and Major Downing, Chief of the Laboratory, was in charge of censoring any communications or pictures which left the base to prevent any useful material from falling into the hands of the enemy. Photos sent home had the mark of the censor stamped on them which indicated that they possessed no valuable information for the Axis. Much of the mail sent was V-Mail, which were pre-printed sheets, photographed onto microfilm and the microfilm shipped to a processing center. In that way, one mail sack of microfilm weighing 45 pounds could replace 37 sacks of mail weighing 2,575 pounds. Once the microfilm was at its destination, it would be enlarged and printed at ¼ the original size and mailed to the recipient. This allowed thousands of tons of shipping space to be freed up for war material. During the war, 555.5 million pieces of mail was shipped on 16mm microfilm from the United States, to military personnel abroad and 510 million pieces were sent home from overseas. (11) Of all the letters sent home by Richard Smith, none made specific mention of the hospital and after D-Day he made no mention of it at all or about the increased work with which he was faced.

Ted Benedict commented about his role as censor:

> "I was also, functionally, the unit censor. Captain (and Major, later) Downing was officially the censor, but he delegated that clerical job to me, and made the decisions about problem communications. I was amused about this, because, as a part of my college study in history I had taken out a subscription to the 'The Daily Worker', the official newspaper of the American Communist Party. That subscription followed me into the army, and I had some problem getting it turned off. I worried that there would be conjectures about my being a communist, and so here we could have had a communist serving as censor of all out-going enlisted mail to see that no secret military information was being sent out." (8)

Courtesy Raymond Bungard

Visit by General Eisenhower

General Dwight David Eisenhower visited the 67th General Hospital on several occasions. Mildred Butler, ANC recalls taking his chauffeur, Kay Summersby, to her quarters on several occasions after she had chauffeured General Eisenhower to the hospital. (The women chauffeurs were called "Free Fannies".) The opthalmologists at the 67th General Hospital, including Dr. Otis B. Tibbetts, took care of an eye problem that the General was experiencing. Upon the authors's request, an archivist in the National Archives checked available records, which he stated to be "very thin" but did state that Ike spent 27 May 1944, with his old friend, U.S. Army V Corps Commander Leonard Gerow. This information was obtained from the wartime diary of a non-medical associate, Captain Harry Butcher. Captain Butcher's diary states, "Ike returned with a sore eye. He has had to consult the doctor and is using hot applications. The doctor says the eye has suffered too much strain." Whether this was the visit to the 67th may never be known, but he did, in fact, make several visits to the 67th for various reasons and one visit, at least, was for treatment of his eye. Mildred Butler, ANC mentioned that she regularly shopped in one of the same establishments frequented by General Eisenhower when he was in Taunton. (1, 9)

Leisure Time and Travel

The period between the arrival of the 67th General Hospital in Taunton, and the activity which followed the D-Day invasion was a time of relative leisure. The men traveled, took courses, were guests in the homes of the local English people, and used their passes to faraway places. Raymond Bungard and his sidekicks in the laboratory--Ted Benedict and Wayne Hixson, made many trips to places throughout the county and surrounding areas. Most of the enlisted men, officers and nurses did the same. Raymond Bungard recalls taking the boat to Belfast, Northern Ireland, and riding back on a military cargo plane. This time of relative leisure gave other opportunities to those so inclined. Ted Benedict was able to read and prepare reports on ninety significant books during this time. One of the modes of travel of the threesome was to catch a train along with their bicycles, take the train to a stop about sixty miles away and ride the bikes back to the post. All three were photographers, and swapped their tobacco allotments to the chemist in the shop in town where they traded, for their 35 mm film. None of them smoked, so that sweetened the deal even more. (8)

Mildred Butler ANC recalled taking time off to sightsee in London, and to visit local people in their homes. During one such visit to a nearby manor house she was introduced to Alice Mountbatten, sister of Earl Mountbatten. There were also trips to Wales and to Plymouth. She spent a week in Balliol College in Oxford. She recalled making some excellent British friends and related a story of two nurses from the 67th General Hospital who were residents of Taunton, Massachusetts. The mayor of Taunton had visited their home town in the United States, at one time, so the two nurses decided to pay him a visit. She recalled that he was most gracious to them and when Christmas came, some of the nurses and officers were invited to the ball held in town. (1)

First Sergeant Joe Bullock recalled trips to Weston-super-Mare, London, Torquay, Bristol, Weymouth, Edinburg, and Glasgow. Joe freely admitted that being First Sergeant made it relatively easy to get a pass, since the passes came through his office. The men could travel anywhere they wished as long as they could get there and back on their three day pass. (4) Photographs and postcards from the collection of the author's father, Richard Smith, reveal his travels to Bath, London, Wells and Weston-super-Mare. Additionally, he had photographs of himself on a bicycle during an outing and pictures of various bomb damage that he encountered on his travels.

Bike Rack
Photograph by and Courtesy of Ted Benedict

Wells Abbey Photograph in Collection of Author

Postcard from Torquay
Postcard Courtesy of First Sergeant Joe Bullock

Cockington Forge
Postcard Courtesy of First Sergeant Joe Bullock

A letter from Alvin Hamblen Morrison, son of Major Alvin Alward Morrison, recalled his side of the war, as he wrote about his father:

"He was a prolific writer of V-Mail to my Mom & me. Occasional censorship of V-Mail was mindless, but he could easily rewrite the offending statements using very personal nonsense that was easily translatable by us. Therefore he could be quite descriptive of his off-duty activities, and my Mom & I could catch his travel pitches using maps & books. The homefront wives also pooled their data constantly. Dad bicycled around quite a bit, and made several British friends. By train he went to Scotland. Once he even got himself out over the Channel aboard a Liberator (B-24). While he was in Taunton he turned 40, and in Portland, so did my Mom, and I turned 10. Being apart 'For The Duration' seemed like forever to all three of us. But, alas, all that once-vitally-bonding V-Mail apparently was junked long ago, and now I'm the only one left in the family to remember any of it, my Mom having died in 1973." (12)

Raymond Bungard had some revealing memories of traveling about in England:

"The food was good (at the 67th). Always powdered eggs. Fresh eggs on furlough only. The hospital personnel traveled over England, Scotland, North Ireland and Wales. Food was obtainable to the civilian population only with food stamps so restaurant fare was somewhat limited. On one furlough to the resort town of Torquay, a first class restaurant had two items on its menu: tripe (animal intestines) and calves head with brain sauce. (I took the calves head.) Many of the hospital personnel were befriended by the civilians. The welcome mat wasn't out among the English military men. We were 'overpaid, oversexed, and over here' (Stealing their women of course.)

Transportation for the GI's was bus, train, and bicycle. With many towns so close together, it was possible to cycle from one to another. English train stations are constructed to allow direct access to compartments without climbing steps. This made it convenient to load a bicycle. Hospital personnel had a three hour access to London via rail and I believe most of them took advantage of it. Travel by London subway was the fastest and most convenient. I observed people sleeping in the subways for air raid protection. (Thousands did.)

In spite of air raids theatres in London remained open. Instead of a sloped auditorium perhaps 7 or 8 tiers arose straight from the floor. One play running was *'The Doctor's Dilemma'* by George Bernard Shaw. Vivien Leigh was the star actress.

H. M. TENNENT Ltd.
Productions

ALDWYCH Theatre :
DIANA WYNYARD
ATHENE SEYLER
in
ANTON WALBROOK
MARGARETTA SCOTT
"WATCH ON THE RHINE"
by LILLIAN HELLMAN

6D.

POLLO Theatre :
"FLARE PATH"
A New Play
by TERENCE RATTIGAN
Directed by ANTHONY ASQUITH

CAMBRIDGE Theatre :
Thursday, 18th March
ROBERT DONAT
ISABEL JEANS
in
EDITH EVANS
DEBORAH KERR
BERNARD SHAW'S
"HEARTBREAK HOUSE"

DUCHESS Theatre :
KAY HAMMOND
CECIL PARKER
in
IRENE BROWNE
AGNES LAUGHLAN
"BLITHE SPIRIT"
by NOEL COWARD
LONDON'S LONGEST RUN.

GLOBE Theatre :
OWEN NARES
CONSTANCE CUMMINGS
HARTLEY POWER
in
SHERWOOD'S BRILLIANT COMEDY
"THE PETRIFIED FOREST"

ST. JAMES' Theatre :
In association with Bronson Albery
MICHAEL REDGRAVE
VALERIE TAYLOR
RONALD SQUIRE
in
"A MONTH IN THE COUNTRY"
TURGHENEV'S COMEDY
Adaption and Production by EMLYN WILLIAMS

COMING SHORTLY :
ERIC PORTMAN and BEATRIX LEHMAN
in
"UNCLE HARRY"
JOHN GIELGUD'S Production of
"LOVE FOR LOVE"

FOR TIMES OF PERFORMANCES SEE DAILY PRESS

Lowe & Brydone Printers Limited, London, N.W.10

Program Courtesy Raymond Bungard

THEATRE ROYAL HAYMARKET

6D.

VIVIEN LEIGH
in
"THE DOCTOR'S DILEMMA"
by
BERNARD SHAW

Photo by Angus McBean

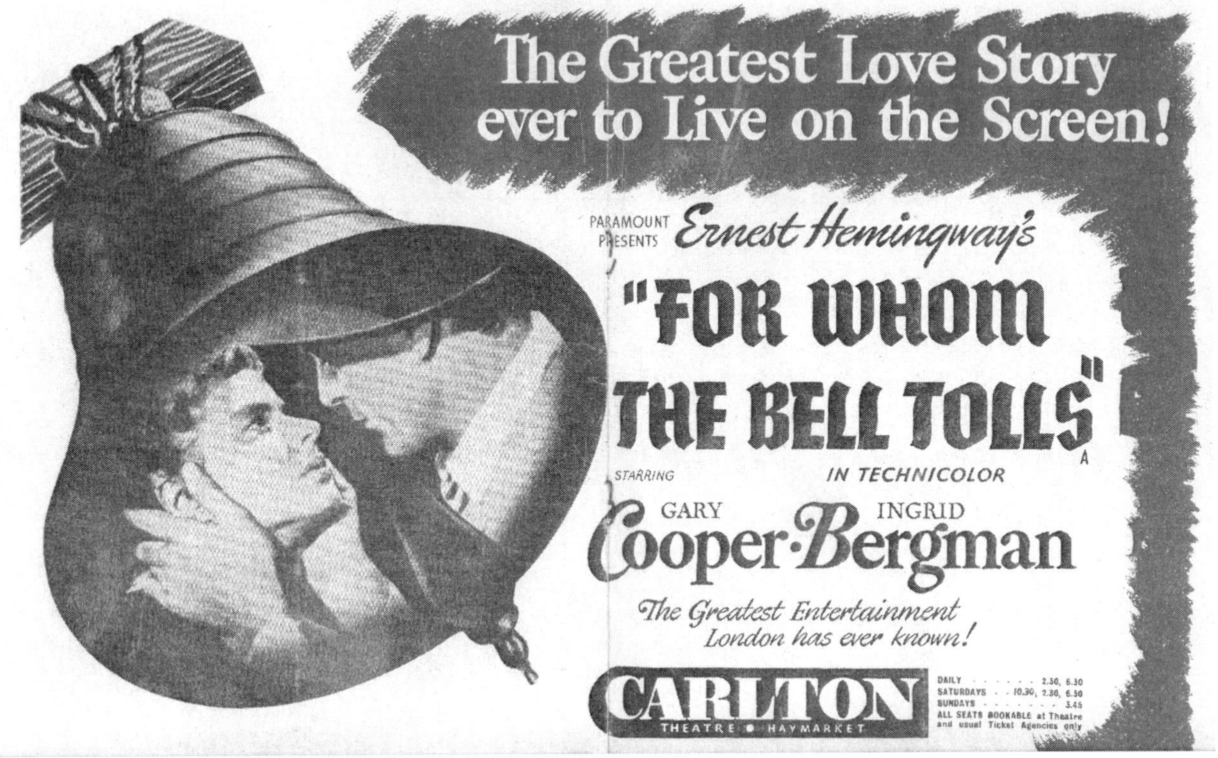

The Greatest Love Story
ever to Live on the Screen!
PARAMOUNT PRESENTS
Ernest Hemingway's
"FOR WHOM THE BELL TOLLS"
A
STARRING
IN TECHNICOLOR
GARY
INGRID
Cooper·Bergman
The Greatest Entertainment
London has ever known!
CARLTON
THEATRE ● HAYMARKET
DAILY - - - - - - 2.30, 6.30
SATURDAYS - - 10.30, 2.30, 6.30
SUNDAYS - - - - - - - - 3.45
ALL SEATS BOOKABLE at Theatre
and usual Ticket Agencies only

Courtesy Raymond Bungard

Produced and Directed by

Laurence Olivier

in close association with

The Editor, Reginald Beck

PAUL SHERIFF	*The Art Director*
Carmen Dillon	*Assistant Art Director*
ROGER FURSE	.. *The Costume Designer*
Margaret Furse	*Assistant Costume Designer*
DALLAS BOWER . ..	*The Associate Producer*
Alan Dent	*The Text Editor*
ROBERT KRASKER ..	*The Director of Photography*
JACK HILDYARD	*Operating Cameraman*
John Dennis & Desmond Dew	*Sound Recordists*
Phil Samuels ..	*Production Supervisor for L.O. Productions*
Wilfred Newton	.. *Photographer of Still Pictures*
Music by	WILLIAM WALTON
Conducted by	MUIR MATHESON
Played by	THE LONDON SYMPHONY ORCHESTRA

Length: 12,296 ft. Cert: U. Running Time: 2 hrs. 17 mins.

PRICE ONE PENNY. Entire proceeds devoted to the Gaumont - British Comforts for **The Royal Navy Fund.**

LAURENCE OLIVIER'S
presentation in
TECHNICOLOR of
HENRY V
by William Shakespeare
MARBLE ARCH
PAVILION

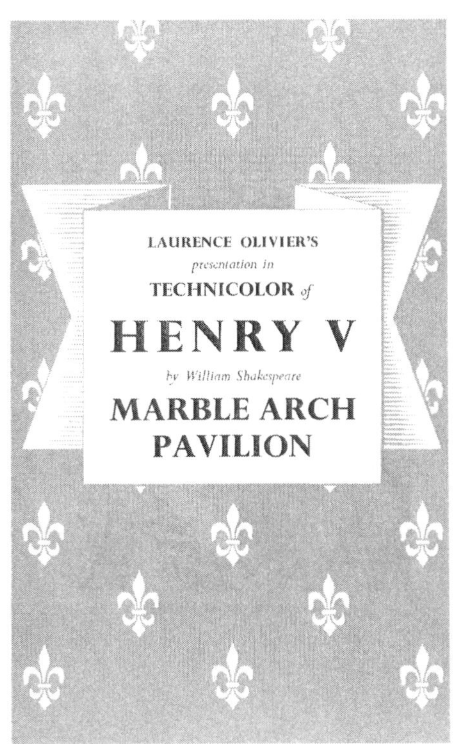

Courtesy Raymond Bungard

THE SERVICES' GUIDE TO LONDON ENTERTAINMENT

WHAT'S ON

NOVEMBER 26th, 1943 **in London** 9th Year of Publication

Incorporating "London Week," "London Day by Day" and "Londoner's Diary."

THE LONDONER.S OWN MAGAZINE

COMPLETE DETAILS OF ALL OF GREATER LONDON'S AMUSEMENTS

WHEN?
WHERE?
HOW GOOD?
HOW MUCH?

Vol. 15 No. 421

3d.

And at the **RITZ,** Leicester Square *(next to the Empire)*

"GONE WITH THE WIND"

now in its 4th Year!

Magazine Courtesy Raymond Bungard

After the war some of us were bussed to Stratford-upon-Avon to see the Shakespearian actors in 'Othello'. Hospital personnel were entertained by traveling USO and others. Bob Hope visited the 67th. The Red Cross 'donutmobile' came by with coffee and donuts once weekly. Movies were shown on base. We were allowed to vote in the presidential election. Payday was followed by gambling. Mostly throwing dice. I'm sure not a few were broke till the next payday. We were paid in Pound notes worth about $4.00 at the time." (6)

Ted Benedict added:

"We were told by the Mess Sergeant that if we were invited to meals by friends in the community we could take butter or other food items as gifts to our hostesses. This was a very welcome gesture of friendliness, since much of the food available to the British was strictly rationed, with no allowance made for guests." (8)

Racial Relations

Betty Wells, a British secretary for the Red Cross Unit, remembered that the dieticians in the kitchen were horrified that the English girls would go out with the Mexican enlisted men. (14) A very close relationship between a Mexican soldier and an English woman finally ended when they came to realize that their cultural differences were too great to sustain a marriage in the United States.

Lt. Bob Walker, of the Quartermaster Corps, recalled several incidents of racial strife. In one incident, a soldier who went by the name of Dixie, stopped his car, dragged a black man out of the hedgerows who was at the time consorting with a white woman, and beat him. In another incident, he recalled a story about a riot in a town south of Taunton, which required the presence of submachine guns to quell. He also recalled an all-Negro engineering or transportation battalion, stationed near Taunton. (13)

The English girls were fascinated with the black soldiers and had no innate prejudice against them. One story related that the black soldiers told the English women that they had been injected with something to make them dark and invisible at night. (39) The competition for the few single females created considerable strife between the black and white soldiers. The Army was mostly segregated and there was little contact between white and black troops except when on leave or on a pass. To reduce the tension and fighting between the men, passes were alternated with white camps given passes on nights that black soldiers would not be in town--white nights and black nights. Problems arose when the soldiers would "go over the fence" on the "wrong" nights to check on their girlfriends, and confrontations were almost a certainty. (8)

Black men accompanying white women were a curiosity to the white soldiers, particularly those from the South. Some took photographs of white women with black men together, since such pairing occurred so infrequently in the USA. In the decade of the 1940's, this was unusual and disturbing to most of these men since the Detachment Medical of the 67th General Hospital was composed of men who were primarily from the South.

As a response to a question posed by the author about race relations between the Negro soldiers and the white soldiers, Raymond Bungard responded:

> "We could have a nightly pass to Taunton and surrounding towns. That all changed when a Negro engineering unit was stationed nearby. From then on it was alternating Negro and white night passes to town. Listening to some of the threats of the enlisted it was a good idea and prevented injuries and may even have saved some lives. This was all new to me. Having grown up in Port Angeles, Washington, I had seen only one Negro till I was 16 years of age--he was the town's shoe shine 'boy'." (6)

Black troops were not used initially as combat troops. They were placed into work, engineering and support battalions and used to load ships, move ammunition and other dangerous and less desirable work. The initial intention was to have separate medical facilities for black patients, with black nurses and black doctors but this type of segregation became more and more impractical. Black patients were integrated into any medical facility which could offer them the best care. The 67th General Hospital was host to a number of soldiers who happened to be black and who were serving their country. The blood bank gladly accepted blood from the black soldiers and fully integrated it into the blood supply pool. (8)

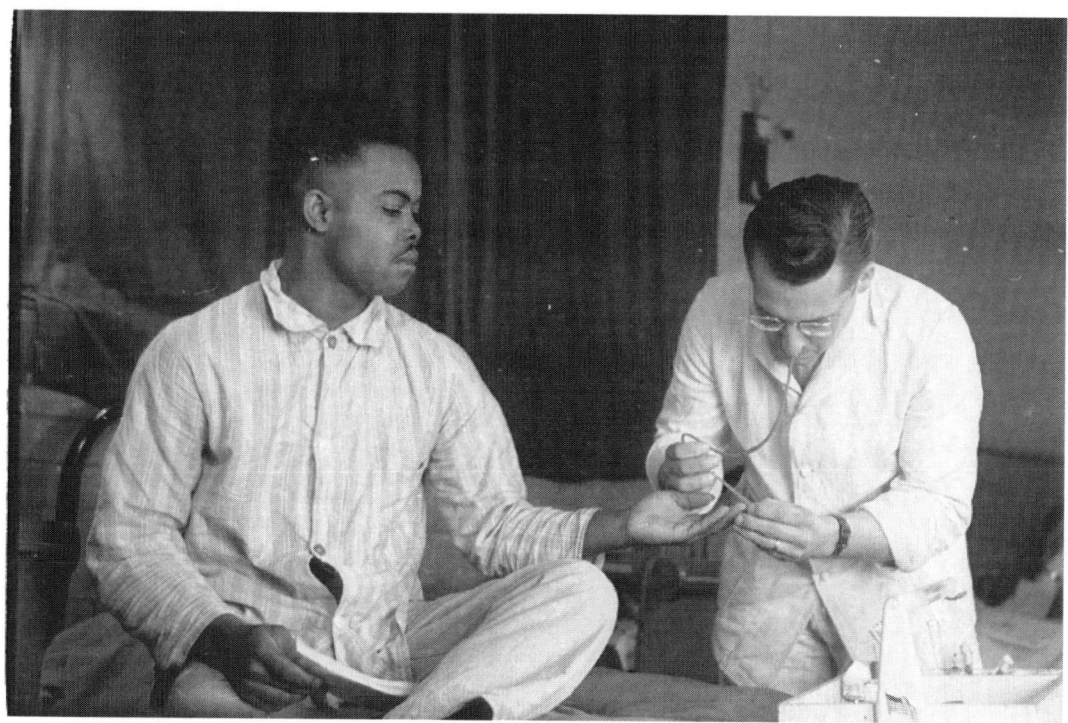

Sirceling Taking Blood from Negro Soldier on Ward at Musgrove Hospital
Photograph by and Courtesy of Ted Benedict

Disciplinary troubles were few in number. The proximity of the town and the impossibility of furnishing sufficient guards to cover the entire perimeter of the post made it comparatively easy to leave without permission. Ambulatory patients who may have been without leave for a long period sometimes succumbed to temptation, but on the whole these offences were rare and prompt disciplinary action was an efficient determent. (16)

A drink made of apple juice was prevalent in Somerset. It was called scrumpy and many of the soldiers acquired a taste for it. The taste of ale was foreign to many of the soldiers, but they drank it anyway. Leading from the town of Bishops Lydeard, in Somerset County, to the 185th General Hospital, which was established up the hill in and around an old manor house, is a small lane. This lane is referred to as "Whiskey Lane" to this day because of the large number of empty whiskey bottles consumed during World War II and discarded along the lane after the soldiers left the pubs and finished the bottles as they headed back to camp. (5, 15)

Whiskey Lane in 2004
Photograph by and Courtesy of Dr. Joe Braly

A story was related concerning an officer in the Dental Service, who was colorful by virtue of his personality and behavior:

> "He had bought a gasoline scooter of the Vespa type, using it for his own transportation around Taunton. To leave or return to the post we had to pass through a guard gate that included a shelter for the guard on duty, and at night the usual 'who goes there?' ritual was invoked, especially when it was very dark. One night, both late and dark, he returned to the 67th and was challenged by the guard. His inebriated response was some obscenity, with the warning that he was 'coming through!' He did, crashing through the gate and guard post, wrecking the scooter, and putting himself into the hospital as a patient." Another story about this officer was that he found several Italian prisoners who had been silversmiths as civilians and used them to make custom jewelry for private sale." (8)

Gambling was the predominant sport and helped pass the time on the Queen Elizabeth as it zig-zagged across the Atlantic to Scotland. It was outlawed, but when a game was broken up, another was started momentarily down the hall. The gambling did not stop with the arrival on dry land and became a frequent activity in the camp, particularly after payday. T5 Richard Smith sent a respectable amount of money home which he had won by playing dice and this served as seed money to buy a house when he returned home.

Drinking and gambling were both prohibited activities under the regulations of the Army and the 67th General Hospital, and of course almost everyone failed in some way in following those particular regulations.

Entertainment and Activities Calendar

Entertainment at the 67th General Hospital which benefited the officers, nurses, men of the Detachment Medical and patients was provided by the men themselves and by cooperative efforts of the Red Cross and the Special Service Officer, Dr. Eugene P. McManamy. The Red Cross was responsible for scheduling events and insuring that things went smoothly.

When the Red Cross first arrived at Musgrove, they were assigned a building formerly known as the Arts and Crafts Building It was brick and shortly after arrival, a large Red Cross was painted on its front. The first room, 26' by 64', contained easy chairs, writing tables and the radio and cabinets with supplies. One corner of the room contained the library. The room had ten casement windows which brought in much light, making the room bright and cheerful. The other room was slightly larger, at 26' by 69', and was used as the game room. This room had ten casement windows also, with a French door at the end. The two rooms could be opened to each other, creating one large room. The floor was of a beautiful inlaid Gujan wood, described as a cross between mahogany and teak. At the time that they took possession, there was no covered ramp to connect it to the other hospital buildings or wards which made it difficult to move patients from their wards to the Red Cross for activities and thus, initially, programs were carried out on the wards.

The Special Service loaned the Red Cross a Victrola and a piano so that music would be available to the patients. Supplies were obtained through the Medical Supply Officer, Captain McDavitt, the Detachment Supply Officer, Lieutenant Walker, of the Quartermaster Corps, and the Utility Officer. The Utility and Motor Pool under the direction of Lieutenant Edward H. Weitzen provided transportation, electrical needs and carpentry work. Captain Faulk provided food and drinks for teas, dances, etc. on various occasions. (10) A request for a piano and small radios for the wards was made at the end of 1942. (10) Additionally, comfort articles were borrowed from the Red Cross in Bristol until the supplies for the 67th Red Cross contingent arrived.

In 1942, only a small lounge room was available for the enlisted men and requests were made for a much larger recreational building. When its building was not being used for patients, the Red Cross had activities for the Medical Detachment, the nurses and the doctors. (10) The enlisted men who used the Red Cross facilities were able to help out with duties as well as care for the patients. A small Officers' Club and a Nurses' Lounge building were available and there was no need for the nurses and medical officers to use the Red Cross building for their recreation. No athletic programs were put into effect in 1942, because they arrived in England during the winter and faced constantly wet weather. A large field was available but it needed grading and plans were made to prepare the field as soon as weather permitted. Special Services provided an amount of athletic equipment and this, when added to the small amount of equipment brought from Fort Bliss, was sufficient. (18)

On 9 December 1942, the Red Cross began distributing American Red Cross Christmas cards to the wards. Movies were shown on the wards in the afternoon and in the Red Cross building in the evening. The ward with the largest patient census was chosen and ambulatory patients were invited to come to the ward to watch the movie with them. During one week they had movies on the G.U. wards and additionally used the recording machine on the G.U. wards for a musical program because those patients were confined to their wards. (17)

A dance was given for the enlisted men of the Medical Detachment on 14 December 1942. There was food and an orchestra with arrangements made by the Red Cross and the men bore the expense.

The Red Cross reported that:

> "On December 15th, through Chaplain Powers, our building was used for a lecture given for the doctors and nurses by Professor Channon of Queens College. December 16th, we had 'Mrs. Miniver' showing on the wards in the afternoon and in our building in the evening. On December 19th we held a community sing for the patients as well as the entire Unit. Through this get together, an enlisted men's choir was started and they practiced Christmas carols for the holidays. On December 21st, an afternoon program was given by the enlisted men that ended up in a community sing. We had open house on December

22nd. Our hours were from 3:00 to 5:00 and 7:30 to 10:00. During the afternoon we had a recording machine we borrowed from the Special Service Unit and played soft music while our guests drank tea and chatted. We had nurses pouring and one in charge of our guest book. The guests numbered around four hundred. In the evening we had an orchestra playing and the tea ended up in a tea dance. The patients were allowed to stay until 9:00 and they were reluctant to leave so early. That same evening a group of thirty-five townspeople came out to sing Christmas carols to the patients.

On the 24th, we had a dance for the enlisted men and made all the arrangements for them. Before their dance, they sang carols for the patients on the wards. On Christmas morning we all took the ditty bags and small packages of cellophane wrapped cakes and cookies to put on the trays. The patients were so grateful for everything and we all felt that we had had a mighty fine Christmas by making the patients happy. We had a tree in our reading room which was decorated with stick candy and small bags of candy. After the 24th, the patients were allowed to strip the tree. One of our chaplains fixed a manger on the stage in the game room and we gathered evergreen branches to bank the stage. We went out in the woods and collected holly, mistletoe, and evergreens to decorate the building. For our Christmas dinner the Red Cross arranged to have an orchestra to play during the meal and Miss Kellum served as hostess. After the dinner, the orchestra was moved from the mess hall to our building and they played for the patients until 8:00. Then the hall was cleared for the dance for the officers and nurses. The Red Cross made all the arrangements for the food and the orchestra but the financial end of the party was taken care of by the officers and nurses. They all thanked us for a grand time and everyone was so well pleased with the dance. On December 30th, we had a bingo party for the patients in the afternoon and they liked it so well that we scheduled another one by request for the same evening. The next day we had a movie on the wards 'Rio Rita' in the afternoon and in our building in the evening." (17)

The theater for the 67th General Hospital opened on 31 January 1943, with a local talent three act comedy, "Quiet Wedding", for which Special Service provided a piano and a pianist. Part of the decoration included mosquito netting shipped across the Atlantic with the 67th General Hospital when it was uncertain as to their final destination in the war theater. (Many thought they were going to Africa.) (7) In the Red Cross Recreation Hall, activities were provided by Special Services but many were impromptu. The Recreation Hall was busy every night with both Detachment enlisted men and patients enjoying the facility. In January, " they had at least one visiting program, one local talent show, one picture show, one dance, occasionally two, one game tournament, one quiet night, one night for practice of musical instruments, one night for dance practice." (19) Two or more shows per week were planned since there was now a theater for shows and stage performance. The patients had a night of their own for an amateur hour and weekly contests in bingo, card games, darts, checkers, and ping pong were held. Posters, made by the patients, advertised The theater for the 67th General Hospital opened on 31 January 1943, with a local talent three act comedy, "Quiet Wedding", for which Special Service provided a piano and a pianist. Part of the decoration included mosquito netting shipped across the Atlantic with the 67th

General Hospital when it was uncertain as to their final destination in the war theater. (Many thought they were going to Africa.) (7) In the Red Cross Recreation Hall, activities were provided by Special Services but many were impromptu. The Recreation Hall was busy every night with both Detachment enlisted men and patients enjoying the facility. In January, " they had at least one visiting program, one local talent show, one picture show, one dance, occasionally two, one game tournament, one quiet night, one night for practice of musical instruments, one night for dance practice." (19) Two or more shows per week were planned since there was now a theater for shows and stage performance. The patients had a night of their own for an amateur hour and weekly contests in bingo, card games, darts, checkers, and ping pong were held. Posters, made by the patients, advertised the daily programs.

Christmas Dance for the Enlisted Men
Photograph by and Courtesy of Ted Benedict

By January of 1943, fifteen wards had been opened. Recreation was limited to indoor activities for the patients due to the weather. Games played included Monopoly, Rook, chess, Parchesi, cards, checkers, Chinese checkers, jig saw puzzles, ping pong, rubber horseshoes, dominoes, Pig Dice, Shake, Sorry, and Touring. There were on-going checker and bingo tournaments. Games were taught to the patients as well as to the ward boys and nurses, and any interest in a particular activity was reported to the recreational workers so that they could fine-tune their programs. The ward doctors and nurses collaborated with the Red Cross workers as to the best activities for the men. Many of the patients were preoccupied with their particular problems and were depressed and restless and slow to respond to anything new. Involving them in activities helped to pull them out of their shell and restart them in every-day activities. (19)

Music was provided to the wards by a number of sources. The Special Services Unit provided a roller piano, piano player and singer for concerts at least twice a week with popular, semi-classical and classical entertainment. A radio combination which played records, radio and transcriptions of plays, musical programs and other entertainments was also furnished by Special Services. Red Skelton and Bob Hope programs were particularly popular. Two portable Victrolas, belonging to the Red Cross, were used on the wards on a rotating basis. (Finding needles for the Victrolas was an ongoing activity.) Additionally, the enlisted men formed quartets and quintets and serenaded the wards. A cowboy band, consisting of guitar, mandolin, violin, and harmonica players entertained the wards as well as themselves. Their functions included serenading those having birthday celebrations and playing for square dances and "Jitter-bug" contests. (19)

There were approximately 10 entertainments including outside entertainment and teas in addition to the three shows weekly in March, 1943. The program at the 67th General Hospital was promoted through the Red Cross Headquarters who took care to coordinate the programs with the medical officers and have them approved by Colonel Moore.

Programs for March 1943

Monday March	**1**	**Open**
Tuesday	**2**	**2:00 p.m. Show in Theater Hut** **7:00 to 9:00 P.M. Ping-pong Tournament (patients only)**
Wednesday	**3**	**Afternoon: music on wards: Sgt. Kane and Cpl. Sharkey** **7:00 to 9:00 Community Sing: Sgt. Kane and Cpl. Sharkey**
Thursday	**4**	**2:00 P.M. Show on wards** **7:00 to 9:00 P.M. Show in Theatre Hut**
Friday	**5**	**3:30-4:30 P.M. Tea party (for patients)** **7:00-9:00 P.M. Dance Recordings**
Saturday	**6**	**Afternoon: new games** **7:00-9:00 P.M. Bingo Party**
Sunday	**7**	**2:00 P.M. Show in Theatre Hut** **7:00-9:00 Classical recordings**
Monday	**8**	**7:00-9:00 P.M. Community Sing**
Tuesday	**9**	**Movies 2:00 P.M.; 7:00-8:30 P.M.** **Quiet games, 7:00-9:00 P.M.**
Wednesday	**10**	**7:00-9:00 P.M. Bingo Party**

Thursday	**11**	**Movies 2:00 P.M.; 7:00- 8:30 P.M.** **7:00-8:30 P.M. Popular Recordings**
Friday	**12**	**Open-Bingo Party on Wards**
Saturday	**13**	**Afternoon-2:00-4:00 P.M. Ping-Pong Tournament** **Serenade on wards-7:00-8:00 P.M.** **Serenade in Hall-8:15-9:00 P.M.**
Sunday	**14**	**Movies 2:00 P.M.; 7:00- 8:30 P.M.** **7:00-9:00 P.M.-Classical Music Hour**
Monday	**15**	**Radio Program-Special Service** **Wards in afternoon. Hall 7:00-8:30 P.M.**
Tuesday	**16**	**Movies 2:00 P.M.; 7:00-8:30 P.M.** **7:30-8:30 P.M. Cowboy Band**
Wednesday	**17**	**Amateur Hour- 7:00-9:00 P.M.**
Thursday	**18**	**Movies 2:00; 7:00-8:30** **Visitors Night 7:00-8:30 P.M.**
Friday	**19**	**Open-Bingo on Wards**
Saturday	**20**	**Outside Talent**
Sunday	**21**	
Monday	**22**	**Beetle Drive**
Tuesday	**23**	**Show. Sing-Paul Kane**
Wednesday	**24**	**Open**
Thursday	**25**	**Show. Bingo Party**
Friday	**26**	**Open**
Saturday	**27**	**Popular Recordings. Quiet games.**
Sunday	**28**	**Show-Classical Recordings**

The "Amateur Night" of 17 March 1943, was attended by Mrs. Miller from the Red Cross Public Relations Department and Private Baum of Army Pictorial who photographed the event. (20)

As spring approached in 1943, sunset did not come until late and there was light until after 10 o'clock, which allowed extended hours for outdoor activities and blackout curtains did not have to be pulled until that time. England instituted "Double Daylight Savings Time" (8) which extended the daylight hours in the summer by two hours. Ted Benedict remembered taking Kodachrome pictures (Weston/ASA 08 or 10) at eleven o'clock p.m. (8) This is, of course, very slow film requiring considerable amount of light which is normally not available at this time of the day.

There was an influx of patients after March 1, primarily British patients from the invasion at Oran. Movies on the ward were cancelled due to over-crowded conditions. Ambulatory patients then went to the "Theater Hut" (soon to be renamed "Nissodrome") for afternoon matinees three times weekly. Four enlisted men were trained to use the movie projector, which was interesting work to them because they liked machinery Music remained the prime form of entertainment..

One amusing story involved a patient who was suffering from arthritis to such an extent that he was barely able to get out of bed. When one of the pianist was beating out a blues song, he jumped up out his bed, threw on his robe and moved around the piano.

By the end of April, 1943, twenty-two wards were open and the need on the wards for more of everything was growing. There was only one portable victrola and the pianist supplied by Special Services was leaving for combat duty, with the singer expected to leave at any time. There were guitar players on the ward and they were used to provide ward entertainment. (22) A billiards table was located. The Special Services Orchestra put on a musical program once a week on each ward, on Wednesdays. Captain McManamy collaborated with the Red Cross to plan and prepare a three-act play.

Concert in the Motor Pool Area
Photograph by and Courtesy of Raymond Bungard

Most of the patients were ambulatory in July of 1943, and were able to stay outside longer and take advantage of the sunlight and extended Daylight Savings Time. Skills were discovered among the officers and enlisted men which allowed them to contribute their expertise to the recreational programs for the patients. Red Cross shows, outside talent shows, parties and teas all helped to occupy the men's time.

Bob Hope and Frances Langford

Bob Hope and Frances Langford visited the 67th General Hospital at Musgrove Hospital on 14 July 1943. Bob Hope was reported as being his usual entertaining self despite being tired and suffering from an eye problem which was treated by one of the eye specialists of the 67th, Dr. Otis B. Tibbetts. They gave two performances and visited the wards to visit with the patients. (24) Bob Hope, Frances Langford, as well as other entertainers traveled from base to base entertaining the troops through USO Camp Shows, Inc., and were known as "Soldiers in Greasepaint." These performances were not only entertaining, but "they provided a link to the folks back home, another way to tell these soldiers that they had not been forgotten and were missed by those back home". (25)

Frances Langford and Bob Hope at the 67th
Photograph Courtesy of Betsy Larson Crumrine

Bob Hope Leaving the Stage at the 67th
Photograph Courtesy Bobby Burns

The visit of Bob Hope and Frances Langford coincided with a contest to name the new theater which had been converted from a Nissen hut into as close to a state-of-the-art theater as possible under the circumstances. It was a well-equipped theater building, built of salvage material by Unit labor and equipped with curtains and backdrops, foot lights, etc. Milk cans were used to provide changing light reflections. It had a stage, dressing rooms for the stars, and dyed curtains made of burlap which gave the stage a panel effect. (26) Part of the stage was covered with slate which made it easier to dance. (24) This Nissen hut was christened the "Nissodrome" after the name was submitted by Sergeant Joe Bullock during a contest which drew hundreds of entries. He was the winner, and received a certificate, which he still treasures, in a ceremony before the evening movie, pinned to an easy chair, signed by Bob Hope, Frances Langford and the pertinent officers of the 67th General Hospital. (4)

Certificate of Award
67th General Hospital
E.T.O.

This is to certify that Joe C. Bullock has been awarded Ye Grand Prize for having submitted the outstanding name for The 67th General Hospital Theatre, to be known for all time as The "Nissodrome". He shall have, hold and enjoy for "The Duration" the sole rights and privileges of Ye Grande Award hereby conferred this 16th day of July, 1943, A.D.

Signed by:

Roland B. Moore, Colonel, M.C.; Stephen A. Cobb, Lt. Colonel, M.C. Executive Officer; Eugene P. McManamy, Captain, M.C., Special Service Officer; Bob Hope and Frances Langford.

(The certificate was prepared by Sergeant Petefish, who functioned as the Artist in Residence at the 67th General Hospital.)

The significance of the award was that it gave Sergeant Bullock the right to sit in an easy chair wherever he chose for every performance in the Nissodrome for the rest of the war, plus six months, taking precedence over officers or any others of importance. Sergeant Bullock still has this certificate and displays it proudly for any who want to see it. The actors from the U.S.O. show stated that, "It is the nicest and best equipped stage on which we have performed". (24) Several personal stories have been uncovered about the visit of Bob Hope and Frances Langford. One of them, told by Betsy Crumrine was that when Frances Langford needed to rest, Betsy provided her cot for Ms Langford to take a nap. In another story Ted Benedict and Ray Bungard were frequenting a local tea room when Bob Hope and Frances Langford arrived for their refreshment.

In the month of August, 1943, there were approximately 20 entertainments for the patients and Medical Detachment. A "jam session" band was formed which included patients and two enlisted men. One leg of the pianist was in a plaster cast and the piano was rolled from ward to ward for him to perform for the ward patients. The instruments for the orchestra were obtained from the nurses who bought or rented them. The enlisted men played for a downtown orchestra and used the instruments they had been issued. In the recreation hall, there was a surprise party of some kind every night, which was eagerly anticipated by the men. (27)

Also in August, the Detachment Medical asked the Red Cross help them produce a play and to set aside one night a week to practice in the "Nissodrome." The set-up at first was similar to what was being done with the patients on their amateur nights--performing a variety of skits, singing, playing musical instruments, organizing quartets, duets, trios, choruses, speaking through the microphone, and working out shadow acts. The original group consisted of 10 men and grew to about 50. They called the activity, "Play House" or "Little Theatre". Captain McManamy became interested and organized talent and materials. They began working on one play, "The Patsy", and one comedy, similar to "Hellzapoppin", which they made up, and gave it the name, "G.I. Gang". The nurses asked to join in to help out with the work. (27)

" Olson & Johnson, a popular vaudeville and burlesque duo of the `30's and `40's produced a show called 'Helzpoppin'.

'Helzapoppin' was a low-grade comedy review. It consisted of a series of sketches and running gags. One ... favorite involved a delivery boy, who would come down the aisle at various intervals with a plant, calling for a specific patron. 'Mrs. Anderson? Mrs. Anderson!?' he would call. Mrs. Anderson was never found, and with each successive entrance, the plant that the delivery boy carried would get bigger and bigger, till he could hardly carry it. Finally, as the audience left the theatre at the end of the show, they discovered the delivery boy in the branches of a tree in the lobby, still calling, 'Missus Aannderssonn!' Straightforward, simple, silly humor.

In a similar running gag, an actor would run out on stage during various sketches and shout that the city had been invaded by spiders. Closer and closer they would come. Finally, right before intermission, he came out and yelled,' They're here! They're here. The spiders have invaded the theater!' Just then, all the lights were turned out, and a shower of rice fell from the ceiling onto the spectators.

People screamed!" (28)

Amateur Night--Facts and Comments

"1. G.I. Queertette: Sgts. Chism, Hatton, Bullock, Presson.

All men are from Texas. They call themselves 'Queertette' because of the 'queer times they've had since joining the army, the queer voices they have, and the queer songs they sing.'

2. Nurses Stunt: 'Inspection'

A take off on our Colonel and General Lee when they enter the wards for inspection. The nurses taking part were:

1. Lena L. Carey, acting the Ward Sergeant, is from Holliston, Maine. Prior to the army was Night Supervisor, Frominghon Union Hospital.

2. Mildred A. Judkins, acting as Ward Nurse, is from Bluehill, Maine, and worked in the Bluehill Memorial Hospital.

3. Mary Louise Scott, acting as General Lee, is from Beverly, West Virginia. Prior to Army was Supervisor in Toledo Society for Crippled Children, Toledo, Ohio.

4. Gladys Wilkins, acting Colonel Moore, is from Heltonville, Indiana. Worked as Ass't Supervisor Rotary Convalescent Home, Indiana University Medical Center.

The stunt was a hollowing (sic) success. Roars of laughter from the patients and entire audience all during the act.

3. Solo: By the fair-haired friend of the patients Ruth Fairbanks, who hails from Portland, Maine, and did X-ray work in the Portland Hospital.

Accompanist: Capt. Miner, a patient, and a brilliant pianist.

4. Hill-Billy Duet:

Nick Nichols from Conway Ark.
Bob Laughlin from California.

Bob and Nick are always popular with the entire command with their unique acts.

5. Solo: Sgt. Michael Murphy, Chicago, Illinois.

Accompanied by Miss Florence Trask, Head of Physiotherapy. Miss Trask, too, hails from Portland, Maine, and is so cooperative in helping the boys in the field of music.

6. Magician: Stanley Sezerjekowski, unusual acts and grasping challenge to the audience.

7. Solo: Edward Sanders, Irish lad who held the audience spellbound with his two numbers, especially 'Ireland'. One patient remarked, 'His soul spoke in that song'.

8. Solo: Mike Sadowski, Philadelphia, Penn: another Bob Hope with his witty personality, humorous jokes and songs.

9. Jam Trio: Sgts. Dewey Force, Wilmar, Minn:--Saxophonist.
Mason Eastman, Duluth, Minn:--Guitarist.
Bob Lyons, Evanston, Ill:--Pianist.

What a jam trio! Benny Goodman takes second place. They call themselves the 'Boogie Band'. Believe me, they really let out on 'Boogie' too. " (27)

Left to Right: First Sergeant Earl Barton, MSgt. Andrew Leon Hatton, Sgt. Glendon Presson, TSgt. Harold Chism and Sgt. Joe Bullock. This Group, Less First Sergeant Earl Barton, Participated in the "Amateur Night" (Program Above) as the "Queertette"
Photograph Courtesy First Sergeant Joe Bullock

First Anniversary

On 1 September 1943, the 67th General Hospital celebrated the First Anniversary of its Activation (Organization Day) on 1 September 1942, in Ft. Bliss, with activities planned the entire day. The ordinary activity of the hospital was suspended whenever possible. Organization Day was celebrated as a holiday featuring a formal review and flag raising, competitive drills, a baseball game and other outdoor sports, picnic meals, stage entertainment and dancing in the evening. (29) The drill band was provided by the 354th Engineers whose commander was Colonel M.E. Sorley. Colonel Moore sent a money order with his thank you note as appreciation to buy music or whatever the band might need. Colonel C.O. Thrasher, G.S.C., Headquarters, South Base Section and Brigadier General Paul R. Hawley, A.U.S., Headquarters, ETOUSA were invited but were unable to come.

On the reviewing stand were Colonel Roland B. Moore, Lt. Colonel Elton R. Blaisdell, Lt. Colonel Stephen A. Cobb, Lt. Colonel William V. Cox, Lt. Colonel William B. Jordan, Lt. Colonel Jack Spencer, Lt. Colonel Arthur B. Thomas, Major Brian T. Brown and Captain Irene L. Zwisler.

Men Passing in Front of Reviewing Stand
Photograph by and Courtesy of Raymond Bungard

Band of the 354th Engineers Passing in Front of Reviewing Stand
Photograph by and Courtesy of Raymond Bungard

Nurses Passing in Review for First Anniversary Program
Photograph by and Courtesy of Raymond Bungard

Organization Day Ceremony
Photograph by and Courtesy Raymond Bungard

Colonel Roland Moore Addressing the 67th General Hospital
Photograph Courtesy Raymond Bungard

The program advertised:

"First Birthday Anniversary" "Somewhere in England".

On the back cover an amusing poem was printed to set the mood of the day:

"Calisthenics

There'll be no calisthenics in the morning
There'll be no calisthenics in the morning
For the order is official,
With the Adjutant's initial
There'll be no calisthenics in the morn!

In the morn-In the morn!
You can slumber 'til you hear old Gabriel's horn.
For the Colonel has admitted
That roll-call will be omitted;
There'll be no calisthenics in the morn!"

67TH

General Hospital

United States Army

FIRST

BIRTHDAY ANNIVERSARY

"SOMEWHERE IN ENGLAND"

1ST SEPTEMBER 1943

The **Program** for the day was as follows:

1000 hrs.	**Opening Ceremony** Headquarters
	ON ATHLETIC FIELD
1020 hrs.	**Platoon Drill** Detachment Medical Department
1040 hrs	**Litter Drill** Detachment Medical Department
1100 hrs.	**Specialty Drill** Detachment Medical Department
1120 hrs.	**Platoon Drill** Army Nurse Corps
1200 hrs.	**Buffet Lunch** (served continuously all afternoon in Mess Tent)
1315 hrs.	**Softball Match** Detachment Medical Department "Reds" v. "Blues"
1500 hrs.	**Races** **Tug-of-War** **Comedy Stunts**
1600 hrs.	**Softball Match** Nurses v. Field Officers
1730 hrs.	**Picnic Dinner** (Mess Kit Service)
1930 hrs.	**U.S.O. Show** for Enlisted Men in **Nissodrome**
2000 hrs.	**Dance** for Officers and Nurses in **Officers Club**
2300 hrs.	**Special Movie** for Enlisted Men in **Nissodrome**
	Refreshments at Red Cross between Shows
0000 hrs.	**"TAPS"**

On his copy of the program (30), T5 Richard Smith wrote, "I hope we don't have another one of these." This was very wishful thinking, as it turned out.

Ted Benedict noted the occasion of the First Anniversary Celebration in his diary:

"Today is Wednesday; and here is the story. This morning we worked until 9:30, then all the fellows except me took off because of the celebrations. Before they left, we all went through a formal review, in front of the Hqs. Building. The day is the first anniversary of the fml trf (formal transfer) of the old 51st boys to the 67th General Hospital in El Paso, really the activation date, although the officer and nurse quota was made up somewhat before then. The Chief Surgeon was to have been here, but due to pressure of official business couldn't make it. The unit hasn't been permitted to fly a flag up to this time, but got special dispensations (to quote the CO) to put ours up today, and so this was a part of the review. The ceremony went off pretty well with photographers on top of all the buildings, two platoons of nurses and one of officers and 6 of em (enlisted men), and almost perfect drilling. A colored band was imported from one of the near-by engineering outfits, sounded off and gave some music for the sports events down in the field during chow. It wasn't more than an hour or so after they had arrived that there were a good many rumors circulating about them. These rumors ranged all the way from the story that two of the band members had been with Cab Calloway's band to the tale that nine months ago none of them had known how to play a note of music. Judging from the performance, I think that there was more truth in the last one.

Yesterday the yardbirds, the colonels and anyone else who was interested put up a big circus-type tent in the lower field, and chow was served down there today picnic style. The EM got along all right, for it wasn't much different from the regular meals except that it was grasshoppers instead of wasps that got into our synthetic lemonade; but the officers and nurses had a hard time learning what to do with the various parts of their mess kits.

Somewhere there was free beer. Consequently, by evening show time most of the personnel were in a happy mood. When I went down to eat at 6:00, nearly a fourth of the personnel was visibly crocked, including nurses and majors. It was raining, and there wasn't room for everyone under the tent, so many were sitting outside in the wet grass, picnic style, just as if there had been good weather. Perhaps these Maine officers and nurses are accustomed to taking their picnics in the rain. I never saw anything quite so crazy; I still don't think that it was entirely true. Over in one spot there was a tanked sergeant and a lieutenant colonel wrestling in the long wet grass; nurses eating nonchalantly sitting in the drizzle in their uniforms; and everyone as happy as if they had good sense. It took the beer to make the em like the occasion, for the idea seemed to them to be a party for the officers and the nurses, who are Yankees, while the em (enlisted men) are all from the south.

Tonight, the USO put on a show, and then at ten o'clock, a movie is going one. This seems to be designed to keep as many of the boys in camp as possible; for yesterday was payday." (8)

By September, 1943, the census continued to grow as did shortages of magazines and books. The westerns were particularly popular and there was always a chronic shortage. The *"A*

Little Theatre" and Choral Club were popular. A Literary Club was organized and Round Table Discussions were held on various topics with the British educational system and the topic of the war among the subjects of discussion.

Around Thanksgiving, the craft shop made miniature turkeys for the patient's mess hall and confined wards. Sergeant Hetzler, who was a craftsman by trade, made a large movie reel which would hold an entire movie, thus freeing the projectionist of the necessity of changing reels halfway through the movie. (32)

Thanksgiving 1943

There was much to be thankful for on Thanksgiving Day, 23 November 1943. The war was going well for the Americans, the 67th General Hospital was snug and well-supplied. R.B. Moore, Colonel, M.C., Commanding Officer, wrote a message to the men in the souvenir menu: (30)

"This holiday, initiated by the Pilgrim Fathers in New
England, is perpetuated throughout our Homeland
As a time for counting our blessings and giving
Thanks to God for them. We, who find ourselves
In this Hospital in Old England, either as personnel
Or patients, should be grateful for the comfort and
Security that is ours today. May our thoughts be
With our Fighting Men, in humble gratitude for
What they have accomplished, and in confident
Expectation that we may all spend the next Thanks-
Giving Day in our own family circles."

The menu consisted of fruit cocktail, crisp celery, roast turkey with sage dressing and giblet gravy, mashed potatoes, buttered peas, boiled onions, cranberry sauce, fresh salad, pumpkin pie with cheese, assorted candy, fresh fruit, sweet cider, hot rolls, butter and coffee.

One of the activities in September, 1943, was "Date Nite" One night per week had been set aside for the previous three months to allow the patients to invite their girls. A few extra were invited for those without a girl and games and dancing was enjoyed. (31) Another dance was held in August. The Red Cross report stated:

> "Our dance was a huge success. The patients gave the names of the girls to the Recreation Worker, so that passes could be secured for them, then the employees on the post were invited, plus 20 good looking nurses from the local hospital. As the guests entered the building a paper flower with A.R.C. in the centre (made by the patients) was pinned on each girl. The patients were in the receiving line to greet their girls. The hall was beautifully decorated with assorted flowers and posters. The hall, flowers, and other decorations were arranged by two patients, florists by profession. A seven-piece orchestra

furnished the music, composed mostly of our own enlisted men and patients. Sgt. Force, who plays the saxophone in the orchestra, took charge of the program of dances. Colonel Moore, our Commanding Officer, was invited, but was called out of town and couldn't attend. The Executive Officer, Colonel Cobb, and Adjutant, Captain Faulk, the two Chaplains, and Captain Johnson, head of Convalescent Huts, were present. The patients enjoyed having them. They too got a kick out of seeing the patients have fun. Some fellows were in their uniform, some in maroon bath robes. One of our workers, a patient, and Captain Faulk, the Adjutant, served the patients and their guests cocoa. A great time was had by all." (31)

On 6 December 1943, two orphans who had been adopted by the 67th General Hospital in 1943, came to visit the post and were given a birthday party. Toys made by the patients were selected and given to them for Christmas. The children visited every ward, met every one on the post, had lunch with the enlisted men, and had a Christmas party with the officers and nurses in the nurses' recreation room. They received clothes, gifts, and a vast array of food to eat. Before the party was over, the activities of the day caught up with them and they fell asleep in Colonel Moore's lap. What made the day truly special was that it was the children's birthday as well as the First Anniversary of the hospital, the hospital being taken over by the 67th General Hospital on 5 December 1942. (16, 33)

Colonel Moore and Adopted Orphans--Christmas, 1943
Photograph Courtesy of Raymond Bungard

One Year in England Had Passed

The enlisted men had the formal opening of their new Enlisted Men's Club on 23 December 1943. The First Sergeant accepted a huge white key with a red ribbon from Colonel Moore. Colonel Moore made a short speech and the sergeant acknowledged the comments.

On the same day of the opening of the Enlisted Men's Club, Richard Smith wrote his wife Bessie and displayed his loneliness and frustration resulting from being away from home.

"1943 December 23 67th General Hosp. APO NY

Dearest One,

It seems as though I will never hear from you again as its been some time since I last heard surely you aren't sick or some of the folks would let me hear I hope I would give most anything to see you this evening.

I enjoyed the afternoon as I finally got the half day off for the second one in five weeks I did aim to go to town but decided that I needed the rest much more every one is trying to have the flu so far I have got around it some way. I did have the headache all night last night but feel better outside of a little indigestion. Now we had apple pie for dinner.

I wonder if you are still at your Mothers and will be there for Thanksgiving. I remember taking dinner with you one Thanksgiving at home we sure did have a nice time I thought.

Everyone is seeming to be having a big Xmas as packages are coming in pretty fast. I got one today myself the one from mother. I wished that I hadn't opened it until the day but some times the things won't keep that long such as cookies, etc. I hope you all don't mind…I have got a job to do tomorrow. I have got to wash a suit of o.d.'s and will have them pressed at our tailor shop. We burn coke in our stoves and do clothes get nasty fast it's a hard matter to get anything done as far as cleaning around here.

Believe me I am ready to go back to the Unites States. Myself I'll never forget what I was doing a year ago tonight.

We have a picture show here it will start in the next thirty minutes so close for this maybe I'll go up for a while just something to be doing keep on writing maybe I'll get your mail some time well bye dearest and be good. Love

Richard Smith" (10)

Before the Red Cross moved to their new facility, there was a final dance in the soon-to-be old Red Cross building in December. After the move, the week before Christmas, Christmas decorating was in full force. There was more office space and the new building was very homelike despite the smaller square footage. Chairs were arranged around the stoves for warmth, which had not been necessary in the previous building due to the central type of heating. The patients liked the building better than the previous one, possibly because the new building was theirs and it wasn't necessary to share it with the enlisted men of the Detachment Medical. A plan was worked out with the Rehabilitation Officer to allow a detail of patients under the supervision of a sergeant, to help care for the fires, put up blackout curtains, mop the floors, and clean the men's latrines. This left their English housekeeper to do the rest of the cleaning which was more or less a constant thing due to the dust and ashes from the stoves. (34)

Christmas 1943

Preparation for Christmas was extensive. The craft shop made a wide array of items to be used for gifts and manufactured the Christmas decorations with available materials. Unbreakable Christmas ornaments were mailed from the states. Red Cross workers and helpers traveled into the woods to gather mistletoe and holly to decorate the hospital. The R.A.F. came with lights and decorated the trees in the Red Cross as well as the tree in the Enlisted Men's Club.

On Christmas Eve, rounds were made of all the wards, passing out gifts which had individual personal greetings inscribed on each package. A Santa Claus suit had been sent from the States and Santa Claus, played by one of the officers, was part of the entourage, with Santa Claus dragging around another of the officers who was dressed as Hitler. Some of the enlisted men accompanied the group, playing on guitars and singing. One of the nurses was dressed as a clown and Colonel Moore accompanied the group as it went from ward to ward. An enlisted man, a nurse and a patient were picked up at each ward and by the time the last ward was reached, the group was of significant size. Christmas carols were sung on each ward as the gifts were passed out and all were wished a Merry Christmas. After seeing the patients and personnel enjoy the festivities and the decorations in the hospital, Colonel Moore said, "It's the best Christmas I have ever had." (33)

A Christmas card was available which was embossed with the motto "Servimus Sanando" , the shield with the pine tree, cactus and red cross, and with "67th General Hospital, Somewhere In England, Christmas 1943". Inside, it read:

"With quiet faith in every heart
Let's carry on and do our part
Confident that war will cease
And Victory bring a lasting peace."

"With the Season's Greetings and every good wish for the New Year" (35)

Irving Berlin

On 29 December 1943, Irving Berlin visited the hospital on a quick trip, held a short song session in the Red Cross building with the patients and visited some of the wards. "The patients enjoyed his presence more than they did his playing the piano and singing." (33) Irving Berlin had been touring Britain with his musical, "This Is The Army" an all-soldier production with 150 United States soldiers. Proceeds from the tour went to British Service Charities. Many of the personnel, nurses and officers attended the performance when it was playing in Bristol.

Victoria Rooms, Clifton

BRISTOL

THE UNITED STATES ARMY

presents

IRVING BERLIN'S

All-Soldier Musical Show

'THIS IS THE ARMY'

Sponsored and all Proceeds Distributed by

The British Service Charities Committee

(of the Charity Organisation Society)

and the British Service Charity Committee (Bristol)

Music and Lyrics by **Irving Berlin**

Musical Numbers and Dances Staged by

Sgt. Robert Sidney

Scenery Designed by

2nd Lt. John Koenig

Costumes Designed by

Pvt. Joseph Fretwell III

Musical Director

Sgt. Milton Rosenstock

Entire Production Staged Under the Personal Direction of Mr. Irving Berlin

If an air raid warning be received during the performance the audience will be informed. The warning will not necessarily mean that a raid will take place and in any case it is not likely to occur for at least five minutes. Those desiring to leave the theatre may do so, but the performance will continue and members are advised in their own interests to remain in the building

PROGRAMME

OVERTURE ... ... THIS IS THE ARMY Orchest
Captain: Cpl. Ralph Magelssen. Sgt. of the Guard: Sgt. Alan Manson. Guards: Sgt. Gene Berg and Cpl. Paul Drap

OPENING CHORUS ... ... Compa

" THIS IS THE ARMY, MR. JONES "
Sung by the Selectees: Sgt. Julie Oshins, Cpl. William Roerich, Pfc. Hank Henry, Pfc. Henry Jones, Pfc. Arthur Gilmo Pvt. John Hederman and Pvt. Daniel Longo.

SGT. DICK BERNIE

" I'M GETTING TIRED SO I CAN SLEEP "
Sung by Sgt. James Burrell.
Assisted by Sgt. Zinn Arthur, Pfc. William Collier, Pvt. James Farrell, Pvt. Roger Kinne, Pvt. Orville Race, P Donald McCray, Pvt. Earl Lippy and Pvt. Carl Nicholas.

" DON'T SING—GO INTO YOUR DANCE "
Sung and Danced by Cpl. Pinkie Mitchell.
Sgt. of the Guard ... Sgt. Sidney Salzer. Guards ... Sgt. Maurice Kelly and Pvt. Nelson Barclif

SGT. JULIE OSHINS

" MANDY "
Sung by Cpl. Ralph Magelssen. Mandy Herself: Sgt. Richard Irving. Her Boy Friend: Sgt. Fred Kelly.
Girls: Cpl. Jack Lenny, Pfc. Eugene Jarvis, Pfc. William Pillich, Pvt. Charles Dickson, Pvt. Charles Ta Pvt. Alfred Danieli.
Boys: Sgt. Joseph Johnson, Cpl. Clarence Jaeger, Cpl. Phil King, Pfc. Carmine Capuozzo, Pfc. Joseph Wojcikow Pfc. Stephen La Marr.

MILITARY VAUDEVILLE
Juggler: Cpl. Larry Weeks. Mess Sergeant: Pvt. Daniel Longo.

LADIES OF THE CHORUS
Girls: Sgt. Robert Sidney, Pfc. Hank Henry, Pfc. Arthur Gilmour, Pfc. Henry Jones, Pvt. John Hederm Pvt. Joseph Fretwell.
Boys: Sgt. Sidney Salzer, Pfc. Norman Stuart, Pfc. Kenneth Bates, Pfc. Richard Browning, Pvt. Daniel Lon Pvt. Richard Reeves.

MILITARY VAUDEVILLE
Acrobats: The Allon Trio (Sgt. Geno Erbisti, Cpl. Louis Bednarcik, Cpl. Angelo Buono).
Sgt. Gene Berg, Sgt. Arthur Steiner and Cpl. Pinkie Mitchell.

" WITH MY HEAD IN THE CLOUDS " and " AMERICAN EAGLES "
Sung by Sgt. Robert Shanley and Company.

" WHAT THE WELL-DRESSED MAN IN HARLEM WILL WEAR "
(Dance Staged by Cpl. Pete Nugent).

Sung by Pvt. James Cross.
Assisted by Sgt. Clyde Turner, Sgt. Jack Brodnax, Cpl. Orlando Johnson, Pvt. George Anderson, Pvt. Robert Jack
Danced by Cpl. Pete Nugent, Pfc. Melbourne Scott, Pvt. Thomas Lee, Pvt. Al Martin, Pvt. Randolph Cal Pvt. William Smith, Pvt. Charles Johnson.
Dance speciality: Cpl. Billy Yates and Pvt. James Cross.
Spoons specialty: Cpl. Marion "Spoons" Brown.

FINALE ... ... The Compa

INTERMISSION

ENTREACTE ... ... THIS IS THE ARMY Orches

STAGE DOOR CANTEEN
Dancers: Sgt. Robert Sidney, Sgt. Arthur Steiner, Sgt. Maurice Kelly, Sgt. Gene Berg, Pfc. Carmine Capuc
Canteen Hostesses: Sgt. Joseph Johnson, Cpl. Clarence Jaeger, Cpl. Stephen Sandes, Cpl. Jack Le Cpl. William Roerich, Cpl. Phil King, Pfc. Ray Goss, Pfc. Norman Stuart, Pfc. Bert Whitley, Pfc. Ar Gilmour, Pfc. Harvey Prael, Pfc. Kenneth Bates, Pfc. Eugene Jarvis, Pfc. Joseph Wojcikowski, Pvt. Jo Fretwell, Pvt. John Hederman, Pvt. Larry Gengo, Pvt. Alfred Danieli.
Jane Cowl: Sgt. Alan Manson. Gypsy Rose Lee: Sgt. Julie Oshins.
Vera Zorina: Pvt. Nelson Barclift. Jack Benny: Sgt. Dick Bernie.
Donald Duck: Pvt. Joe Allen. Rochester: Pvt. James Cross.
Ronald Colman: Cpl. James Kearney.

" I LEFT MY HEART AT THE STAGE DOOR CANTEEN "
Sung by Sgt. Earl Oxford. Eileen: Pvt. Charles Tate.

Victoria Rooms

WEDNESDAY, DEC. 29
6.30 p.m.
THIS IS THE ARMY

Ground Floor
£1 1s.
Row B

Nº 22

A report detailing the activities of 1943, stated that,

"A Special Service Officer, (referring to Captain McManamy) detailed from the hospital personnel, has devoted more than eight hours a day to the supervision of recreational activities These include sports, motion pictures, USO Shows, musical organizations, educational lectures, dances for enlisted men, tours to points of interest in the immediate vicinity and other forms of entertainment.

One hundred ninety-six motion picture entertainments were shown during 1943, with an average attendance of 230. Films are exhibited three times a week, for patients in the afternoon and for personnel in the evening." (29)

1944

Joe Louis

In March of 1944, Joe Louis went overseas and served with the Special Services. He presented a program in the motor pool area at the 67th General Hospital some time after his arrival in England. (8) He performed a comedy routine with another black soldier who accompanied him on his tour and refereed a sparring match between two soldiers of the Detachment Medical of the 67th General Hospital. At the time, Joe Louis was the "Heavyweight Champion of the World". During World War II, he fought 96 exhibition matches, attended numerous bouts like the one at the 67th, personally donated more than $100,000 to Army-Navy Relief and retired from the Army with the rank of staff sergeant. The author remembers meeting Joe Louis in his capacity as a greeter at Caesars's Palace in Las Vegas, and was amazed at the size of Mr. Louis' hands and by his graciousness. Quite a guy.

Joe Louis at the 67th General Hospital, Musgrove Military Hospital
Photograph by and Courtesy of Raymond Bungard

Joe Louis at the 67th General Hospital Refereeing Match in Motor Pool Area
Photographs by and Courtesy of Raymond Bungard

Joe Louis at the 67th General Hospital
Photograph Courtesy Bobby Burns

Purple Heart for the 67th

Another event happened on 14 March 1944, when Sergeant Wesley Carter of the Detachment Medical of the 67th General Hospital received injuries while on leave in London, resulting in the award of the Purple Heart. He was lying in bed with a lady friend when an incendiary bomb pierced the roof and various floors of the hotel in which he was staying and struck him in the chest. Luckily his luck held and it did not explode. He was not seriously wounded, but afterwards, always claimed that the injury had affected his dice throwing hand. This was the only Purple Heart received by any member of the Unit. (54) Another account stated that he was hit with falling plaster in a London hotel, his duties at the moment being "hardly official". (8) First Sergeant Joe Bullock added to the story:

> "I recall one Purple Heart being rewarded to a sergeant who was shackin' up in a hotel in London, when an air raid occurred and an incendiary bomb came through the roof and landed on his hand and chest, while he was lying in the bed, although it did not explode, causing multiple breaks and disfigurement." (4)

Activities Continue

Little Jenny, the eight-year-old British girl continued to visit and entertain the patients and men. She appeared in one of the "Amateur Nites" and sang for the enlisted men at their dances. The U.S. Navy Band gave a stage show for the patients and played for their dance. A comment was made about the different colors on the dance floor: maroon, blue, orange, brown and checked bathrobes, and some G.I. uniforms. Additionally, the Welsh Band and The Prince of Wales Band from Buckingham Palace performed and the Nissodrome was packed for both performances.

The Nissodrome had its moments in February of 1944, as the Red Cross reported:

> "We have been fortunate in having officers from off the post to come in and entertain the patients either in the afternoon or evening. A Flying Officer from a nearby British post gave a most delightful and interesting talk to the patients in the hall on February 16. The hall was filled to capacity with patients, enlisted men, officers, and nurses. Officer Hartley was a Prisoner of War in the last World War, and he held the audience spellbound with his unique manner of delivery on 'How Prisoners of War Were Treated in the Last World War!' A chaplain from a nearby unit comes often to sing and play for the patients in the hall. The bed patients enjoy him too, when he tours the wards with the rolling piano. The fellows always appreciate celebrities such as James Cagney, who performed in the Theater and visited bed patients on the wards." (37)

The hospital settled into a routine by April of 1944, with the Unit well assimilated into the community--one depending on the other for various things. With known sources and resources, the work was smoother and the attitude tended to be an acceptance of a more or less permanent situation. Those who liked action were tired of the lack of variety and wanted change and those who were more security oriented wanted things to remain the same. (24) Things would remain the same for one more month.

Entertainment for April of 1944, kept most of the old favorites such as informal sing-outs, musical quizzes, bingo and community sings. An Anglo-American ping-pong tournament was held with men from a nearby convalescent depot. A melodrama called "Love in Bloom or Meet Me at the Lamp Post, Nellie", was written and produced by the patients. The best of the month was one that the patients gave with their own master of ceremonies, singers and musicians and a former British patient who sang, along with Little Jenny and the Anglo-American Band which was originated and organized at the 67th. Following the performance, ice cream, which had been frozen by the patients was served in paper cups topped by a piece of hard candy. Another all-patient program came from a convalescent orthopedic ward with a quartet, black-out skits, soloists, dramatized jokes and a community sing for a finale. The April Birthday Party was held outside and featured a white cloth on the table and candles in lieu of a cake. Birthday presents were wrapped in white with blue and yellow ribbons and iced chocolate milk made by the patients was served. Some patient programs were taken on the wards. One particularly good one was "Irish" who sang ballads from Ireland. Others were a Unit program called the 67th Inkspots, some classical piano, and "a spot of jive". The Special Service would often include talent found on the wards into their shows. (39)

Williams, Allen at USO Show
Photograph by and Courtesy of Ted Benedict

The Recreation Hall was filled with spring flowers such as rhododendrons, anemones, gorse, iris, forsythias, violets and lilac and brought by the women who visited the patients, the nearby British Convalescent Depot, the English staff of the Red Cross, the Detachment personnel and the patients. Cyclists from the post would collect them alongside the road and bring them in to the hall. In April of 1944, the weather allowed the patients of all the orthopedic units to play bingo in the sun and hold outdoor tournaments, play card games, hold informal musical moments as well as magic hours and tricks. (39)

In May of 1944, a Red Cross Post Art Exhibition was held in the Red Cross building and brought much critical praise. Little Jenny had her eleventh birthday and a real American birthday party, complete with a decorated cake prepared for her. The soldiers tried to think of games that were played when they were eleven and all decided on musical chairs, wink-em and other similar games. A new game called "Rekop Dice" was started (Rekop is poker spelled backward). In this game, everybody throws five dice and the one with the best poker hand wins the throw. To prolong the game, the winner could be the one who:

> " wins the most out of a given number of throws or based on so many points for each kind of hand and a score card for each player. This too, could be done in two ways: winners for the one who reaches a certain score first, or winners for the one who is ahead after a given length of time. The value of a game of this type is that it can be made to last for fifteen minutes or all afternoon." (40)

D-Day Invasion

The world turned around for all on 6 June 1944—D-Day, the invasion of Europe. Increased demands were made on all supplies. The Red Cross suddenly needed more toilet articles, especially for the hospital train. There were more letters to be written for the men and Purple Hearts to be packed and mailed. The activities for the men continued:

> "The highlight of our month's program in the recreation hall was last night's birthday party, one of the best program parties we've ever had at the 67th. Complete to a birthday cake with candles, ice cream, a professional magician (and one of the best, now a G.I.), trumpet music from a detachment patient, hot jive by an air corps lieutenant and Miss Ward, who worked a 'two at one piano' routine as well as playing separately, and our own 'Little Jenny' we write about so much, it was, as one of our patients told us, the very best birthday party he's ever had. We had with us some of our best English friends, including one little girl with a June birthday who has been 'adopted' by Sgt. Hetzler.
>
> Little Jenny and Miss Ward have been coming out every Tuesday night for our weekly combination amateur shows and musical quizzes. As the fellows say, 'If Jenny is going to be there, so will I', and she has become our 'sweetheart of the 67th'. We think our musical quiz has been the musical story about 'The Three Little Sisters'--'Dolores', 'Ice Cold Katie' and 'Sweet Rosie O'Grady', who were quite a problem to their mother, like Katie who went to the 'Basin Street Ball' with her sailor, 'Jim' and got the 'Jersey Bounce' when she tried the 'Strip Polka'. Or Rosie, who was mother's hope, but 'Nobody's Baby', and how the fellows love them. Our 'amateur' talent has not always been amateur, for we have had some wonderful showmen with us. 'Pat Patterson' from Station WLW, Cincinnati, who has been our MC; Ernest Delmer, snake dancer par excellence; 'Lord Bozo' an English patient, who has since been accepted for E.N.S.A. and who organized some real variety shows for us while he was here. His unit had done 14 African hospitals with a spontaneously organized 'British I' show, and it was easy to see why. He was a real joy to have around, and while he was in the craft shop, he made a flute out of airplane parts. While he was here, he sang twice in Chapel with Miss Larson as accompanist. He had been a choir boy at York Cathedral, and everyone was impressed by his singing. Mrs. Morgenthaler has also sung several times at Chapel. Other special features were a games tournament, a classical music hour, an informal silly quiz night, with an English

accordionist to furnish peppy tunes, and a radio hour. Regular features of our program are Wednesday night Anglo-American ping-pong tournaments, arranged through our good friend Captain Callander of the English convalescent depot, weekly snooker tournaments, Sunday night bingo, Tuesday Amateur Hours, Tuesday, Thursday and Saturday afternoon movies at the theater. On the wards we have been able to show a movie every night through the help of one of our detachment X-ray men who gives up every evening to help our patients. Needless to say, the patients really appreciate it. We also had Sgt. Jack Covich, a pre-war professional magician, who gave a wonderful show on every ward, that left the patients chattering long after he had left about how he did it. There were also several members of a G.I. Special Service show who went out on the wards. One afternoon, we were able to remember every ward with flowers, thanks to an English woman from our town."

Second Organization Day Anniversary

On 1 September 1944, the 67th General Hospital held its Second Organization Day Anniversary celebration and all unnecessary personnel were excused from duty. A Retreat and Review was held and at the formation, a history of the organization and an address was given by Colonel Moore. A dance was held for the officers and enlisted men, a U.S.O. Show was presented to the enlisted men and a concert was given by the Devonshire Regimental Band. (44)

By September of 1944, the high turn-over of personnel at the hospital and in the units around the hospital made it more difficult to carry on regular entertainment programs. For example, the recreational workers in the Red Cross were down to one worker from a previous level of three. Things changed so rapidly that an event could not be planned ahead more than one week, due to the probability of some of the participants being transferred out. A G.I. band near the Unit which had come weekly to play in the Hall or on the wards was transferred out with their units. A British unit which used to come in for snooker and table tennis tournament play was also transferred out. Special Services helped take up the slack as far as recreation was concerned. They supplied new books and provided movies to the wards. (43)

A Crooner's Contest was added to the variety of activities already available, and an engraved plaque was presented with the details of the contest. (31) The officer patients were given a small recreation room in September, 1944, decorated with pictures and furnished with games, books, magazines, writing equipment and a radio. A club room was maintained by the Officers Mess for the officers of the 67th General Hospital. (24).

On 29 October, T5 Richard Smith wrote another letter to his wife Bessie, again showing his loneliness and some of his activities to fight it.

"Dearest One

Just a few lines to let you hear from me again this leaves me well and doing fine but wish I could hear from you it being several days since I last heard. I wish you were here to go with me to the picture tonight here in camp its been a long time since we were to a picture together. As to that matter any place. But surely it can't last always this has been a long Sunday for me I have worked all day anyway I have been on duty which is just about as bad but we have supper served and cleaned up and still have a hour and a half to wait…I see on the patients red cross door that they are having a big blow out there tonight.

I haven't checked on my furlough to see if it has been approved of if so I guess I'll be going about the 1st or 2nd. I'm sure planning on a big rest the fellow that's going with me has a girl friend there in town and she said to him I'm not worried if your going with Richard he won't let a floozy get away with you . I told him that the kind of talk my wife should hear, ha ha. But I don't suppose you have been doing any worrying on that matter. Well dearest there isn't any thing new to write about from here its just the same thing every day. Will say bye for now with all my love, Yours

Richard Smith" (10)

The hospital seemed to relax a bit in October and November, as reflected by the activities reported in the Recreation Narrative Report submitted by Betsy Larson Crumrine, Senior Recreation Worker:

"The many and colorful activities going on constantly in the recreation hall have given it a constant face lift, and a festive atmosphere. Our Military Wedding occasioned our room to be converted into a chapel atmosphere. Autumn leaves, berries and branches graced our back drop behind the pulpit, windows, stoves and stove pipes, while candle light enhanced the quiet dignified surroundings appropriate for a wedding. Our two English girls, pianist and singer, were formally dressed, so up to the entrance of the bride we had every G.I. completely fooled. The chaplain, a patient, was really a chaplain, and he was the best sport officiating at the wedding. He brought the house down when ending the ceremony, by giving the bride and groom a pair of boxing gloves saying 'May the best man win'. A guest book was made, and each patient guest had to sign the book before coming in. As long as we can remember, there hasn't been so many clean shaven lads as there were that night. One patient asked the nurse for a clean bath robe because he was going to this wedding and wanted to look presentable. All the costumes were made by the patients, and we even borrowed a full dress suit for the bride's father to wear. An officer patient took the initiative in this affair, and the other patients participating were sworn to secrecy, so until the entrance of the 'bride', with the pianist changing from Lohengrin to Chopin's funeral dirge, we had the audience guessing. We fooled the fellows, and they all thought it was the best fun they had ever had. We had a record of 300 patients packed in the hall. Hot chocolate and cookies were served at the reception.

One evening a colonel on the post showed the patients colored movies of his travels in England and Scotland.

The Red Cross shows 'Let's Get Acquainted' and 'Three Girls and a Guy' were much enjoyed by the patients and we could use more shows of this type.

The Halloween party was as much like home as we could make it. The physical set-up was on a progressive basis, starting with silhouette drawing, then a psychoanalysis booth, fortune teller, apple ducking, apples suspended on string attached to a pole, string chewing contests, ring toss, horse race, dart throwing, and the middle of all this was a hillbilly band whooping up a storm.

A democratic Thanksgiving and Birthday party was combined for November, and even our Thanksgiving theme was carried out in a wall frieze with turkeys for window and wall decorations. A special treat for the November birthday patients was their portraits drawn by two other patients. Our hillbilly orchestra furnished the background entertainment for patients unable to participate in all the active games.

Our regular weekly programs of musical quizzes, community sings, impromptu jam sessions, tournaments and games are all highlights in the hall activities." (45)

Thanksgiving, 1944

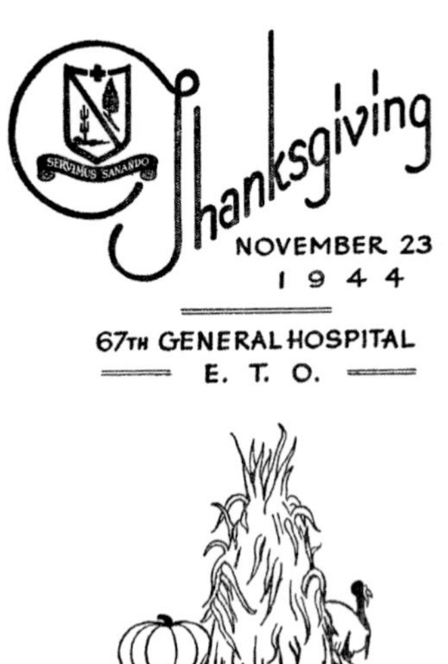

On 6 December 1944, a birthday party was held for Jean and Colin, the adopted orphans of the hospital. The Detachment entertained them at the noon meal and the officers and nurses did the same in the afternoon. A Christmas tree was decorated and their Christmas presents were presented to them by Colonel Moore, the officers and the nurses. (16, 46)

Also, on 6 December 1944, T5 Richard Smith wrote his wife Bessie:

> "Dearest One,
>
> …I certainly appreciate what you and the rest have done toward trying to give me a big Xmas, but nothing would be like being at home with you but I would say the chances of getting back before this is not as bad as I hate to think about it….
>
> If you were here …We could have a few bitters commonly known as flat beer over there provided we wish to be in society. I'm getting so darn tired of this part of the world. I can't explain through mail how or why we are having a lovely evening here its raining as usual I would like to write you something interesting to read but there isn't anything worth while so will close for this time all my Love Yours,
>
> Richard." (10)

And again on 19 December 1944:

> "Sweetheart I have my box filled with Xmas now and look as though I'll never use half you and Mama have sent me the cookies were fine I could eat for a week and still have plenty left over. I hope your mother has that chance to cook me a big dinner some day soon tell her I'm all for it well by Dearest Love Yours, Richard." (10)

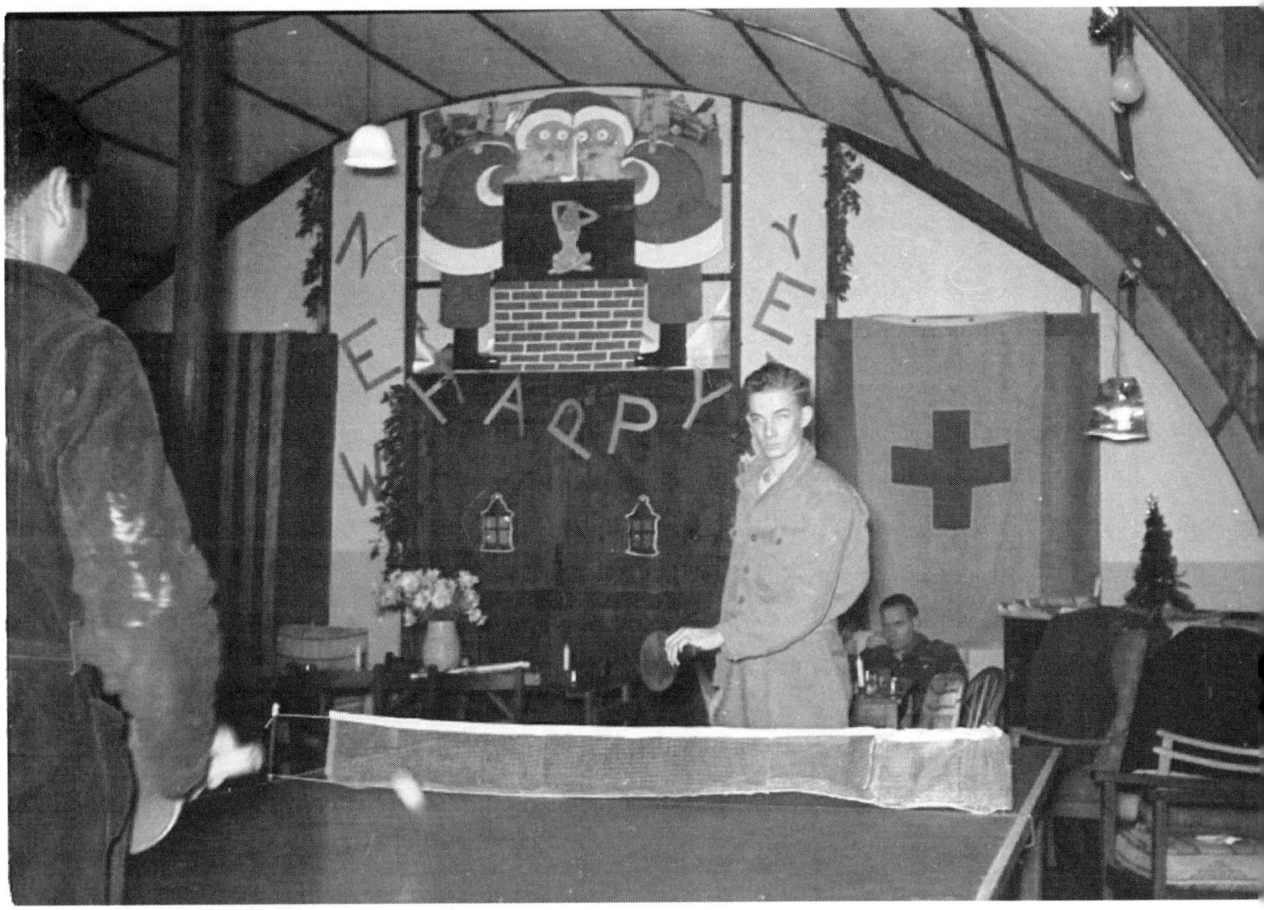

American Red Cross Christmas Decorations
Photograph by and Courtesy Ted Benedict

1945

Entertainment in January, 1945, included skits, soloist, an exceptional Negro quartet, guitarists and choral music involved in producing four shows, "Show Time", "School Days", "Dixie Hall" and "Bathrobe Bizness".

> " 'Bathrobe Bizness' featured a fortune teller from Tul-sa Ok-la in authentic costume and make-up and the singing of our second Choral unit, the 'Red Coats' with a return engagement of the Engineers' quartet completed the program.The other high spots were the appearance of the ENSA shows 'Globe Trotters', 'Picadilly Commandos' and the C.E.M.A. artists, the best of these being Adilla Fachiri, on the violin and Adrian Holland, pianist. Mme Fachiri was superb and contrary to our original opinion, had the audience eating out of her hand, so to speak." (47)

In February and March, 1945, the 185th General Hospital Band and the 1332nd Engineers Band visited and entertained the men. In addition, the 167th Engineers Quartette came each Sunday and sang on the wards and presented a program in the Hall. The Cathedral choir presented two concerts, there were three E.N.S.A (Entertainments National Service Association) shows, two C.E.M.A. (Council for the Encouragement of Music and Arts) shows, three shows presented by Taunton people and two Red Cross shows. The men designed and executed the decorations for various holidays and parties including stenciling the napkins for Easter and coloring and delivering the eggs. (48)

Because of the improving weather seen in April and May of 1945, there was more interest in the wards in throwing a ball or kicking a football, than in going to the craft shop. Horseshoes were popular and a few of the wards planted some tiny gardens. Movies continued to be popular and it became possible to show up to six ward movies per week, due to the arrival of a second Cinemobile operator. For some reason, more entertainment became available, with two U.S.O. shows, following a long period in which there were none.

Following the signing of surrender documents in France, on 7 May, and in Berlin on 8 May 1944, preparation for moving from Musgrove Hospital began. Certain regularly scheduled entertainments had to be cancelled. Little Jenny made her last appearance after two years of faithful service to the officers, nurses, detachment and patients. (51)

References

(1) Personal communication Mildred Butler.

(2) "Lewiston Journal; Magazine Section." Saturday, October 25, 1969.

(3) Bush, Robin. *A Taunton Diary 1787-1987. Two Centuries of gossip,scandal,success and calamity in darkest Somerset.* Buckingham, England, Barracuda Books Limited, 1988.

(4) Personal Communication First Sergeant Joe Bullock.

(5) Hinton, David J. *An Illustrated Social History of Bishops Lydeard and Cothelstone.* Published by The Rocket Publishing Co., Ltd., and Printed by Taunton Printing Company.

(6) Personal Communication with Raymond Bungard.

(7) Personal Communication Betsy Crumrine.

(8) Personal Communication with Ted Benedict.

(9) Email Communication with Archivist Jim Leyerzapf at Jim.leyerzapf@nara.gov.

(10) Letters from Richard Smith to Wife, Bessie Transcribed and Edited by the Author.

(11) www.si.edu/postal/learnmore/vmail.html.

(12) Communication with Alvin Hamblen Morrison, "Ethnohistorical Anthropologist".

(13) Telephone Interview with Lt. Bob Walker, Quartermaster Corp, with the 67th General Hospital.

(14) Interview with Betty Wells, Red Cross Secretary for the 67th General Hospital, June, 2004, in Taunton, Somerset, England.

(15) Hawkins, Mac. *Somerset at War 1939-1945.* The Dovecote Press. Reprinted in 1997.

(16) "Historical Report of 1943, to the Chief Surgeon, SOS, ETOUSA from R.B. Moore, Colonel, Medical Corps, Commanding Officer, 67th General Hospital, APO 511." Dated 31 January 1944. National Archives.

(17) "Reports to the Red Cross from the Red Cross Unit Assigned to the 67th General Hospital. Narrative and Recreation Report for 31 December 1942." National Archives.

(18) "Annual Report of the 67th General Hospital to the Chief Surgeon, SOS, ETOUSA." Dated 15 January 1943, and signed by Lieutenant Colonel R.B. Moore, M.C., Commanding. National Archives.

(19) "Reports to the Red Cross from the Red Cross Unit Assigned to the 67th General Hospital. Narrative and Recreation Report for January, 1943." National Archives.

(20) "Reports to the Red Cross from the Red Cross Unit Assigned to the 67th General Hospital. Narrative and Recreation Report for March, 1943." National Archives.

(21) "Reports to the Red Cross from the Red Cross Unit Assigned to the 67th General Hospital. Narrative and Recreation Report for June, 1943." National Archives.

(22) "Reports to the Red Cross from the Red Cross Unit Assigned to the 67th General Hospital. Narrative and Recreation Report for April, 1943." National Archives.

(23) "Reports to the Red Cross from the Red Cross Unit Assigned to the 67th General Hospital. Narrative and Recreation Report for May, 1943." National Archives.

(24) "Reports to the Red Cross from the Red Cross Unit Assigned to the 67th General Hospital. Narrative and Recreation Report for July, 1943." National Archives.

(25) http://www.60wwii.mil/Presentation/Education/FS_uso.cfm.

(26) "Historical Report of 1943, to the Chief Surgeon, SOS, ETOUSA." From R.B. Moore, Colonel, Medical Corps, Commanding Officer, 67th General Hospital, APO 511. Dated 31 January 1944. National Archives.

(27) "Reports to the Red Cross from the Red Cross Unit Assigned to the 67th General Hospital. Narrative and Recreation Report for August, 1943." National Archives.

(28) http://www.thestorynet.com/archive/spiders_ah!.htm.

(29) "Annual Report to the Chief Surgeon, SOS, ETOUSA, APO 887, U.S. Army." Dated 31 January 1944. National Archives.

(30) Collection of the Author.

(31) "Reports to the Red Cross from the Red Cross Unit Assigned to the 67th General Hospital. Narrative and Recreation Report for September, 1943." National Archives.

(32) "Reports to the Red Cross from the Red Cross Unit Assigned to the 67th General Hospital. Narrative and Recreation Report for November, 1943." National Archives.

(33) "Reports to the Red Cross from the Red Cross Unit Assigned to the 67th General Hospital. Narrative and Recreation Report for December, 1943." National Archives.

(34) "Semi-annual Report, Medical Department Activities, 67th General Hospital to the Surgeon General, Washington, D.C." Dated 15 June 1945. National Archives.

(35) Christmas Card of 67th General Hospital, 1943.

(36) "Reports to the Red Cross from the Red Cross Unit Assigned to the 67th General Hospital. Narrative and Recreation Report for January, 1944." National Archives.

(37) "Reports to the Red Cross from the Red Cross Unit Assigned to the 67th General Hospital. Narrative and Recreation Report for February, 1944." National Archives.

(38) "Reports to the Red Cross from the Red Cross Unit Assigned to the 67th General Hospital. Narrative and Recreation Report for March, 1944." National Archives.

(39) "Reports to the Red Cross from the Red Cross Unit Assigned to the 67th General Hospital. Narrative and Recreation Report for April, 1944." National Archives.

(40) "Reports to the Red Cross from the Red Cross Unit Assigned to the 67th General Hospital. Narrative and Recreation Report for May, 1944." National Archives.

(41) "Reports to the Red Cross from the Red Cross Unit Assigned to the 67th General Hospital. Narrative and Recreation Report for June, 1944." National Archives.

(42) "Reports to the Red Cross from the Red Cross Unit Assigned to the 67th General Hospital. Narrative and Recreation Report for July, 1944." National Archives.

(43) "Reports to the Red Cross from the Red Cross Unit Assigned to the 67th General Hospital. Narrative and Recreation Report for September, 1944." National Archives.

(44) "Historical Data of 67th General Hospital for Third Period Quarter1944--July, August, September 1944." Dated 14 October 1944. National Archives.

(45) "Reports to the Red Cross from the Red Cross Unit Assigned to the 67th General Hospital. Narrative and Recreation Report for October--November, 1944." National Archives.

(46) "Historical Data of 67th General Hospital for Fourth Period Quarter 1944--October, November and December 1944." Dated January, 1945. National Archives.

(47) "Reports to the Red Cross from the Red Cross Unit Assigned to the 67th General Hospital. Narrative and Recreation Report for December, 1944, and January, 1945." National Archives.

(48) "Reports to the Red Cross from the Red Cross Unit Assigned to the 67th General Hospital. Narrative and Recreation Report for February and March, 1945." National Archives.

(49) Menu of 67th General Hospital E.T.O.—Christmas, 1944.

(50) Christmas Card of 67th General Hospital, 1944.

(51) "Reports to the Red Cross from the Red Cross Unit Assigned to the 67th General Hospital. Narrative and Recreation Report for April and May, 1945." National Archives.

(52) "Reports to the Red Cross from the Red Cross Unit Assigned to the 67th General Hospital. Narrative and Recreation Report for June and July, 1945." National Archives.

Chapter 13
Activities Outside the Hospital and with the Community

Everyday life was not exclusively carried out on the post, but involved other military units, other Red Cross units across the area, the European Theater of Operations' medical establishment, the national and local British Medical organizations as well as local civic and private organizations and individual English citizens all doing their part to support the war effort by supporting the morale of the troops.

In January of 1943, the British Red Cross Library Association of Somerset County, headed by The Honorable Mrs. Mervyn Herbert, donated volumes of books on English classics, poetry and history. The Red Cross reported:

Lady Herbert
Photograph Courtesy Betsy Larson Crumrine

"Mrs. Herbert has also made arrangements to meet at our building one day a week to handle requests for hospitality in English homes. She has had an office in the town, but her committee have felt they were not getting to the soldiers who needed and wanted the hospitality the most. A personal interview is necessary to make the type of placement most desirable, both on the side of the soldier and the British host or hostess. They will plan special trips of interest besides making plans for social events, hunting, fishing, tennis, and swimming. She has had dozens of requests from British residents to extend the hospitality, but they have been unable to get American guests. The plan at our hospital is in the manner of an experiment which if successful will be tried in other camps. (2) (Lady Herbert was an American who had married Lord Herbert. She became good friends with Mrs. Hahn of the Red Cross Unit at the 67th General Hospital and opened her home to the 67th General Hospital on several occasions. She also had a maternity hospital on her estate. (1))

Lady Herbert and to her Immediate Left, Mildred Butler With Patients and Personnel of the 67th General Hospital, on Her Estate
Photograph Courtesy Betsy Larson Crumrine

Miss Evelyn Lowe of the YMCA has visited us (the Red Cross) on numerous occasions and has furnished flowers, games and magazines. She is most anxious that we call upon her for any need she can fill.

Mr. W.L. Ozzard, town librarian who is also a member of the Hospitality Committee and holds the honorary office of Minister of Information, has given the names of the members of our unit to women's clubs in this county whose interests may again fill various needs and requests of patients and enlisted men. From the members of these clubs we will be able to pick the personnel for our volunteer group who will be badly needed when the hospital enlarges. Invitations to attend the meeting of various groups are coming to us and we will cover these to the best of our ability." (2)

As time went by, more books were generously donated by the local community. (3)

To maintain community relations, an informal meeting was held with the townspeople who had shown an interest in working with the Red Cross and their programs. An informal tea was held on 27 January 1943, for patients and other guests from town. The hall was decorated with flowers and the guests seemed to enjoy chatting with the patients. (2) Tea and cookies were served and musical entertainment was provided for everyone's entertainment. (3) On 21 February, a Church Parade was held with the British Home Guard of Somerset County, where Chaplain Powers of the 67th General Hospital preached the sermon. (4)

In March of 1943, The Red Cross reported that they continued to work closely with the Minister of Information, the British Red Cross and the Hospitality Committee. There were a number of people in the community anxious to volunteer their services to the hospital. For those soldiers who could get leave, hospitality was arranged by the local Hospitality Committee. Miss Lowe, of the British Y.M.C.A. brought flowers to the hospital and visited with the patients.

On 9 March 1943, the Public Relations Department, London Headquarters of the Red Cross sent Mr. Lindsay McHarrie of the Public Relations Department who made a transcription of interviews, games and music in the Recreation Hall. The preparation for this broadcast fascinated the ambulatory patients. The program was to be broadcast on the "Stars and Stripes in Great Britain" program on April 4th and 5th, 1943. Mrs. Barbara Miller was sent from the staff of Mr. McHarrie to write casualty stories of the patients and was accompanied by an Army pictorial photographer who took pictures of the patients' variety show. In addition to the interviews for the casualty stories, Lt. Colonel Moore, the Commanding Officer of the 67th General Hospital (later promoted to Colonel) and members of his staff were also interviewed.

Hospitality by the British population was lavish while entertaining individual or small groups in their homes. (5) Not every offer of hospitality was accepted and thus many opportunites were wasted. A Red Cross report from February and March, 1943, discussed this matter:

> "Two years ago considerable effort was directed to working out the program of hospitality in local homes for American soldiers, both patients and others. Even at that time the report indicated there was not much interest shown by the men. This has been available all the time but has been little used. From time to time we have tried to arrange something again, but for the most part it seems the men prefer to find their own friends, and we do know that they have enjoyed the hospitality of many homes in this community even though they have not made their acquaintances through the established committee set up to do this service. The extent to which they do become acquainted and identify with the local neighborhood is well illustrated by the fact that many of them who are having the

opportunity now to take seven days furlough, or delay-en-route to the Reinforcement Depot when they are discharged from hospital, spend the entire time in town rather than using that time to see more of the country. Probably they have done the same in other communities if they have been previously stationed in this country because many of them who have been stationed elsewhere in the United Kingdom spend the furlough in that same vicinity, and always, if we ask why they have decided to go there, the answer is the same, 'I'd rather go where I have friends, it's the next best thing to going home.' It seems well to bring this out, as comments on the soldiers' response to the work of the Hospitality Committee might create a false impression as to their attitude toward the British people in general.

Many of the patients plan to spend the time available to them for passes or furloughs in visiting relatives or friends in other hospitals or stationed elsewhere in this country. We have been able to help many of them in communicating and arranging these meetings. Not only does this seem to mean a great deal to them personally, but as they often remark, 'Now the folks will be happy to know we've got together.' It definitely comes under the heading of 'something to write home about', and must be really satisfying to the families concerned. Often we have discussed with the patients the fact that their families still have the ideas most of us used to have, that this is, after all, a very small country and if two or three of you are in this country it couldn't be so hard to get together."(6)

On 27 March, a detachment of the 67th was dispatched to Bridgewater to march in a "Wings for Victory" parade.

Photographs Above and Below: Soldiers of the 67th General Hospital Marching in Bridgeport Parade. Second from Left is Sgt. Robert Agee. Second from Right is Master Sgt. Leon Hatton and on Right is Lt. Aronson, Detachment Commander.
Photograph Courtesy Betsy Larson Crumrine

A Red Cross Service Club opened in Taunton, in May of 1943, with a recreation center which provided a snack bar, lounge, and game rooms for the soldiers. Community volunteers worked and assisted with the daily operations. (7) The light load of patients allowed the Red Cross workers to use the Clubmobile which was stationed at Musgrove and plan programs at various isolated camps, such as Sandhill.

Clubmobile Serving Patients and Detachment Medical
Photograph by and Courtesy of Ted Benedict

The Clubmobile served doughnuts and coffee and delivered books and magazines. They presented one program on the average per week in areas where there was no Red Cross Unit. The men and patients from the 67th General Hospital participated in presenting these programs with permission of their medical officers and the Commanding Officer, Colonel Moore. (7)

A "Wings for Victory" week, designed to raise funds for the war effort and raise awareness, was held for Taunton in May of 1943, and 500 men of the 67th General Hospital participated. Names of some of the other participating units performing in the parade were omitted due to security concerns. A parade was held on 22 May 1943, and the program was as follows: (23)

“Wings for Victory” Week

Order of March
Saturday, May 22nd
Leaving the Victoria Recreation Ground, East Reach at 5:30 p.m.

Flags of United Nations

Bridgwater Christy Band

Contingent Navy-H.M.S. Bristol

Detachment of Chinese

Contingent Navy-W.R.N.S.

Contingent Navy-Admiralty Creechbarrow House

46 Coy, C.M.P. (T.C.)

114 Convalescent Depot

A.T.S.

R.A.F. Station-Name of Station Not Permitted

R.A.F. Station-Name of Station Not Permitted

R.A.F. Station-67th M.U.

U.S.A. Forces

Home Guard-2nd Bn. “A” Coy

Home Guard-“H” Coy

Home Guard-G.P.O. Coy

Home Guard-M.T. Coy

Taunton School J.T.C. Band and
King’s School, Rochester, Navy, J.T.C., A.T.C.

King’s College J.T.C.

King’s College A.T.C.

Queen’s College J.T.C.

Huish’s School Army Cadets

Huish’s School A.T.C.

1st Taunton Army Cadets

41st Squadron A.T.C.

193 Coy, Girls’ Training Corps

559 Coy, Girls' Training Corps.

Tonight, 7:30-9:15
Vivary Park
Band of Royal Air Force (Fighter Command)
Seating Accommodation for 1,000

On 23 May, voluntary attendance (in formation) of 40 officers, 90 nurses and 100 enlisted men of the 67th General Hospital was made at a "drum-head" service held in Vivary Park, Taunton, by the Home Guard. On 25 May, a baseball game between the officers and men of the 67th General Hospital was held at
the County Cricket Grounds, which netted 246 Pounds Sterling towards the Taunton "Wings for Victory" week. Several other opportunities arose in May, 1943, for cooperation with British civilians and military organizations, in addition to their social contacts

Vivary Park with Castle Hotel in Background
Photograph Courtesy Raymond Bungard

On two nights of the week, two convalescent patients went to the British Hospital and presented an hour's musical program, playing the guitar and singing. Two other patients staged a game of "Horseshoes" at the same hospital for an hour. (7) Administrative staff and nurses from this same hospital visited Musgrove Hospital in June for the "Amateur Night" production. (8)

On 12 June 1943, the hospital staged a two hour performance in a small town nearby with participants from all levels in the hospital--patients, Detachment personnel, nurses, and officers. This program was also for the Wings for Victory Week. The plan was to give the same program in the Theater Hut at Musgrove Hospital. Additionally, there was work on a theater show similar to "Helzapoppin", with plans to present it in the Theater Hut on July 4. Participants included patients who were expected to still be in the hospital. To ensure sufficient available talent, enlisted men were trained as back-up substitutes in case there were discharges from the hospital. (7)

By August of 1943, the Red Cross was supplying two isolated camps and one station hospital with magazines and papers and two cadres of men from the Detachment Medical were guarding other hospitals. (9) They reported supplying the old books, newspapers and magazines to the Station Hospital, airports, and various isolated camps. They even assisted some camps with their entertainment programs.

Colonel Moore addressed two of Taunton's schools for boys in 1943. Local officials and several high ranking British officers were entertained at a formal review and presentation of the Soldiers' Medal to Private James E. Murphy on 6 August 1943. *(The Soldiers' Medal, section 3750, title 10, United States Code (10 USC 3750) was established by Act of Congress 2 July 1926. The Soldier's Medal is awarded to any person of the Armed Forces of the United States or of a friendly foreign nation who, while serving in any capacity with the Army of the United States, distinguished himself or herself by heroism not involving actual conflict with an enemy. The same degree of heroism is required as for the award of the Distinguished Flying Cross. The performance must have involved personal hazard or danger and the voluntary risk of life under conditions not involving conflict with an armed enemy. Awards will not be made solely on the basis of having saved a life.)* (5)

A convoy of Queen's Messengers Relief Trucks for British bombed areas was entertained on 13 August 1943. (4, 5) The Red Cross report of August, 1943, summed up their attitude toward the community as a whole:

> "Although we do not use English Volunteers at this post we still have made our contacts in the community. We have grown to admire the English woman and her unlimited capacity for service. We marvel at the jobs they do and that are pure drudgery. We can learn from their volunteer system which has been organized to the point that everyone is doing something, and doing it where it is needed." (9)

In September, the Red Cross reported:

> "The Commanding Officer of one of the nearby airports asked us to come out in our spare time and assist in directing a G.I. stage show that the enlisted men had written, cast, and composed music and words to the songs used. The C.O. sent transportation, and we went out several times to help all we could in directing, re-arranging the acts, making suggestions, etc. The G.I.'s opened their show for their own unit. It ran for three successive nights, then we had it presented (two performances) in the Nissodrome for the 67th Hospital Unit. Much credit and praise is due, and was given, to the G.I.'s for the hard

work, good talent, and grand show. The Stars and Stripes correspondents and Mr. Husted from Red Cross Public Relations attended the show, and interviewed each actor." (10)

A medical meeting was held at the 67th General Hospital on 22 September, with hundreds of medical doctors from the nearby hospitals and community invited. This was a meeting of the American Medical Association of the European Theater of Operations (AMAETOUSA). (10) An all-day program of scientific papers, discussions and demonstrations was presented and the meeting was a good opportunity to share ideas with other doctors in the Theater. Seventy-five percent of the Surgery Department participated in the program. A dance was held and music was provided by a band provided by the 354th Engineers. On 26 September, a party of officers was sent to form part of the Mayor's staff to review a British parade on "Battle of Britain" Day.

On 11 November 1943, Colonel Moore attended memorial services at Vivary Park, Taunton, on Armistice Day. Paramount News men appeared in November, 1943, to film the patients and Red Cross activities. This aroused considerable excitement and anticipation among the patients who eagerly awaited the release of the film and of course they let all their families know that they were in the movies. (11)

On 4 December 1943, the American Red Cross Service Club in Taunton was dedicated. Speakers were the Club Director, Mr. Robert Smith; Chaplain C. Vander Ark; the Mayor of Taunton Alderman C.H. Goodlano, J.P.; the Commissioner of the A.R.C. of Great Britain, Mr. Harvey D. Gibson; Major General L.T. Gerow, Commanding General of V Corp and Sergeants Barton and Bullock of the 67th General Hospital representing the enlisted men. The program consisted of a reception and inspection of the club, the dedication ceremonies, followed by teas served in the cafeteria. Recordings of interviews with some of the enlisted men and performance by the band was followed by continuous entertainment in the game room.

In December, 1943, a show was put on by the British evacuee children downtown with 50 convalescent patients invited, and 40 other patients on crutches delivered by ambulance. The program was a Nativity Show and was held in the Empire Hall. (9, 12)

Due to the build-up prior to the D-Day invasion, there was a surplus of medical facilities to care for those patients who needed care. As a result, there was a lot of free time available. Social interaction between the Americans and British hosts increased. American doctors were encouraged to join British Medical Societies and allowed to use their libraries. American medical seminars included invitations for their British counterparts to attend. (13) A British Convalescent Hospital was in Taunton, and the staff of that hospital and those of the 67th General Hospital shared teachers, instructors and lectures. (14)

In January, 1944, the Red Cross report detailed several contacts that were made with the community:

> "We have a little British girl, eight years old, who comes out to sing and dance for the patients, enlisted men, and officers. She ('Little Jennie') has won the hearts of every member of the post, and all are anxious to have her come as often as she can. Little Jennie

has appeared on our 'Amateur Nites', has sung for the enlisted men in their talent shows, and at their dances. She too, was a first Shirley Temple in our Paramount film which was made of our hospital. We have taken her on our G.I. shows that we take to places in this area. We are sorry she is afraid of microphones, or else she would have been on some of our broadcasts. A few weeks back Col. Wyman of Southern Base Section called us to bring a show to his base. Little Jennie went with us. Col. Wyman wrote us a very nice letter, telling us how pleased he was with our show. On Feb. 3rd we take the show to a nearby village. We hope to make the best showing ever. By making all these contacts so many necessary materials have been donated to our Craft Shop and Recreation Hall. These contacts have been so helpful in guiding us to the right places to get various things we needed. Too, the little villages, army units, etc., donate salvage of all kinds, to be used as we see fit. Indeed, we are grateful. Too, we enjoy gathering talent from the personnel and producing shows." (15)

In April of 1944, an art show was held in town hosted by the Red Cross Unit at the 67th General Hospital. The hospital sent exhibits. Little Jenny and her accompanist came along with Miss Ward's father, who also sang in some of the programs put on for the patients.

In the first quarter of 1944, the Detachment basketball team won the local league championship (Championship of the Southern District, U.K. Base) and received a trophy. (4) Additionally, bull dozers from a nearby engineering regiment leveled off the field in the rear of the Detachment and made it into an athletic field. The Detachment Medical Department had a baseball team which played several games with other organizations, and a swimming team which entered in the contests sponsored by Southern Base Section. (16) The plans were to use the field for tents if the expansion program went into effect.

Also, during the first quarter of 1944, the Special Service gave the personnel Sunday trips to Dunster Castle, Cheddar Caves, and the Cathedrals at Wells and Glastonbury. A cooking school was begun in the Unit during this time as well. (17)

Glastonbury Ruins, the Purported Burial Site of King Arthur
Photograph by and Courtesy Ted Benedict

National holidays were celebrated appropriately. On 17 June 1944, a detachment of 100 men from the 67th General Hospital participated in a "Salute the Soldier" parade with other American and British organizations. (16)

The invasion caused a loss of volunteers in the hospital. In July, 1944, two volunteers, wives of British Army officers, who had been posted elsewhere, had to leave. Another had a houseful of relatives evacuated from London that she had to deal with, and yet another left to be with a daughter whose husband was in Normandy. The process continued to find replacement volunteers to work in the library and elsewhere. (18) In addition, the work load increased substantially, curtailing many of the extra-curricular activities which had been enjoyed prior to 6 June 1944.

Through Special Services, moving pictures were shown three times weekly in the post theater, and also on the wards for bed patients. Many U.S.O. and E.N.S.A. shows were presented in the post theater, as well as several vocal and instrumental concerts. During 1944, 358 films were shown (204 educational and 154 recreational), 20 U.S.O. or E.N.S.A. shows, 56 amateur performances, 6 mass discussions of current topics, 16 bands and concerts--nine of which were contributed by the band of the Devonshire Regiment. (16)

Nurses and other officers held dances monthly and sometimes more frequently. One of the three neighboring military organizations held dances the other weeks. Guests would often include members of other military units, including the U.S. Army Air Corps. (21) Dances were held twice monthly for the enlisted personnel. (16) The British population continued to entertain individuals or small groups of all ranks in their homes. (24)

The Unit had many opportunities for increasing its general knowledge of events and local history in 1944. Lectures were given to patients and personnel through the British Ministry of Information and other sources on many subjects of political, geographical, and historical interest. Short courses were given at universities and some took advantage of them.

Members of the Surgical Service took an active part in district meetings of hospitals during 1944. In the early months of 1944, hospitals in the district of the 67th General Hospital held monthly meetings in rotation and with the formation of the 1st Hospital Group (Prov), later the 801st Medical Service Detachment (Hospital Center). Monthly meetings were rotated among the various hospitals, and the first meeting was held at Musgrove Hospital. (20)

In October and November of 1944, the Red Cross report included activities involving the community:

> "With Special Service curtain and physio-therapy screens our hall was converted into Hollywood's little theater. The occasion was a skit put on by our local Air Raid Patrol center in our town. A retired English colonel wrote up the skit, in the form of a burlesque on their really serious job. The same set up was used for our 'Juvenile Review' with 24 youngsters from a dancing school near here."

In December of 1944, a theater party was given for 100 "evacuee" children from London who attended one of the Taunton council schools. (20)

On 8 May 1945, celebrations took place in the United States and throughout Great Britain. This was the day after the unconditional surrender of all German forces by General Alfred Jodl, Chief-of-Staff of the German Armed Forces High Command, aptly named Victory in Europe or VE Day. In Taunton, VE Day was celebrated with a civic service on a dais in Castle Green and a day later with sports, dancing, singing and parades in Vivary Park. (21) Flags of England, the United States and Russia covered the buildings on the streets of Taunton. (22)

Flags Hanging From the Castle Hotel on VE Day
Photograph By and Courtesy of Ted Benedict

Flags Hanging From Taunton Shops on VE Day
Photograph by and Courtesy of Ted Benedict

Liberation of Europe was the goal, but liberation of another sort took place at another time when a number of Taunton citizens were convicted of "liberating" thousands of sheets from the Supply Depot at Norton Manor. (21).

During the last few months at Musgrove Hospital, the Special Service was particularly active. There were many opportunities to take tours to nearby points of interest--for both patients and personnel. British homes extended their hospitality and a baseball diamond, a second tennis court and two volleyball courts became available. Softball games were arranged with other nearby American hospitals between corresponding groups of officers, nurses and enlisted men.

Following VE Day and prior to the departure of the 67th General Hospital from Taunton, the "Somerset Gazette" put out a special edition lauding the 67th for its accomplishments and to note the affection in which it was held by townspeople. The Taunton Rotary Club then had Colonel Moore as their guest which gave him an opportunity to thank the town and return their compliments. (21)

References

(1) Personal communication with Betsy Larson Crumrine, Red Cross Worker in 67th General Hospital.

(2) "Reports to the Red Cross from the Red Cross Unit Assigned to the 67th General Hospital. Narrative and Recreation Report for January 1943." National Archives.

(3) "Reports to the Red Cross from the Red Cross Unit Assigned to the 67th General Hospital. Narrative and Recreation Report for March, 1943." National Archives.

(4) Hinton, David J. *An Illustrated Social History of Bishops Lydeard and Cothelstone.* Published by The Rocket Publishing Co., Ltd., and Printed by Taunton Printing Company.

(5) "Historical Report of 1943 to the Chief Surgeon, SOS, ETOUSA." From R.B. Moore, Colonel, Medical Corps, Commanding Officer, 67th General Hospital, APO 511, Dated 31 January 1944. National Archives.

(6) "Reports to the Red Cross from the Red Cross Unit Assigned to the 67th General Hospital. Narrative and Recreation Report for February and March, 1945." National Archives.

(7) "Reports to the Red Cross from the Red Cross Unit Assigned to the 67th General Hospital. Narrative and Recreation Report for May, 1943." National Archives.

(8) "Reports to the Red Cross from the Red Cross Unit Assigned to the 67th General Hospital. Narrative and Recreation Report for June, 1943." National Archives.

(9) "Reports to the Red Cross from the Red Cross Unit Assigned to the 67th General Hospital. Narrative and Recreation Report for August, 1943." National Archives.

(10) "Reports to the Red Cross from the Red Cross Unit Assigned to the 67th General Hospital. Narrative and Recreation Report for September, 1943." National Archives.

(11) "Reports to the Red Cross from the Red Cross Unit Assigned to the 67th General Hospital. Narrative and Recreation Report for November, 1943." National Archives.

(12) "Reports to the Red Cross from the Red Cross Unit Assigned to the 67th General Hospital. Narrative and Recreation Report for December, 1943." National Archives.

(13) "Monthly Sanitation Report to the Commanding Officer, 67th General Hospital, APO 511." Dated 2 January 1943. U.S. Army. Signed by Merrill S.F. Greene, Major, Medical Corps, Medical Inspector. National Archives.

(14) "History of the 67th General Hospital 1 December 1942, till 31 December 1943." Dated 1 January 1944. National Archives, Washington, D.C.

(15) "Reports to the Red Cross from the Red Cross Unit Assigned to the 67th General Hospital. Narrative and Recreation Report for January, 1944." National Archives.

(16) "Historical Report of 1943 to the Chief Surgeon, SOS, ETOUSA from R.B. Moore, Colonel, Medical Corps, Commanding Officer, 67th General Hospital, APO 511." Dated 31 January 1944. National Archives.

(17) "History Memorandum to Base Section Historian, APO 519, U.S. Army." Dated 7 April 1944. National Archives.

(18) "Reports to the Red Cross from the Red Cross Unit Assigned to the 67th General Hospital. Narrative and Recreation Report for July, 1944." National Archives.

(19) "Lewiston Journal; Magazine Section." Saturday, October 25, 1969. Courtesy Betsy Larson Crumrine.

(20) "Semi-annual Report, Medical Department Activities, 67th General Hospital to the Surgeon General, Washington, D.C." Dated 15 June 1945. National Archives.

(21) Bush, Robin. *A Taunton Diary 1787-1987. Two Centuries of gossip, scandal, success and calamity in darkest Somerset.* Buckingham, England: Barracuda Books Limited, 1988.

(22) Photographs Courtesy Ted Benedict and Raymond Bungard in Possession of Author.

(23) Program in Author's Collection.

(24) "Annual Report to the Chief Surgeon, SOS, ETOUSA, APO 887, U.S. Army." Dated 31 January 1944. National Archives.

Chapter 14
Having Left Taunton

The 67th General Hospital officially ceased admitting patients to Musgrove Military Hospital at 2400 hours, 31 May 1945, at which time the four remaining patients were evacuated from the hospital. (2) All wards and buildings were stripped of property and supplies were returned to the appropriate depots. All other property, except that allotted by T/O and T/E, was turned over to the British authorities and the Hospital Plant was finally relinquished on 15 June 1945.

Loading Into Buses to Leave Musgrove Military Hospital
Photograph by Courtesy of Ted Benedict

The 67th General Hospital assumed command and operation of the 4116 Hospital Plant at Benbow Barracks, Pimperne, Dorset, on 9 June 1945.

Interviews of parties in the know reveal that after the 67th General Hospital departed, some of the movable items left behind, such as flagstone and other items, were removed by the local citizens to edge their gardens and in general improve their own lifestyle. Musgrove Military

Hospital was used as a convalescent facility for British troops for some time after the war. It was taken over by the County Council and the Ministry of Pensions in early 1946, and now is a major hospital, Taunton and Somerset Musgrove Park Hospital, a part of the National Health Service Trust. (6, 28)

Camp Blandford

Benbow Barracks, Pimperne, Dorset

An advance party from the 67th General Hospital was sent to the U.S. Hospital Plant 4116, at Camp Blandford, on 1 June 1945. (4) Most of the remainder of the Unit followed on 8 June 1945, and the 67th General Hospital assumed command and operation of Hospital Plant 4116 at Benbow Barricks, Pimperne, Dorset, on 9 June 1945. Except for transportation, all Unit equipment had been left at Musgrove Military Hospital, in Taunton. The Unit inherited the equipment left by the 131st General Hospital, the Unit that was being relieved. The Plant was under the administrative command of the 802nd Hospital Center, later succeeded by the 805th Hospital Center. (1)

Photograph by and Courtesy of Raymond Bungard

The administration of the Post was handled by the Hospital Center which the 67th General Hospital did not have to assume, and this partially compensated for the loss of personnel it had experienced.

The hospital facility occupied by the 67th General Hospital covered 25 acres which was only a small portion of the total area occupied by the 802nd Hospital Center. The buildings covering the majority of the land were of the usual converted British barracks type, arranged in six "spiders" of six wards each. The hospital also had separate buildings for supply, mess, quarters, etc.. The I and E Building was well-equipped and there was an excellent library supplied with 2000 new books as well as the regular text books issued for education courses. Additionally, the hospital featured a large gymnasium, as well as tennis courts, baseball and soft ball diamonds and the men took advantage of all these facilities while they were at the 802nd Hospital Center.

4116 Hospital Plant at Benbow Barracks, Pimperne, Dorset (Camp Blandford)
Photograph by and Courtesy of Raymond Bungard

Patient load gradually diminished there as the war casualties needing the care of a General Hospital decreased, and the men, thus freed of the care of a large patient load, had more opportunity to take part in recreational activities and trips of educational interest to nearby areas. Bournemouth was a popular destination because of its proximity.

Ballgame at Blandford
Photograph by and Courtesy Ted Benedict

Patients continued to be treated at Benbow Barracks and upon arrival, the 67th General Hospital inherited 621 patients who had been under the care of the 131st General Hospital. Between 8 June 1945, and 17 July 1945, there were 311 patients admitted, of whom 92 were surgical and 357 medical. The total number of patients treated in this time period, which included previous patients and new admissions, was 932, of whom 575 were surgical and 357 were medical. Of this total, 64 were returned to duty, and 864 were transferred to other hospitals. Of those transferred to other hospitals, 150 men were sent to the Zone of the Interior. Calculations would suggest that four men were unaccounted for were left at the hospital. No deaths occurred among the patients while the Unit was there.

Fourth of July at Blandford
Photograph Courtesy Ted Benedict

Apparently, not all was peaches and cream. Richard Smith, T5 wrote to his mother on 2 August 1945:

> "Our rations have been cut 10%. It was rotten before that. Momma don't let this worry you any but don't plan on me being at home for several months yet. Of course we haven't had any information to that effect, but it looks to reason according to all the shifting around and again I could be at home in one month but not likely. I had rather you and Bess wouldn't send me any more packages unless I know for sure that I'll be here for some time." (2)

Of interest, between 8 June 1945, and 17 August 1945, 54 Russian patients were treated at Hospital Plant 4116 for pulmonary tuberculosis; of these, 18 had active pulmonary tuberculosis requiring isolation and special nursing care. They were all evacuated to Russia before the 67th General Hospital left Benbow Barracks. After the 67th General Hospital left, the hospital was closed and all equipment was returned to the depot. (4)

War Is Over, Japan Surrenders

On 14 August 1945, Japan surrendered unconditionally. The World War was over, peace was at hand.

Fairford Park, Gloucestershire (Hospital Plant 4118)

The 67th General Hospital was moved again on 17 August 1945, to Fairford Park, Gloucestershire, where it took over Hospital Plant Number 4118, from the 186th General Hospital. An advance party had gone ahead on 13 August to prepare for the arrival. (4) The facilities of the Hospital Plant 4118 were emptied of patients and turned over by the 67th General Hospital, the 187th General Hospital and the 312th Station Hospital for staging purposes. All equipment had again been turned into the supply depots except for transportation. The type of construction was new to the Unit, but the condition of the buildings was admirable. The hospital grounds had 110 beautifully landscaped acres with well-kept lawns and flowers, making it one of the most attractive hospital sites in England. Buildings were Nissen huts, constructed of brick and there were many supply buildings. There was a relatively small patient load which made administration simple despite a high turn-over of officers and enlisted men. Upon arrival, the 67th General Hospital inherited 113 patients from the 186th General Hospital. Admissions between 18 August 1945, and 28 August 1945, totaled 128 men, 50 being surgical and 78 being medical. Of this total of 241 patients, 45 were returned to duty, 40 were transferred to the Zone of the Interior and on 28 August 1945, 156 patients remained in the hospital to be cared for by the 93rd General Hospital, which followed the 67th General Hospital, and replaced them at the facility.

At the above facilities, no fresh battle casualties were admitted. The patients were transferred from other hospitals or received directly from command. Most of the patients were seen in the dispensary and came from a number of units being staged in the area as well as from the American University at Shrivenham. (4) The out-patient department in each Hospital Plant was active and averaged from 40 to 100 patients daily. Most of these were minor cases and required only 1 to 3 treatments. The Dental Outpatient Department was particularly busy and had 282 admissions, with 1274 sittings; 52 dentures were furnished and 41 repaired, in addition to 564 fillings of all types.

Large numbers of personnel changes occurred. The Executive Officer, Adjutant and three Chiefs of Services were lost due to the readjustment program. There were no German prisoners available for the work they had done at Taunton, but with the lighter work load, it did not prove to be a problem. (4)

They remained at Fairford Park for only eleven days.

Cirencester Park, Gloucestershire

On 28 August 1945, under Movement Order Number 2906 dated 27 August 1945, the 67th General Hospital again changed their post, this time to Cirencester Park, Site No. 2, Cirencester, Gloucestershire, to stage for return to the United States. The facility at Fairford Park was turned over, along with patients and facilities, to the 93rd General Hospital as well as equipment and supplies not turned into the proper supply depots. The MEE (Minimal Essential Equipment) required for overseas movement was retained. A small portion of the plant formerly occupied by the 192nd General Hospital was assigned to the 67th General Hospital. Three other units were already staging at the same post when the 67th General Hospital arrived. Only two small buildings were available for Headquarters, and three sheds of moderate size were available for supply. This created a rather crowded facility for the staging. Bathing facilities were overcrowded due to the large number of other troops staging there. Food and mess equipment were in short supply and rations were adequate but lacking in variety.

No patients were admitted and medical activities were limited to health inspections, sick call and the work at the Post Dispensary was done by the 67th General Hospital with assistance of the 231st Station
Hospital and the 347th Station Hospital. All personnel received a dental survey at this time, also.

Upon arrival at Cirencester, an extensive rearrangement of personnel began which included the return to the Unit of most of the members of the original 67th General Hospital who had been assigned or attached during the previous thirty-two months. The readiness date for the Unit was 4 September, but there was a delay because of the transfer in of numerous personnel, mostly enlisted, which delayed the inspection by the Inspector General until 11 September. (4) Additionally, over 300 new members with high ASR (Adjusted Service Rating) scores were assigned to complete the roster, in accordance with T/O 8-550. These men also had to be clothed, equipped and their personnel records completed, requiring an immense amount of administrative work.

Toward the end of the war, the ASR was one of the major considerations as to which men should be sent home and when.

> "During this period the situation was further complicated by the necessity for a general reconsideration of all personnel assignments. The fact that a man with 18 months' service was surplus in Europe did not justify his release from active duty if men with 36 months' service were still being held in the Pacific, and it was essential that there be established a basis for the equitable discharge or reassignment of all Medical Department personnel regardless of current place of duty. This was accomplished by an 'adjusted service rating' (ASR) scored on the following credits:
>
> | | |
> |---|---|
> | Each month of service since 1 September 1940 | 1 point |
> | Each month of overseas service (in addition to points for total service) | 1 point |
> | Each combat decoration | 5 points |
> | Each child under 18 (maximum of 3) | 12 points |
>
> (ASR scores were first calculated as of 12 May 1945; they were later adjusted as of 2 September 1945.)
>
> On the basis of the ASR, personnel overseas were divided into the following categories:
>
> 1. Men with the fewest points were put in units bound directly for the Pacific.
>
> 2. Men with slightly more points were put in units bound for the Pacific after a stopover for furloughs and training in the United States.

3. Men in the median ASR categories were returned to the United States for assignment to a strategic reserve for duty in the Pacific when and if needed.

4. Men in the moderately high point categories were held in Europe for occupation duties until eligible for release from the Army.

5. Highest point men were to be returned to the United States for immediate discharge." (7)

While at Cirencester Park, **Organization Day** was celebrated on 1 September 1945, the Third Anniversary of the Activation of the Unit.

Richard Smith, who had been on detached duty in Reading, wrote these letters to his wife, Bessie from Circencester on 30 August 1945:

"**...**as you see I'm at a new place again I was called off my dispensary job and now I'm sweating out the best news that I ever expect to hear but don't know how soon but Bess I can most assure you I'll see you within one months time and It's possible sooner but things can always be changed...

Well dearest I got here yesterday afternoon and I pulled guard duty this afternoon for six hours I don't like it but we are so short of men now but its so foolish and it rained mostly all day its awful wet and cold here for its been very nice at Readings. I like to of starved there I was mighty glad to get something to eat we had good fried chicken today at noon but not as good if they were fresh...

Sweetheart I'll still continue to write by the time you get this letter I could be on my way home so to make you feel more certain don't write until I'm sure I'll have time to get it before I'm leaving here I hope you have sent your phone number just wait until I get to a phone and say I'm in the good old U.S.A. and just to think as I can see it now I've enough of points to get out. Oh Sweetheart before I start shouting I had better close and save my breath to tell you how much I've missed you all this time. If that could be possible for me to do I'll close for now and always loving you as ever yours Your Husband

Richard Smith

1945 September (Date is not certain, but was probably written 9 September.)

Well I pulled six hours guard duty today. It isn't so nice when its raining right down but surely it won't be long until I can get off of it or get started home. Rumors are flying every way but honest I don't know any thing for sure but my opinion is won't be but for a very short time I still have hopes of seeing you before the month is all gone.

I got a typhoid shot yesterday my arm sure is sore and its been making me feel pretty tough too. I hope it isn't so hot there now and that you haven't had any bad storms. I read about the one in the valley. I wouldn't mind seeing a good thunder storm for a change. I guess every one is celebrating there today VJ day. I can see that there is any change here than any other day in fact every thing on the big day passed off pretty quiet about all one ever hears around here is someone says I'll be glad to get home and get a discharge and me with them ha ha.

Looks as though I'll be broke when I hit the states while I was on Detach service I had to borrow money to eat on and I won't get that back until I get back to the U.S.A. Of course I'll have enough to get along with it wont take much for me. We have a movie in our kitchen tonight. Falcon of Hollywood if you were here I could take you to the movie but I guess I'll go by myself didn't sleep so well either I didn't get up for breakfast I stayed in bed until 9:30…This is Monday morning my shot in the arm is still bothering me some. I still think that we'll be home by the last of the month it will depend on what sort of a ship it takes a long time on some of them…with love, yours,

Richard Smith" (5)

T5 Richard Smith was assigned to a venereal disease clinic in Reading, near London, although the exact time frame of this activity is not clear. Apparently, he returned to the 67th General Hospital while they were in Circencester, to join his Unit. He made application for the money he had needed to borrow while on detached duty and received a refund of his expenses after he returned to the States.

The rapidly decreasing patient census allowed the I and E Program to begin in earnest. Despite the quick receipt of movement order to the United States, many officers and men were able to complete courses in the United Kingdom and on the Continent. Also, classes and group discussions were held on the post, and all who desired were given an opportunity to participate. Due to the constant change in personnel, a regular schedule of training was carried out so far as possible, and emphasis was placed upon "refresher courses" in basic training school of the soldier, military courtesy, etc..

The proximity of Oxford and Stratford-on-Avon, and other interesting places close to Fairford and Cirencester, allowed frequent trips under the direction of the Special Service Officer, and liberal use was made of passes and furloughs. Athletic contests among personnel of the 67th General Hospital as well as between other units and hospitals were encouraged, and most importantly, there was plenty of time to enjoy these activities. The Post Exchange of the 347th Station Hospital was utilized by the men of the 67th when needed.

On 4 July 1945, an enlisted man from the Detachment Medical was killed and another seriously injured on an unauthorized trip and a Board of Inquiry investigation rendered its report.

On 9 September 1945, all transportation was finally turned in to the 231st Station Hospital, and the 67th General Hospital made preparations for shipment to the United States. All Unit property except Minimum Essential Equipment was turned in to supply depots. Enlisted personnel were furnished with necessary clothing and equipment, reception center rosters and passenger lists were prepared, baggage was inspected and sealed and all other required processing was done as directed by ETO-SOP No. 61 (ETO-POM-RED). Inspection by the Inspector General's

Department was performed on 10 September 1945, and the Unit was declared ready for overseas shipment at any time after that date. All hold baggage was sent to the Port of Embarkation on 18 September 1945. On 13 September, 10 officers were redeployed on the basis of their point score and 10 replacements arrived by the 15th of September and were quickly processed. (4) They had been at Cirencester for less than one month.

Some men did not follow the 67th General Hospital on its tour through the English countryside as it left Taunton. Sergeant Ted Benedict was assigned to take charge of closing down a General Hospital near Southampton, although he had applied for an assignment in France, taking university courses. By 4 September, the baggage had been inspected and sealed and a shipping roster had been sent in to U.K. base. The Queen Mary rested serenely in her berth in Southampton, as the 67th General Hospital marched into the bowels of the ship. The Unit departed from Southampton on 22 September 1945. (4)

References

(1) "Period Report, Medical Department Activities, 19 September 1945, for the 67th General Hospital." National Archives.

(2) Letter from Richard Smith T5 to his mother, Maude Kitchens, on 2 August 1945.

(3) Communication with Ted Benedict.

(4) "Historical Data of 67th General Hospital for First Quarter 1945--January, February, March, April to 8th May, 1945." National Archives.

(5) Letters from Richard Smith to his wife Bessie, from Cirencester, England.

(6) http://www.somerset-health.org.uk/t

Chapter 15
Going Home

The entire command was given a physical inspection on 21 September 1945, and the Unit boarded the Queen Mary in Southampton, her home port in the south of England, on the English Channel, on 22 September 1945, for departure to New York. (4) Prior to the end of the war, the Queen Mary had not been docking at Southampton, due to security issues, primarily its vulnerability to German air attacks from bases in France. With the war in Europe at an end, this danger was no longer of concern, and the Queen Mary was able to depart from its home port.

Some members of the 67th General Hospital were allowed to return to the States earlier than others. Betsy Larson (Crumrine), a member of the original Red Cross Unit, left in January, 1945, on the Queen Elizabeth. Others who had been in the 67th General Hospital were allowed to leave earlier, also. Some were transferred to other units. Mildred Butler, ANC transferred out of the 67th and crossed back to the United States, on the Queen Mary, prior to the departure of the 67th General Hospital. Most, however, remained with the Unit and left England together.

Queen Mary at Berth Prior to the Boarding of the 67th General Hospital
Photograph by and Courtesy of Raymond Bungard

The passenger list of the 67th General Hospital showed 53 male officers, 1 male warrant officer, 85 female nurses, 3 female hospital dietitians, three female physical therapy aides, 2 female American Red Cross personnel, and 436 enlisted men. (3) They were only a small part of the passenger manifest for the H.M.S. Queen Mary, leaving from the port of Southampton, on 23 September 1945.

Richard Smith saved his Berth Assignment Card and listed the names and addresses of his bunkmates.

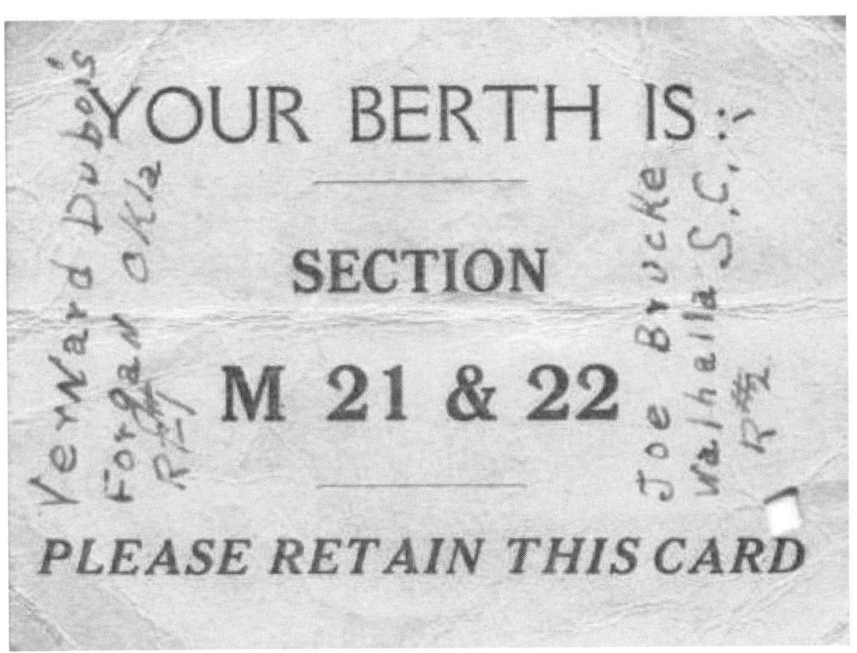

YOUR BERTH IS :-

SECTION

M 21 & 22

PLEASE RETAIN THIS CARD

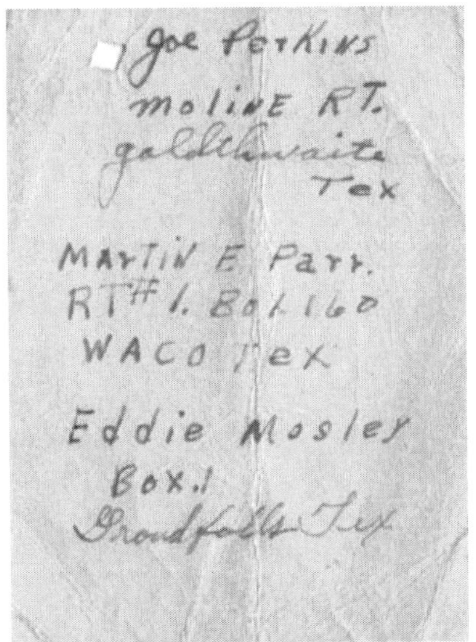

Joe Perkins
Moline RT.
Goldthwaite
Tex

Martin E. Parr.
RT#1. Box 160
WACO Tex

Eddie Mosley
Box 1
Grandfalls Tex

Berth Assignment Card (Bottom Card is the Reverse Side of the Top Card but Has Been Reduced in Size for Editing Purposes)
Collection of the Author

"The Queen Mary was constructed by John Brown and Company, Limited, Clydebank, Scotland, and launched 26 September 1934. She had her maiden voyage on 27 May 1936. She had an overall length of 1,019.5 feet, stood 181 feet from keel to forward smokestack top, had a gross weight of 81,237 gross tons, had a cruising speed of 28.5 knots while consuming a gallon of fuel every 13 inches of forward progress, had 12 decks, carried 1,174 peacetime officers and crew and 1,957 peacetime passengers. It arrived in Long Beach, California, on 9 December 1967, after its last voyage and ownership was turned over to the City of Long Beach." (5) The mileage calculates out to .92 gallons per foot or 4873.8 gallons per mile or .0002052 Miles per Gallon (MPG).

Post Card of the Queen Mary
Courtesy Raymond Bungard

First Sergeant Joe Bullock still remembers that the rails of the Queen Mary were carved and chipped, whereas the rails of the Queen Elizabeth, early in the war, on the way over had been smooth and pristine. (9) It was good judgment for the Cunard Line to remove the carpets and decorative ornamentation before allowing the hundreds of thousands of bored soldiers to cross the Atlantic in their ships.

Sunset Over the Atlantic from the Queen Mary
Photograph by and Courtesy of Ted Benedict

The trip home must have been as crowded as the trip made to England, on the Queen Elizabeth, but the passengers were in much higher spirits. Ted Benedict recalled that on the way home, bunks were placed in the dry swimming pool, with stacks of fifteen high on the deep end. (10) Gone were the zig-zag maneuvers, the dark-outs, the radio silence and the worry of the men about their ultimate survival. In its place was the euphoria they must have felt knowing that their long absence away from their families was finally coming to an end and of a job well-done.

The Queen Mary, under the command of Captain Fall, on a voyage designated as WW#54W, crossed the Atlantic with an average speed of 26.84 knots, traveling 3,131 miles, carrying 14,803 troops, 161 passengers, and 834 crew, with a landing in New York City, on 28 September 1945. (2) An Associated Press newspaper article from the Wichita Falls, Texas, newspaper, *The Wichita Falls Times Record*, stated that the Queen Mary was carrying 14,512 troops including the 254th and 255th Infantry regiments of the 63rd Division; 67th General Hospital; 3000 air corps personnel; 91WACs; 91 nurses; and 279 naval personnel. On the same day, the Santa Maria, the Walter Raleigh and the U.S. Victory arrived in Boston, carrying troops and the Hawaii Shipper arrived in Newport News also carrying troops. (7)

The ship was met by a welcome-home boat complete with girls and band, as it came into the harbor. Signal flags, which few could read or understand, flew from lines on the welcoming boats accompanying them to port.

Welcome Home Launch in New York Harbor Photograph by and Courtesy of Ted Benedict

The piers were adorned in red, white and blue colored buntings. Despite the desire of the troops on the Queen Mary to stand again on American soil, it took several hours from the time they glimpsed the Statue of Liberty in New York Harbor until they marched off the ship. The time needed for the tugs to move the ship to the Cunard Pier at the New York Passenger Ship Terminal on the west side of Manhattan Island, must have seemed like an eternity.

Cunard Pier, New York City Photograph by and Courtesy of Ted Benedict

Raymond Bungard recalled:

"The Statue of Liberty and N.Y. skyline was a welcome sight on our return with flagged escort boats blowing their horns to welcome us home. (11)

View of the Statue of Liberty from the Queen Mary
Photograph by and Courtesy Raymond Bungard

"By the end of the war, the Queen Mary had carried 765,429 military personnel and traveled 569,429 miles, carrying up to 15,000 troops at one time while carrying wounded back to the United States on out-bound voyages. Additionally it transported Winston Churchill three times to conferences and at the end of the war carried 12,886 G.I brides and children, all the time doing it in style." (5) The total gas consumption based on the need for one gallon of fuel per 13 inches of forward motions would have been 2,775,169,174 gallons of fuel for her wartime voyages. Billions of dollars at current prices would have been spent on her fuel.

Camp Kilmer--Again

The men could not simply hop off the ship and go home when they arrived at the Port of New York. That would not be the Army way at all. They marched off the Queen Mary and returned to Camp Kilmer, from whence they came. Other troops entering New York Harbor went to Camp Shanks, near Orangeburg, N.Y. or to Fort Hamilton in Brooklyn. The Port of New York was processing 250,000 returning soldiers per month at that time. The men of the 67th General Hospital were assigned to a Disposition area (one of 10) at Camp Kilmer and assigned a barracks number. They were met by a band and a welcoming orientation program, and were told to stay together as a group to facilitate their processing. After the processing they were encouraged to check in frequently with the unit commander until their departure was set.

The men were urged to get a haircut, have their uniforms cleaned, mended and made to look their best so that when finally released they would present a positive image of the military to the civilians with whom they came in contact. They were reminded to continue acting like soldiers by paying proper military courtesy to the officers they encountered--with a salute. When they went to the mess, they were required to take their knife, fork and spoon. The officers did not have to do this, but had to pay 25 cents when they ate. They were warned not to ship any of their GI issue equipment back home and cautioned to make sure their souvenirs were rendered harmless. Their baggage was delivered to their Disposition area and they were required to turn in unnecessary equipment such as gas masks, helmets and protective clothing.

Cigarettes were referred to as "coffin nails" by the Port Authority, but despite this, the arriving soldiers were given a tobacco rationing slip good for one carton of cigarettes, and told that upon arrival at their Reception Station they would be given a regular Army tobacco ration card good for six packages of cigarettes a week which would be good until 29 October 1945. (8)

There had been a rumor that the Unit would be shipped to China, after they left England. This rumor was based on the indisputable fact that the 67th General Hospital had not been moved from their original base at Musgrove Military Hospital, to follow the troops advancing in battles across Europe as many General Hospitals, which were once stationed in England, had done. The rumor said that the assignment came from resentment in the Army command of cancellation of two previous orders for such a move resulting from influence from the powerful Maine Senator,

Ralph O. Brewster, a friend of some of the officers in the 67th General Hospital. Senator Brewster was a guest at the head table for their farewell dinner prior to the activation of the 67th General Hospital. Whether the rumor was true or not, the end of the war following the surrender of Japan eliminated the need of any further service by the 67th General Hospital.

Telegram and telephone facilities were provided at Camp Kilmer, and Richard Smith elected to send a telegram home.

ARRIVED SAFELY. EXPECT TO SEE YOU SOON DON'T ATTEMPT TO CONTACT OR WRITE ME HERE. LOVE RICHARD F SMITH

The message was delivered at 7:58 P.M. 28 September 1945. (6)

Muster Out Photograph of the Nurses
Photograph in Collection of the Author

Above: Muster Out Photograph of the Officers and Detachment Medical
Photograph in Collection of the Author

Photographs of the Unit were made, orders were received and the soldiers of the 67th General Hospital shipped out to their respective Reception Stations (of which there were 51 across the country) for mustering out. Some were sent home by airplane--primarily to the west coast but the majority of the returning soldiers traveled by train. Ted Benedict recalled flying home and needing to wear his Army overcoat because it was so cold at ten thousand feet altitude and then descending to Albuquerque, where the temperature was almost one hundred degrees. (10) The soldiers used their traveling orders to obtain railway tickets to their respective Reception Stations. (9)

Richard Smith was sent by train to Fort Sam Houston in San Antonio, Texas, where he received an Honorable Discharge from the Army. He had been in the Army for 3 years, 4 months and 20 days. When he walked into his mother's wooden frame house in Wichita Falls, Texas, he took his dog tags from around his neck, and draped them over a nail protruding from the wall behind the door, where they remained for the next 23 years.

The war was over and the men of the 67th General Hospital were home. Like any history, there is no final end just as there is no true beginning. Ted Benedict returned home, was married and finished college on the G.I. Bill, eventually earning a Ph.D. from USC in speech. Raymond Bungard used the G.I. Bill to obtain his medical degree from Loma Linda and became a practicing surgeon. He worked felling trees between school sessions. He currently works part time at the VA hospital in Boise, Idaho. Betsy Crumrine lived in Ohio, on her husband's family farm and still does volunteer work for the Red Cross. Richard Smith resumed his mechanic work, eventually opened a garage and tractor dealership of his own and encouraged his children to pursue a university education and all did. Joe Bullock returned to Texas, earned his degree with the assistance of the G.I. Bill taught school in El Paso, for 28 years, and served as assistant principal at Burgess Junior High School and Messita Elementary School. C.L. Robberson used his experience in the operating room to decide not to be a doctor and when he returned to Oklahoma, he became a teacher, and then principal in Ada, where he retired after 35 years of teaching. Most of the doctors returned home to Maine, and resumed their medical practices. Others pursued medical specialties, including Dr. Maynard Colley, who became an anesthesiologist after the war.

Many who were in the 67th General Hospital returned to their previous lives, only to find that they would never be the same, that the world had changed and that they had changed. The GI Bill allowed men of few means to pursue a college degree and even advanced degrees at little or no cost to them. This enabled them to get an education which was beyond their reach before the war began. Men who returned to the farm were able to acquire formal training in agriculture to improve the performance of their farms and ranches. The overall effect was to elevate the economic and intellectual level of the country. There were other effects of the war, especially in the relationship between races and the acceptance of the woman as more of an equal to a man, since many women had been doing a man's job while they were at war. The industry and commerce of the United States was intact at the end of the war. There was no need to rebuild a devastated infrastructure, and because of this, it was ahead of the rest of the world economically.

The economic stimulation of the War dissipated the Great Depression. The War for many reasons served as a catapult to propel the United States to the position it now holds in the world.

Most of the men and women who served in the 67th General Hospital—all part of the Greatest Generation now have grandchildren, or even great-grandchildren, who are the same age as they once were when they marched into the side of the Queen Elizabeth, and sailed to the greatest adventure of their lives. What do these children have to look forward to that will have an equivalent impact on their lives and on their country?

References

(1) Personal communication with Betsy Larson Crumrine.

(2) Harding, Steve. *Gray Ghost: The R.M.S. Queen Mary at War.* Missoula, Montana: Published by Pictorial Histories Publishing Company.

(3) "Unit Recapitulation Passenger List for Unit Service Number RE 7355-KK, the 67th (US) General Hospital." Courtesy First Sergeant Joe Bullock.

(4) "Period Report, Medical Department Activities to the Surgeon General." Dated 19 September 1945. (1945-2 Semiannual). National Archives.

(5) Brochure from Queen Mary, Long Beach, California. Collection of Author.

(6) Original Telegram Sent from Richard Smith to Wife Bessie on 28 September 1945. Collection of Author.

(7) Newspaper Clipping. Collection of Author.

(8) "NYPE News Special Edition for Overseas Veterans". Collection of Author.

(9) Personal Communication with First Sergeant Joe Bullock.

(10) Personal Communication with Ted Benedict.

(11) Personal communication with Raymond Bungard.

Epilogue

The doctors and nurses of the 67th General Hospital volunteered for an experience that training did not totally prepare them to fulfill. The enlisted men, for the most part, were drafted and put into a totally foreign environment and asked to learn and do things that they would never have imagined in their lifetime. But it did work, and a statement from *Voices of War* sums up the reason it did work.

> "So how did these new soldiers manage to accommodate themselves to a life they'd never known before? There is one theme common to every veteran's experience: a determination to see it through. Serving in wartime always involves a personal mission of some kind. It may be a yearning to succeed; it may also involve a quest to bring some clarity to an unfocused life. And for some recruits, determination may also be as simple as making the best out of a perplexing, frustrating, grueling, and sometimes discouraging experience."(1)

The 67th General Hospital treated approximately 24,000 patients during its time in England, with only 71 deaths. This was a remarkable achievement. Of all the men evacuated from the Continent, less than one percent died of their injuries after reaching England. No one faced blazing guns or faced death to accomplish their mission. No one was able to turn their wartime escapades into a Hollywood career or seek high public office from notoriety gained from their time serving the 67th General Hospital. By serving on a day-to-day basis, quietly doing what they had been trained to do, and doing it well, the 67th General Hospital did its part to facilitate the final outcome of the war.

References

(1) Wiener, Tom, Editor. *Voices of War (The Library of Congress Veterans History Project).* National Geographic Society, Washington, D.C. 2006.

67TH GENERAL HOSPITAL

Appendix One
Rosters of Personnel

Roster of Personnel as of 31 December 1942 (4)

(Allotted by T/O 8-550, WD 1 April 1942)

	Authorized	Assigned
Commissioned		
Medical Corps	41	42
Dental Corps	5	6
Medical Administrative Corps	7	6
Quartermaster Corps	2	2
Corps of Chaplains	2	2
Army Nurse Corps	105	106
Warrant Officers	1	1
Physiotherapy Aides	3	2
Hospital Dietitians	3	2
Enlisted Men	500	492
American Red Cross		5

"All of the personnel with the possible exception of about three percent of the enlisted men were considered suitable for the duties expected of them. Those excepted were illiterate or did not speak sufficient English to carry out difficult or involved commands or to read written orders. It was felt that the remaining personnel with further training would make an excellent organization. It was felt that more experienced clerical workers would greatly increase the efficiency of all departments." (4)

There were no civilian employees in the hospital other than physiotherapy aides and dietitians. The recommendation was made to employ British civilians as maids in nurses' quarters, gardeners, painters, carpenters, etc. Authorization had been requested at the time of the annual report of 1942." (4)

"In August of 1943, there were two cadres of the Detachment Medical who were used elsewhere to guard hospitals." (6)

"The Annual Report for 1943, suggested that a third dietitian would lighten the load imposed upon two dietitians. A breakdown of the civilian workers showed 1 foreman,

2 stenographers, 3 typists, 5 storekeepers, 6 telephone operators, 1 file clerk, 1 plumber, 1 plumber's mate, 3 gardeners, 2 painters, 1 seamstress and 16 stokers. Because of a ruling by the British Employment Office, this number of civilian employees was to be greatly reduced during the ensuing year." (15)

"Medical Staff Meetings and Clinical Conferences continued to be held regularly on a weekly basis. Medical officers were rotated in ward assignments and different services, so that they could fulfill multiple functions as the occasion arose." (2)

Roster of Personnel as of 31 December 1943 (1)

(Allotted by T/O 8-550, WD 1 April, 1942, as Amended by Cl 5 October, 1942.)

	Authorized	Assigned
Commissioned		
Medical Corps	41	41
Dental Corps	5	5
Medical Administrative Corps	8	7
Quartermaster Corps	2	2
Corps of Chaplains	2	2
Army Nurse Corps	100	103
Warrant Officers	1	1
Physiotherapy Aides	3	2
Hospital Dietitians	3	2
Enlisted Men	500	481
American Red Cross		5
British Civilians Employed		42

"A change was made to the Table of Organization (T/O 8550) on 3 July 1944. This change reduced the number of enlisted personnel to 450. This change coincided with the heaviest demands on the hospital following the D-Day invasion and resulted in long hours of work and careful adjustment to maintain previous standards of patient care. Additionally, many officers and enlisted men were needed to go on Detached Service or Temporary Duty with other units, and at times there were as many as fifty to sixty men absent for considerable periods. This resulted in the loss of many trained men who were replaced by 'limited duty' personnel from combat units who required training when everyone was already working at their utmost speed." (2)

"It was understood that a change in T/O would soon be effected, reducing the number of enlisted men to 450. This necessitated even more careful distribution of duties, as it was difficult to provide adequate coverage of the increased number of wards with properly trained enlisted personnel. The demands for personnel for D.S. (Detached Service) and T.D. (Temporary Duty) sometimes meant that as many as 62 men were absent for several weeks at a time. During the latter part of 1944, there was steady demand for men to be reassigned to combat duty and replaced by 'limited duty' personnel. As the replacements were wholly untrained in medical duties, it was difficult to train them at a time when wards were full and every individual was working to capacity. However, the men showed a willing spirit and an eagerness to learn so that the standard of nursing course suffered little, if any by the change. This reflected the situation reported in 1943." (2,3)

"In 1944, the British civilians employed included: 1 foreman, 3 stenographers, 7 telephone operators, 1 plumber, 1 plumber's mate, 4 gardeners, 1 painter, 2 seamstresses, and 14 stokers." (4)

Roster of Personnel as of 31 December 1944 (3)

(Allotted by T/O 8-550, WD 1 April, 1942, as Amended by Cl 5 October, 1942.)

	Authorized	Assigned
Commissioned		
Medical Corps	37	34
Dental Corps	5	5
Medical Administrative Corps	8	9
Quartermaster Corps	2	2
Corps of Chaplains	2	2
Army Nurse Corps	83	81
Warrant Officers	1	1
Physiotherapy Aides	3	2
Hospital Dietitians	3	3
Enlisted Men	492	480
American Red Cross	5	4
British Civilians Employed		34

"The officers, nurses and enlisted men remained basically intact until VE Day and by the end of the war, some were detached for duty elsewhere." (5)

References

(1) "Annual Report to the Chief Surgeon, SOS, ETOUSA, APO 887, U.S. Army." Dated 31 January 1944. National Archives.

(2) "Historical Report for 1 January to 31 December 1943, for the 67th General Hospital." Signed by Roland Moore, Colonel. Dated 31 January 1944. National Archives.

(3) "Annual Report of the 67th General Hospital to the Surgeon General, United States Army, for 1944." Dated 31 January 1945. Signed by Roland B. Moore, Colonel, Medical Corps, Commanding Officer. National Archives.

(4) "Annual Report of the 67th General Hospital to the Chief Surgeon, SOS, ETOUSA." Dated 15 January 1943 Signed by Lieutenant Colonel R.B. Moore, M.C., Commanding. National Archives.

(5) "Lewiston Journal; Magazine Section." Saturday, October 25, 1969.

(6) "Reports to the Red Cross from the Red Cross Unit Assigned to the 67th General Hospital. Narrative and Recreation Report for August, 1943." National Archives.

Appendix Two

Professional Services of Musgrove Military Hospital

Activities of the Various Services
Of the 67th General Hospital While at
Musgrove Military Hospital

Activity of the Medical Service

Activity	1943 (6)	1944 (3)
Admissions to the Medical Service	2212	4602
Discharged from the Medical Service	2029	4659
Returned to full duty		2273
Sent to the Replacement Depot		554
Transferred to other hospitals		1061
Sent to Zone of the Interior		771
Consultations requested by the Medical Service	1864	3294
Consultations completed by the Medical Service	1117	2125
Deaths		9
Electrocardiograph tracings	183	411
Basal Metabolism tests	170	256
Final diagnoses (as follows:)	2494	5630
A. GASTRO-INTESTINAL DISTURBANCES		
1. Anklyostomiasis		7
2. Appendicitis	2	5
3. Colitis	2	15
4. Cystitis		1
5. No Disease, ill-defined condition of the G.I. tract		134
6. Duodenum, ulcer of	88	160

7. Hemorrhoids	3	8
8. Diverticulitis	1	1
9. Cholecystitis		5
10. Diarrhea, acute	2	13
11. Enteritis	24	53
12. Peptic ulcer		3
13. Malnutrition		3
14. Hematemesis		3
15. Strongyloidosis, severe		1
16. Gastritis	14	25
17. Constipation, atonic		7
18. Ulcer, gastric	9	2
19. Other diseases of the digestive system	30	2
20. Intestinal obstruction		1
21. Teniasis		2
22. Diarrhea, fermentative		1
23. Enteritis, gastric	2	29
24. Fissure, anal		21
25. Hypochlorhydria	1	1
26. Proctitis		2
27. Intestinal indigestion	8	2
28. Pylorospasm		1
29. Nematodiasis	1	2
30. Stomach, ulcer of		1
31. Enterocolitis	5	
32. Peritonitis	1	
33. Gallstones	1	
34. Ankylostomiasis	3	
35. Hyperchlorhydria	8	
	215	491

B. RESPIRATORY DISORDERS

1. No disease, ill-defined condition of the respiratory system		7
2. Asthma	35	89
3. Bronchiectasis	5	10
4. Bronchitis	37	64
5. Nasopharyngitis	725	559
6. Pneumonia, lobar		48
7. Pneumonia, primary atypical		162
8. Rhinitis	1	2
9. Sinusitis, maxillary		26

10. Tonsillitis, follicular		133
11. Tuberculosis, pulmonary, active	7	37
12. Observation for tuberculosis		1
13. Pleurisy, serofibrinous		25
14. Pharyngitis	1	1
15. Pleurisy, fibrinous		15
16. Tuberculosis, pulmonary		7
17. Tubercular abscess, chronic		1
18. Tuberculosis, pulmonary, miliary		3
19. Tuberculosis, pulmonary, arrested	3	7
20. Hayfever	6	6
21. Hematemesis		2
22. Laryngitis	11	18
23. Pleurisy, suppurative		2
24. Pneumonia, broncho-		17
25. Sinusitis, ethmoidal		1
26. Sinusitis, frontal		6
27. Tonsillitis, hypertrophic		11
28. Hemothorax		2
29. Pleuritic adhesions		4
30. Tonsillitis, chronic		1
31. Tonsillitis, parenchymatous		4
32. Hemoptysis	1	2
33. Sinusitis	21	1
34. Tonsillitis	62	2
35. Pneumonia, unclassified	68	28
36. Pleurisy	12	
37. Cyst, right lung	2	
38. Adhesion, left base	1	
39. Pneumothorax, spontaneous	1	
	999	1,304

C. DISEASES OF THE LIVER AND BILE-DUCTS

1. Hepatitis,catarrhal		90
2. Cholecystitis		2
3. Hepatitis	30	
4. Cholangitis		
	31	92

D. DISEASES OF THE MUSCLES, BONES AND JOINTS

1. No disease, ill-defined condition of the muscles, bones and joints		33
2. Arthritis	14	120
3. Hernia		3
4. Pes Planus	14	28
5. Rheumatic Fever	7	46
6. Osteoma		3
7. Sprain	1	2
8. Arthralgia		5
9. Bursitis	2	3
10. Myotonia		1
11. Strain		9
12. Lumbago		3
13. Scoliosis		7
14. Synovitis	1	8
15. Myalgia	13	15
16. Other diseases of the locomotor system		6
17. Sacralization, bilateral		2
18. Myositis	8	4
19. Atropy of muscle	2	3
20. Myoma		1
21. Myelitis		1
22. Deformity of spine		1
23. Deformity of foot		1
24. Gout		1
25. Spina bifida	2	4
26. Ganglion		1
27. Tenosynovitis	1	2
28. Deformity of upper extremity	1	1
29. Exostosia	1	
30. Strain, lumbo-sacral	1	
31. Deformity of chest	1	
32. Hammer toe	1	
33. Deformity of elbow	1	
34. Hallux rigidus	1	
35. Lupus erythematosus	2	
36. Metatarsalgia		
37. Deformity of leg	1	
38. Deformity of lower extremities	1	
	91	314

E. NEUROPSYCHIATRIC DISTURBANCES

1. Observation for mental disease		7
2. Alcoholism		7
3. Combat exhaustion		1
4. Constitutional psychopathic states		325
5. Dementia praecox		94
6. Epilepsy		27
7. Mental deficiency		68
8. Psychoneurosis		456
9. Psychosis		31
10. Neurocirculatory asthenia		1
11. Hysteria		3
	210	1020

F. DISEASES OF THE SKIN

1. Dermatitis	106
2. Fungus infection	45
3. Folliculitis	13
4. Herpes progenitalis	3
5. Herpes zoster	7
6. Pyoderma	3
7. Psoriasis	13
8. Seborrhea, sicca	1
9. Scabies	19
10. Urticaria	14
11. Trichophytosis	7
12. Other diseases of the skin	82
13. Impetigo contagioso	3
14. Cellulitis	15
15. Epithelioma	2
16. Plantar warts	2
17. Verruca warts	10
18. Eczema	1
19. Acne vulgaris	13
20. Furunculosis	9
21. Erythema multiforme	3
22. Ichythiosis	5
23. Intertrigo	2
24. Pityriasis rosea	3
25. Trichorrhexis	5

26. Mycosis		1
27. Trichomoniasis		1
28. Sycosis, vulgaris		2
29. Tinea, favosa		1
30. Callosity		2
31. Skin, ulcer of		1
32. Hyperhydrosis		1
33. Ketatosis, senilis		1
34. Pruritis, ani		
	217	318

G. DISEASES OF THE GENITO-URINARY TRACT, INCLUDING VENEREAL

1. No disease, ill-defined condition of the Genito-Urinary System		11
2. Balanitis		8
3. Chancroid	1	11
4. Lymphogranuloma		1
5. Gonorrhoea	8	194
6. Lymphopathia, venereum		1
7. Prostatitis	1	26
8. Glycosuria, renal		1
9. Syphilis, hereditary	3	4
10. Syphilis, new primary	17	144
11. Syphilis, secondary	2	25
12. Syphilis, old, primary	391	112
13. Syphilis, tertiary		9
14. Syphilis, unclassified	4	23
15. Neurosyphilis	1	5
16. Venereal warts		3
17. Urethritis, non-venereal	5	52
18. Epididymitis	2	16
19. Eneuresis, nocturnal	8	9
20. Menopause, artificial		1
21. Penile ulcer		10
22. Verruca, penile		2
23. Nephritis		6
24. Hematuria		1
25. Stricture, urethra		1
26. Calculus, urinary		1
27. Atrophy of testicles		1
28. Orchitis		3

29. Phimosis, congenital	4	7
30. Salpingitis	1	2
31. Spermatorrhoea		1
32. Hydronephrosis	1	4
33. Ureteritis		2
34. Hypospadia, penile	1	
35. Albuminuria, organic type	2	
36. Pyelitis	1	
37. Orchitis, non-venereal	1	
38. Hydrocele	1	
39. Syphilis, old	10	
	114	697

H. DISEASES OF THE NERVOUS SYSTEM

1. Other diseases of the nervous system	3	59
2. Neuritis, multiple, non-alcoholic		1
3. Neuritis, peripheral		4
4. Neuritis, unclassified		1
5. Poliomyelitis		1
6. Paralysis of nerve	8	10
7. Neuralgia	2	2
8. Neurasthenia		2
9. Sciatica	3	2
10. Ganglionitis, geniculate		1
11. Neuritis	1	
12. Herpes Zoster	1	
	18	83

I. DISEASES OF THE CIRCULATORY SYSTEM

1. Other diseases of the circulatory system	81	59
2. Angina pectoris	3	8
3. Arterial hypertension	8	23
4. Arteriosclerosis	7	15
5. Raynaud's disease	1	4
6. Valvular heart disease: Aortic insufficiency	1	1
7. Valvular heart disease: Mitral stenosis	2	4
8. Valvular heart disease: Mitral insufficiency	1	8
9. Valvular heart disease:		

Unclassified		10
10. Varicose veins	2	10
11. Thrombosis, coronary	3	6
12. Auriculo-ventricular block		1
13. Pericarditis		4
14. Endocarditis		3
15. Cardiac hypertrophy--ventricular defect	1	1
16. Heart block		6
17. Sclerosis, disseminated		2
18. Heart, congenital disease of		3
19. Myocardial insufficiency		1
20. Myocarditis		2
21. Cardiac arrhythmia	1	5
22. Tachycardia, simple		
23. Cardiac murmur (not organic)	1	7
24. Angioneurotic edema	1	9
25. Coronary sclerosis		3
26. Cardiospasm		3
27. Infarction, myocardial	1	2
28. Buerger's disease		1
29. Ill-defined condition of neuro-circulatory system		6
30. Phlebitis		2
31. Mitral regurgitation	1	
32. Phlebitis	2	
33. Tachycardia, paroxysmal	4	
34. Cardiac disorder, functional	1	
35. Pericarditis, fibrinous	1	
36. Acrocyanosis	5	
37. Sclerosis	1	
	56	201

J. DISEASES OF THE BLOOD

1. Anaemia, simple	2	6
2. Leukemia, myelocytic		1
3. Leukemia, aleukemic		1
4. No disease, ill-defined condition of the blood		2
5. Anaemia, pernicious	3	2
6. Mononucleosis, infectious		2
7. Leukemia, lymphocytic		1
8. Hemolytic jaundice	1	

K. MALARIA

1. Malarial fever, tertian		138
2. Malarial fever, estivo-autumnal		15
3. Malarial fever, unclassified		24
4. Malarial fever, mixed type		1
	8	178

L. COMMUNICABLE DISEASES

1. Dysentery, amoebic		3
2. Dysentery, endamoebic, acute, caused by *Entamoeba Histolytica*		2
3. Typhoid fever		1
4. Meningitis		20
5. German measles	20	18
6. Mumps	6	104
7. Measles	5	26
8. Meningococcemia		1
9. Erysipelas		1
10. Whooping cough		1
11. Chicken Pox		10
12. Scarlet Fever	4	22
13. Diptheria	1	
14. Meningitis	3	
	39	209

M. DISEASES OF THE GLANDS

1. Other Diseases of the ductless glands		1
2. Hypothyroidism	2	1
3. Pituitary Gland, hypofunction of		1
4. Lymphadenitis	7	14
5. Goiter, Colloid		1
6. Goiter, Exophthalmic		3
7. Goiter, Simple	1	3
8. Other Diseases of the Lymph Glands	4	2
	14	26

N. DISEASES OF THE EYE, EAR, NOSE AND THROAT

1. Abscess, periapical		28

2. Blepharitis		3
3. Defective hearing		29
4. Stomatitis		19
5. Conjunctivitis, catarrhal		7
6. Conjunctivitis, vernal		2
7. Otitis media		12
8. Myopia		3
9. Rhinitis		1
10. Vincent's angina		17
11. Abscess, peritonsillar		9
12. Defective vision		3
13. Otosclerosis		1
14. Otitis externa		2
15. Myringitis		1
16. Cornea, ulcer of		2
17. Keratitis		1
18. Aphonia		1
19. Nasal septum, deviation of		9
20. Speech impediment		1
21. Mastoiditis		2
22. Fistula, antra, oval		1
23. Gingivitis		5
24. Tinnitus		1
25. Other diseases of the eye, ear, nose and throat		1
26. Hemoptysis		1
27. Otitis interna		1
28. Pterygium		1
29. Astigmatism		1
30. Chalazion		3
	86	168

O. DISEASES OF METABOLISM

1. Diabetes mellitus		10
P. MISCELLANEOUS	106	68
Q. INJURIES DUE TO EXTERNAL CAUSES	46	122

R. ADMINISTRATIVE ADMISSIONS	61	139
S. ADDITIONAL DIAGNOSES		175
T. NO DISEASE	168	
U. CARDIOVASCULAR DISTURBANCES	9	
	2494	

Activity of the Surgical Service

Category		1943	1944
1.	Major operative procedures	401	919
	Minor operative procedures	1731	2857
	Total operative procedures	2132	3776
	Plaster applications		1661
	Diagnostic procedures		382
	Out-patient procedures in OR		325
	Total procedures		6144
	2. Anaesthetics		
	Total number of anaesthetics	1534	4144
	Total number of inhalation anaesthetics	143	279
	Total number of regional anaesthetics	773	1803
	Total number of intravenous anaesthetics	347	1575
	Total number of combined anaesthetics	198	485
	Total number of endotracheal anaesthetics	63	175
	Total number of rectal anaesthetics	2	None Listed
	3. Blood transfusions and intravenous fluids		
	Fresh whole blood	25	88
	67th bank blood		394
	ETO bank blood		33
	Plasma transfusions	13	
	Liters of intravenous fluid administered	600	

4. Consultations

Total consultations seen by the surgical service	2632	4220
5. Total surgical patients boarded for transfer to the Zone of Interior	227	1763
Transferred to Zone of Interior, (boarded in other hospitals)		704
Transferred to other UK hospitals		2611
Returned to duty		3575
Returned for limited duty (during the time period this was possible.)	74	
Total surgical patients considered by the Disposition Board	301	
Transferred to other service in hospital		462
Increase over surgical census of 31 December 1943		373

DIAGNOSES:

GENERAL SURGERY

1. Appendicitis	148	197
2. Hemorrhoids	104	108
3. Varicose veins	63	74
4. Pilonidal sinuses	51	78
5. Hernias	108	163
6. Cholecystitis	4	13
7. Cholelithiasis	4	10
8. Burns	32	69
9. Gunshot wounds, lacerated, penetrating and perforating		1328

10. Infections	140	84
11. Other surgical diagnoses	135	1774
12. Amputation of limbs		43
13. Chest and intrathoracic injuries		175
14. Aneurysms		25
15. Gunshot wounds	496	
16. Wounds, lacerated, penetrating and perforating	174	

NEUROSURGERY

1. Peripheral nerve injuries	36	467
2. Cerebral concussion and contusion	59	189
3. Penetrating wounds of skull		181
4. Spinal cord injuries		82
5. Brain tumors		5
6. Fractures of the skull	17	

ORTHOPEDIC SURGERY

1. Fractures of femur	48	140
2. Fractures of humerus	33	91
3. Fractures of os calcis	17	34
4. Fractures of vertebrae	41	108
5. Fractures of tibia	113	203
6. Fractures of fibula	121	167
7. Fractures of patella	11	34
8. Fractures of bones of foot		216
9. Fractures of bones of hand		241
10. Sprains	59	132
11. Strains	216	257
12. Dislocations	61	96
13. Ruptured ligaments	43	74
14. Fractures of other bones of body	520	309
15. Fractures of pelvis		90
16. Other orthopedic diagnoses	562	598

UROLOGICAL SURGERY

1. Nephrolithiasis	4	4
2. Gunshot wound, kidney		8
3. Gunshot wound, bladder		10
4. Varicocele	24	25

5. Orchitis	10	5
6. Phimosis	75	78
7. Epididymitis	23	41
8. Prostatitis	18	24
9. Cord bladder		30
10. Other diseases of the GU tract	318	413
11. Lues, old	37	
12. Lues, new	85	
13. Gonorrhea	191	

ENT SURGERY

1. Tonsillitis	136	169
2. Otitis media	72	129
3. Mastoiditis	22	42
4. Other ENT diagnoses	242	583
5. Diseases and wounds of the eye	182	277
Total diagnoses	4755	

Activity of the Dental Service

Work Done	**1943** (5)	**1944** (2)
Sittings	14,890	15,139
Fillings	7,516	4,359
Extractions	1,440	1,633
Missing teeth replaced	1,168	
Prosthetic restorations (all types)		1,453
Bridges--all types	10	
Full dentures	75	
Dentures repaired	122	
Dentures, partial	201	
Dentures reconstructed	86	
Prophylaxes		1,846
Examinations		3,630
Routine admissions	2.150	
Emergency admissions	596	
Miscellaneous operations (gum treatment, post-operative treatment, etc.)		6,124
X-rays		5,946
Plastic eyes (Made by Captain Smith)		57

Fractured jaws (new fractures reduced only at this hospital)	14	27
Fractures of maxilla	6	
Reduction of fracture	20	
Vincent's stomatitis	157	
Vincent's stomatitis, treatment of	638	

The Annual Report of 1943 classifies the military personnel as of 31 December 1943, as 18 in Class I, 33 in Class II, 4 in Class III and 595 in Class IV.

Activity of the Laboratory Service

Procedures	1943	1944
Bacteriology Section:		
Cultures of all types	1728	2712
Smears of all types	3951	7222
Feces examinations	1400	1501
Agglutination tests	135	152
Sputum pneumotyping	242	
Miscellaneous examinations	not listed	71
Serology Section:		
Blood qualitative Kahns	6837	13411
Blood quantitative Kahns	79	550
Blood Wassermans	75	80
Spinal fluid Kahns	173	447
Spinal fluid Wassermans	93	309
Colloidal gold curves	261	655
Darkfields	214	666
Hematology Section:		
Routine blood counts	24867	48921
Spinal fluid counts	291	898
Miscellaneous examinations	1583	4469

Chemistry Section:

Total blood procedures	2053	7048
Total spinal fluid procedures	503	1140
Gastric analyses	312	352
Miscellaneous procedures	5	26

Urinalysis Section:

Routine examinations	not listed	17534
Miscellaneous examinations	not listed	2455
Total examinations	10412	

Immunization Section:

Tetanus	716	838
Small-pox	752	217
Typhus	763	1517
Typhoid	652	738
Autogenous vaccines	12	37
Mantoux tests	8	59
Schick tests	8	not listed

Pathology Section:

Surgical specimens	352	521
Autopsies	8	53

Total examinations	not listed	114599

Activity of the Roentgenological Service

Examination	1942	1943 (4)	1944 (1)
Chest	67	2585	3438
Chest (portable)		390	415
Thorax		None listed	40
Bronchogram		14	36
Heart		105	190
Extremities	69	2362	5641
Spine and pelvis		660	1590
Spine	14		
Pelvis	10		
Skull	3	206	715
Mastoids	1	111	97
Sinuses	6	452	447
Facial bones	3	131	311
Eye		4	None listed
Sweet eye localization		8	28
Ventriculogram		1	2
Encephalogram		1	None listed
Abdomen		Not listed	30
Gastrointestinal examination	6	818	1062
KUB	4	68	134
Retrograde pyelogram		79	162
Intravenous pyelogram	2	91	113
Myelogram		4	44
Cystogram		1	Not listed
Urethrogram		5	Not listed
Gall bladder		348	318
Number of portable examinations		460	859
Fluoroscopy:			
Gastrointestinal		Not listed	1062
Others		Not listed	178
Number of new patients	120	3768	9177
Number of check-up examinations	54	3917	5794
Total radiographic examinations	174	7685	14971

Expendable Property Used by the Roentgenological Service

Property Used	1942	1944 (1)
Films, small		4884
Films, medium		8933
Films, large		10404
Total films used		24221
Barium sulfate, 10 lbs.		101
Powder, developing pkg		143
Powder, fixing pkg		134
Lipiodol, bottle		42

References

(1) "Annual Report of the Roentgenological Service for 1944." Dated 8 January 1945. Submitted to the Commanding Officer, 67th General Hospital, by Lieutenant Colonel Jack Spencer, M.C., Chief of X-Ray Service. National Archives.

(2) "Annual Dental Report for 1944, to the Commanding Officer, 67th General Hospital, APO 511." Dated 4 January 1945. Signed by Lieutenant Colonel, DC., Chief of Dental Service. National Archives.

(3) "Annual Report of the Office of the Chief of the Medical Service to the Commanding Officer, 67th General Hospital, APO 511." Dated 9 January 1945. Signed by E.R.Blaisdell, Lt. Colonel, Medical Corps, Chief of the Medical Service. National Archives.

(4) "Annual Report of the X-Ray Service to the Commanding Officer, 67th General Hospital, APO 511." Dated 30 January 1944. Signed by Jack Spencer, Lt. Colonel, M.C., Chief of X-Ray Service, National Archives.

(5) "Annual Dental Report for the period 1 January 1943 to 31 December 1943." Signed 4 January 1944, by William B. Jordan, Lt. Colonel, D.C., Chief of Service. National Archives.

(6) "Annual Report of the Medical Service to the Commanding Officer, 67th General Hospital, APO 511, U.S. Army." Dated 12 January 1944, for the year 1943. Signed by E.R. Blaisdell, Lieutenant Colonel, M.C., Chief of Surgical Service. National Archives.

67TH GENERAL HOSPITAL

Appendix Three

Patient Census By Periods

Patient Census at Musgrove 5 December 1942 to 31 December 1942 (5)

	To be Accounted for			Dispositions				
	Remaining 5 Dec. 1942	Admissions	Total	Duty	Died	Transported Other Hosp.	Total	Remaining 31 Dec. 1942
	152	246	398	175	0	2	177	221
Army:								
Officers	5	19	24	15	0	0	15	9
Nurses	10	25	35	24	0	1	25	10
Enlisted Men	134	193	327	131	0	1	132	195
Navy and Marine Corps								
Officers	0	0	0	0	0	0	0	0
Nurses	0	0	0	0	0	0	0	0
Enlisted Men	2	0	2	0	0	0	0	2
All Others	1	9	10	5	0	0	5	5
Total	152	246	398	175	0	2	177	221

Patient Census 1 January 1943 to 31 December 1943 (1)

	To be Accounted for			Dispositions				
	Remaining 1 Jan. 1943	Admissions	Total	Duty	Died	Transported Other Hosp.	Total	Remaining 31 Dec. 1943
	221	5082	5303	3352	6	1277	4635	668
Army:								
Officers	9	306	315	241	0	50	291	24
Nurses	10	194	204	189	0	10	199	5
Enlisted Men	195	3845	4040	2547	5	928	3480	560
Navy and Marine Corps								
Officers	0	15	15	13	0	1	14	1
Nurses	0	0	0	0	0	0	0	0
Enlisted Men	2	117	119	67	1	8	76	43
All Others	5	605	610	295	0	280	575	35
Total	221	5082	5303	3352	6	1277	4635	668

The number of patients in the hospital varied from 166 on 15 June, to 912 on 6 November, the average daily number for period 1 June 1943, to 31 December 1943, inclusive being 430.7. There were 157,236 patient days for this period, of which 88,345 were Medical and 68,891 were Surgical cases. Five hundred twenty-nine patients were transferred to the Zone of Interior for further hospitalization during the calendar year. (1) Of the 5,082 patients admitted, 2,212 were Medical and 2,870 were Surgical. (5)

During the first quarter of 1944, the hospital was running to near capacity in number of patients. (3)

Patient Census 1 January 1944 to 31 December 1944 (4)

	To be Accounted for			Dispositions				
	Remaining 31 Dec. 1944	Admissions	Total	Duty	Died	Transported Other Hosp.	Total	Remaining 31 Dec.1943
	668	14136	14804	6539	59	6816	13414	1390
Army:								
Officers	24	892	916	362	8	476	846	70
Nurses	5	155	160	83	1	63	147	13
Enlisted Men	560	12548	13108	5662	45	6102	11809	1299
Navy and Marine Corps								
Officers	1	15	16	13	0	3	16	0
Nurses	0	0	0	0	0	0	0	0
Enlisted Men	43	170	213	167	3	43	213	0
All Others	35	356	391	252	2	129	283	8
Total	668	14136	14804	6539	59	6816	13414	1390

Patient Census 1 January 1943 to 31 May 1945 (2)

	To be Accounted for			Dispositions				
		Admissions	Total	Duty	Died	Transported Other Hosp.	Total	Remaining 31 May 1945
	152	23159	23311	11423	71	11817	23311	0
Army:								
Officers	5	1441	1446	657	9	780	1446	0
Nurses	10	432	442	348	1	93	442	0
Enlisted Men	134	19954	20088	9590	55	10443	20088	0
Navy and Marine Corps								
Officers	0	33	33	28	0	5	33	0
Nurses	0	0	0	0	0	0	0	0
Enlisted Men	2	300	302	241	4	57	302	0
All Others	1	999	1000	559	2	439	1000	0
Total	152	23159	23311	11423	71	11817	23311	0

Patient Census 8 June 1945 to 17 August 1945 (2)
Benbow Barracks, Pimperne, Dorset

To be Accounted for			Dispositions				
Patients in Hospital 8 June 1945	Admissions	Admissions Total	Duty	Died	Transported Other Hosp.	Total	Remaining 17 August 1945
621	311	932	64	0	864	932	4

Ninety-two of the admissions after 8 June 1945, were Surgical and 219 Medical.
Of the total Admissions, 575 were Surgical and 357 were Medical

Of the patients transported to other hospitals, 150 were sent to the Zone of the Interior with 60 being Surgical and 90 being Medical.

Patient Census 18 August 1945 to 28 August 1945 (2)
Fairford Park, Gloucestershire-Hospital Plant 4148.

To be Accounted for			Dispositions			
Patients in Hospital Remaining 18 August 1945	Admissions	Admissions Total	Duty	Died	Transported Other Hosp.	Total Remaining 28 August 1945
113	128	241	45	0	40	156

Fifty of the admissions after 18 August 1945, were Surgical and 78 Medical.

Of the patients transported to other hospitals, 40 were sent to the Zone of the Interior with 12 being Surgical and 28 being Medical.

References

(1) "Annual Report to the Chief Surgeon, SOS, ETOUSA, APO 887, U.S. Army." Dated 31 January 1944. National Archives.

(2) "Semi-annual Report, Medical Department Activities, 67th General Hospital to the Surgeon General, Washington, D.C." Dated 15 June 1945. National Archives.

(3) "History Memorandum to Base Section Historian, APO 519, U.S. Army." Dated 7 April 1944. National Archives.

(4) "Annual Report of the 67th General Hospital to the Surgeon General, United States Army, for 1944." Dated 31 January 1945, and signed by Roland B. Moore, Colonel, Medical Corps, Commanding Officer. National Archives.

(5) "Historical Report of 1943, to the Chief Surgeon, SOS, ETOUSA from R.B. Moore, Colonel, Medical Corps, Commanding Officer, 67th General Hospital, APO 511." Dated 31 January 1944. National Archives.

Index Available Upon Request

C000203315

BY THE SAME AUTHOR

In Search of the Forty Days Road

Shoot to Kill

A Desert Dies

Impossible Journey

Thesiger

Sahara (with Kazoyoshi Nomachi)

Phoenix Rising – The United Arab Emirates, Past, Present and Future (with Werner Forman)

THE LAST OF THE BEDU

In Search of the Myth

MICHAEL ASHER

With colour photographs by
Mariantonietta Peru

VIKING

VIKING

Published by the Penguin Group
Penguin Books Ltd, 27 Wrights Lane, London W8 5TZ, England
Penguin Books USA Inc., 375 Hudson Street, New York, New York 10014, USA
Penguin Books Australia Ltd, Ringwood, Victoria, Australia
Penguin Books Canada Ltd, 10 Alcorn Avenue, Toronto, Ontario, Canada M4V 3B2
Penguin Books (NZ) Ltd, 182–190 Wairau Road, Auckland 10, New Zealand

Penguin Books Ltd, Registered Offices: Harmondsworth, Middlesex, England

First published 1996
1 3 5 7 9 10 8 6 4 2
First edition

Set in 12.25/14.25 pt Monotype Bembo
Typeset by Datix International Limited, Bungay, Suffolk
Printed in Great Britain by Clays Ltd, St Ives plc

A CIP catalogue record for this book is available from the British Library

ISBN 0-670-83370-9

This book is dedicated to my son Burton,
who made me aware of the future.

And to Mariantonietta, again.

Future Prospects. The Arabian Desert, until about 1940, had remained practically unaffected by other cultures, and particularly Western culture. In the future one may anticipate change . . . The desert, nevertheless, will remain the desert, although it will become less isolated, more comfortable, and possibly more productive. The question that remains to be answered, however, is whether or not the Arab individuality will become merged into an urban anonymity.

(*Encyclopaedia Britannica*)

A myth is a kind of story told in public, which people tell one another; they wear an air of ancient wisdom, but that is part of their seductive charm. Not all antiques are better than a modern design – especially if they are needed in ordinary, daily use. But myth's own secret cunning means that it pretends to present the matter as it is and always must be . . . But, contrary to this understanding, myths aren't writ in stone, they're not fixed, but often, telling the story of the same figures – of Medea or of dinosaurs – change dramatically both in context and meaning. Myths can lock us up in stock reactions, bigotry and fear, but they're not immutable, and by unpicking them, the stories can lead to others. Myths convey values and expectations which are always evolving, in the process of being formed . . . but never set so hard they cannot be changed again . . .

(MARINA WARNER, *Managing Monsters: The Reith Lectures*, 1994)

CONTENTS

LIST OF ILLUSTRATIONS

All the photographs were taken by Mariantonietta Peru with the exception of no. 28, which was taken by the author.

AUTHOR'S NOTE

Most of the journeys recorded in this book took place over a period of about three years, but formed part of a single quest. Several other experiences, from an earlier era, have been brought into the text because of their relevance to the development of ideas about the Bedu over a period of fifteen years. The events recounted are all factual, but the chronological order has occasionally been changed to give continuity to the text. The names of several individuals have been changed in the interests of privacy, and sometimes to prevent confusion.

I have spelled Arabic words according to my own phonetic system, though there is inevitable friction between this and some accepted spellings of Arabic words in English. The ancient Sheban capital, generally spelt Marib, has been rendered Maʿrib – the ʿ representing the consonant ʿain, not found in English but familiar to Arabic speakers. The same consonant occurs in the word Saʿudi Arabia, but since an Anglicized version of this is in common use, I have excluded it here as unnecessary. The oasis I refer to as Palmyra is generally called Tadmor by Syrians, though both names are known to locals. When in doubt I have followed the spelling in Nigel Groom's excellent *Dictionary of Arabic Topography and Place Names* (1983).

I have thanked all those who played a part in the creation of this book separately, but I would like to record here my debt of deep gratitude to both the Bedu and the Hadr of whatever tribe, who gave me unstinting friendship and hospitality.

MICHAEL ASHER
Stamford and Edinburgh, UK,
Sanur, Bali,
and Frazione Agnata, Sardinia,
7 April 1992–31 March 1995

ACKNOWLEDGEMENTS

I am deeply grateful to the following:

Dr Steven Simms, Associate Professor of Anthropology, University of Utah; C. Vance Haynes, Professor of Earth Sciences, University of Arizona; Donald Powell-Cole, Professor of Anthropology, American University of Cairo; Dr Darius Campbell and Alan Rowe of the joint Royal Geographical Society–Royal Jordanian Government Badiya Project, Jordan; Dr Edward Allonby and Dr Jane Allonby, Amman; The American Centre for Oriental Research, Amman; The London Library; The Library of the School of Oriental and African Studies, University of London; Edinburgh City Library; Faber and Faber Ltd for permission to use an extract from T. S. Eliot's *Four Quartets* on page 54; The Royal Geographical Society; Janet Williamson and Mbarak bin Musallim ash Shahri; John and Jo Crowther, British Council, Salalah, Sultanate of Oman; Eleo Gordon, of the Penguin Group; Anthony Goff, of David Higham Associates, Literary Agents; Mariantonietta and Burton.

PRELUDE

A Colony of Sphinxes Moulded by the Winds

In Cairo, I booked into a hotel on the third floor of a crumbling Corniche tenement, with a Bedouin called Selmi. The hotel had a vast vacant hall beneath, like an ancient Egyptian temple, its dome festooned with spider-webs and its walls with flaps of peeling paint like sloughing snakeskin. A statuesque Egyptian girl with an elaborate coiffure of black curls watched our toings and froings suspiciously from behind the reception desk. Yes, she had said it was all right to put our luggage in the store, but she had hardly been expecting filthy sackcloth camel-saddles and palm-fibre panniers that leaked chaff all over the lobby. Selmi handed her his identity card apprehensively. 'Aren't you going to fill in the registration form?' she asked.

'I can't write,' Selmi said, gruffly. 'My father never thought it important in our profession.'

Selmi's profession was indeed a time-hallowed one. He was a rock-salt gatherer – an occupation listed on a tomb-inscription on Elephantine Island, Aswan, dating from the time of the Pharaoh Ramses II. He was one of the last group of Bedu – perhaps no more than two dozen in all – who still used camels to transport rock-salt long distances in the deserts of Egypt.

Selmi and I planned to trek with camels across the Western Desert from the Mediterranean to Upper Egypt – a journey of 1,000 miles. Both of us knew that it was a formidable undertaking.

Our path lay through the Great Erg or Sand Sea, a desert-within-a-desert that was smaller but more treacherous than Arabia's Empty Quarter. Its dunes rose to 500 feet and in places formed an impenetrable labyrinth that could be crossed by neither camels nor motor-cars. The Sand Sea itself lay within the frame of a much larger region, known – variously and confusingly – as the Egyptian Sahara, the Libyan desert, the Western Desert and the eastern Sahara. Whatever you chose to call it, it remained one of the least inviting, least hospitable, least familiar areas in all Africa. No major routes passed through it, no friendly Bedui pitched his tent there, no veiled Tuareg grazed his flocks. Outside its oases it had supported no human population in modern times, and in places no plants, no mammals, no birds, and no insects. In much of it there was no accessible source of water, no ancient wadi-systems carrying run-off, no rain-tapping massifs. Its Nubian sandstone core sucked down into deep aquifers the rain that fell in places once every forty years. Its temperatures were ferocious, its evaporation rate the world's highest, its surface grilled by the sun for exactly 96 per cent of daylight hours. In its southern part the sun stood so high in its zenith that at the summer solstice a man had virtually no shadow. In winter Siberian winds lashed it from the north and the water in goatskins had been known to freeze solid. In early summer came the dreaded Ghibli, the hot southern wind that was still regarded with superstitious awe. So alien was the Egyptian Sahara that even the geologists had likened it to the surface of Mars.

It had been difficult to explain to Selmi why I wanted to travel in this alien place, and why, to me, the journey would have no meaning without a Bedouin companion. The Great Sand Sea was the true desert of Western imagination, and Selmi belonged to the only group of Bedu I had heard of who still clung tenaciously to their camels when they might have used motor-cars instead – the only ones to take on this desert-of-deserts in the traditional way purely out of choice. My true object was to discover the Bedu, and all they had become in the last decade of the twentieth century. To know them fully, I knew, I had to travel in the environment that had moulded them, that was familiar to them as it was to no one else.

Although Selmi had not actually crossed the Sand Sea before, the prospect of its dangers did not daunt him. He had been travelling with his family's salt-caravans into the deepest deserts since the age of twelve, and his apprenticeship had been a rude one. On his very first trip his companion had simply dropped dead while cooking the evening meal. Selmi had been watering the camels at the time, and had come back to find him lying against a saddle. At first he had thought the man had been stung by a snake or a scorpion. Then he realized that he was dead, and started to cry from fear. He was twelve years old and had never seen anyone die before. When he arrived back home he swore that he would never go with the salt-caravans again, but within six months he had been off with the camels, and after that had made two or even three journeys to the salt-oasis every year – except for his three years of military service, of course. Now, at thirty-one, he had covered more than 40,000 miles by camel, making him the most experienced caravaneer I had ever known.

I had met Selmi a week earlier in Baghdad, a village in the Kharja oasis. It lay at the base of a crescent-shaped mound where – since Persian times at least – a spring had watered gardens of date-palms, *fuul*-beans and clover. The palm groves were a brilliant halo of green against the pastel wastes of the sands: beyond this haven of moisture the Sahara stretched on and on like an endless ocean – 3,000 miles from here to the Atlantic coast.

It had been mid-morning when my car pulled up by the colony of mud-brick houses where a dozen camels stamped and snorted in a tight alley paved with a decade's camel-dung. Energetic piebald doves squabbled continuously on the cab of a rotting tractor, and around it barefoot urchins performed acrobatics in the dry manure. A slim man in an ankle-length jallabiyya and high-rise turban came out to welcome me. He had a face as grave as a Ramessid statue, and the tan-line at his neck showed that his complexion had been acquired from an outdoor life. His skin was prematurely wrinkled around the eyes, adding several unwarranted years to his age, but his broad, gleaming smile made him a rakish youth again. He was tall and lightly built with a spindly, camelline stride. This was Selmi walad ʿEid.

He drew me into a mud-brick room, where a handful of Bedu with pickled-walnut faces were sitting on the floor. Each one of them stood up to shake my hand. They were dressed in jallabiyyas of striped pyjama cloth with turbans like squashed white doughnuts. Their hands had the feel of wizened buckskin, and they had a way of gripping your palm and grunting 'Welcome!' as if they really meant it. They looked like a colony of sphinxes carved and moulded by the Ghibli winds.

ʿEid, an old Bedui with a nose like a purple onion and a mouthful of chiselled teeth, was Selmi's father. The other Bedu were Selmi's brothers, cousins and uncles, all recognizably out of the same mould as Selmi himself. ʿEid had been born in a black tent at Sohaj in the Nile Valley, and as a young man had walked 1,000 miles to Kassala in the Sudan, to visit relatives. He had stayed there long enough to watch British bombers pounding the Italian garrison, and had thriftily exchanged a goatskin of water for the rifle of a parched Italian trooper. Returning home to Sohaj by boat and train, he had later submitted to family pressure and married his cousin – then a little girl of nine. At thirteen she had produced the first of six strong, graceful sons. The third of these was Selmi.

A fat ewe had been slaughtered in my honour: 'Every guest must get his due!' ʿEid said. I hunkered down with the others at a calf-high table on which Selmi's youngest brother laid a tray of roasted meat, stew, intestines, a salad of tomatoes, green onions and white radishes, flaps of bread, and gooey Jew's mallow. After we had eaten the table was cleared, and a boy came round with a pitcher of hot water, a bar of soap, and a steel basin from which we washed our hands. He carried a white towel on his arm like a wine-waiter. Selmi, his father and a couple of brothers sat cross-legged on a rug opposite me. Flies settled on their faces and they flicked them away with ease. Outside, the camels puffed and rumbled as they chewed the cud. A squall of wind-borne grit scratched at the shutters on the door.

For a moment there was silence. Then ʿEid asked: 'How can we help you?'

When I explained that I wished to cross the Great Sand Sea, ʿEid and his sons looked at each other perplexed. 'You aren't looking for antiquities, are you?' one of the boys inquired. 'They put you in prison for that.'

I assured them that I was not looking for antiquities.

'But how will you find your way?' ʿEid asked. 'That is dangerous country, and none of us here has ever crossed it. The worst sin in the desert is thinking that it's easy to find the way! Why, there are plenty of Bedu born and raised in the desert who lose the way and die! Remember that man who went with us once to the salt place, boys? When he came back he said, "Now I know the way, I'll go there with my own camels." We tried to stop him, but he was so cocksure! He took a caravan of camels with him and his son, who was just a boy. They never came back. They're probably still out there somewhere – what's left of them!'

'But I *can* find my way,' I said, holding up my flat Silva compass, 'with this?'

'Let me see that thing!' ʿEid said, chortling through his sharp teeth. He examined it carefully, tapped it and screwed round the bevel, then put it down bemused. I explained that the red needle always pointed north, and that you would thus always know the other directions. 'I don't need a needle to show me north!' ʿEid shrugged. 'I wouldn't put my trust in that machine, any day!'

'I doubt if you'll get anyone to go with you across the Sand Sea,' Selmi said. 'Too far! Too far!'

I felt my spirits sink. It had taken me months – actually years – to trace these Bedu. Now, it seemed, they were not even interested in the journey I proposed. I was just about to get up and beat an ignominious retreat, when ʿEid said, almost casually, 'A journey across the Sand Sea would need a tough companion. Now what would you be willing to pay for a man like that?'

I hesitated for a moment. 'I reckon it'd be worth a hundred Egyptian pounds a day,' I said.

For an instant – and only for an instant – the sphinx-like faces lost their inscrutability and registered decided interest. In Egypt £E100 was a good monthly wage. 'Boy!' 'Eid bawled to one of his sons. 'Where's that tea, by God!'

Selmi's younger brother, a slightly less weathered, more clean-cut version of Selmi, strode in balancing a brass tray that bore glasses and an aluminium teapot. He poured out glassfuls of tea and held one out to me, but I declined. It was time to leave them to discuss my offer in private. While Selmi and the others sipped tea, I walked through dung-carpeted streets to the edge of the village where the unfettered desert wind held the spicy scent of dust. Far off to the west I could see the fringe of a dune-belt – dunes that had not existed at all in Roman times – where the folds and counterfolds of soft sand fell along the sparse cultivation and tiny dust-demons unreeled across the dune-crests like smoke. In their path stood a picket of drunken palms nursing palm-doves, postage-stamp patches of wheat, furry pencil-cedars, sprouts of tamarisk on the sandy hillocks. A battle was being fought there – the old battle between the desert and the sown. Often, the desert won. There was an abandoned village called Arbaʿ – now reduced to a roofless maze of melted mud-brick and belly sand. The creeping dryness had turned the soil to dust long ago, and the wind had threshed it away leaving only a griddle of lines that had once been irrigation canals.

Suddenly, someone touched my arm. Selmi stood there, regarding me with a basilisk stare. 'It has been decided,' he told me with simple gravity. 'I will go.'

It was New Year's Eve in Cairo, and the Corniche was choked with honking taxis and expansive holiday crowds. In Tahrir Square gangs of young people in silver witch-hats were shooting off firecrackers and clapping hands around musicians playing lutes and tablas. Selmi and I spent a fruitless hour trying to navigate through the Metro subways: 'It's a lot easier finding your way in the desert,' he grumbled. A group of excited schoolboys made a circle round him hand in hand, chanting 'Saʿidi! Saʿidi! Man from the south!' Selmi broke out of the circle scornfully. 'Just because we wear jallabiyyas and turbans they think we're stupid!' he said. It was one of the few times I saw him angry.

We sat at the tables outside the Hilton and ordered tea and hookah pipes. The waiter, done up in bottle-green mess-tunic and dicky-bow, sniffed at Selmi superciliously, but made no comment. We puffed gratefully at our hubble-bubbles. 'The pipes are wonderful but the tea is rubbish!' Selmi said. Gazing wistfully at parties of immaculately dressed Egyptian girls with sparkling eyes and red mouths, he said: 'I'd like to marry one of those girls. My wife is a good woman – but she's my cousin and we've been friends since we were small. We've got four children – we had five but one died – and she gets very tired. When I come home she's always asleep these days.'

Next morning we took a taxi to the camel-market at Imbaba. A freezing wind had blown up from the Delta, bringing with it the winter rains. At Imbaba the streets had become liquid chocolate, and portly ladies tiptoed through the mire with their skirts tucked up. The camel-market was a swamp of mud and manure – three great intersecting yards where Arabs sat under awnings and camels shivered in miserable gaggles in the corners. Most of them had come down from the small markets in Upper Egypt, where they had arrived after a 1,000-mile trek on the hoof from the Sudan. They were not accustomed to this winter dampness, for the rains in the Sudan came in summer.

As we walked through the gate, a beefy, beaming Arab threw his wrestler's bulk on Selmi, bawling, 'Welcome! Welcome!' This was ʿAlaysh, a steward of the market and an acquaintance of Selmi's one previous visit. He had a pumpkin-sized face with a moustache like a bramble-bush, and his head was lapped up in a mottled shawl against the rain. His green wellingtons looked as though they pinched his large feet. 'Welcome, Selmi!' he roared. 'Welcome, friend!' Flinging bear-like arms around us, he marched us to the nearest teashop.

An Arab boy brought three small tumblers of tea on a tray and ʿAlaysh doled them out officiously. 'Drink! Drink! By God, you are my guests here!' he thundered.

Selmi told him that we would need five good camels – strong beasts capable of lugging the immense quantity of food and water we should require on our trek.

'You will have the *very best* camels!' ʿAlaysh declared. 'Oh, the *very best*! Selmi knows me, Omar! My heart is white! I will find for you the *most perfect* camels and I don't want anything in return! Nothing at all! I will do this for you because you are a foreigner and Selmi is my good friend. Of course, any little thing you should want to give me – any trifle – would be acceptable. My heart is completely white!'

'How much do you want?'

'Nothing! The very idea of it! Nothing at all!'

'How much?'

'Only a mere trifle – the merest of trifles would suffice!'

'Which would be?'

'Only – let's say – twenty pounds commission on each camel. A mere trifle. It's nothing, really. My heart is like snow!'

'Ten pounds.'

'Make it fifteen.'

'Done!'

All morning we wandered around the yards looking at camels, prodding camels, poking camels, feeling humps and haunches, putting camels through their paces, chatting with camel-merchants and men who were buying camels for rides at the Pyramids. By the end of the morning I had bought Shaylan, a great off-white Bishari reared by the Beja in the Red Sea hills. 'This is a *most perfect* camel, Omar!' ʿAlaysh declared. 'Been to the

Sudan and back twice that camel has!' He leaned over and raised a whiskery eyebrow. *'Smuggling!'* he growled.

It took us eight days to assemble five camels and all our provisions and equipment, and half-way through Selmi took to sleeping at the camel-market to protect our investment. One morning I strolled into the market to find him deep in conversation with two Saudi Arabs in expensively cut dishdashas and speckled red headcloths. One of them wore a drooping Sancho Panza moustache, and the other a pair of reflecting sunglasses. The one with the sunglasses struck me as being familiar.

'We want to offer Selmi a job,' one of them said. 'A permanent job in Saudi Arabia, looking after our camels.'

'But he won't go,' added the other. 'He says he's working for you.'

'Why don't you let him go? We're giving him a really good chance. A good wage and all found.'

'I can't go,' Selmi said. 'I've already agreed with Omar!'

I called him aside and explained that I was prepared to let him go. 'It's a good chance,' I said, 'and I'm only giving you temporary work. We could send a message to Kharja and get your brother Ahmad to come with me instead.'

'No, my word is my word. All is written. If those Saudis had come to me first I would have agreed with them and kept my promise. But God brought you first, and a Bedui never changes his word. I am your man.'

I had often heard the Bedu dismissed as grasping, and occasionally I had found them so myself. But I knew this was as fine a display of personal integrity as I was ever likely to see.

Before the Saudis left, I remembered where I had seen Sunglasses before. I had seen him at Shepheard's Hotel on the Corniche, drinking beer and dining with a pretty Egyptian girl. I mentioned this to Selmi. 'Yes,' he said, 'last night he had a celebration in the market for his new marriage.'

'He has just married an Egyptian girl?'

'Yes. He married her yesterday, and in a few days, when he goes back to Saudi Arabia, he'll divorce her. That way it's all legal you see!'

The next morning a four-ton truck pulled up at the loading-ramp at Imbaba. The driver, a lanky Cairene with a truculent look, jumped out and leaned on the bonnet smoking a Cleopatra cigarette. ʿAlaysh and a few brawny friends helped Selmi and me to coax our camels up the ramp, then cajole, heave and shove them into the truck, until they were wedged and trussed up like chickens. Then we humped aboard our mounds of gear – saddles, panniers, 300 kilos of sorghum for camel-feed, bags of sardines and bully-beef, packets of tea and pokes of sugar, ropes, rugs, blankets, hobbles and nose-bags, five kilos of olives, ten packs of cheese, a sack of flour, twenty plastic jerrycans, twenty kilos of pasta and two large waterskins. When all had been squeezed in and lashed down, I paid off ʿAlaysh's crew, while ʿAlaysh leaned panting on his stick. 'Well, Omar,' he said, 'I got you the camels. I haven't fallen short, have I?'

'No, you haven't,' I said, and handed him exactly twice what we had agreed.

His lower lip quivered. 'Only a hundred and fifty. After all the work I've done!'

Selmi fixed the big Bedui with a piercing stare. I had never seen him look so intimidating. 'You agreed to fifteen pounds a camel, and Omar has given you twice as much. It is twice as much as you deserve, judging by this display. Put it away and don't make a further disgrace!'

The giant wadded the money into his pocket with ham-like fists and stalked away. I looked at Selmi: 'A Bedui never breaks his word?' I said, grinning at the retreating figure.

'The Arabs say, "Never trust a man who talks too much",' Selmi answered sternly. 'There are Bedu and Bedu, like anyone else!'

I

Cain and Abel

It was far from Egypt, but in another desert country – the Sultanate of Oman – that I first conceived of the idea of seeking out the last of the world's Bedu, the nomadic Arabs who have played such a dramatic part in the history of Western imagination. I was in Mughshin, a grille of ornate buildings in space-age Moresco set in the midst of sweltering, featureless sands, as a guest of an old Bedui called Musallim bin Tafl, once the companion of Wilfred Thesiger, the British explorer whose biography I was then researching.

In the early morning I accompanied the old man on his rounds, padding the periphery of his small kingdom as he always did, carrying the rifle presented to him by the Sultan of Oman's Special Forces. The wind was drifting off the desert, uncorking scents of salt and dust, and though the opal sky held a pledge of baking heat, at that early hour the air was cold across the naked sands. Among the salt-bush Musallim happened upon the spoor of a young gazelle. He crouched down to examine the V-shaped nicks, cut cleanly into the sand, and smiled. 'Allah is truly great!' he muttered. 'For He has brought back even the beasts of the wilderness!'

The old man never ceased to marvel how water had worked its magic on a land that had known nothing but aridness and drought for 10,000 years. Where the Bedu not long ago had licked parched, cracked lips as they searched desperately for a single, sulphur-smelling spring, gallons of groundwater now gushed from steel cocks, sousing the sand and coaxing it to life. Here, in the deserts of southern Arabia, where for generations the Bedu had eked out a precarious living from the barren soil, feeder-canals carried bubbling water amid new forests of palm-trees that dappled the earth with their shade.

Musallim paused often to listen to the magical sound of water flowing in the desert. He breathed in the bittersweet smells of leaf-mould, humus and moss, the perfumes of oleander and jasmine, that now toned the chalk smell of the sands he had known from childhood. With the trees had come the shrubs, and with the shrubs the grasses. With the grasses had come the darkling beetles, the lizards, the skinks, the butterflies, the spiders, the ants and the moths, the kangaroo-rat, the gerbil, the fennec and the Ruppell's sand fox. Now the greater animals were returning too. One day, perhaps, even the oryx would come back just as it had reappeared on the bitter plains of Jiddat al Harasis, where it had been extinct for a generation.

Following the slim path beaten by the passage of his bare feet each morning and evening for years through the mesquite and the camel-thorn, we reached the garden of melons, cucumbers and tomatoes Musallim himself had had planted. He called his Punjabi gardener, a gaunt brown man named Mohammad, from his tiny thatched hut in the garden, to have him start the fresh-water pump that fed the crop. Mohammad, clad only in a chequered loincloth, but carrying his bean-pole body with assurance, stepped out of his house and stared at us. He knew that there was no need to irrigate the garden now, but Musallim never grew tired of watching the pump work – of seeing before his eyes the miracle of water where all his life there had been only sand. The Punjabi climbed down to the oily lump of machinery and jerked the starter until, with a gunshot crack, the exhaust-pipe spat a single guff of smoke, and the cogs and ratchets rattled suddenly into action. A few moments later, clear water surged in a foaming torrent out of the conduit and into the feeder-canals. Musallim laid down his rifle and dabbled both hands in the stream, beaming, and splashing it over his face. 'Praise be to God!' he intoned. 'This is what I dreamed of when I was a boy. Water and green trees where there was only desert! Running streams where men used to die of thirst! No God but God, we live in a wondrous world!'

Despite his pleasure in the gardens and the palm-groves, though, it was evidently Musallim's discovery of gazelle-tracks that excited him the most. He had been a hunter since he could hold a rifle, and by the time he was twenty had become one of the most renowned marksmen in the Sultanate of Oman. So famous was his shooting, indeed, that small-arms instructors in the Sultan's Armed Forces would ask their best shots, 'Are you trying to equal Musallim bin Tafl?'

Not that Musallim had any further ambitions in the hunting line: his eyesight had been so poor for the past few years that he would, he admitted freely, have been lucky to have hit a camel at twenty metres. Still, he yearned for the game as he yearned for an old friend – it was something that had always been there in the old days when the larder was empty. 'In those days there *was* game, by God!' he told me. 'There were Barbary sheep in the canyons at Mughsayl, there were oryx in the steppes, and you saw gazelles in hundreds – as many as goats! I find the track of one baby gazelle in the wadi today, and I am as thrilled as a little boy!'

Even at seventy-odd, Musallim was an impressive figure. Small, squat, barrel-chested, and slightly bow-legged, his head was squarely symmetrical, his face a complex of wrinkles that formed and broke like rivers on the map of a drainage-system, his nose crooked, his eyes slightly blank – more from the ocular problems that had beset him in recent years than from nature. The features which defined him most, though, were his feet. They were wide and leathery, the toes hard-grafted and splayed, the heels cracked into clints and grykes by the interchange of heat and cold. These were not the feet of a townsman: together with his scarred and calloused hands, they looked out of place against the milk-white dishdasha, the multi-coloured headcloth, the silver cartridge-belt and the bone-handled dagger in its filigree scabbard that befitted his rank of Sheikh and Vice-Wali of the Government Administration Centre here at Mughshin on the edge of the great Empty Quarter, the Rubʿ al Khali.

The dream of creating a town out of this wilderness had come to Musallim, he said, when, during a border crisis between Saudi Arabia and Oman, Sultan Qaboos had sent word to Dhofar that Mughshin must be occupied at all costs, lest it fall into the hands of the Saudis. He had gathered a dozen Bedu tribesmen who bolted up to Mughshin on their camels, and waved an Omani flag facetiously whenever the Saudi spotter-plane hummed over. Thereafter, at his own expense, Musallim had built an Arab-style castle not far from the spring, which he had manned faithfully until the government disbursed two million dollars for the modern centre, which was sited a couple of kilometres away.

The dazzling new centre struck you at first like a mirage from the *Arabian Nights* – an enclave of quaint zinc-white houses sealed against the heat, their crenellated roofs giving them the look of miniature forts; a mosque with a marble dome of delicate jade-green; a modern hospital, a school, a generating plant, water-towers, guard-posts, all disguised as a sort of kasbah. It didn't take you long to notice that there was something missing, though: the centre had few inhabitants. Mughshin lay in no man's land on the edge of the world's largest single expanse of land, the Empty Quarter, 300 kilometres from Salalah and 600 from Muscat. Few people, at present, anyway, cared to live there. 'But the people will come,' Musallim assured me. '*Inshallah* they will come!' He was sitting in his *majlis*, a room of staggering dimensions – ice-box cool from purring air-conditioners – in which moisture-seals on the outer doors went 'Shooosh' as they closed. It was a gaudy palace that might have been dreamed up in Bedu imagination. The reception room was carpeted wall to wall with electric-blue deep pile, its main furnishings a score of gilt baroque chairs, padded with blood-coloured velvet and standing with their backs to the four walls. There was a glass-lined bookcase containing leather-bound volumes, and on the wall blown-up, out-of-focus photographs of Musallim mounting a horse and Musallim shaking hands with the Sultan. An entire platoon of retainers and relatives – mostly young men with earnest, bearded faces in working dishdashas – occupied the plush chairs, passing around tea in a giant vacuum-flask and listening to our conversation intently, like a tribunal.

Musallim had been born around 1920 in the Wadi Mughsayl, west of the town of Salalah, among gorges that, for half the year, were swathed in soupy sea-mist. The gorges were now traversed by a multi-million-dollar highway of switchback hairpins that spanned sheer cliff-faces where protruding rocks had simply been shaved away by the construction teams. Such a thing had been as undreamt of in Musallim's youth as a camel-race on the moon: his was a poor family of a poor Bedouin tribe. 'We had about twenty goats and no camels,' he told me. 'We lived on our goats, what we could shoot, a bit of trading with the towns in butter, wool, and skins. Apart from our goats, we had waterskins, a leather well-bucket, ropes and hobbles we made out of palmetto-fibre, cooking-pots, a coffee-set, fibre mats and goatskins for sleeping on, rifles, cartridge-belts and daggers and the clothes we stood up in. That was about the total of our possessions. Some Bedu would tend the incense trees that grow on the north side of the mountains, but our family didn't.'

'Then what are the Bedu?'

'The Bedu are those who live in the desert. They are tribesmen, and are loyal to their blood-relatives. They are strong, they can fight and they carry weapons. Not all Bedu are Arabs, and not all speak Arabic. But those who are permanently settled – the people of the towns and villages who never move from their dwellings, are not Bedu. They are called Hadr or Fellahin. Bedu and Hadr are different, but like two branches of a tree. Some tribes, like the Murrah in the north, have both Bedu and Hadr sections.'

'What distinguishes the Bedu from the Hadr?'

'The Bedui is more generous and more hospitable. Those are his most important qualities. He is also brave, but then bravery and generosity are almost the same thing, because when you are poor you have to be very brave to give away even what little you have. If your family depends for its livelihoood on twenty goats, it is very hard to kill one to feed to a guest, but that is what the Bedui would do. No one would be turned away from his camp, not even an enemy. If anyone stole from the guest or did him any injury under the host's roof, the host would avenge the insult for the sake of his reputation. Among the Bedu reputation counts for everything. A man *is* his reputation.'

I could see that the old man was growing restless, looking around him and inching nervously forward on his seat. Soon he was buckling on his cartridge-belt and dagger and calling for his rifle. We were going on a tour of the hospital and the school, I was informed. We marched across the hot sandstone of the square in a horde, Musallim at point, striding fast and furious, hardly pausing in his endless commentary, with myself struggling to keep up, and the rest lagging behind, armed to the teeth as if on a foraging raid. The hospital was spotlessly clean: six beds, well-stocked drugs cabinet, laboratory with microscopes, emergency clinic, operating theatre with state-of-the-art accessories. A friendly Indian doctor turned out to accompany us. 'We haven't got any patients at the moment,' he said, apologetically. 'In fact, we've never actually had any.' I had to admit that the lack of patients did tend to spoil the effect of it all.

'I was only three years old when my mother died giving birth,' Musallim said. 'There were no hospitals then. The Bedu had a hard life. A woman used to go on working until she felt the birth-pains coming on, then she would just sit in the shade under a tree and if there was no one there she would deliver the baby herself. My people never had any tents anyway. In the rains we would live in caves in the wadi sides, and the rest of the time we just lived under the trees. The Bedu were tough in those days, tougher than they are now. But being tough and being strong are not the same thing, because knowledge is strength also, and in those days the Bedu were completely ignorant of anything but their own lives. What good is toughness when your mother dies under a tree? We saw our children dying of sickness in front of us and had nothing to give them but a cup of camel's piss! We couldn't even read the Holy Quran or write our own names! What good is toughness when you have a dagger and a rifle and the others have tanks and aircraft? To be tough is a good thing, but – God have mercy on her – it wasn't enough to save my mother. Of course, it was Fate, and we all die when it is time for us to die. But Allah helps those who help themselves, and I wanted to have a hospital and a proper doctor here at Mughshin, so that our daughters would no longer die in childbirth under a tree!'

The school was a little more active than the hospital: it boasted three classes, three Moroccan teachers, and about eight pupils. The classrooms were air-conditioned and fully equipped with brand new desks, tape-recorders, videos, and every modern teaching aid. The pupils, intimate cabals in the front row, were all boys. And, I learned quickly, all were the sons of Musallim's relatives or his guards. 'I never learned to read or write,' Musallim commented. 'In those days no one thought it was important for a Bedui. Your school was the desert. You learned to look after goats and water camels, to shoot and to ride, to read the tracks of men and animals. You might be sent to herd the goats from when you were very small and you had to guard them against wolves and leopards – and you had to be on the lookout for raiders too. If you saw raiders coming you would just mount your camel – if you had one – and run away. There was no honour to be gained in fighting ten or twenty men, when all you had was probably a dagger and a stick. Then the families would band together and pursue the raiders on camels. Sometimes they would catch up, and there'd be a tremendous battle and people would be killed on both sides. Anyway, before I reached manhood, my uncle – who brought me up after my father died – was shot by Mahra raiders in one of those battles, and the wound festered and he died. I swore that I'd get revenge on his head from the Mahra, and by God that's what I did! Years later I went into Mahra country, and found a man from the section of the Mahra who had killed my uncle, and shot him. I didn't feel guilty about it at the time, because after all they had robbed me of my uncle, and that was the law of the blood-feud, a life for a life. Now I realize how futile it all was and what a waste of life, but I didn't then. When we had the opening festival here at Mughshin, with feasts and camel-races, I recognized the son of the man I had shot among the crowd. He was my guest. I saw that he had fallen on hard times. I felt sorry for him, so I gave him a sum of money. It was then that I realized how pointless it had all been. Things are far, far better now that Sultan Qaboos has brought peace. At least you can travel anywhere you want without being afraid that someone will put a bullet through your head!'

Back in the cool interior of his house, two great platters of mutton – whole joints of roasted sheep set on a bed of rice moist with fat – were brought in and placed before us on the floor. Musallim fussed about, directing the Indian servants to bring water, soap and towels, supervising the hand-washing, distributing various members of his guard around the trays. The Bedu knelt around the food, assuming the prayer-like posture they had grown accustomed to since childhood, with both feet tucked beneath them. Musallim busied himself in breaking open leg-joints and rib-cage and handing succulent titbits out to various people: pieces of liver and heart ended up on my side of the tray. 'In the name of God,' he said, 'let's eat!' Hands began scooping rice, moulding it delicately into round pellets which were popped into the mouth by a single finger; then began the tearing of the meat, the deft, carefully calculated selection of a joint, the daggers coming out of their scabbards to part flesh from bone.

I felt strangely ambivalent. All this was very different from the Arabia of which Thesiger and the other Western travellers had written: the land in which a herdsboy would lie down naked in a trench on a freezing winter night with only his shirt to cover him, in which a man would ride 300 miles by camel just to obtain news, in which travellers would make fire by striking a flint against a dagger-blade, kindling the spark with a strip of their own clothing. The Bedu Thesiger travelled with in the 1940s – bin Tafl among them – had known no other world but their own, and accepted the hardships of their lives as a small price for their freedom. They met every challenge, he wrote, with the proud boast, 'We are Bedu!'

For centuries the desert Arab had haunted the Western psyche as the epitome of all things chivalrous. He was the quintessential warrior archetype, lusting for deeds of glory and heroism, enduring incredible hardship for trivial gain, competing for personal distinction through fantastic acts of hospitality and generosity. He was famous for his individualism and natural democracy, for his pride of race and the purity of his blood, but above all for a spiritual perfection which accrued from his lack of attachment to material things. All that was best about the Bedouin, the Orientalists believed, came to him from his poverty and from the utter hardship of his life. Always, the Bedouin character was expressed through a polarity which compared it favourably with that of the settled farmer. As early as the fourteenth century AD, the Arab historian Ibn Khaldun wrote of the Bedouin that 'they were closer to the first natural state and more remote from the evil habits that have been impressed upon the souls of sedentary people . . . sedentary life constitutes the last stage of civilization and the point where it begins to decay. It also constitutes the last stage of evil and remoteness from goodness. Clearly the Bedouins were closer to being good than sedentary people . . .'

This polarity, with its overtones of Cain and Abel – the eternal conflict between the nomad and the settler – seemed so perfectly natural to the Western colonialists that it became an unquestioned part of their picture of the East: 'The two professions . . . stock-breeder and agriculturist never became united,' wrote John Bagot Glubb. 'The inhabitants of these countries remained, for thousands of years, divided into two distinct halves, the graziers and the cultivators, the nomadic and the settled. These two distinct manners of life produced entirely different characters and entirely different communities, often at bitter enmity, and regarding one another with contempt and aversion.' The distinction between nomad and farmer was useful, because by any other terms the definition of a Bedouin was hazy. Glubb wrote that a Bedouin must be a nomad who bred and kept camels, and must be able to trace his descent back from certain recognized pure-bred tribes. This definition might have suited the region of northern Arabia in which Glubb operated, but it was clearly unsuitable in other parts of the Arab world. In southern Arabia, for instance, men could have goats, cattle, camels and even cultivation and still be called Bedu, and as for having 'noble blood', in the Yemen even Somalis – an African people – were regarded as 'Bedouin'. In North Africa, where the term 'Bedu' was rarely used, nomadic tribes – even those who bred camels exclusively – were known simply as 'Arabs', a term which in Glubb's scheme of things meant 'shepherds'.

Wilfred Thesiger defined the Bedu as 'the nomadic camel-breeding tribes of the Arabian deserts', and wrote of them passionately: 'I knew I should never meet their like again. I had witnessed their loyalty . . . I knew their pride in themselves and their tribe; their regard for the dignity of others; their hospitality when they went short to feed chance-met strangers; their generosity with money they so badly needed . . . their absolute honesty; their courage, patience, endurance and their thoughtfulness. Constant raids and counter-raids with the blood-feud dominating their existence made them careless of human life as such, but no matter how bitter a feud, torture was inconceivable.' Thesiger bewailed the nascent modernization and settlement of the nomads as a tragedy: 'I realized that the Bedu with whom I had lived and travelled . . . were doomed,' he wrote. 'Some people maintain that they will be better off when they have exchanged the hardship and poverty of the desert for the security of a materialistic world. This I do not believe.' Later he added, 'I have encountered individuals among many races with high standards of conduct, but only among the Bedu were such standards generally observed. I was fortunate enough to know them before the discovery of oil in southern Arabia destroyed forever the pattern of their lives. The years I spent with them were the most memorable of my life.'

Taking Thesiger's as the definitive Western statement about the fate of the Bedu in modern times, I had come to Mughshin convinced that I would find the dull monotony of a desert suburbia, a once proud people now condemned to the humdrum of modern life. I had found instead something different – a traditional culture in the actual process of change, and, though I regretted the passing of the old life, I had to admit that the transformation had its fascinating aspects. Thesiger and the Orientalists had condemned the apparent acquiescence of the Bedu in their own modernization and settlement as a 'betrayal'. Now I found myself wondering who or what had been betrayed. It occurred to me that Ibn Khaldun had a lot to answer for: it was the notion of 'distinction', of 'polarity' – Cain against Abel, the 'pure' nomad against the 'corrupt' settler – which was to blame for this sense of moral outrage. I wondered if the terms Bedouin and cultivator had ever really been as mutually exclusive as some liked to believe. The celebrated Israeli scholar Emanuel Marx recorded in 1967, for example, that 16,000 Bedu still living in the Negev were 'primarily farmers' who also reared camels, sheep, and goats and worked for wages, yet considered themselves and were considered by the settled population 'true' Bedu. There was, in fact, an almost infinite variety of definitions of Bedu and 'true' Bedu, even among the Arabs.

Viewed in a different light – a light in which nomads and settlers were not polarities, but merely alternating stages of organization that the same groups used in response to changing conditions – the settlement of these Bedu at Mughshin looked less like 'betrayal' than flexibility. For centuries they had wandered across the harsh landscape of southern Arabia, from the hills of the Yemen to the soaring heights of inner Oman. For centuries they had fought a running battle with the wilderness. Here at Mughshin the wanderers had come home. Here, for a time anyway, the great battle had been won.

I asked Musallim whether it was true that the Bedu had lost their traditional qualities since adopting a more affluent life. He laughed dryly. 'Of course, something is lost when the old ways change. There are advantages and disadvantages. The Bedu certainly aren't as tough or enduring as they were. I don't suppose many of these boys could ride a camel for even a day without getting tired. The Bedu are not so hospitable or generous as they used to be, but then people are not so poor. When I was born the Bedu were unbelievably poor and anyone who wants to go back to being poor must be absolutely crazy! Old Bedu today will tell you that some things about the old days were better – and they were. But you won't find one of them who really wants to go back to those old days. Where do you think we would be today if we were still riding about on camels carrying our mother-of-ten-shots rifles, when our neighbours were flying aeroplanes? They would take our country from us as easily as raiders with rifles used to take the camels from an unarmed herdsboy. The world belongs to the survivors. Those who do not change with it will simply be destroyed.'

It was difficult to resist Musallim's rhetoric. I had assumed that the Bedu either did not want change or were naïvely unable to cope with its pitfalls. But my meeting with Musallim had shown me just how little they shared the Western vision of their future: by the very nature of where and how they lived, they were pragmatists rather than romantics. In the 1950s, Thesiger had written that they were 'doomed'. Now I questioned how much and in what ways that was really true. Had the skills and qualities that had made the Bedu famous – their bravery, endurance, hospitality, generosity, honesty and loyalty; their ability to read tracks, to handle camels, to live in the desert – survived into the last decade of the twentieth century? As we sped back to Salalah on the desert highway the next day, I resolved to travel in as many Arab countries as possible on a quest for the last of the Bedu – and what remained of their traditional way of life.

2

Snow upon the Desert

It was midwinter, and the tribes had descended from the mountains to graze their sheep on the plains of Palmyra.

A famished wind was prowling the Baadiyat ash Sham – the Syrian desert. The plains were packing out in umber and ochre, spreading to infinity and reducing our vehicle to a mote under the great crystal dome of light that was the sky. Nomad tents – segmented like immense black caterpillars – were pitched in the lee of the barren hills, and sheep advanced everywhere in close columns that speckled the landscape with their colours.

'But God, it's cold!' Ahmad said, dragging deeply on his cigarette. 'I think it's going to snow.'

This was the first time I remembered hearing a Muslim predict the weather.

It was two hours since we had left Palmyra, and Ahmad was nursing the pick-up across a surface as brittle as pack-ice. It was Ahmad who saw the camels first. He took the cigarette from his mouth and gestured towards them casually, as if he had known where to find them all along. They were flowing slowly in open formation across the range, not less than 100 of them, their behemoth bodies picked out and magnified by the crystalline light. Among them – almost under their feet – was a flock of sheep whose fleeces glowed like molten gold. I could also see the dark perpendicular shapes of humans – a boy riding a camel, a girl at his feet, an old man among the sheep by a donkey wadded with a blanket. As we drew near, the girl peered timidly at our city-white faces. Suddenly she made off in terror, sprinting helter-skelter through the ranks of placid camels, her layers of ragged clothing flying and her plastic flip-flops going slap, slap, slap on the hard earth. The boy, clinging on to the hump of a pot-bellied bull-camel, steered carefully away. Ahmad pulled up near the old man, a bone-thin, leathery figure, cackling through the gold fangs that were all that remained of his teeth. 'Ha! Ha! Frightened the life out of them!' he chortled. He had a jutting chin and a sliver of beard, and his knuckles were tattooed with wandering blue squiggles. Though he wore a heavy fleece-lined coat against the cold, he was on the move constantly, weaving and ducking as if to avoid the blows of an imaginary opponent. The Siberian wind seared across the frozen landscape with the sound of rending cloth, and in our shirtsleeves we were immediately quivering breathlessly. We plunged back into the car for our jackets and headcloths. The old man shook hands with us and jerked his head towards the donkey. 'Come and share my food!' he said. 'Come on!' The donkey was hobbled to a stake in the ground, and she wheezed, stamped and shuffled as the spider shadows of the camels floated by. 'Afraid of camels, this donkey!' the old man announced, jiggling bundles of dirty cloth from the animal's saddle-bags. 'Bought her from the Kurds. Kurds don't have any camels. She's a good beast, but she's not used to camels.'

He crouched down and unwrapped some flaps of thin bread, a pot of yoghurt and a bowl of fat. 'Only simple shepherd's fare,' he said. 'It's simple, but it's good!' He remained crouching, but his head assumed the task of movement, nodding and jerking from side to side. He broke off a piece of bread and dipped it in the yoghurt. 'Come on!' he said again. I followed his example, but Ahmad hung back and lit another cigarette. 'I'm not hungry,' he said.

I asked the old man if the camels belonged to him.

'God bless you, they aren't mine!' he said. 'No, no, I don't have any camels! Not me! Only Bedu keep camels. Those camels belong to the Bedu!'

'Aren't you from the Bedu, then?'

'No, not me, no never! I am an Arab, not a Bedui. The Bedu keep camels. The Arabs keep only sheep.'

After we had finished eating, he stood up and waltzed about in the wind. He pointed out a black tent, standing alone on a bleak ridge far in the distance. 'That's where you'll find the Bedu!' he said. Then, as a sort of parting gesture, he jumped up and down making a warbling sound from his throat. Instantly the sheep halted in their tracks, swerved around and came pelting towards us, led by a ferocious, shaggy belwether with broad horns, looking like the incarnation of the Pharaonic god Khnum. The belwether hurled itself at the shepherd's legs with such gusto that he was obliged to fight it off, laughing and cackling. He evidently took this as a sign of affection: 'See!' he said. 'You wouldn't get camels to do that!'

A little later we halted at the Bedu tent. In this pristine light, each detail of the tableau was highlighted perfectly: the long shank of fraying black wool with its peaks and troughs, tightly guyed and shuddering in the wind; a thick-bodied woman in a black dress dragging a heavy sack from a pile; a fluffy white sheepdog baring her fangs at us over a nest of puppies; small children with gold streaks in their hair, playing around a stack of basins made out of rubber tyres; two tractors in day-glo orange; a pair of Bedu boys tinkering under the engine-farings, who grinned at us through teeth that were stained dark with grease. A tall man wearing a fine camel-hair cloak and a shamagh was coming to meet us. His face was parched hide-brown with heavy features: high brow-ridges, deep eye-sockets, sad eyes, pursed lips, a moustache that was completely grey. He did not smile as he shook hands, but held himself grave and aloof as he sized us up. 'Welcome!' he said. 'Come into my tent! You will be my guests for the night!' The magic words, I thought. There might be tractors outside the tents, but the old code of hospitality still reigned supreme.

Inside the guest-section of the tent, neatly cordoned off by wool hangings, a fire of camel-droppings was smouldering dismally in a hearth. The stout woman bustled in and greeted us without shaking hands, shouting, 'Rest! Rest! Make yourselves comfortable!' She pulled out rugs and hard woven cushions, and arranged them around the fire. Although her thick dress covered her body from neck to ankle, her face was bare, displaying a mandala of woad-blue tattoos. We sat down at the hearth and our host – Salim – brought in a pile of spiky brushwood, arranged it over the camel-dung, and added a nip of kerosene. 'Watch your feet!' he roared, as he stabbed a tongue of flame at it from a disposable cigarette-lighter. A mushroom cloud of smoke belched up in our midst, and when it had died down we sat with our freezing hands outspread across the welcoming flames. 'Allah alone is all-knowing, but it is cold enough for snow,' Salim said. 'This *rimth* doesn't give out much heat, but it's better than camel-dung, and it's all there is at this time of year!'

He sat down on a rug, and a horde of small children in pyjama-cloth jallabiyyas rushed in and bounced upon him, chattering. Salim made tea methodically and poured the amber liquid out into small glasses. He refilled them every time one of us set a glass down. At last he asked Ahmad, 'Where is this foreigner from?'

'He is from England.'

'Where?'

'England . . . you know, Britain!'

'Where's that?'

'Haven't you ever heard of London?'

'Yes, I've heard London on the BBC. Do they speak Arabic in London? All the people I hear on the BBC speak Arabic perfectly!'

'What is your tribe?' I asked diffidently.

'Syria.'

'No, I mean your *tribe.*'

'We are Bedu. What can a foreigner know of tribes?'

'I know a little.'

'Very well, then. We are ʿAnaza. Do you know the ʿAnaza?'

Indeed I did. My 'handbook' to the tribes of Arabia – *Notes on Bedouins and Wahabys*, compiled by John Lewis Burckhardt in 1831 – listed the ʿAnaza as 'the most powerful nation in the vicinity of Syria, and . . . one of the most considerable bodies of Bedouins in the Arabian deserts'.

I was in the tent of one of the last families to rear camels in the Syrian desert – in the company of perhaps the most authentic and most aristocratic Bedouin tribe of all.

When I stepped off the Damascus bus in Palmyra only two days earlier I had despaired of finding any Bedu in Syria. The first thing I noticed was a chipboard sign nailed to a tree, with a straggling arrow pointing to some unknown object beyond: 'TOYRISTS WELCOME!' it read.

Chuckling, I humped my rucksack to the Zenobia Hotel, a French Colonial style oblong the colour of Gruyère cheese, which had been built when privileged tourists first began motoring to Palmyra across the desert in the 1920s. It stood right in the middle of the most impressive classical ruins in the Eastern world. The size and scale of the ancient town was breathtaking. The architecture spoke of fabulous wealth and deliberate ostentation: the vast entrance portals of the temples and the great arches suggested that they had been built to admit giants. There was nothing cowering to be glimpsed in Palmyrene style: power and confidence were writ large in wide expanses, towering tombs, dozens upon dozens of Corinthian pillars. As I walked through the fields of fallen masonry later, I was able to savour the same privilege that the exclusive tourists of the 1920s must have experienced: there were no other visitors in the ruins – I had the place completely to myself.

Except, of course, for the Arabs. Inside the perfectly preserved Roman-style theatre, there were two round-faced tribesmen warming their hands over a blazing wood fire, and in the colonnaded street outside there was a lanky boy in a full-length jallabiyya who tore after a clutter of fat-tailed sheep, vaulting over fractured pilasters and skimming stones calculated to miss them by inches. It was clear that the shepherds had been at home among the ruins for centuries: in the inner sanctum of the temple of Bel Shamim – the largest and most interesting section of the ruins – the ceiling was black with the smoke of their cooking-fires. By the time Islam arrived, Palmyra's expansive, confident civilization had long since shrivelled to a fearful defensiveness and suspicion. The Muslim Arabs had torn down the carefully crafted stones and pillars and turned the temple of Bel Shamim into a makeshift fort. The ancient caravan-city of Palmyra might have boasted a population of hundreds of thousands, yet the first Westerners to investigate the ruins thoroughly – a group of English merchants from the Aleppo trading colony, who arrived here in 1691 – found them inhabited by only thirty or forty families: 'poor, miserable people', whose 'little huts made of dirt' were installed inside the temple compound.

Freezing sleet began to sift down as I left the Bel Shamim temple. A Bedui – his face a diamond of chapped flesh between the folds of his shamagh – was sheltering against the wall near two very hypothermic camels. The man squared his shoulders expectantly as I passed. 'You ride camel, mister? Very nice!'

'Not the weather for camel-riding!' I said, in Arabic.

He shrugged, abandoning his hustling tone. 'It's going to snow. We haven't had weather this cold for two or three years. God is generous, but it's bad for the tourists!' Then he sank back with resignation into the shelter of his wall.

I took refuge from the rain in the Ethnological Museum, housed nearby in a fortified villa that had once been the residence of the Ottoman governor. A guide called Marwan, a gangling man who wore a permanent grin, ushered me around rooms filled with Fellahin tools, jewellery, and carpets, delivering a set speech in Arabic with English footnotes on each item. In the 'Bedu Room', two full-sized plaster models of camels displayed the traditional north Arabian riding-saddle, the *shadad*, and the ceremonial women's litter – the *markab* – which, with its great bow-shaped wings, had once been used to transport the new bride. Known as the 'Ark of Ishmael', after the father of one branch of the Arabs, the litter had traditionally been occupied in battle by the Sheikh's daughter – her hair flowing like a standard – and was the tribe's rallying-point, beyond which the warriors were not supposed to retreat. Burckhardt recounted the tale of Jedwa ibn Ghayan, notorious for having slain thirty Bedu in a single encounter, who sacrificed his life by charging through the enemy ranks to fell the camel carrying their *markab* with a blow from his scimitar. He was shot dead by a Bedui with a firelock only moments later, but, heartened by the fall of the standard, his own side rushed forward and routed their foes, leaving 500 enemy warriors dead on the field.

Marwan told me that the Bedu no longer used these artefacts: 'The bride is carried by car, now,' he said. 'They have forgotten how to make camel-saddles. The only real riding-saddles you will see are on the camels they use for tourists.' Marwan told me that no Bedu families reared camels now, anyway. 'I don't suppose there are more than two thousand camels in all Syria,' he said. 'In my father's day the ʿAnaza alone had hundreds of thousands of them – probably millions. In the 1930s the bottom dropped out of the camel-market, because the Egyptians – who used to import thousands of camels for meat – could get them more cheaply from the Sudan. The camel-tribes were rich, but started to become poor: they had these masses of camels, but no one would buy them. The money was in sheep, so most of the Bedu went over to raising them instead. In fact, if you think of the Bedu as camel-rearing nomads, you can say that there are no Bedu left at all.'

When the rain had eased, I walked disconsolately through a date-market that occupied a stretch of the main road. Syria had seemed the obvious starting-point for my quest for the last of the Bedu, yet apart from the tribesmen in the ruins and the man hiring out camels to tourists, I had encountered none at all. I walked slowly past the stalls of sackcloth and nylon fibre erected around racks of peach- and wine-coloured dates cut freshly in bunches from the tree, noticing that they were not the hard dates of Bedu tradition, but the squishy ones eaten by Westerners at Christmas. Palmyra had been a ruin for more than seventeen centuries, I reflected, yet the date-palms for which the Romans had named the oasis 'Place of Palms' still flourished today. Indeed, it occurred to me that the great tousle-headed columns which I had taken to be Corinthian were not Corinthian at all: they were the architectural equivalent of the palm-trees which had always surrounded this settlement on the desert floor. Some of the vendors were lighting brushwood fires with kerosene, and one of them waved a kettle at me. 'Welcome!' he bawled in a voice set some decibels too high. 'Arab *hospitalité!*' Nearby was a large sign on which was painted in English, 'DATSES FOR SALE HERE.'

The Ottoman citadel lurked on a pinnacle above the town, dark and brooding like a single crushed molar. Later, I climbed up to it by the steep and shaly pathway. After the lightness and feeling of space in the ancient city, the keep seemed wretchedly claustrophobic. If the Muslim Arabs had dined in the ruins, the Turks had withdrawn from them entirely to the peak of this natural spire. They had lived in more dangerous times than the ancient Semites – times of muskets and artillery – during which they sat astride this desert place uneasily as a foreign ruling élite. Whatever it was that the Turks had feared, they had gone to great pains to protect themselves from it: the castle itself stood on an island of rock completely surrounded by a deep, sheer-sided fosse which had been quarried out of the belly of the hill. The only means of entry was by a perilous wooden bridge to a heavily fortified doorway. As I approached the bridge, I met a big-bodied, grey-bearded man coming the opposite way. He was the custodian of the ruins. 'I've just closed,' he told me. 'There aren't many tourists about today. Because it's so cold. But I'll open it up for you if you like.' The interior was dank and crumbling, but from the parapet above there was a lovely view of the oasis. The ruins, their pieces laid out like bits of a gigantic jigsaw, were vast, but their scale was humbled by the sheer wild immensity of the desert. The wind up here had an arctic chill to it, and the sky was trawled by a stream of dark clouds which cast the Baadiya into a patchwork of light and shade. To the west lay the mirror-sheen of the Wadi al Ma salt-lake, and to the east, desert and sky mingled along the rim of a horizon that hid the distant Euphrates.

The forbidding yet fertile steppeland I could see from the parapet might well have been the birthplace of the Bedu. The word *baadiya* itself provides an important clue, since while in one sense it means merely 'desert' or 'desert steppe', in another it implies 'the beginning of life'. 'Bedu' is derived from the same root, and means 'the people of the *baadiya*', though the word cannot be traced back to any great antiquity.

Forty centuries ago, a people called the Amorites lived on the fringes of the cultivated land. Although they possessed neither camels nor horses, their lives were similar to those of later Bedu, for they herded sheep, cattle and goats and used donkeys as pack-animals. While some of them remained close to the cultivation, others roamed farther afield. A thousand years later a tribe known as the Aribi or Aribu, perhaps the descendants of the Amorites, appears on the Kurkh Monolith – an account of the battle of Qarqar in 853 BC – as one of a number of Syrian peoples that were defeated by the Assyrian king Shalmaneser III. The Aribi were led by a chief called Gindibu – the first individual Arab in history – and though it might never be known whether in fact the Amorites and the Aribi were one and the same, it is certain that, by the time of Shalmaneser, the people of the Baadiya had acquired the camel.

The idea of the Baadiya as the cradle of the Bedu is supported by Arab legend. Tradition has it that there were two main branches of the Arab family: the sons of Ishmael – Abraham's eldest son – and the sons of Qahtan, a descendant of Shem, son of Noah. The division was originally a distinction between southerners and northerners, for while the Ishmaelites settled around

Mecca and the Hejaz, the Qahtanites were based in the Yemen. According to a lesser-known legend, though, neither of these branches were 'true' Arabs but acquired their language and culture from a third group, the 'lost Arabs' or 'Arabizing Arabs' who originated in the semi-fertile steppes of the Baadiyat ash Sham. If they were originally the people of the Syrian desert – where the camel was hardly known before about 1000 BC – then the 'true' Bedu were originally humble shepherds, and not camel-men at all.

It was only from the vantage-point of this high keep that I began to understand the drama of Palmyra's history, the romance of the caravan-road on which its fabulous wealth was built. Through this place the ivory, ebony, spices, pearls and jewels of Persia and India were freighted on the backs of camels. Over these horizons had marched caravans laden with Cathay's silks and jade. Palmyra's burghers had grown fat on the caravan trade, and the public coffers overflowed with gold from the duty charged on every commodity brought through the town. The most telling monument to old Palmyra, indeed, was not the great temple of Bel Shamim, but the Palmyrene Tariff – a stone slab one and three-quarter metres high – which had once stood at the main gate. Dating from AD 137, and inscribed in both Greek and Aramaic, the Tariff listed the duty payable on slaves, dry goods, purple, cloth, cattle, water and salt. No trade was too shameful to escape the scrutiny of the Tariff-maker, as a fascinating clause of the tablet showed:

> Also, the publican will collect from prostitutes, from the one who charges 1d or more he will collect 1d [per month], from the one who charges 8 As he will collect 8 As [per month]. As for the one who charges 6 As he will collect 6 As [per month] etc.

Of such significance was the Tariff that it bequeathed a new word to the languages of Europe.

The name Zenobia is inextricably linked with the history of Palmyra. Her story was of a drive for power which led ineluctably to the downfall of the Palmyrene state. Zenobia was both beautiful and ruthless. She was intelligent, cultured, and as fluent in Greek and Persian as in Aramaic. A superb military strategist, she was the Diana of her time, excelling in the hunt and marching on foot with her regiments during her campaigns. She came to prominence as the second wife of Odaynath, doyen of Palmyra's leading family, who took the part of the Romans in their war against Persia, and was recognized by them for his partisanship with the title *dux* or viceroy of the east. Zenobia almost certainly arranged her husband's murder, and declared herself regent in the name of her son, Wahb Allah.

After her successful *coup d'état*, she rebelled against Rome, smashing the Roman legions sent against her and bringing the entire Province of Syria under Palmyrene control. She then marched to the Hauran and razed the town of Bosra, adding to her orbit the Province of Arabia. To the astonishment of the world, she went on to lead her army to Alexandria and actually succeeded in wresting Egypt from Roman grasp. By AD 270 this tiny palm-oasis in the Syrian desert had acquired an empire that stretched from Asia Minor to the Nile. A year later she renamed her son 'Augustus', in direct challenge to the Roman Emperor, Aurelian. This was too much for the dignity of Rome. Aurelian dispatched a punitive expedition which engaged the Palmyrene army near Homs, and for the first time the Semitic forces were soundly whipped. Zenobia fell back on Palmyra with Aurelian's legions in hot pursuit, but the town's defences could not sustain a determined siege. Aurelian quickly seized it and put a number of prominent citizens to the sword. Zenobia herself escaped, but was taken while attempting to cross the Euphrates. She was deported to Rome and paraded through the streets at Aurelian's triumph, shackled in chains of gold. Palmyra never recovered from this blow. In the following centuries the trade routes were diverted to the north, and its halcyon days forgotten. Only the olive-groves and date-palms remained.

What lessons did the rise and fall of Palmyra have to teach me about the Bedu, I wondered? Though classical Palmyrene culture incorporated Greek and Persian elements, it was essentially indigenous and Semitic – as Philip Hitti has put it, 'an illustration of the cultural heights which the Arabians of the desert are capable of attaining when the opportunities present themselves'. If the Bedu really did lay the foundations of Palmyra – and traces of them have been found here dating back as far as 2000 BC – then it is an illuminating example of the way in which nomadic and settled life were continuously fluid and interchangeable, and by no means fixed in eternal opposition as traditional authors maintained. In this case, clearly, the nomads had not remained poor out of preference for the freedom of the desert, neither had their ways been immutable. Here was an unmistakable parallel with what was happening in Arabia at the end of the twentieth century: a situation in which the Bedu had taken advantage of new opportunities, and adapted to a different mode of existence in order to survive.

The wind dropped as the day bowed towards sunset. Blue ribbons of smoke from among the palm-groves now curled up vertically to the darkening sky. The hills glowed like firecoals in the clear, cold, midwinter light. The custodian was growing impatient, shuffling and coughing on the parapet. As I finally followed him down the broken stairs, he said, 'There is no entrance fee. You can give me anything you like.' I took out my wallet and handed him a fifty-lire note. The old man crinkled it in his palm and regarded it mournfully. 'The last person here gave me a hundred,' he said.

I was walking back through the date-market, wondering what my next move should be, when I met Ahmad, sitting patiently in his new, polished Toyota pick-up, waiting for tourists. He was a shy, thoughtful young man of about twenty-four with a bristly red face, not handsome, but trim and athletic. I learned later that he had just finished his three years of national service in the army, and had bought the pick-up out of his savings.

'Where do you want to go?' he inquired.

I explained that I was looking for traditional Bedu – nomads who still bred camels in the Syrian desert. 'But they told me there aren't any left!' I said.

'Nonsense!' Ahmad said. 'I know where there is a family who still rear camels – real Bedu. Their tents are pitched near the oil-pumping station, T4.'

I arranged for Ahmad to meet me at the Zenobia the next morning. When he arrived I slung my rucksack into the back of the pick-up, and we followed the route of the old silk caravans, heading east. At first the way wound ponderously through the sandstone crags, as if wary of the infinite space beyond, but soon it turned arrow-straight and raced on over the ochre plains with a sense of uplift to the boundless sky. Suddenly, as the hills fell away behind us, a wonderful sight met my eyes: the desert was smothered by sheep in massed battalions, and black tents lay along the spreading skirts of the hills. 'The tribes have gathered here from everywhere this year,' Ahmad said. 'For ten years we had no rain, and this year there was a deluge! Look at that pasture! Just look at it!'

The pumping-station popped up out of the desert like a tiny oasis – shining industrial plant, ringed in mesquite trees and stone pines. Outside a tin shack full of automobile parts, an Arab in an overall was prising the tyre off a rusty wheel. We asked for directions to the camels, and he waved a spanner vaguely towards the north: 'That way!' he said.

I was excited to meet the ʿAnaza because they were one of the seven or eight great tribal entities of the Syrian desert, and traditionally regarded themselves and were regarded by other tribes as 'true' Bedu. They were a vast family of Ishmaelite clans which had migrated to Syria tent by tent, lineage by lineage, over a century and a half, building their power, attracting clients from other tribes, until, in 1860, they had expelled their Qahtani rivals – the Shammar – and chased them back into Iraq and the deserts of the Nejd. The multitude of their tents and the great quantity of their animals was a byword, and was explained among them by a story about their ancestor, Wayl. He had happened on the correct instant, they said, on the Night of Destiny – the twenty-seventh of the fasting month of Ramadan – when God was bound to answer men's prayers. Placing one hand on his she-camel and the other on his phallus, Wayl prayed that both her seed and his own should multiply and prosper, with the result that, by the 1940s, the ʿAnaza numbered 37,000 men and owned over a million camels.

My first surprise in the ʿAnaza tent was to learn that these 'noble' Bedu owned cultivation. 'We've got quite a few hectares,' Salim said. 'The barley's about knee-high now and coming on well. But heavens, it is hard work! Most days I am working there from dawn to sunset.'

They moved only a few kilometres a year, since their herds were no longer dependent for survival on the grazing. 'I can remember what it was like before we had motor-cars and tractors,' Salim said wistfully. 'We had no cultivation then and we used to go off scouting on *dheluls* (trained riding-camels) and then moved the tent to wherever the pasture was. We still have some *dheluls*, but we don't have any saddles. In the past we moved farther than we move now. It used to take five camels to carry the tent and everything. In those days we ate less bread and more dates and milk, but we bought flour and we sold our animals in the towns. It must have been a good diet, because then there was no disease.'

Ahmad sniffed doubtfully. 'There's always disease!' he said.

'Well, what I mean is that whoever was going to die, died, and whoever was going to live, lived, and there was no lingering on with medicines. We did have our own treatments. We used to give people the branding-iron. You can't beat the branding-iron when someone is sick, but if we use it today the doctors refuse to treat us. Then we had our own doctors too. They belonged to the Solubba, who were a weak people and so terrified of us that if a Bedui arrived they would run away. But they knew a lot of secrets. They knew more about sickness, about plants and animals and tracks, than any Bedui, by God!'

'Are there still Solubba living in the desert today?'

'No, none at all! They all went off to Saudi Arabia and Kuwait and became rich men!'

The wind was whipping the fabric of the tent above us and wafting the acrid smoke into our eyes. Salim's wife hurried back from the women's side and began to adjust the poles and guy-ropes expertly. In a moment she had sealed off the open side of the tent against the wind and opened the other side, giving us a view across a blasted expanse of *rimth* humps and ground gouged and scored by the feet of camels. It suddenly came home to me how beautifully adapted the tent was to the desert: it was architecture at its most mobile – in itself a symbol of the nomadic way of life. Because of the impermanence of its material, perhaps, little is known about the antiquity of the black tent, the use of which is spread from the shores of the Atlantic to the highlands of Tibet. Certainly it is not man's most primitive structure, for it is highly sophisticated in comparison with the windbreak or the grass-and-timber hut. If the Old Testament may be relied upon, then the tent existed in the time of Abraham – about 4,000 years ago – when the Patriarch left the city to tend flocks with his nephew, Lot, and pitched his tents in the land of Canaan.

A little later the woman returned carrying a tray laden with dishes, which she set at our feet: melting butter, yoghurt, and balls of sheep's cheese. She opened an old coat which contained flaps of moist bread. I expected her to return to her own part of the tent, but instead she sat down on the rug and began stitching a sheepskin coat, watching us eat.

'Was the old life of the Bedu better than the new?' I inquired.

Salim considered the question. 'It was better in some ways. It's true that in those days there was no peace, no security. The strong used to take from the weak: that was the only law. There was slaughter between the tribes. Of course, the Bedu were the bosses then, and it didn't bother us that the strong took from the weak, because we were the strong.'

'It was a hard life, because we had no water,' Salim's wife cut in. 'The water was far away, and we had to bring it on camels in waterskins – it tasted horrible. That was the hardest thing – no water, and never enough to eat. Now we have plenty.'

'But in those days, we had freedom,' Salim continued. 'There were no borders then – we could go to Iraq or Saudi Arabia or Jordan – we could move where we liked. We were free.'

'We were free, but we were hungry and thirsty,' the woman said. 'We could go where we wanted, but we only moved because we had to find grazing for the animals. Now we spend most of the year here: if only there was a school, our children could learn to read and write.'

Salim sent an irritated glance in her direction: 'Yes, and who would look after the camels if the children went to school? They don't need to read and write. The desert is their school!'

'Every Fellah's child can read and write. Why should their children have schools and not the Bedu?'

I asked if there was any fundamental difference between the Bedu and the Fellahin.

'In the past we had nothing to do with the Fellahin, and they had nothing to do with us,' Salim said. 'The ʿAnaza are of noble blood, and we looked down on them, and all the other tribes.'

'What does "noble blood" mean?'

'It means power. The ʿAnaza were the most numerous tribe, and had the most tents and the most livestock – tens of thousands of tents and hundreds of thousands of sheep and camels. Once we were so strong that all the villages near the desert, and all the weak tribes paid us *khuwwa* – "brotherhood tax". That's gone now, of course. Most of the ʿAnaza moved to Saudi Arabia because of the oil money. Now only the government is strong, but there are still tribes that we would never give our girls to, and never take wives from – like the ʿAwazim and the Shararat and the Solubba. They are just like slaves – white slaves. We still wouldn't marry into them, no matter how rich they were. That's a matter of blood! It is true that we aren't nomads like we used to be, but we still live in black tents. We could easily have a house in Palmyra if we wanted, but we prefer it in the desert.'

It was almost sunset, and the cold had become more intense. When I stepped outside the tent for a minute, it was like walking into a freezer. The sun was lodged on terraces of cloud above the horizon, sending vapour trails of brilliant colour along the frozen ground. Ghost figures were migrating across the periphery of my vision, and I turned to see the camels coming towards me, loping madly in twos and threes, pursued by the herdsboy's shrill cries. Soon they were gliding in from all directions, converging on the water-tank that stood on a farm-cart behind the tent. Salim tramped out and opened the water-tap, and the camels began to roar and tussle, entwining their great necks. 'We water them every day now,' he told me on his way back. 'In the old days we had to take them to the wells. Now we bring them water with the tractor and trailer.' He advised me to fetch my things in from the car and make myself at home, and as I was collecting my rucksack, Ahmad appeared. 'I'd better be going now,' he said.

'Wait a minute! I thought we were staying the night here.'

'It's perfectly all right for you, but I'm not used to it. I've never slept in a tent before.'

'Not even in the army?'

'No. I was an ambulance-driver. I've never slept in a tent in my life!'

I could see that there was no changing his mind, and I let him go with instructions to pick me up soon after sunrise in the morning.

It was dark in the tent now, except for the flickering light of the fire. As soon as the sound of Ahmad's pick-up had petered out in the night, there was an ominous silence – the harbinger of a distinct sea-change. After a while, Salim asked, 'What exactly do you want in the tents of the Bedu?'

'Only experience.'

'Who was that man who came with you?'

'A driver. A townsman from Palmyra.'

'Are you sure he doesn't belong to the government?'

'I don't think so.'

'How much are you paying him?'

'That's my business.'

'What profit do you make from staying here?'

'Directly – none.'

My rucksack had been laid in the corner of the tent and while Salim was grilling me the children started to open the straps and examine the contents – my sleeping-bag, my water-bottle, my small tent. Salim looked on, interested but unconcerned: 'What have you got in there?' he inquired.

'Just my sleeping and washing things.'

'Have you got any spare shoes? I could do with a new pair of shoes.'

'Sorry.'

The boys were unrolling my sleeping-bag, and unscrewing my torch. I watched, trying to conceal my concern. 'Don't worry,' Salim said, making no effort to stop them, 'your things are safe in a Bedui's tent. Much safer than you would be in a hotel. How much did you pay for your hotel in Palmyra? See, you are getting a bed here free! No one is as hospitable as the Arabs! Tell me, in *your* country could you just turn up at someone's house and unroll your blanket?'

I had to smile, assailed by visions of a Bedui arriving at a semi in suburban England and bedding down happily on the lawn. 'Look, it's not that my people are inhospitable,' I told him, 'it's just that we don't live in the desert. It's a different way of life!'

We were joined by Salim's eldest son, a lad of eighteen with an inquisitive face, who was on leave from his military service in Damascus. He seemed friendly when he shook hands, but as soon as he had sat down at the hearth, he asked his father: 'Who is this man? What does he want here?'

'He is a Christian.'

'Perhaps he is a spy!'

His opinion obviously weighed heavily on his father, for afterwards Salim seemed to fall into a kind of lethargy, sinking back upon his cushions and answering my attempts at conversation with monosyllables. Instead I tried to strike a rapport with his son. 'I was a soldier once,' I said. 'Parachutist. In some ways it's a good life. What unit are you in?'

'I'm the servant of an officer.'

'Oh. Do they give you plenty of leave in the army?'

'You should know, if you were really a soldier once!'

Salim and his son began rolling stubby cigarettes from a pouch of tobacco: 'Don't you smoke?' Salim asked.

'Yes, I smoke a pipe.'

'Smoke it! Smoke it! I want you to be at ease here!'

When I did, though, it caused consternation. 'What's that stuff he's smoking?' Salim demanded.

'It could be hashish and you wouldn't know!'

The children had left off sorting through the contents of my rucksack and had gathered around me, giggling and chattering too fast for me to understand. When I got up to go outside I tripped over a box hidden in the darkness, and they roared with laughter. Some of them even followed me outside to watch me pee.

Back inside the tent, Salim's son said, 'Aren't you afraid to sleep in the desert?'

'No. Why should I be?'

'Well, there are wolves and hyenas here,' he said. 'There are some bad people too!'

I suspected that this was a rather puerile attempt to frighten me, for even Salim roused himself from his doze long enough to say, 'That's nonsense! In a Bedu tent you are completely safe! Just think of what you would have to pay in a hotel! In the tents of the Arabs it's free!'

This was the last sentence he uttered all evening, and before long his wife entered with a sheaf of heavy blankets and allowed me, thankfully, to retire.

I was awoken by the sound of camels being hustled out of the camp to the clicks and shrieks of the herdsboys. A little later came the roar of tractor-engines being fired. The sun was up bleary-eyed, swathed in cotton cloud: the bell-clear brightness of yesterday was gone. Salim peeled back his covers and built up the fire, warming his hands until his wife entered with a pot of fresh tea. We sipped in silence, until Salim said, 'God knows all, but there might be snow today. Last time it snowed our tent was almost buried. The shepherds had to bring their sheep inside their tents and light big fires until help came: sheep can't stand the cold, but camels can resist it well enough.' Later, he watched me packing my things away in my rucksack, scrutinizing each item carefully. Quite nonchalantly he said, 'I need a new pair of shoes, size eight. If you come again, you must bring me a pair!'

His wife surfaced again with yoghurt and bread for breakfast, but after I had taken two mouthfuls the dish was mysteriously whipped away.

I took it that they were waiting for me to go.

Almost at once I heard the buzzing of an engine, and Ahmad's pick-up came bumping into view. We watched it through a gap in the tent, increasing in size until I saw his whiskery face smiling through the windscreen. I was very glad he was here. I loaded my rucksack into the back, and as I shook hands with Salim, I asked him, 'Since no one rides camels any more, and people don't eat them, why do you bother raising them anyway?'

'People buy the *dheluls* to give rides to tourists!' he said.

Much later I discovered that some small items had disappeared from my rucksack: trifling things such as my razor, some soap, and the toggle-rope for my shamagh – and I was sure that the small Bedu children had taken them. It didn't bother me, but when I thought of Salim saying, 'Your things are completely safe,' and the huge investment the myth-makers had made in the sacred inviolability of a Bedui's guest, I could not suppress a wry smile. I had achieved what few travellers before me had achieved: I had been robbed in the tents of the ʿAnaza – the noblest Bedu tribe of all!

I refused to be perturbed by my first contact with the 'noble' Bedu of the Syrian desert. Once, I might have explained their less than gracious behaviour by claiming that they had been 'corrupted' by contact with civilization. To the traditional travellers, Bedu who became semi-settled had somehow 'failed' the desert's rigorous selection-test: they were 'rejects of the desert' or nomads for whom the nomadic life had been too much. These 'failures' were considered to have little moral worth, and indeed were 'reputed to be thievish, treacherous and untrustworthy; whereas there were few known instances of travellers receiving anything but good treatment from Syrian nomads . . .'

Now, it occurred to me that the 'corrupting' influence of civilization was an illusion. The 'freedom' travellers had claimed to find among the Bedu was surely the projection of their own delight in being freed from the constricting demands of European society. The 'true' nomad – clinging to the remote desert, shunning all contact with the outside world – has probably never existed. There were never any nomads who lived exclusively in remote deserts – oscillation between the fertile or semi-fertile steppes in summer and the desert in winter had always been the nomadic way. Burckhardt noted, a century and a half ago, that the ʿAnaza – the *crème de la crème* of the Bedu – did not stray far from the settled country in spring and summer: 'Their principal residence . . . during that time,' he wrote, 'is the Hauran and its neighbourhood, where they encamp *near and among the villages*.' In fact, the nomad who lived entirely on his own animal products was another figment of the romantic imagination. On the contrary, it is well known that the Bedu ate little meat. Apart from milk, their main diet was always bread and dates, obtained in one way or another from the 'despised' but vital Fellahin.

The conversion of 'noble' Bedu to 'morally worthless' semi-nomads or settled farmers was lamented by the traditionalists, because they wanted to believe that the East had always been static. The life of the Bedu had, they imagined, remained unchanged since the beginning of time, until they were rudely forced out of their ancient ways by technological and economic development, and obliged to settle down. In fact, there was absolutely nothing new in the process of settlement: the various means of livelihood which travellers observed in the Arab world were actually part of a sliding scale of survival along which lineages and households had moved backwards and forwards throughout the millennia. Men do not willingly look for a 'death in life' – as T. E. Lawrence described the nomad's lot. They seek always the best means of survival the ecological and political conditions can provide.

Many cultivators, semi-nomads and shepherds were once camel-breeding Bedu, and settled, not because they had 'failed', but because conditions were favourable for a more settled way of life. Conversely, when conditions became unfavourable for cultivation, due to drought, disease, disaster, or high taxes, for instance, these families would make for the desert – perhaps after decades or even centuries as farmers – and take on the mantle of the Bedu once again. There may not have been – as T. E. Lawrence claimed – a single settled Arab unmarked by the brand of the nomad, but neither was there a single Bedui, no matter how 'blue-blooded', who did not have a Fellah's planting-stick in his saddle-bag.

Not long after we had regained the asphalt road that led east to the Euphrates, the snow began, drifting down across the gaunt plains. The sky was pregnant with white and soft purple, and the distant hills dissolved into mist. 'It's snowing!' Ahmad said, 'Let's go back to Palmyra!'

'Not unless it gets really bad!'

We were heading for Qasr al Hayr ash Shariqi – a brace of desert fortresses built during the Ummayyad era – near the ruins of which there was supposed to be a large Bedu encampment. All along the road the Bedu had lit fires from discarded tractor-tyres, whose smoke wreathed up among the snow in coal-coloured spirals. Men in sheepskin coats and headcloths congregated around the pyres shoulder to shoulder, hands outspread, while others lay on the ground beneath the falling snow, transforming their sheepskins into miniature tents. The sheep stood in miserable wedges head to tail and flank to flank. Tractors came drumming up the wet road carrying Bedu swathed tightly in cloaks, scarves and headcloths. We hummed through Sukhna – once a caravanserai on the Silk Road, now a mean town of deserted streets. In the open door of a breeze-block store a cluster of boys and men stared at us from the comforting glow of a brazier. Beyond the town we left the road and headed once more across the desert. A bleak weirding wind gusted against us, and fizzles of snow fell upon the windscreen like cold volcanic ash. Ahmad had lost the way. He had been to Qasr al Hayr many times before, but never in such white-out conditions as these. The country pitched and yawed under the blizzard. There was a billiard-table green in the surface, and shortly there was an armada of long-coated sheep, brown-and-white and red-and-white, led by a bare-headed man in a cloak. Ahmad jumped out to talk to him: the air seeped in and it was unbelievably cold. In a moment he was back, saying, 'It's only two kilometres from here!'

Fifteen kilometres on, we were still searching for Qasr al Hayr, and Ahmad was cursing silently. 'The Bedu have no idea of distance!' he said. 'They'll tell you it's two kilometres when it's twenty, and twenty when it's two!'

The snow seemed to be easing, the sky clearing, and for a moment we glimpsed in the distance feldspar hills veined in blue like Stilton cheese. Then, very suddenly, a great edge of masonry sprang out of the desert – an L-shaped wall, many feet thick. I stepped out into the burning cold to inspect it, while Ahmad warmed himself with yet another cigarette. My guidebook said that this was a 'khan' or caravanserai, associated with the two sister-fortresses of Qasr al Hayr which stood four kilometres away. It was easy to observe how that conclusion had been reached: the wall was so perforated by Moorish arches along its length that it could not possibly have been a defensive structure. Standing on the Silk Road as it did, in proximity to two forts, it might therefore have been a halting-place for caravans.

In fact, the entire distance from here to the fortresses was marked by traces of a mud wall whose external and internal buttresses show that it was no military bulwark, but the boundary of an immense area of cultivated land. *Qasr al Hayr* means 'fortress of the enclosed garden', and in the period Westerners call 'the Dark Ages' the Arabs actually created a man-made oasis here in the remote ranges of the Syrian desert. The crops were fed – perhaps – by a rain-harvesting system from which the collected liquid was funnelled along feeder-canals. These arches were sluice-gates put in place to drain off the excess water.

It was too cold to linger, but as we rattled along the remnants of the boundary-wall, I reflected that the garden planted here as early as the eighth century AD marked yet another triumph of adaptability for the nomadic Bedu, and yet another indication that the Syrian desert was not the utterly inhospitable wasteland it was often supposed to be.

The snow had stopped, and we had a clear view of the ruined castles standing in a perfect hollow on the desert surface. From a distance the desert's vast scale reduced them to models, and it was only when we pulled up between them that their true size became apparent. They were squarish, built of two-metre-thick blocks of peach-coloured stone, with bulging turrets topped with brick domes. The easternmost and smaller of the structures had but one gate, which directly faced the entrance to the larger castle across a corridor no more than 100 metres wide, marked by a square watch-tower. The iron grille across this gate was locked, and of its interior we were able to glimpse only some fine Corinthian pillars of the same style as those found in Palmyra. We wrapped our shamaghs around our heads against the biting cold, and walked through the gateway into the larger citadel, where great vaulted arches seemed to be perched tentatively on the most fragile of supports, and top-heavy slabs of masonry hung out of the walls at perilous angles. There were the remains of mud buildings inside, but their structure had been obscured by the quarryings of Bedu, intent on buried treasure.

Constructed by the Caliph Hisham in AD 728–9, Qasr al Hayr is the oldest fortified structure in the Islamic world yet dated. This, and the man-made oasis it helped to guard, were products of the so-called 'Golden Age' of the Ummayyads, when Islam still remained firmly in the hands of the Arabs from whom it had derived. The Ummayyads were one branch of the Quraysh, the settled townsmen from Mecca whose ancestors had once been Bedu, and among whom the Prophet Mohammad had been born. Drawing their support partly from the Bedu tribes of Syria, they presided over an era in which tribesmen were settling in urban centres such as Damascus in great numbers. Nevertheless, Hisham and his brothers – three of whom also ruled as Caliphs – retained an affection for the Baadiya, where several of them had been sent as children to hunt, ride, shoot, drink wine, and compose oral poetry in the tents of the Bedu. Their affection manifested itself in the foundation of many such estates, hunting-lodges, and country residences in the Syrian desert.

We emerged from the far gate to see a pair of Bedu boys grazing their sheep among the *rimth* bushes. They were wearing heavy sheepskin coats with stiff empty sleeves that stuck up like vestigial wings, giving them the appearance of amiable penguins as they hopped about in the cold. 'Who used to live here?' I asked the boys, after we had shaken hands. 'We don't know!' one of them answered. He pointed north, to where I could see a village of mud-brick houses and black tents, about a kilometre away. 'That's where *we* live!' he said.

The Bedu village might have been less monumental than the Ummayyad ruins in whose sight it stood, but it was a fascinating illustration of the successful integration of desert and sown. The houses were plain, windowless boxes of mud-brick, centred on sheepfolds of twisted thorn and low walls. For each house, though, there were one or two battered black tents, and despite the cold it was in the tents that the life of the settlement seemed to be going on. To the north I noticed an elliptical pool of burgeoning wheat, bottle-green like the waters of a deep and placid lake. Goats and long-haired sheep skulked around the houses, and flocks of turkeys grazed the stony ground beyond. We halted outside one of the houses to inspect some baked-mud monoliths that looked like traditional grain-silos, but were in fact sealed stores of firewood. A woman whose face was a horoscope of spiralling tattoos bustled out of the nearby tent to call us in for tea.

In the smoky recesses of the tent another woman sat cross-legged on a mat, working with a Singer sewing-machine. A younger woman and a girl of no more than five were sitting by a fire, both contentedly smoking cigarettes. The women were strikingly nun-like in their enveloping black dresses tied at the waist with rope, and their pointed, wimple-like headcloths. They wore only narrow kerchiefs to provide the hint of a veil when drawn across the mouth. Our presence seemed of insufficient weight to urge them into a show of respectability, though, which was fortunate, as the younger woman was remarkably beautiful, despite a mouthful of gold teeth. Ahmad sat down next to her on the rug, and his rubicund face blushed yet more redly when she smiled at him and said, 'You are from Palmyra. You look exactly like our teacher here. Perhaps you are his brother!'

'You have a school here?' he asked.

'Yes. All our children can read and write.'

As the older lady poured out tea, she told us that, like the Bedu I had stayed with last night, the people here belonged to various branches of the ʿAnaza. 'We have our fields, and our sheep,' she said, 'but we don't have any camels. We got rid of them thirty years ago, because they were no good any more. Cars are more comfortable. In the wet season we take our tents out into the desert, and we carry the sheep in trucks. Sometimes we go as far as Homs.'

I asked about the *markab* – the traditional camel-litter for brides with its curious sweeping arms. The young woman giggled. 'The bride is carried by car now,' she said. 'No one has used the *markab* for a very long time!'

'But are you still Bedu now you have houses?' I asked.

'Of course,' the old woman replied with a touch of indignation. 'Houses don't make any difference. We are still Bedu, just the same!'

The woman with the sewing-machine worked away silently during our conversation, hunching uncomfortably over the device, turning the handle with terrible concentration. I watched her with interest for a moment, and realized suddenly that this Singer was a genuine antique. 'That's an old machine,' I commented.

The old lady paused and glanced up at me, her face a pattern of tattoos on tanned leather. 'It certainly is!' she said. 'It belonged to my mother. It's a *Sanja*, by God! A foreigner like yourself once came here – an Italian he said he was – and offered me four thousand lire for it. "I won't sell, by God!" I said. "This *Sanja* belonged to my mother! I wouldn't exchange it even for a hundred goats! And besides, if you are ready to give me four thousand lire, it must be something very special indeed!"'

As we drove back along the wall which, 1,000 years ago, had marked the boundary of gardens which the Bedu created out of the desert, I wondered if indeed very much had changed. Nomads who reared camels exclusively had always been a tiny minority even among the pastoral population of the Arab world. In the Baadiya, with its oscillation between fertility and barrenness, it had always been those who combined agriculture with livestock-rearing who had been most in evidence. If there was a norm in the Arab way of life, it was surely this, for in a changing environment it was those who were the least specialized who had the greatest chance of success.

On the way back to the road, we halted at a modest tent made of jute sacks, where 500 head of sheep were guzzling grain from dozens of rubber bowls. Two white-haired sheep-dogs bounced towards us, snapping, as we left the car, but they were called off by a young man in a jallabiyya, with a mop of tousled black hair. He bade us sit down at the hearth inside the tent, while his wife – a dark, lively gypsy of a woman – made tea on a spirit stove.

His name was Habib, and he too belonged to the ʿAnaza, though he worked as a professional herdsman for a merchant from the town. 'These sheep belong to him,' Habib said, 'and they're all rams – no ewes at all!'

'How do the flocks increase?' I asked.

'They don't. We buy the lambs from other shepherds and rear them here. Then we sell the lot for meat in Damascus, and buy another lot. The government gives us barley to feed them on, but when there is good grazing, like there was this year, the price of sheep goes up.'

'Goes up? Surely, if conditions are better the price will go down. Isn't it the law of supply and demand?'

'It doesn't work like that. If the grazing is poor we have to buy more grain, and to do that we have to sell more sheep in the market, so the market is flooded and the price of sheep goes down. For us a year of poor grazing means poor prices.'

Habib had only recently been married and had just acquired his first tent. 'I haven't made enough to buy a proper tent of goats' wool,' he explained. 'They cost about thirty thousand lire to make. The women still make them, but we have to buy the goats' wool because the Bedu don't have goats these days. Sheep's wool is no use for making tents. The women can only work in the summer and it takes months just to weave one section of the tent. Unless you buy bits of it from other people, making a full tent is the work of years!'

There was a gas-lamp attached to a cylinder in the tent, and a chest of drawers, upon which Habib's wife was unscrewing plastic jars. She produced a tray loaded with balls of cheese, black olives, bread, and a delicious pickle called *fetr* made from local mushrooms. We crouched around the meal together. Habib looked at his wife with the affection of a newly-wed. 'In your country, do you get married for love?' he inquired.

'Usually, yes.'

'We got married for love. My wife belongs to a different tribe. I was herding the sheep near her family's tent, and we fell in love at first sight.' The girl grinned and laughed uncomfortably. 'What I want now is to earn enough money to get my own tent, and to have children. As many as God sends. I would like them to go to school, because I never learnt to read and write. I have spent my whole life in the desert, except for the two years of military service, which I did at Homs – a dirty, noisy place! You feel trapped in the city. Give me the desert any day!'

Within minutes after we left the tent it was snowing again, and this time the snow was coming down in large, flat flakes like feathers. The plains were transmuted from ochre to alabaster, under a sky that was grey and so low that it caressed the ragged peaks of the hills. There were drifts along the edges of the highway, and the pyres of the Bedu had been soused, the tractor-tyres spluttering and choking for air. The only living things moving in the desolate landscape were the dark figures of shepherds and their flocks, but as we whizzed past, they too were frozen for an infinite moment in our memories, as they plodded at snail's pace towards black tents that were already sagging under massed white wedges of snow.

3

The Land of Edom

Sunset in Damascus was the tramp of grey-robed men out of streets smeared with the day's drizzle. It was the sun like a wan eye blinking feebly through the last shreds of flaccid cloud. On the Avenue of the Revolution the traffic was an endless scream of brakes and tyres, jostling and jerking forward in a roil of benzene and burned rubber smells. The crowds in Martyrs' Square were a tide ebbing out into the main arteries, mingling with the traffic like stragglers across a raging torrent. From the grid of alleys behind the Hejaz railway station emerged a three-wheeled refuse truck. A man leaned out of his cab, honking a brass horn like some prehistoric trumpet, miraculously clearing a swath through the fevered cars. Below the Avenue, the Barada river issued unnoticed from a cloaca, a grey surge of foam running shallow over stones, weaving and writhing beneath the decrepit buildings that hung over it on tenterhooks. It was difficult to believe that this shallow froth was the inspiration for the sacred river Alph in Coleridge's *Xanadu*, or indeed that without the Barada this city would not be here at all.

This was the hour I chose to lose myself in the warren of Old Damascus – the Ummayyad town that lay along the Barada's banks. I watched the rags of the day rinse away into the scurrying waters, and turned into the covered market, where the night-globes were already firing up, brindling the flow of humanity with bars of sulphur-coloured light. Disconnected faces floated before me: Arab, Sudanese, Mediterranean; men in shamaghs and hats and heavy turbans, women wearing masks and veils and coloured *hejabs.* Along the walls of the Ummayyad mosque, men were sitting around glowing braziers on little stools. The Street Called Straight was a dark conduit where vehicles were shooshing past, scarcely visible but for blazing headlamps and an aura of petrol fumes. I hurried through pools of light cast out from the doors and windows of shops, each one a glimpse of a self-contained planet: a man sharpening a knife on a grinding-wheel in a shower of sparks; another shaping a coffee-pot on a press; three cross-legged boys in white skull-caps embroidering carpets; a butcher shaving strips of flesh from a loin of hanging meat; a barber enveloped for an instant in a halo of cigarette-smoke as he rested from shaving his client. This street would always be associated for me with the figure of Charles Montagu Doughty, one of the greatest of Western explorers in Arabia. He had been here almost a century before, yet I could sense his presence. I had this irrational feeling that if I hurried I could somehow catch him up. It was as if Doughty and I were linked by this street on a level where the barriers of measured time no longer constrained us:

> Time present and time past
> Are both perhaps present in time future,
> And time future contained in time past . . .
> What might have been and what has been
> Point to one end, which is always present.

I savoured these thoughts for a moment as I marched, for I knew that time and change were the central themes in Western ideas about the Bedu and the East in general. Doughty and three other nineteenth-century British travellers in Arabia – Palgrave, Burton and Blunt – had done more than anyone else to generate the idea of the Bedu as a race which had preserved the primeval innocence of mankind, a people who, it seemed, were impervious to the normal process of history. The Bedu were 'static while the world moved', Rana Kabbani has written, 'pure of all corrupting influences, a purity that greatly endeared [them] to a Western eye so appreciative of symbolic horoes'.

In Doughty's time, Europe was undergoing a period of change so rapid that it was difficult to comprehend: in the East there remained to artists, travellers and philosophers a vision of the immutable – the unchanging landscape of the biblical era. 'As for the nomad Arabs,' Doughty wrote, 'we may see in them that desert life, which was followed by their ancestors, in the Biblical tents of Kedar . . . we almost feel ourselves carried back to the days of the nomad Hebrew Patriarchs . . . And we were better able to read the bulk of the Old Testament books, with that further insight and understanding, which comes of a living experience.' So enticingly unimpeachable was this concept that Doughty's words were still being paraphrased uncritically a century later: 'The Bedu . . .' wrote the naturalist Bryan Nelson in 1973, 'practise a specialized and demanding way of life almost exactly as they did in pre-biblical times.'

But no culture truly remains outside the process of history, not even the camel-rearing Bedu of Arabia. Indeed, the biblical scholar W. F. Albright says that there is little archaeological evidence that camels actually existed in the region during the time of Abraham – the nineteenth century BC – nor are there any references to camels in the records of Mesopotamia from that epoch. Albright claims that biblical references to Abraham's camels were added to the scriptures later by scribes attempting to bring them up to date. If the camel existed at all in those times, it must have been in such small numbers that it had no impact on the economy of the day. If Doughty had indeed been transported back to the biblical tents of Kedar, he would have been surprised to find that the way of life he believed so timeless simply did not exist.

Yet as I dashed through the darkness on the Street Called Straight that night, I could not restrain a sense of empathy with Doughty, as one who went before, who risked all to live and travel among the Bedu. Nor could I deny the dewdrops in my eyes when I recalled his encounter – after all his privations in the desert – with an old friend, on this very street: 'Tell me (said he) since thou art here again in the peace and assurance of Ullah, and whilst we walk as in former years, towards the new blossoming orchards, full of sweet spring as the gardens of God, what moved thee, or how couldst thou take such journeys into the fanatic Arabia?'

Next morning I was at the taxi-station behind the Hejaz railway terminus, where rows of cabs were parked fender to fender in muddy puddles, and drivers in leather jackets were hustling for passengers. A man called Abdallah agreed to take me to Amman in his taxi, an enormous Chevrolet, originally white, but now almost coral-coloured from the rust. 'Don't worry about the car,' Abdallah said, 'it is highly trustworthy. I do this run from Jordan and back almost every day!' Abdallah was small and carelessly dressed in jeans and biker-jacket: blue chin, cavalry moustache, long black hair swept back in a brylcreamed slick. He said that he was from Amman, but it was not difficult to guess that he was Palestinian. 'I'm originally from the Negev,' he admitted. 'You know the Bedu? I am a Bedui. My tribe is the Tarabin.'

As it happened I had heard of this tribe, because only recently I had read *Bedouin of the Negev* by Emanuel Marx. The Negev Bedu were particularly interesting, because while they were mainly offshoots of the great Bedouin tribes of the Hejaz, they included cultivators and herdsmen under the tribal aegis. 'I understand the Negev Bedu are doing very well,' I said. 'The Israelis have given them tractors and things and they are better off than ever.' Abdallah scowled over the driving-wheel as he piloted the Chevrolet out of the bleak streets of Damascus. 'Maybe they are,' he said, 'but those who remained in the Negev after the Israelis came were not true Bedu!'

Here was yet another definition of 'true' Bedu to weigh against my favourite one – that of the anthropologist Shelagh Weir: 'the Bedouin are pastoral nomads whose traditional way of life is based mainly on herding animals, and partly on small-scale farming, smuggling, protection of trade routes and other activities.'

Abdallah wore modern clothes and drove a taxi, but – according to Weir's definition, at least – he had not abandoned at least one aspect of the 'traditional way of life'. This became evident when he pulled up next to a shop, disappeared, and returned a moment later with 1,000 Marlboro cigarettes in five cartons sealed in plastic covers, which he secreted behind the dashboard and in cavities under the bonnet. We drove off and coasted along in silence for a while, then Abdallah said, casually, 'Taxis normally drop their passengers off at the taxi-station in Amman. But I will take you to wherever you are staying.' He was too discreet to add, 'As long as you don't say anything about the cigarettes,' but we both knew that a bargain had been struck. Since the air had been cleared, I felt free to ask him what he was doing with the cigarettes, anyway. 'Syria is a free market for cigarettes,' he explained. 'They come into Damascus from Beirut. In Jordan they are more expensive. I take some back with me every time I come to Syria, just to make a few dinars extra. Times are hard and petrol is expensive – you know!'

Damascus fell behind us, and we raced through rolling limestone country – red land, shell-white stones as thick as fallen leaves, stands of Aleppo pine, stone pine and peeling eucalypt. There were mountains in the distance trimmed with snow and sombre farms stitched into the contours of the landscape, with fig-trees in rows planted with military precision. At Daraʿa, there were interminable queues at immigration. At the last barrier, a rotund Syrian guard in Ruritanian khaki with a woollen hat pulled over his ears turned up his collar to the freezing drizzle. He took a handful of melon seeds from his pocket, and chewed them while he examined our documents. He weighed my oversized passport with exaggerated wonder, and said, 'This is not a passport. This is a *book*! Ha! Ha! Ha! Ha!' Then, with the skins of melon seeds hanging from his upper lip, he waved us on.

Jordan was a bleak stony hillside washed by the rain. At Ramtha we halted in the customs-tunnel, and a man in civilian clothes ordered me to bring my rucksack for inspection. 'Bring your rucksack!' Abdallah bawled. The official laid the contents out along the table, while Abdallah watched me, frowning. 'Have you got a video-camera?' the man asked.

'A video-camera?' Abdallah parroted nervously.

'No.'

'All right. Get moving!'

'Come on!' Abdallah shouted at me, so belligerently that even the customs-man stared at him. 'Are you in a bad temper?' he inquired.

'No! No! Of course not!' Abdallah said, but he looked uneasy and beads of sweat were gathering along the line of his forehead. If I had been the customs-man, I should certainly have suspected him. The official waved us on, however, and as soon as we were through the last barrier Abdallah let out a whoop, and stabbed his foot joyously down on the accelerator: 'Marlboro country!' he yelled.

True to his word, he dropped me at ACOR – the American Centre for Oriental Research – where I had booked a room. It was a place of almost monastic calm, overlooking hills smothered in adobe-block houses. Here, on the outskirts of Amman, country and city coalesced: there were ploughed fields among the flat-blocks, men shepherding goats along the wet roads, and horses tethered on overgrown plots. It was in ACOR's library that I met Steve Sims, a small, reed-slim man who was associate professor of anthropology at the University of Utah. Sims, an expert on Native American culture, was now applying his expertise to the Bedu of Jordan. Over coffee in his tiny room, I asked his opinion of the traditional view of Bedu immutability: 'Anthropologists always like to divide and comprehend,' he said, 'but while we were excavating at Petra, we were constantly coming up with traces of pastoral nomads in the strata. I mean, they have been able to adjust to new political, economic, climatic and technological conditions throughout history. The desert and the sown were never completely distinct. There was always a continuum between them.'

'What do you think of the idea of the Bedu as pure nomads?'

'I prefer to take an ecological view. When you think of it, why should you call certain nomads "pure" just because they herd camels and migrate over long distances rather than herding sheep and migrating over shorter distances? Or because they obtain their grain by trading for it rather than growing it? It's a subjective value-judgement which is totally meaningless. You can't pigeonhole things so neatly, because nomadism is so diverse anyway – it is an adjustment to a set of ecological conditions along a continuum of numerous possibilities. It was never fixed, but dynamic – some people were always dropping out of nomadism and others going in.'

'But it is true,' I said, 'that among some Arabs, only the camel-herding tribes were regarded as being "real" Bedu.'

'Yes, but even the Arabs themselves aren't the final arbiters of the truth. We have to look at the evidence, and the evidence doesn't fit the concept that only the "noble camel-rearing tribes" are "true" Bedu. There are many tribes who regard themselves as Bedu who don't rely on herding camels – even some who are settled, like the Bedu of Petra. In fact, it's possible to say that "Bedouinism" *never* entails a monoculture of camels – even the supposedly "pure" nomads like the ʿAnaza had always interacted with others.'

'What about the idea of "noble blood"?'

'The Bedu liked to preserve genealogies which showed their descent from a noble ancestor, and this seemed to fit in with a Victorian concept which influenced a lot of the writers and travellers of the first half of this century. They were obsessed with the idea of inherited blood and race, and made the fundamental mistake of confusing things like race and culture. People liked to believe that the Bedu had kept their blood "pure" due to isolation in the desert, but it is clear that they were always in contact with the outside world, and in reality their gene-pool must be amazingly diverse if you look at it at the macro-level. The point is that the traditionalists believed that some races were "pure" and therefore superior. They wanted to arrange races in a hierarchy with themselves at the top.'

Next morning I was in a Mercedes taxi nearing Petra, where Steve Sims had suggested I should start my quest for the last of the Bedu. He had advised me to contact a man called Dakhilallah – a Sheikh of the famous Bedouin tribe called the Bedul, who had until recently lived within the ancient rock city itself. As we drew nearer, the landscape became increasingly mountainous, coarse limestone on which grass grew with the sparseness of receding hair. There were pockets of Aleppo pine here and there, with apple orchards and figs. Suddenly the high ground dropped away beneath us into a great valley – the valley of Petra, in which a shapeless mass of purple and burgundy sandstone seemed to have boiled like confectionery out of the centre of the earth and set hard. You could see nothing of the rock city itself from up here, but the basin in which the sandstone core stood was battened in on all sides by chalky sheep-ridden hills. This was as dramatic as it was unexpected. I had always imagined, somehow, that Petra would be an oasis like Palmyra, surrounded by waterless desert on all sides. But this was not real desert at all: this was the sown land. Wadi Musa – the village standing at the entrance to Petra – was a crescent of white blocks crawling up a fertile mountainside that in Roman times was even more intensely cultivated than it is today. Rather than the 'desert citadel' it had often been called, you could fairly say that Petra was a city on the rim of the sown.

It was noon by the time I reached the Bedul village, and the only thing that seemed to be moving was a mangy camel, trying to insinuate itself into a crack of shade by a cinder-block wall. Dakhilallah's was the penultimate house in the village, a concrete cube notable mainly for its great size and astonishing lack of character. Again, this was unexpected. I had imagined this Bedu tribe living in snug one-roomed houses of mud, like the ʿAnaza at Qasr al Hayr in Syria. Instead, this village seemed to have combined so many of the most sterile features of modern design – or lack of it – that one could only believe that it had been done on purpose. There was, at least, a donkey tethered at the back of the house, and – albeit amid a dozen crates of empty cola bottles – a rolled-up black tent on a steel frame. These alone were good signs.

I found Dakhilallah at the front of the house, supervising three Egyptian labourers in baseball caps, who were stripping wood off recently set concrete pillars with chisels and hammers. 'I'm extending the house,' he said, after greeting me. 'It's going to be a new salon. In the summer I'm going to let the whole house to archaeological parties.'

'Where will you go?'

He pointed to the lump of woven wool standing on the steel frame nearby. 'I have my tent!' he said.

He was a wiry man with a grizzled face, wearing what looked like a khaki ranger's uniform and a loose lounge jacket. His black and white checked shamagh and the toggles looped around his crown were his only concession to tribal dress. Later, as we crouched on a hot mattress in the doorway of his house, sipping glasses of tea, oppressed by small, squeaking girls in dungarees, he made an imperious motion towards the valley. 'Have you seen Petra before?' he asked.

'No, this is my first time.'

'That is Petra!'

Thousands of feet below us, across bubbles and stacks of stone and scree, beneath chiselled faces of crimson rock, lay Petra's only free-standing monument. Known to the Bedul as 'The Castle of the Pharaoh's Daughter', it was actually the temple of Dushara – Dionysus to the ancient Nabataeans who had built the rock city of Petra, and whose human remnants – two millennia on – Dakhilallah's people claimed to be.

I wondered that Dakhilallah wanted to extend his house, for it was already a mansion. From the inside it was a curiously asymmetrical amalgam of rooms and passages that blossomed organically out of each other without any suggestion of planning. My room contained two unmade beds crammed close together, and smelt distinctly of human excrement. It was only after a time that I discovered the reason for this: the smell emanated from the upstairs toilet in which a modern pedestal had been fitted without the benefit of modern plumbing.

And there was an explanation, too, Dakhilallah told me later, for the lack of design: 'The government built these houses for us, when they moved us out of Petra,' he said. 'They promised to build us houses with two hundred and forty square metres of floor space but in the end the space was only forty-eight metres square. I've been able to add to mine bit by bit, but many of the others don't have the money.'

Dakhilallah was one of the Bedul who had grown up inside the confines of Petra. In the winter they had lived in the caves that honeycombed the rock city, warmed by fires of brushwood they collected freely from the wadis. There were plenty of caves to choose from – natural as well as man-made – and families would own several – one for the men, another for the goats, a third for the women and a fourth for guests. Some of the caves they occupied lay high up in the valley sides because of the danger of flooding, and they would build dry-stone walls across the cave-mouths to prevent the young children from falling out. In summer, when the caves became unbearably hot, they moved up to the plateaux, and pitched their tents. Traditionally they depended on goats, and grew a little wheat, barley and tobacco, keeping a handful of camels to transport their crops to Maʿan along the Wadi ʿArabah in the pilgrim season. Their possessions were almost ludicrously few: an iron cooking-pot, an iron griddle for making bread, a tin for carrying water, a basin, a chest for clothing, and perhaps a gun. In the past the Bedul would hunt the rabbits and gazelles that abounded in Petra, and kill the hyenas, wolves and leopards that harried their flocks.

As early as 1925, when Thomas Cook built the first tourist camp in Petra, a few Bedul were employed in the seasonal tourist trade, though the tribe remained so poverty-stricken that in the 1930s the archaeologist Margaret Murray had commented of their physical condition: 'The Bedul were not only ignorant but weakly, and were very different from the strong, hard-working Fellahin of Egypt and south Palestine,' she wrote; '. . . the [Liyathna] were better fed and therefore stronger, but they suffered from the disadvantage of extreme bumptiousness, a vice from which the Bedul were free. This was not from a natural virtue on the part of the Bedul, but was probably due to the weakness of malnutrition.' The Liyathna were the settled inhabitants of Wadi Musa – neighbours and age-old rivals of the Bedul. Though considered Fellahin or cultivators, from the 1860s onwards they had dominated the Bedul by force of arms – a situation in contrast to the classic Orientalist concept of Bedu raiders terrorizing settled farmers and disappearing camel-borne back into the desert. Rivalry between the tribes had remained sufficiently fraught by the 1930s, when Margaret Murray began her excavations at Petra, that she was obliged to recruit an equal number of labourers from both tribes, lest the Liyathna murder the Bedul tribesmen out of jealousy. Murray called the Liyathna village – Wadi Musa – 'the most murderous settlement in Transjordan'.

Until the 1960s, visitors to Petra remained a trickle – no more than 100 a day – but with the world-wide boom in tourism afterwards, the numbers swelled to thousands. The Bedul, based within the site, were well placed to serve the new invaders, selling trinkets and snacks, or renting out camels and horses. Bedul tribesmen who had never lived in the caves, but had continued in their traditional means of subsistence, were attracted into Petra to join the bonanza being enjoyed by their clansmen. 'Then, about ten years ago, the government comes along with Unesco and turns the place into a National Park!' Dakhilallah said. 'They said that we were getting too many and that in twenty years' time the place would be full of Bedul. In a way they were right, we saw that – we didn't want to do anything to put off tourism, because that's what we depended on. Anyway, they promised to build us houses here in Umm Sayhun that would be big enough for us and they turned out to be these middens! I think there was some dirty business involved, because I once saw a truckload of baths turn up that must have been meant for our houses, but they disappeared. Who knows what else disappeared too! Anyway, we moved here even though we were happier in our caves, and at least we were near enough Petra to carry on working with the tourists. Well, now they say they are going to move us again, somewhere far away. Umm Sayhun is going to be turned into a tourist village with hotels and local handicrafts, and someone will make a fortune at our expense.'

'Don't these houses belong to you?'

'That's the worst thing: we don't have any written agreement to prove that they're ours. The government won't even let us plant trees! They are just moving us around like baggage, and if the truth be known Petra is rightfully ours, because we lived there before there was a state called Jordan. We were far better off when we were in the caves – everything was free, and we were accustomed to living there: our fathers used them and our fathers' fathers used them right back to the Nabataeans, our ancestors.'

From out of northern Arabia, from the margins of the sown land, the Nabataeans came: some have even called them 'the first Bedu'. Their appearance in the region of Petra – the biblical Land of Edom – was part of an upheaval in the balance of power taking place in the Middle East throughout the last half-millennium BC. The sheep- and goat-herding Bedu tribes of northern Arabia and the Syrian desert had known the camel for centuries as a pack-animal bred and managed by foreign caravaneers from the Yemen. The Assyrians had experimented with the animals as war-beasts, but found them wanting, for the simple reason that the saddle – a pad behind the camel's hump – was too unstable a platform for warriors trying to wield a spear or loose an arrow. The Bedu tribes had learned to rear camels from the Yemenites, though – since wheeled vehicles were still in vogue among the settled peoples – their usefulness was limited to the long-distance carrying-trade. Only by supplying pack-camels for the caravans were the nomads able to benefit from the fabulous wealth in incense and other commodities that had been pouring across the Arabian Peninsula for 2,000 years. The control – and the fat profits – of this trade lay in the hands of foreign city-states too powerful for the desert tribes to challenge with ease. Then, around 500 BC, all this had begun to change. The catalyst was a simple technological innovation – the *shadad*, or double-poled camel saddle – yet the revolution it brought about over the next 600 years has only been paralleled in the modern era by the advent of the motor-car.

Shadad means 'the firm one' in Arabic, and the saddle placed the rider over the camel's hump rather than behind it, providing the stability necessary to use a long sword, a lance or a bow without promptly being pitched off. The advantage this conferred on a camel-borne warrior was, in its day, equal to that enjoyed later by the machine-gunner mounted in a light car. The Bedu of the fringe-lands were now more than a match for the heavily defended caravans, and steadily they began to take control of the incense trade. Some tribes exacted tolls on caravans passing through their territory, while others offered them protection against the predatory bandits of the remoter desert. One of these newly powerful Bedu tribes – the Nabataeans – went further: they cut out the middlemen and entered the caravan business for themselves. For 400 years, their capital at Petra dominated the route from the kingdoms of Yemen to the Mediterranean shore.

The Bedul village guarded the rear entrance to Petra, but I preferred to experience it first from the Wadi Musa approach, by which Burckhardt, disguised as a Muslim, had rediscovered the site in 1812. I hitched a ride to Wadi Musa, and the driver dropped me near the ticket office, where I faced the attendant through an iron grille.

Attendant: 'Do you want a ticket for one day at twenty dinars, for two days at twenty-five dinars, or for three days at thirty dinars?'

Self: 'For three days at thirty dinars.'

Attendant: 'You can't, because tomorrow is the King's birthday, and it is free. You will have to buy a ticket for one day at twenty dinars.'

Self: 'All right, but what about the day after tomorrow – is that free too?'

Attendant: 'No, then you will have to buy another ticket for one day at twenty dinars.'

Self: (amazed) 'Wait a minute! That means I have to pay forty dinars for three days, when one of them is free. The free day is costing me ten dinars!'

Attendant: (pensively) 'Very well. You will pay for three days at thirty dinars.'

I walked away nursing my ornate ticket, and it was not until I had actually passed through the gate that my mistake dawned on me. If two days cost twenty-five dinars, I was still five dinars short!

Inside the gate dozens of horses belonging to the Bedul and the Liyathna were stamping and whinnying as Arab boys in jeans leapt on and off their backs. The air was redolent of horse-urine and horse-dung. As I walked past the pickets, the boys yelled at me to take a horse. I ignored them and walked down the sandy track that dipped between limestone terraces covered in tamarisk.

The first inkling of what is going to happen to you in Petra comes on this initial approach, when you fall unexpectedly upon the tombs of yellow sandstone that at first sight seem to be elongated storage silos with dark entrances at their bases. You realize with a thrill, however, that they have been deliberately and painstakingly separated from the rock wall by adzes and chisels, and shaped into perfect boxes by craftsmen whose skills were rather those of the sculptor than of the architect or engineer. The next surprise is the 'obelisk temple', whose weathered edifice has the effect of op art. The rock here has been transformed into the recognizable façade of a classical church, with columns and cupolas, but is so eroded that you seem to be looking at an out-of-focus version of something familiar, a building melted out of kilter and warped by time in a way no true building could ever have been warped and remained intact. And then it suddenly strikes you that this is *not* a building at all, but just a cave whose exterior has been ingeniously fashioned to resemble one.

These are overture and beginners – an antipasto for the feast of Petra. The road narrows. You enter a gorge called the Siq – in places almost a tunnel between walls that rise sheer above you to hundreds of feet. Each twist and turn brings you to new wonders. The Siq is a fault-line that bisects the massif, created by surging earth forces that have caused the mountain to swell and rupture. Over aeons it has been polished by water, and there are many fine grades of colour in the rock. In places the sand underfoot is stippled with primary hues, and sunbeams drift along the walls in bars and brindles. At times, the flat echoes and these tricks of light and shade produce the feeling that you are walking in an undersea cavern. Occasionally you find yourself obliged to stop and stare upwards at the soaring walls, sheared into bulbs and peduncles, where the patina has fallen away completely to expose burrows beneath like the lairs of giant worms, or where the wine-coloured rock seems to have trickled down the face like syrup. All these are natural marvels. After about twenty minutes' walk through the tunnel, though, there is a mallow-pink flush of light in the dimness, and you glimpse through the slit in the rocks a miraculous transformation. You step through into the blazing light of an amphitheatre and there before you the stone has been magically refashioned into the vast, elaborate frontage of a cathedral, ten storeys high – the Khuznat al Firun – perhaps the temple of the Nabataean god, She'a al Qum, patron-deity of caravaneers.

It was late afternoon when I reached the Khuzna, and happily the crowds were already dwindling. A troop of Bedul elders in shamaghs and jallabiyyas were sitting in the shade of the rocks, tapping their slender camel-sticks and sniffing the breeze. The air was layered with fine dust and the odour of horses. Cavalry contingents trotted by – aged foreigners on mounts being led by Arabs – and I could not help overhearing one matron with bottle-blonde hair telling her attendant in an unmistakably English accent: 'Actually, you know my father was here in 1918. Of course, it was called Mesopotamia in those days. He was here for eight years and he simply *adored* it. He rode camels and horses. He lived with the Bedouin!' The horse-boy looked singularly unimpressed: yet I was fascinated. Perhaps her father had never really 'lived with the Bedouin' – perhaps he did not even speak Arabic – but her enthusiasm for the myth brought home just how deeply the idea of the Bedouin was etched into our national psyche.

The Khuzna is hewn out of a square fissure in the rock, but gives the impression of having been built inside it. Six Corinthian-style 'pillars' yield the illusion of supporting a grand pediment, above which the complementary halves of another pediment stand like bookends either side of a beautiful, cylindrical cupola, with a domed roof and a great urn on top. The Bedu of Petra traditionally believed that this urn contained gold and jewels hidden out of human reach by 'the Pharaoh', and the bullet-marks which riddle it are testimony to their past attempts to crack it open.

The interior was a cool, square womb sculpted in rigid angles that slashed through the grain of the rock, exposing a shimmering progression of colours – blood, milk, hyacinth, wine-purple – that merged, swelled and ran like those on a hand-made Persian carpet. Lofty portals on each side of the room had lost their sharp edges and the spectrum of colours spread across their ornamented frames. A great fissure in the rock spanned the place from floor to ceiling on both sides, a crack so wide that I was again reminded that this was only the illusion of a man-made structure.

I surfaced into the bright light of day once again and followed the straggle of horses and foot-sloggers around the corner into another narrow chasm, past Bedul boys selling multi-coloured sand in bottles, past minor tombs, past a Roman theatre in marbled colours carved out of a single piece of rock. Above me the shoulder of the gorge had broken out in all manner of gothic façades:

flat gargoyle faces pitched and tilted at uncomfortable angles and flashed back the molten sunlight like polished brass. I stood still beneath them and tried to cradle the whole overwhelming effect of Petra in my thoughts. On one hand it was no more than an incredibly elaborate practical joke – natural rock made to look like tombs and churches, pillars that never supported anything, prodigiously sculpted doorways to what were no more than dark caves: this was form without function, style without content. At the same time, the experience of Petra was not the result of human intervention alone: one wondered at the tombs as one wondered at the Pyramids and temples of Egypt, but there was a difference. Petra would have been an impressive place even without a single human indent – the marbled colours, the textures, the shapes in the sandstone were alive with images before ever the Nabataeans came: the sculptors merely liberated them from their cold sleep in the rock and gave them form according to the highest religious icons of their day.

Near the temple of Dushara, beyond the paved Colonnade Street built in Roman times, I drank a glass of tea at a café with a view of a sloping headland strewn with pebbles and potsherds. It was on this shelf of rock that the actual Nabataean living-quarters were sited, for in fact the people of ancient Petra never inhabited the caves as the Bedul were later to do. Instead they constructed a town of single-storey, flat-roofed stone dwellings, each centred on its own courtyard, with only small windows giving on to the tortuous alleys outside. At its height this town had housed a population of 30,000.

The Nabataean occupation of Petra was less the consequence of invasion and conquest than a leisurely massing of tribesmen who first pitched their tents on the marches of the cultivated land, and in time assimilated themselves completely to the ways of the Edomites. The two tribes claimed common descent through daughters of Ishmael, and since Arab genealogies tended to reflect *de facto* power-relationships, this must at the very least have been an expression of mutual ground. The people of Edom had, anyway, been decimated in their wars with the Judaeans – spectacularly by King David, whose objective, it seems, was little less than their genocide. There were also new stars rising in the firmament of Mesopotamian power. In 587 BC the Babylonians captured the Judaean capital at Jerusalem, torched Solomon's Temple and Palace, and led off the Jews into captivity. The remnant Edomites, gleeful over the destruction of their ancient enemies, flocked out of Edom to occupy Judah's green swards. The vacuum this diaspora created was readily filled by the encroaching Nabataeans, who by 300 BC had so swamped the remaining Edomites with their numbers that theirs had become the dominant culture in Petra.

Like the Bedu tribes who were later to create Palmyra – indeed, like all Bedu – the Nabataeans were exceptionally versatile, with a talent for commerce and organization. Not only were they remarkably skilled architects and sculptors, they were also engineers of the highest order, whose farms and settlements have been discovered in thousands all over the Negev and as far north as Damascus. In the deserts beyond Petra they developed a sophisticated spreadwater irrigation system, collecting rain whose volume was too limited to be productive when spread over twenty acres and directing it via an ingenious network of cisterns and feeders to a single acre, where it brought forth an abundant crop. The Israelis have estimated that if all the rain falling on the 2½-million-acre southern Negev were harvested by this system, 125,000 acres of desert could be turned into productive land. The Nabataeans constructed reservoirs and aqueducts that are still watertight after 2,000 years, and every drop of rain falling on their villages was channelled into public catch-basins. Israeli engineers who have studied Nabataean methods in the Negev have declared that even with the benefit of modern technology they are still unable to equal this ancient people's success in greening the desert. If there is a single conclusion to be drawn from the Nabataean migration to Petra and their subsequent achievements, it lies once again in the fluidity rather than the immutability of Bedouin ways.

It was dark by the time I arrived back in Wadi Musa. The taxi-driver who motored me to Umm Sayhun belonged to the Liyathna – the ancient adversaries of the Bedul. When I mentioned that I was staying with Dakhilallah, he said: 'Dakhilallah is an old fox! Don't take a bit of notice about what he says! He'll tell you the Bedul liked it much better when they lived in the caves, but you just try getting them to go back there! They've got the foreigners thinking that they've been unfairly treated, and they are trying to force the government to hand over the sites in Umm Sayhun to them, by acting the aggrieved party. As soon as the sites belong to them they will sell up. Just think of the value of that land to the hotel chains with the new boom in tourism! Overlooking Petra, right near the back entrance: it'd be worth millions!'

There is no direct evidence apart from their own testimony that the Bedul are the descendants of the Nabataeans, or even that they have inhabited Petra for more than 150 years. In 1812 Burckhardt found the ruins of Petra unoccupied, though the fact that his Liyathna guide went in fear of bandits is taken to suggest that he expected some human presence there. Burckhardt did, however, encounter some Bedul outside Petra and recorded that not only were their tents unusually small, but they were too poor to offer him coffee: 'our breakfast or dinner therefore consisted of dry barley cakes, which we dipped in melted goat's grease,' he wrote. The first detailed account of the Bedul comes from the traveller John Wilson, who visited Petra in 1843 and was startled when a Bedul Sheikh claimed that his tribe was descended from the 'Bani Israel' or Hebrews. On closer analysis, though, it appeared that 'Bani Israel' was the name the Bedul gave to the ancient inhabitants of Petra, the Nabataeans, and that far from claiming to be Jewish, the Sheikh was merely asserting his tribe's link with the ancient past. Nevertheless, stories concerning the Bedul relate that they were originally Jews who became Muslims or originally pagans who became Jews, the theme of apostasy being supported by the fact that the name Bedul shares its root with the Arabic word *badala* – to exchange. On the other hand, since the consonants 'l' and 'n' are often interchangeable in Arabic dialects, Bedul may be a corruption of *bdun* – literally 'without', indicating that the tribe were social pariahs in origin – a view supported by the fact that none of the prestigious Bedu tribes they claim to be related to will intermarry with them.

What happened to the Nabataeans after their kingdom was annexed by the Roman Governor of Syria, Cornelius Palma, in March AD 106, remains a mystery. For some time the caravan-trade from the Yemen had been in decline, and many merchants had drifted away to the new hub of commerce at Palmyra. Certainly the Nabataean town of Petra contracted: many of its citizens may have taken to the desert as nomads, spilling into southern Jordan, Egypt and the Hejaz as the famous Bedu tribe of Huwaytat. Others – a handful – may possibly have readopted a semi-nomadic existence in the region of Petra, as the Bedul.

Dakhilallah and his wife – a cheerful, robust woman who chain-smoked cigarettes – were sitting on the floor watching television when I arrived. The programme was a loop showing and reshowing images of King Hussein amid adoring crowds, set to saccharine songs and music. 'Tomorrow is the King's birthday,' Dakhilallah said. 'Everyone loves the King, because he is of the line of the Prophet Mohammad. I'd trust him above any one of his ministers. That's why we're making up a petition to ask him for the deeds to these houses.'

The TV stayed on all evening, and Dakhilallah and his wife were evidently much attached to it.

'No TV in the caves!' I commented.

'We could always get our own generator!' Dakhilallah said, but I wondered about what my Liyathna driver had said. I wondered too about the constant extensions to this house and the profit my host must make from letting it out to tourists during the high season. Despite the rhetoric, he seemed to be doing well in Umm Sayhun. An illiterate Bedui he might be, but he was well versed in the machinations of the wide world.

I remained with Dakhilallah's family for three days. I never tired of the sights of Petra, nor of my conversations with the Bedul. I climbed up to the so-called 'Monastery' on the high plateau, and met Dakhilallah's son, Mohammad, a swarthy, thickly bearded man, who kept a coffee-shop there. He pointed down the precipitous gorge and described the dangers of Petra after heavy rains: 'Only last month a woman was drowned going down from the Monastery,' he said. 'The floods come so quickly that you can't do anything about it. Two women were carried off, but the Bedul managed to save one of them. Nobody realizes how important the Bedul are to the safety of people in Petra.' He also had a fascinating story about the Israeli youths who until recently would undergo a sort of initiation test by racing across the border at night, with the object of reaching Petra and getting back on to Israeli soil by sunrise the next morning. Inevitably many of them got lost, dehydrated or exhausted, only to be rescued by Bedul trackers.

On the last evening of my stay I returned to find Dakhilallah and his wife glued once again to the TV. 'Sit down! Sit down!' Dakhilallah said, without looking up. 'This is about the Bedu!' In fact it was a weekly soap in which ham actors dressed as Bedu made melodramatic speeches and came and went between very clean-looking tents on camels and horses. 'That one is the villain!' Dakhilallah told me breathlessly. 'He is trying to ravish that young girl. And the hero – that one – is trying to stop him!' I dropped the idea of conversation and muttered excuses before retiring. My abiding memory of the 'Last of the Nabataeans' will be of them sitting glued to a TV set watching a soap opera that presented a pale imitation of a life they had left only a decade before, but to which they would never return.

Sombre clouds were massing over the Petra valley. At Wadi Musa a contingent of tourist guides in dungarees and baseball hats was lounging in the lobby of the Rest House, talking of snow. Mas'ud, a Liyathna taxi-driver in a yellow cab, agreed to take me to Wadi

Rum across the mountains: 'But you'd better leave right now,' he said, 'or the passes are going to be blocked and you'll be snowed in for three days!' I took this as sales-talk, but I got in, and as soon as we were above the valley I saw that I had misjudged him. There were rashes of snow on the crests, and below us clouds gyrating in a kaleidoscope, strobing the sunlight into starfish shapes, providing snatched glimpses of the boiled-brain rocks of Petra beneath. As we drove higher freezing cotton-wool mist shrouded the road. Masʿud slowed down to a snail's pace and gripped the wheel till his knuckles turned ashen, but even then I could feel the tyres slipping on the ice. There was silence: the tension was palpable. Suddenly the windscreen was splashed with water that converted it instantly into a freezing blindfold, and the vehicle careered desperately across the road. Masʿud jumped, then threw the wiper-switch. A second later the wipers had clawed a translucent patch on the windscreen just enough for him to steer by, and he brought the car under control, gritting his teeth. 'Thank God there were no other vehicles coming!' he said, his voice shaking slightly. 'I don't want that to happen again!'

We continued to slither along until, almost imperceptibly, we were losing altitude. The snow-drifts cleared and the black ice gave way to wet asphalt road. At Ras al Nagab the sun was exhaling light freely across the valley. Streams of fire snaked along the cool ground, unhitching blurs of mist which distended like smoke rings around massive sandstone polyhedrals. We hauled past breeze-block hamlets, shredded old gunny-bag tents with chimneys, oblong sheepfolds, sheep-dogs, children in cloaks and mufflers, tractors billying smoke. Soon we were turning off the main road and speeding into Wadi Rum.

In Rum a bone-biting wind was blowing out of the Arabian Peninsula. The Rest House was hemmed in on both sides by cliffs so grooved horizontally that they might have been cut by a giant cheese-grater. I paid my entrance fee in a tiny office, where a man dressed as a Bedui answered my Arabic in English and handed me a ticket on which was written 'Genuine Bedouine tea or coffee free with this ticket!' The House was crammed with tourists, and in the dining-room a Jordanian singer with a voice like gravel was retching out a local pop-song to the thrum of a lute, while the audience cheered deliriously and beat time. I asked to see the manager of the House, and as I sipped my genuinely anaemic Bedouine tea, he agreed to fix me up with camels and a guide to take me as far as Aqaba. He led me through the Bedu village, where black tents were pitched inside shanties of timber and cinder-block, and the sand was scattered with rusty machine-parts and bits of dead car frames. An unruly camel shrieked as it dashed down the track, its jaws open and its tongue bulging in a diabolic rictus. Boys in red-specked shamaghs raced after it, screeching. At a one-roomed shop, a man called Sleiman emerged from behind an alp of sardine-cans, a tiny figure with a long Bedouin nose peeking out of his shamagh. 'I will take you to Aqaba,' he said. 'The journey will be four days, and you will pay two days for my return: six days at thirty dinars a day.'

Like all the Bedu in Wadi Rum, Sleiman belonged to the Huwaytat, the famous tribe of T. E. Lawrence's ally Auda Abu Tayyi, which was spread across Jordan, the Hejaz, and Egypt. If there were ever a 'middle class' in Bedu society, the Huwaytat would fit this niche, for though they looked down upon lesser tribes such as the Bedul, they themselves were shunned by the mighty clans of the ʿAnaza, with whom they shared a traditional enmity. Huwaytat history was a fine example of the fluid response of Bedu tribes to changing conditions. Originally they were traders, and settled farmers along the shores of the Red Sea. At the end of the nineteenth century they acquired the fertile Sherah plain from the Neumat tribe, and began to practise both cultivation and animal husbandry in conjunction. In the days of their warrior-sheikh Auda Abu Tayyi, though, they took to raiding on a large scale, abandoning their farms or renting them out to Fellahin, within a short time gaining a reputation as the most warlike tribe in Arabia. After 1918 many of them reverted once again to cultivation. The Huwaytat were perhaps the second most powerful tribe in Jordan, and in the Rum–Aqaba region alone numbered at least 1,000 tents.

The camels were grazing behind the shop in a field full of old tyres and broken saddles. Sleiman bridled three of them – two for riding, he said, and one, an untrained calf, as a 'spare'. A crowd of little peanut-coloured boys and girls led them out, jumping and shouting piercingly, and couched them by the shop door. Saddle-girths were lapped and buckled, woven saddlebags and my rucksack slung on, a plastic jerrycan was attached. 'Don't worry about food,' Sleiman said, 'all that is taken care of!' Within minutes we were leading three camels out into the great spaces of the Wadi Rum.

The glacial wind had splintered the cloud into quills of smoke, and the sky was radiant. Rum was more than a mile wide here, an imperial boulevard between smelt-coloured stacks that receded from us in diminishing perspective to their vanishing point on the high horizon. There were no dragons and demons in the hills of Rum as there were at Petra: instead there was a grain to them – the grain of old timber, chased and bevelled. They looked like the buttresses of unbelievably large trees whose trunks had snapped off and fallen into the desert behind them. The valley floor was a soft meniscus lapping at the cliffs, brick-dust and burnt umber, a-whiffle with plants whose oilskinned undersides gave the place a feel of wetness. Bedu tents stood along its edges like the abdomens of huge dismembered black scorpions.

We tramped into the eye of the wind, and for an hour I tried to engage Sleiman in meaningful conversation. He was a young man, shoulder-high, no more than twenty, wrinkled up like a prematurely senile turtle into the folds of his shamagh and his camel-hair cloak, stalking on silent and resentful. I sensed that he regretted having to travel to Aqaba by camel when he might have made more money more easily in a motor-car. I felt too that he was taken off guard by my Arabic, accustomed to using a few well-honed foreign phrases to control visitors. Like almost everyone involved in mass tourism, he regarded foreigners as a predictable herd species without the attributes of individual humanity. Tourists were the new flocks of the Huwaytat in Wadi Rum.

He emerged from his shell to ask me: 'Do you want to go to Aqaba itself, or only to the main road?'

'We agreed on Aqaba.'

'It won't matter if it takes less than four days, will it?'

'Yes it will. I'm paying for four days!'

Sleiman fell silent for a few moments, then he asked: 'Do you want to ride?'

'No. Why, do you?'

'No. Of course not!'

Presently, we came to a tent pitched by a well, inevitably called 'Lawrence's Well', below a deep chasm cleft by water running down the rock. Because of its proximity to Rum village, this must have been the most photographed Bedouin tent in the world. Certainly, it was the only one I ever recalled seeing that was surrounded by a fence of rickety plywood. This bespoke a siege mentality that was uncharacteristic of the Bedu: the tent had not been designed originally to close its occupants off from the desert, but to allow them to merge with it. Certainly the place was not picturesque in the romantic sense, for the tent lay within an orbit of mechanical debris: the rusted frames of stripped Land-Cruisers, fractured camshafts, antique cylinders, a cracked engine-block to which an ugly black donkey was moored. Five or six camels were kneebound by the fence, next to a wire coop of squawking chickens. I recalled Steve Sims telling me, 'When you're digging and you get down to what we call the "chicken line", you say, "Aha! This was when they stopped being nomads!"' My feeling of 'siege-mentality' was confirmed when an old woman with a determined jaw marched up to the fence and shouted, 'No photographs! If you want to take photographs you pay me five dinars!'

We passed the tent and struck on into the wadi. 'Are you ready to ride yet?' Sleiman asked.

'No. But you must ride if you want to. Don't wait for me!'

'I do not ride yet. I am a Bedui.'

A little later he pointed out camel-riders like ants, far away across the valley.

'Military patrol!' he said. 'They still use camels. They sometimes stay with the Bedu, but they don't go far.'

'What is their job – I mean, are there any bandits here?'

'Never! There are no dishonest people in Rum. They do it just for show – or to encourage the tourists, to help the Bedu – that sort of thing.'

The wadi walls had lost their grain here, and the buttresses were fractured into abstract entities like piles of jellyfish or columns of parachutes. We moved through the scrawny neck of a pass and into another long bed of apricot sand.

'Do you want to rest for the night here?' Sleiman inquired, 'or to stay with the Bedu?'

'To stay with the Bedu.'

'But they may be a long way ahead.'

'That's no problem. Why, what do you want to do?'

'My only wish is for your comfort.'

We marched on while the clouds rolled over us like liquid splashes, drowning the sun and leaving only a lemon-coloured stain along the hills. The night hid us in its coils, and the dark walls of the wadi receded to a thickening of shadows on the rim of our vision. The night brought no stars, but it brought silence – the aching silence of infinite spaces, ruptured only by the reassuring sound of our own tramping feet. 'Do you want to ride?' Sleiman inquired, more insistently this time. I could feel his frustration when I refused again. Despite his claims to the contrary, I was beginning to suspect that he was more concerned with his own comfort than mine. He wanted to ride but could not bring himself to do so before a foreigner. His continual badgering only made me feel more stubborn, and it was a cool, crisp evening – a wonderful time for a long walk, anyway.

We had been going several hours when two pinpoints of light flickered out of the darkness. 'Bedu!' Sleiman said in a voice full of anticipation. We made for the nearest light, stumbling over loose rocks, until we came upon a canvas tent slung over a make-shift frame, furled in the odours of invisible camels. A thickset man loomed up out of the shadows and shook hands with us grumpily, then turned sharply away. '*Fut! Fut!* Come into my tent!' he said.

Sleiman hung back. 'Are you with your Arabs?' he inquired, meaning, 'Are you with your womenfolk?'

'No. There is only me and my brother.'

Without another word, Sleiman pulled his camels off into the night.

When we were out of earshot, I asked him why.

'He is a crazy man. He did not know a guest!'

'But he invited us into his tent!'

'He didn't mean it. They were just empty words, that's all.'

I recalled the brusque manner and the sharp turning aside. Sleiman had read these nuances much more acutely than I. For him, 'Come into my tent!' might just as well have been 'Clear off!'

We moved towards the second light, which resolved into moonbeam rays of fire dancing upon the flap of a black tent as if upon a screen. As we came within shouting distance, watchdogs began to bark. A Bedui in a cloak appeared in the doorgap, a coal-coloured cameo outlined in light and smoke. He told us to unbelt the camels and come in out of the cold. I had not realized how cold I was until I was toasting my hands and feet before the fire. The brushwood crackled, illuminating the faces of our hosts: Gasim of the Huwaytat, a teenaged boy, and a blind old man with slits for eyes. 'Who is it? Who's come?' the old man whined.

'It is an Englishman, uncle,' Sleiman said.

'The English! I know the English! I am more than ninety years old! I can remember the days of al ʿAurens and Auda Abu Tayyi, by God!'

'Glubb, that was another of the English,' Gasim said, grinning wickedly, dispensing glasses of tea. 'He wanted to be the king. He *was* the king, really – Abdallah was only king in name. But you know, Glubb helped the Israelis by moving the Arabs out of their villages and letting the Israelis in. Then Hussein came. He kicked Glubb out. There was no Jordan before Hussein. I have nothing against the English personally, but we don't want colonialism any more!'

For a man who lived in the desert, it seemed to me, Gasim was extraordinarily well informed, but he soon jarred me out of my prejudiced notion: 'We have a house in Rashdiyya, with a TV,' he said. 'We have our own farm, and I keep a shop in the village. I am a shopkeeper in the morning and a Bedui at night. I prefer to sleep among my goats and camels. No, I don't think cultivation is a disgrace for a Bedui. There is no real difference between a Fellah and a Bedui, and if a Fellah bought goats and lived in a tent, he would be as good as a Bedui any day.'

'But you wouldn't let your daughter marry him.'

'Of course not! There are degrees of blood!'

'Do you think you will live in the tents for ever?'

'Why not? There's nothing wrong with tents. Having a house doesn't change that. We have tents, houses, livestock, crops, a shop, cars and tractors, and our children go to school. Why give up tents? We have the best of everything!'

'Don't cars and tractors mean the end of the Bedu?'

'Pooh! The Bedu are people who herd goats, sheep and camels. Motor-vehicles just make that easier.'

'What about the children? Don't you think they will want to change?'

'The young ones are even more keen on the tents than the old ones. Some of them will always come back to the desert. But if one of them wants to be a doctor or a shopkeeper, he has the chance. The more choices you have the better off you are!'

Later, I asked the old man how long it used to take in the past to travel from Rum to Aqaba by camel. His answer was unequivocal: 'Two days,' he said, 'going slow!'

Sleiman avoided my gaze and poked at the fire listlessly with a stick. His phrase, 'It won't matter if it takes less than four days, will it?' clanged in my mind. 'Ah, but the camels get tired, uncle!' he

1. Mohammad walad 'Eid. One of a small group of Egyptian Bedouin – perhaps no more than a couple of dozen – who still use camels to carry rock-salt from the Sudan.

2. The ruined heart of Shali, Siwa oasis, Egypt. The population of Siwa oasis moved to the village of Shali in AD 1203, and their descendants remained there until recently, when the government condemned the old mud-built houses as dangerous.

3. Ruins of classical Palmyra, Syria. In the third century AD, under Queen Zenobia, this tiny oasis in the Syrian desert had an empire stretching from Asia Minor to the Nile.

4. Bedouin woman of the ʿAnaza, Syrian desert. She wears the traditional gold earrings given to her as part of the bride-price.

5. Bedouin woman with facial tattoos, Syrian desert.

14. The Mahra coast, Yemen. It was probably somewhere along this coast that the camel was first domesticated, around 3000 BC. Tribes living in this area continue to use camels today.

15. Mosque at Al Qarn, south Yemen coast.

16. Old fisherman, the Tihama, Yemen. Using rafts made out of driftwood lashed together, such fishermen range into the Red Sea as far as the coast of Eritrea.

17. Ruins of the Maʿrib dam, Yemen. Built perhaps as early as 1800 BC, the dam was the centrepiece of a vast system of irrigation-works which transformed southern Arabia into a rich and fertile land. Arab legend ascribes the diaspora of the Bedouin tribes to the bursting of this dam, which drove the settled farmers into the desert.

said sheepishly. 'Aqaba is a looooong way! It's no good me losing a *dhelul* worth fifteen hundred just for a few dinars!'

'Losing a *dhelul*! No God but Allah, who ever heard of losing a *dhelul* between here and Aqaba!'

'What's the point in rushing? Take it easy, that's what I say. I wanted to make camp back there at the pass, but the Englishman insisted on staying with the Bedu! I keep on asking him to ride, and he says, "Not till you do!" God gave us camels for riding didn't he? He's paying for them but he just wants to walk all the time! What's the matter with the English, I'd like to know?'

Gasim weighed the question for a moment, then he smiled with understanding.

'Did you ever see that film *Lawrence of Arabia* – the one they made here in Wadi Rum? I've seen it many times. Well, that was the way al ʿAurens behaved with the Bedu. This Englishman must be trying to copy him!'

I carried the laughter that followed this to my sleeping-bag, but as I rolled myself up for the night, I realized that Gasim was perfectly right. I must have seen *Lawrence* a dozen times myself, but I had forgotten completely that it was filmed here in Wadi Rum. On reflection, though, I could remember the scene precisely – the one in which Lawrence was travelling by camel with his Bedouin guide on his apprentice journey in the desert:

Guide: 'Drink!'

Lawrence: 'Do you not drink?'

Guide: 'I am Bedu!'

Lawrence: 'Then I will drink when you drink!'

I hadn't once thought of the film, but the soundtrack – a distillation of all my culture's notions about the Bedu – must have been playing secretly in my unconscious all day as I travelled with Sleiman.

It took only minutes to load the camels in the morning. The new day unwrinkled from the tatters of darkness in a long procession of hues: quince, Persian red and chrome yellow, riding like beacons on the galleries of cumuli. The sandstone pinnaces were racks of ruby light and purple shadows. A flap of woodsmoke hung over the tents, and as we set off the flocks were already streaming from the nightfolds in the wake of dark-robed women, a procession of soft-edged shapes upon the golden meadows. We had scarcely reached the lip of the gorge when Sleiman asked if I would like to ride. When I refused, he couched his own camel and slid gracefully into the saddle. Today, pride had assumed second place to comfort. We travelled for an hour into rasping cold, until we spied a girl in a scarlet dress herding goats on a scree, and beyond her a Bedouin camp tucked under the hem of the sandstone. 'Bedu!' Sleiman said, gratefully.

We hobbled the camels and approached the tents, where a few plump sheep were penned up next to a Chevrolet pick-up so bashed-in that it was hardly recognizable. An old man with a blade face and a quill of a beard popped up and beckoned us towards the hearth. I asked why he had these few sheep penned up in the camp. 'Those are the ones we sell,' he answered. 'Sheep aren't clever like goats. They're all right in a big flock of their own kind, with dogs to keep them together, but if we let them go off with the goats they'd get lost!'

He told me that his family had no cultivation, but he owned a house in Rashdiyya. 'I don't go to the village much,' he told me. 'We move camp whenever there is some fresh grazing. We drive the flocks on foot and we carry the tent in our car. That old jalopy is no good on the road any more, but it's all right for driving around the desert.'

I asked him my standard question: 'Who are the Bedu?'

'The Bedu are those who live in the desert,' he told me. 'The Bedul? Yes, the Bedul are Bedu, but not *real* Bedu – they are Bani Israel. We Huwaytat wouldn't give a daughter to the Bedul, no indeed!'

Sleiman asked the old man if he would look after the camel-calf we had brought with us from Rum, which had proved a nuisance. 'Just for the night,' he said.

'I can't,' he replied. 'I'm on my own here. I have too much to do. It might die or get lost and I can't take the responsibility. Why on earth did you bring it, anyway?'

'There was no one to feed it in Rum, and I thought there would be plenty of chance to graze on the way to Aqaba. But this Englishman wants to keep moving all the time.' He fell quiet and stared at the fire moodily, displaying no eagerness to leave.

'I think we'd better be going!' I said.

We meandered on for another half hour, then Sleiman said: 'Why don't we halt here? The camels have to eat, you know. Otherwise they will die!'

So mournful was his expression that I almost forgot for a moment that we were talking about the same hardy animals which had given the Arabian Bedu dominance over their Peninsula for more than 1,000 years: which caravaneers in the Sahara still used to carry 300 kilograms of baggage fifty kilometres per day, day in day out: the same animal on which I had crossed the world's greatest desert from west to east through sandstorm, rain and withering cold – a distance of 4,500 miles in nine months. It was scarcely mid-morning, and the camels had been going for an hour and a half. They had covered about seven kilometres, I estimated. Not only were they virtually unladen, but I knew that Sleiman had with him a large bag of barley – the heaviest thing in our baggage – and on this alone the animals could quite easily have survived. Sleiman's ploy came into perspective with devastating clarity: Aqaba was two days' slow journey from Rum, and he hoped to do two days' work and get paid for six.

'Sorry,' I said, 'but I've never heard of a camel dying after one and a half hours' march. I cannot pay you thirty dinars a day to graze your camels. You agreed to take me to Aqaba.'

I led my camel on into the wadi and Sleiman followed reluctantly, letting his camels browse on every tree he passed until I had left him far behind. I realized that this was hopeless, and waited for him to catch up. 'The main highway to Aqaba is very near,' he said. 'Why don't you just pay me the money and go to the road and catch a bus?'

'If the road is so near, then we will go back to Rum, and I'll tell everyone why!'

'No! No! That would be a disgrace! All right, I'll take you to Aqaba. It's just that it's so cold. The camels can't stand the cold. You wait till you see the route to Aqaba – it's really hard going! Real mountains! You'll see!'

When we had climbed the next scarp we came to a valley covered in stones and green shoots, beyond which the landscape curved up towards peaks of biscuit-toned granite, whose sides were jagged and sheer compared with the grooved massifs of Wadi Rum. 'See! See!' Sleiman cried in apparent exoneration, but I saw that the track we were following was not at all steep, undulating gently beneath the peaks. 'That's not difficult going for a camel,' I said. 'You won't even have to get out of the saddle to do that!'

Sure enough, and despite his constant protests, Sleiman didn't bother to descend from his camel on the next climb. The hills opened into a hollow, where Huwaytat tents were pitched, and where rabbles of goats were scurrying after jogging herdsboys. Murky cloud spun in a majestic vortex, striping the ground in a slow carousel of light and shade. 'It's going to rain!' Sleiman announced, swinging down from his saddle at last. 'It will kill the camels, by God! I'm going to stop for the night in those tents!'

'The night! It's only just passed noon!'

'But I'm so cold! Feel my hands! It's no good. You walk too fast! The camels are exhausted!'

'The camels must be very poor animals indeed if they are exhausted so easily, when they are carrying almost nothing. I haven't even ridden mine. And I am hardly the world's fastest walker. You are a young man, half my age. And you are a Bedui.'

'What's the point in going on for hardship's sake?'

I saw that he was right. What was the point, after all? This was a country of cars and buses. Sleiman was twenty years old, born in the 1970s, in an era when motor-cars had already become more familiar than camels. Ironically, I had been riding camels when he was still a small boy. I knew that I had come to Jordan expecting too much. To him, travelling by camel when one could go by car was pointless: here in Jordan, the life of camels and hardship – the old life of the Bedu – was gone.

We couched the camels by a canvas guest-tent some distance from the Huwaytat camp, and a middle-aged, bearded Bedui in an embroidered sheepskin coat appeared and invited us inside. Once we were seated by the fire, I handed Sleiman a crumpled wad of ninety dinars.

'What's this?' he asked.

'Since you insist on stopping the night, I shall be going on alone from here.'

He shrugged with apparent relief, then counted the money. 'But this is only three days' pay!' he said. 'I want four! You were supposed to pay me four days for the journey to Aqaba, and two to return!'

'We only set off yesterday! You've worked one and a half days at the very most. It was your decision to stay here, when we haven't even done half a day's journey!'

Sleiman appealed to our host for support, but the Bedui stroked his beard and declared: 'It is fair.' Then he added in a soft voice: 'You should not let him go alone from here. Don't you know it is forbidden in the sight of God to abandon your travelling-companion when you have agreed to take him somewhere?'

'What does it matter?' Sleiman countered miserably. 'These aren't the old days. The other tourists I've been with only wanted to ride a camel!'

I shook hands with the two of them, and, shouldering my rucksack, I strode out into the valley. Not five minutes after leaving the tent, the rain came down in buckets: Sleiman was right about that, anyway.

By sunset it was still raining, and I found a small sheepfold – a square of piled dry stone – and erected the waterproof sheet I was carrying. All night a stiletto wind struck in gusts out of the hills, but by morning the rain had ceased, and I hiked as far as the main road where after an hour's wait I halted a minibus heading for Aqaba.

The town stood at the head of the Rift Valley, on the shores of a sea that was bronze and sparkling. A great cargo ship was spitting black smoke as it banked corpulently in the smooth waters. I walked along the parade of palms on the Corniche, past the foundations of the port that may have stood here in the time of Solomon, when Aqaba was a crucial link in the sea-route to southern Arabia. A camel in gaudy trappings was tied to a palm-tree, next to a horse and gharry, and across the road hung a sign upon which black tents and camels were painted. 'Come and visit!' the sign exhorted me. 'Bedouin Home!'

For a moment I wondered if this was where retired Bedouin went to die.

4

East of Aden

Shukri braked the Peugeot in the dry stream-bed that ran through the village of Nabi Hud, and cut the engine. 'Say what you like,' he said, 'but I'm not going any farther!'

Around us block-houses of carved mud were dwarfed by the sheer walls of the Wadi Hadhramaut. The houses were hulking redoubts of several storeys with façades punctured by scores of loophole windows, their surfaces sun-crisped and crinkled like biltong from the furnace heat. Half-way up the cliffs, reached by an expansive alabaster staircase that would not have disgraced a rococo palace, stood the shrine of the Prophet Hud, a white block-building perched under a dome of fragile eggshell brilliance, around which kites swung in silent orbit. Apart from the kites, not a creature moved in the deserted place. Shukri kept his hands on the wheel and stared about glumly. 'This village is inhabited by Jinns,' he said. 'That's why there are no people here. The Jinns have driven them out!'

As I stepped out on to the uneven floor of the wadi, oily heat engulfed me. There was indeed an evil, brooding silence to the village. I looked up uneasily, following the dozens upon dozens of slit windows, wondering if there were hidden eyes watching me. If the houses had been ruined, the absence of people would not have been so disturbing. But they were generally in good repair, as if the population had moved out only the day before. Their heavy wooden doors were barred from the outside by planks, and fenced with branches of thorn-bush against marauding goats. Guffs of dust skimmed along the wadi and spiky tumbleweeds were urged forward by the wind. I leaned through the open window of the car. 'You're not coming then?' I said.

'Not on your life! If you meet any Jinns shout. I'll shout back!'

'What do they look like?'

'Ugly. And they have donkeys' feet!'

I left him in his car and struck off alone to explore the shrine of the Prophet Hud.

Shukri had been recommended to me as a driver by the concierge of the Movenpick – Aden's only good hotel – and it was in the hotel lobby, a week earlier, that I had met him for the first time. He was a podgy, puffy-faced, unfit-looking man in his late twenties, dressed in a clean shirt and *futa* – the wraparound kilt most Yemenis wore. I noticed he was agitated even before he blurted out, 'I'm very nervous! I'm a bloody fool! It's so long since I spoke to a foreigner. My father told me to get dressed up, to put on a tie and look respectable. He made me put on my best *futa*. I bought it in Saudi Arabia. It cost one thousand shillings. What a bloody fool I am!'

I began to wonder if he was entirely sane.

Shukri proposed to drive me to the Hadhramaut in his eight-seater Peugeot. I told him I would think it over, and as soon as he was gone I took a taxi to visit a 'Tourist Agency' at Steamer Point, which the concierge had told me about. The office was entirely vacant except for a table where a forlorn-looking manager in Western clothes sat by a telephone. I spoke to him in Arabic, he replied in French. He had studied tourism in France, he said. 'Yes, I can get you a car,' he told me, 'next month. Maybe next week, I don't know. We don't get many tourists here. I haven't seen a tourist in weeks.' On the way back to the Movenpick, the taxi-driver told me, 'You'll be lucky to hire a car in Aden. Everything here has gone to pot. It was the Russians who ruined us, you know. We got rid of the British and we walked into the hands of the Russians – who were worse. I wouldn't pick up a Russian if one hailed me in the street. They started a car-factory here, making Ladas. By God, you can't drive a Lada ten kilometres before it breaks down! Yet there are Morris Minors that have been going forty years!'

I had desperately wanted a four-wheel-drive vehicle, but I soon realized that in shell-shocked Aden there was no alternative to Shukri and his Peugeot. In the evening I phoned him, and the next morning he was in the lobby at the crack of dawn. 'I had a bad impression of you yesterday,' he told me frankly. 'My father told me not to phone you, but I was very worried that you wouldn't take me. I came up to the hotel twice in the afternoon, but you were out. My father said it was a waste of time: "If he wants you he'll call you!" he said. He was right, of course. See! I'm always talking about my father. Maybe it's because I haven't grown up!'

Before we left, Shukri insisted on giving me a guided tour of the city. Locked around its harbour by the pressure of sweeping mountains, the tranquil aquamarine waters trawled by flamingoes, Aden could easily have been the jewel of the Arabian Sea. Instead it was an urban carcass eviscerated and picked clean. Alps of debris lay in the gaping blind alleys. Street lights had been shot out. Buildings were warped and buckled, riddled with millions of bullet-marks and shell-holes. Only four years earlier, during the uprising against the communists, 10,000 people had died on these streets in a matter of days. Foreign expatriates had been evacuated from the beaches by the Royal Marines. 'I saw communist tanks driving over traffic-jams,' Shukri said, '*on the roofs of the cars!* There were women and children in them who were just crushed to death! I'll never forgive them for that.'

Trade still hadn't recovered – whole streets of shops were shuttered and of the few that were open, none seemed to have much of substance to sell. As we coasted about, motor-vehicles honked and stuttered past – mobile junk-heaps, hammered, scored and held together by rope. We wheeled around Muʿalla, Sheikh Othman, Crater, Steamer Point – names from an Englishman's dream of the Empire – and Shukri pointed out the barracks that had watched scores of British regiments on parade in starched khaki drill, the parade-ground now a no man's land of broken brickbats, the buildings skewed out of true by bombs and bullets, peeling walls scrawled with communist slogans, windows glassless and ringed with the marks of fire. He showed me the famous Crescent and Rock hotels, once the pride of the city, now gloomy, flea-bitten dens with fractured doors and cracked windows, whose view was blocked by the massive Russian memorial to the Unknown Soldier. Muʿalla was a grand canyon between featureless Stalinist-style apartment-blocks, their balconies sealed with chicken-wire, their rows of windows like sightless eye-sockets. Shukri stopped to let me see a poster on the wall displaying the Muʿalla flat-blocks in better days, with the legend, *'Another Product of the Glorious Revolution!'* printed across the picture. 'What a cheek the communists have!' he said, sputtering with laughter. 'It was the British who built those flats. They were the married quarters for the British garrison!'

We drove through 'White City' – formerly the British officers' lines – once-neat villas mildewed and crumpled, their lawns now jungles littered with old bicycle-frames and rusty tin cans. 'The Bedu live there now,' Shukri said. 'People from the countryside. They just break the locks and take the houses for themselves. It's a scandal!' We passed the wreck of the Sheba cinema – still in operation judging by the garish posters of Arabic films pasted outside. 'When I was a kid you had to wear a collar and tie to get in there,' Shukri said. 'Used to be called the "Regal" in those days!'

The only institution which seemed to be flourishing in Aden was the qat-market. At eight o'clock in the morning, crowds of men in kilts and headcloths were milling like ants around the open backs of shiny new Land-Cruisers whose windscreens and side-windows were covered with blankets against the sun, transforming them into sinister black caverns. Inside lurked truculent, bearded qat-traders amid piles of shoots tied into bundles like coiled streamers. Trading was brisk, loud and acrimonious. Many of the men – buyers and sellers – were already chewing, their faces bloated on one side like toothache-sufferers. They chewed furiously, stripping the succulent green leaves from the qat stems with their teeth, simultaneously puffing hungrily on cigarettes. Qat was a way of life in the Yemen: men chewed it, women chewed it. Shukri's mother ground the qat leaves in a machine for his old father who had lost all his teeth and now had to eat it with a spoon. Thousands of acres of fertile ground had been given over to growing it, the fields so valuable that tribes which once specialized in stealing each other's goats and camels now stole each other's qat, and watch-towers had been erected in the qat fields to house armed guards when the qat was ripe. In shattered, burned-out Aden qat seemed the one thing that was keeping the economy going.

Qat was first thing on Shukri's list of equipment for a journey to the Hadhramaut. 'No one here makes a long journey by car without qat,' he said. 'It stops you dozing. Watch the drivers we pass and you'll see their cheeks swollen with it!'

At the open door of a Land-Cruiser, he weighed two wheels of qat in his hands, held them up to the light, picked a strand and sampled it, pronounced it good, and wrangled for ten minutes over the price. As we nursed the two green spirals nervously through the jostling crowd to the safety of Shukri's car, an officer in down-at-heel combats touched my arm. 'Do *you* chew qat?' he inquired in apparent amazement.

'Why shouldn't he?' Shukri answered, tensing with clownish hostility. 'It's legal, isn't it?'

At a stall nearby he bought two clean hand-towels and sprinkled them with water from a plastic bottle: 'Otherwise it will get dry!' he explained. He wrapped each bundle of qat gingerly in a damp towel, then edged the bundles into two plastic bags, knotted them, then made punctures in the bags with a nail: 'To let it breathe,' he said.

He laid the two bundles on the gearbox-faring, and turned his attention to the rest of the provisions: four bottles of Canada Dry Cola, which, sipped while chewing the qat, would sweeten it: six packs of Marlboro cigarettes, to enhance the effect of the narcotic. At a stall near the harbour we bought fifteen bottles of mineral water, which Shukri poured one by one into a plastic cooler, followed by three bagfuls of ice. He replaced the cooler's lid firmly: 'We've got everything we need!' he said.

It was a relief to get past the guards at the roadblock and to hear Shukri running through the gears smoothly as we rolled alongside the ocean: onyx waters, black lava-sand, the occasional palm tree, isolated buildings encircled with barbed wire, camels drawing two-wheeled carts along the water's edge. To the north there were brazen, fluted hills, puddled low dunes, and once we passed a squadron of camels pouring out of a gully, driven on by two Arab boys in tattered check *futas* and tight headcloths. 'Bedu,' Shukri said. 'In the Yemen, anyone who lives outside the city is Bedu. Bedu are tribesmen: they are tough fighters and they lead hard lives. They eat soap and think it's chocolate!'

'The Aden people have no tribes?'

'Everyone has a tribe. My grandfather was a Bedui from the northern desert – the Jauf – but he killed someone in a vendetta and had to run away to Aden. He settled down there and in time forgot about his tribe. We don't keep in contact with any of our people, because of the blood-feud – they would use it as an excuse to attack us. We became city people in two generations. I suppose you could say that we are still Bedu, but once you leave the tribe it doesn't have any meaning. We married townswomen and became townsmen. Adenis are jokers, not fighters. We don't really give much importance to Islam. I mean, we are Muslims like the English are Christians. The Bedu are crude, unsophisticated and superstitious. Adenis are people of the modern world.'

Shukri told me he had been a bright student, top of the class and head boy of the school, but at the age of sixteen he had suddenly lost interest in his studies. Instead, he had gone off to Saudi

Arabia and after working there for a while, he and his friend, flush with cash for the first time in their lives, had booked a vacation in Thailand. 'It was for the women,' he admitted, 'and by God, there was one girl there that I'd have married – she was so shy and modest. But Mahsin, my friend, would have told everyone she was a whore. Anyway, we had girls, we got drunk on whisky, we even ate pork. Mahsin said, "We can't eat that, it's forbidden!" I laughed at him. "We've just been making love to whores and drinking whisky," I said. "We're not going to prove we're good Muslims by not eating pork!"'

Glistering hills passed, a crumbling, powder-dry communist town with paintings of Martyrs to the Revolution, a village where men were loading camels with stacks of firewood. The sea was out of sight, and we were driving across a rocky plain covered in a wild tangle of tamarisk and acacia trees. 'Well, who's going to start?' Shukri asked, placing a plump hand on the qat.

'It'll have to be you,' I said. 'I don't know how to do it.'

Shukri opened the package with one hand, flipped back the moist towel, and broke the fragile string holding the bundle. He selected a twig of qat – green leaves on a stem, almost like privet – and began rubbing the leaves gently between finger and thumb. 'First you clean it like this,' he said, 'then you pluck the leaves off down to the stem. Don't chew it straight away, just store it in your cheek and let the juices flow. The effect of qat depends on the type. Some makes you feel horny. Some makes you feel like walking till you drop. Some makes you feel like sitting on your arse for hours.' I began cleaning the leaves with attention. Shukri guffawed. 'You've got to do it a bit harder. Pretend you're masturbating!' he said.

I plucked the leaves off and began storing them inside my cheek, remembering that the Arabic word for chewing qat actually means 'to store'. The taste was incredibly bitter. Shukri rumbled with laughter as he watched me. Later, he took a bottle of Cola and pierced the cap with a rusty nail. 'Just sip it very, very little at a time,' he said. 'That takes the bitterness away.' At first I tasted only the bitterness, then, slowly, my cheek turned numb. Desert unfolded outside – dustbowls, claws of thorn-trees, palm-groves, clumps of houses, cactusoid Indian figs with fruit like yellow hand-grenades, women in blazing colours carrying great nests of firewood and waggling broad behinds, grinning men on camel-carts laden with sugar-cane, trickles of shorn sheep wrapped in cloaks of gold-dust, methyl-blue sky in which falcons and kites banked with the exquisite slowness of mobiles on strings, great plains opening up into mile after mile of silvery waste. Suddenly we were sailing along uplifted through the sky like clouds, rhythmically chewing, our cheeks bulging balloons, our eyes glittering jewels, and the world seemed a very, very beautiful place indeed. 'This is good qat,' Shukri said. 'It is qat from the south. The qat from the north is big and bushy but a lot of the leaves are dry.'

We stopped for lunch at an open-sided shack, where we spat our gobs of masticated qat unceremoniously into the sand. My jaws ached as Shukri had warned me they would, and as he had bits of green leaf stuck between his teeth, I supposed I did too. A robust, sweating Arab with a protruding paunch and a moustache shaped like a horseshoe brought us fried chicken, fresh bread, and water in a plastic jug. He charged me twenty-five shillings for the meal. 'You are charging him too much because he's a foreigner!' Shukri said. The perspiring man wiped his forehead with a hand. 'No, I'm not,' he said. 'A whole chicken is a hundred shillings, and that is a quarter of a chicken, so it is twenty-five shillings.'

Shukri grinned. 'It's correct,' he said. 'There are no thieves in Yemen. In Sanaʿa maybe, but not here!'

As soon as we were out of town we began to chew again, floating in gauze across dramatic volcano country. Great orbs of coagulated stone rose before us, a waste of black lava slates, gullies with dragonflies and hummock-grass.

'Why do you want to go to the Hadhramaut?' Shukri inquired.

'I want to meet the Bedu,' I told him.

A playful smile quivered on his lips. 'You are one of those Englishmen like Lawrence,' he smirked. 'I have seen the film. But most of those who were interested in the Bedu preferred men to women.' He let this sink in for a moment, then inquired with a mischievous grin, 'Are you married?'

'Yes. And I have a son.'

He heaved a false sigh of relief. 'That's got *that* out of the way!' he said. 'I've got a son too. I'll be seeing him when I get back from this journey with you. I see him once a week, but he won't play with me. Sometimes I think my ex-wife shows him a photo of me and says, "Woo! Woo!" to put him off me. But no, really, we'd both like to get married again, only we can't. You see, in Islam if you divorce your wife three times you can't remarry her unless she has married someone else in between and been divorced by *him*. And they have to have slept together, so you can't fake it. We've been divorced three times, so we're stuck!'

I looked at him aghast. 'How on earth can you divorce a woman three times?'

'You'll think I'm terrible if I tell you why.'

'Go on.'

'The first time I just told her: "I'm going to sleep and if you wake me up I'll divorce you!" She woke me up so I divorced her. Just like that. Then someone told me I shouldn't have done it, and I thought, "Hey, this is something really big!" and I wanted her back. I felt guilty. In a day or two I fixed things up. You see, in Islam you only have to say, "You are my wife!" to get married and "I divorce you!" to get divorced. It's easy!'

I chewed my qat, thinking this was the most flippantly irresponsible view of marriage I had ever heard. 'What about the other two times?' I asked.

'Well, that was because of a dispute with her family.'

'You don't have to tell me unless you want to.'

'No, I want to.' He took a deep breath. 'All right,' he said, 'let me start right at the beginning. There I was in Saudi Arabia. I wanted to get married, but no Saudi family would have given me a girl, and my own family would only really have accepted a girl from Aden. I couldn't cope with the idea of going home, marrying, and then migrating back to Saudi Arabia again with all the bureaucracy that entailed. Then a colleague of mine, an Adeni, solved the problem. He suggested that I should marry his sister. "She's staying with me here in Saudi," the brother told me. It was so convenient that I didn't bother to consider why the girl should be with her brother rather than at home with her parents in Aden. Anyway, I agreed to marry her right out. I never met the girl before our engagement day. I never even saw her in a photo. You may think it's odd, but I didn't want to see her because I knew I'd change my mind then, and I wanted to get married. The brother said she was neither ugly nor beautiful, which at least was the truth. When I removed the veil on our engagement day, she stood modestly, eyes downcast, which was suitable. "Do you agree to marry this girl?" the *qadi* asked. I said yes and the girl agreed and nominated her brother to speak for her. We agreed on the bride-price and made a contract, the brother specifying that, if I divorced her, I would have to pay twenty thousand riyals compensation. He left me alone in the room, and then he pushed the girl in. She was very nervous. "You realize I'm now your husband?" I asked. She didn't answer. That was good – if she'd been too forward it would have been a bad sign. We stood there in silence for a minute, and then I asked, "Is there any tea?" She said "Yes!" and almost ran out. That was a good sign too.'

'The second time I went, I asked her to remove the veil. Then we talked for a bit, but she always took any opportunity to leave the room. After a few visits, though, I managed to persuade her to sit on my knee. I stroked her hair. At last, I kissed her on the head. Then in the ear. Then I began to kiss her on the mouth. I wanted to make love, but she said, "Wait till we're properly married." Everything went all right, until the night of the actual wedding. Then I realized that she was a woman, not a girl, you see what I mean?'

'She wasn't a virgin?'

'That's it. I discovered it on our wedding night. We made love, then I put the light on. "Where's the blood?" I asked her. "I don't know!" she said. She looked so surprised – I mean it didn't seem like an act. She swore that she'd never been with a man before – that she'd lost it by . . . well, by playing with herself, you know. I said, "I believe you. But I'd better take you to the hospital tomorrow to make sure. If you have anything to tell me you'd better do it now, because at the hospital they will certainly tell me the truth." She said nothing, but in the morning I saw her reading the Holy Quran. That meant either she was asking God to help her disguise the truth, or to make sure the hospital revealed the truth. Anyway the doctor said that there was a hole, but she couldn't tell if it had been made by a man or a finger. I should have sent her back to her family right then, and demanded the bride-price back, but she said, "They'll kill me!" – I mean really *kill* her – so instead, I hushed it up. But I found I couldn't stop thinking about it. I decided to get rid of her on some silly excuse, like waking me up.

'It's true that I took her back after a few days, but then my mother came to visit. She sensed there was bad feeling between us, and she told my wife that she ought to look after me better. My wife called her a bitch, and they had a blazing row. "You don't like me having Shukri!" my wife shouted. "You're jealous!" That was too much! "Shut up and get out!" I told her. Then she went back to her brother, who asked to see me a few days later. He said, "Shukri, you are not a man because you never revealed that my sister wasn't a virgin!" I was shocked! I had never mentioned it to anybody. How did he know? Either he had known before I married her, or she had told him later – which she said she was terrified to do because the family would kill her. Anyway, since he had brought it up, not me, I had no option but to divorce her again. Then the brother said, "All right. Now you'll have to pay me twenty thousand riyals compensation!"

'It struck me suddenly that the whole thing had been a trick. Two things were suspicious. First, why did the family send her to Saudi Arabia to get married? Secondly, why didn't her brother come the morning after our wedding night to see the blood on the sheet that proved she was a virgin? It is the custom even in Aden to do that – we call it "asking for one's *sharf*" – one's "honour" – because virginity reflects a family's "honour". Anyway I remembered thinking it funny at the time that he hadn't come for his "honour". Perhaps she'd been playing around in Aden and the parents had sent her away from wagging tongues – to make a clown of me! I felt that the brother knew all the time that she wasn't a virgin and had made the compensation clause in the contract to fiddle me, that son of a bitch! I refused to pay, so he took me to the High Court in Saudi Arabia, and he told the judge I drank alcohol and played with women and chewed qat – all enough to hang me in Saudi. I had to tell the truth – that my wife wasn't a virgin. The judge asked the brother to swear that she'd been a virgin before the wedding and he wouldn't, so he lost the case. The judge said, "It's forbidden in God's sight for you to live with this filth ever again!" and he made us marry and divorce again as a formality so that it was finished for ever. The funny thing was that by then, I loved my wife, and having the baby made it worse, of course. I wouldn't have divorced her if the brother hadn't revealed publicly that she wasn't a virgin, and forced my hand. I came home from Saudi Arabia, and explained it all to my father. I asked him, "Did I do right or wrong?" He said, "It was a mistake from the beginning. You should have acted like an Arab. Now you'll have to deal with it!'

The qat lifted me euphorically. I found myself clinging on to Shukri's story with all its twists and turns as to the most fascinating epic – it was a brilliantly illuminating window into the heart of Arab society. I could have listened all night. Outside, the landscape was pulpy gold now, the sun lowering, losing its hard edge. We passed rolling plains where the light hung on tamarisk-trees like threads of fleece. Stiff grasses puffed out of the ground like strands of smoke. Flat-capped acacias whisked in spinning vortices. The sand-and-gravel country faded, giving way to tattered hills where forts staggered on the brink of cliffs, where rock-falls littered the valleys, where the gneiss had been sculpted by time into claws and pedestals that were in the process of detaching themselves from the mother-lode. There was a muzziness in the air, sheaths of mist lurking in faery vales of palms, wadis with beds of burnished ivory pebbles, ant-heap villages of mud-block where house had been piled on house over generations, where the mud seemed to have oozed into almost every available space before setting hard. Houses with galleries of tiny windows and studded wooden doors had mushroomed organically into Gothic dream-castles. Sprouting towers evolved into spires that scratched the sky. In cramped alleys beneath them there were goats and black asses and bony oxen, tended by girls in masks like alligator heads. We followed a great trunk wadi where water trickled between plunging walls, an entire village cast in bronze on a slice of island in the stream. For me this was a new Arabia, a rich, Brothers Grimm, Lord-of-the-Rings world of phantastical geometry and faery textures.

After dark we came down to the sea, and parked for the night on a damp beach by a ruined fisherman's hut. The beach was churned up by the tracks of a million crabs, and in the moonlight I could see them – energetic spider-shapes scuttering along the edge of the surf. I spat out the last ball of qat, unrolled my sleeping-bag, and made myself as comfortable as possible in the sand. As soon as I was out of the car, Shukri locked himself inside. 'What's the matter?' I asked.

'There are Jinns in places like this,' he said through the open window. 'I don't want some ghostly hand coming in and throttling me while I'm asleep! You can sleep in the car if you want, but if you sleep outside and I see any Jinns attacking you, I'll just drive off, I warn you! There's no way you can fight Jinns!'

I remembered Shukri's withering remarks about the 'crude and superstitious' Bedu versus the 'sophisticated' townsman. Some things could not be erased in two generations, I thought.

And maybe he was right about the Jinns anyway.

★

Breakfast in Mukalla: from afar it was a crystal-white city tucked under lofty mountains – a spit of land in pellucid waters where fishing-skiffs like dark needles rode placidly at anchor. From inside, though, it was a seething mass of confusion: half-wrecked cars belching smoke, crowds spewing along deep avenues beneath crippled housing-blocks, men milling on a corner with shovels and picks, waiting for someone to offer them work. We parked the Peugeot in a rubbish-strewn back-street where boys were kicking a punctured football, and goats clambered on the bonnet of a burned-out car. We sat at a greasy table in the street, and an old man in a skullcap brought us fried eggs on flaps of bread, and sweet red tea.

Later we visited the palace of the former Quʿaiti Sultan, a ramshackle Gormenghast of a building overlooking the deep curve of the harbour – half a dozen styles, predominantly Indian, hanging together on the edge of collapse. The place had been turned into a museum, and amidst a jumble of Indian crockery and furniture, Soviet machine-guns, pre-Islamic carvings of dolphins and sea-horses, and sepia-tinted prints of stern-looking British officials, we found a framed letter from the British government to the last Quʿaiti Sultan of Mukalla, informing His Excellency that the British would presently be pulling out of their Aden Protectorate and that they could 'no longer extend their protection to him or his heirs'. Shukri, whose English was very good, read the letter in silence. After we had set off for the Hadhramaut, though, and he had started on the second package of qat, he burst out, 'What bastards the British were, just leaving the Quʿaitis in the lurch like that! I don't mean it personally, but all the trouble we've had with the communist government was the fault of the British. They encouraged the communists because they wanted them to destabilize the region – they wanted to find themselves needed in the Gulf. My family fought against the British. My uncle shot a British soldier. He told me they were coming up in a patrol of six and he could see this soldier, who was very young. When my uncle shot him, he fell down and shouted, "I want to live!"

My uncle said he couldn't shoot him again. He hadn't the heart for it. I don't mean it personally – I think the British should pay for what they did here. God, if there were any concessions to governments for rebuilding Aden, I wouldn't let the British in!'

The Peugeot was juddering up into the Jol – the rocky region that divided the sea-coast from the Hadhramaut – twisting and turning around fearsome hairpins, with plunging arid valleys far below us, their sides brittle schist looking like liquid toffee that had run, cooled and clotted into blebs and bubbles. Sometimes the road passed within inches of a sheer drop on both sides. Shukri chewed hard in concentration, but today he chewed alone. The qat had kept me awake the previous night, and had made me shaky and washed-out all morning.

We passed a sign that read 'Beware!' in Arabic. Some witty scholar had added a feminine plural case-ending to the imperative with an ink-marker, so that the sign now implied 'Women Beware!' Shukri laughed darkly as he pointed it out to me. 'That's right,' he said. 'Women should beware. They should know their place. Take my sister, for instance – she's training to be a doctor, and she's got her nose up in the air and won't take orders. I don't speak to her any more. I told my father that when she gets married she'll have to wash and cook. She'll have to put her nose down – especially if she marries a bastard like me. How can she accept a husband as boss if she can't accept her elder brother as boss? By God, she'll be divorced in a week! I'm only doing my duty to her – I want her to be a good wife – it's *sharf* – honour – just like my wife not being a virgin. My father was right about that. If I'd done what Arab custom dictated and sent the girl home as soon as I found out she wasn't a virgin, the problem wouldn't have arisen. *Sharf* – that's the whole root of Arab society for townsmen or Bedu – the root of Islam itself. For an Arab "honour" doesn't necessarily mean fighting or courage – it's entirely to do with the purity of our women. That's why your writer Salman Rushdie got into trouble, because he suggested that the Prophet Mohammad's wife committed adultery. By God, there's a man who deserves to die! I believe in mercy, but there should be no mercy for a man who insults the honour of the Prophet Mohammad!'

Shukri seemed very steamed up, and I was surprised. Since we had left Aden he hadn't once stopped the car to perform the prayers required of a devout Muslim. The previous morning he had happily described his sexual experiences in Thailand, and even admitted to guzzling pork: 'We are Muslims like the English are Christians,' he had said. Yet here he was, a self-admitted 'joker', fuming about Salman Rushdie, an Indian-born British writer whose books he had never read. 'I don't understand,' I said. 'I mean Muslims accept that the Prophet Mohammad was just a man – not God – so surely the things that happen to other men could perfectly well happen to him?'

'No,' Shukri said. 'How could the wife of a Prophet commit adultery? If the Prophet Mohammad hadn't even got the respect of his wives, he couldn't have gained the respect of millions of followers, who all swear, "There is no God but God *and Mohammad is the Prophet of God!*" If Mohammad's wife committed adultery it would mean that he had no *sharf*, and if he had no *sharf* it would mean that God didn't care about him, and didn't care about Islam. It would mean that he wasn't a Prophet. If he had no honour then the whole of our history means nothing. Even the descendants of the Prophet are called *"The Honourable Ones"*. Honour is the root of everything – why the Bedu here would kill you at once if they thought you had insulted their honour! Honour is more important than Islam – that's the truth – because without honour Islam is meaningless. If my sister appeared in a pornographic film, for instance, I would kill her for dishonouring all the family. What would you do in the same situation?'

'Well, I'd advise her against it. I'd be very angry with the people who'd got her to do it. But in the end it would be her choice. I'd be more concerned about her than about the family, because she's an individual.'

'That's the difference between you and us, you see. It's *sharf* –

the honour of the family and the tribe – that makes us what we are. Individuals mean nothing.'

'I don't think Margaret Thatcher would have agreed with you: she said, "There is no such thing as society: there are only individuals." '

'Rubbish! Margaret Thatcher is a woman, anyway, and men shouldn't be bossed about by women! That's typical of the West! In the West today women act as if they were men. That's why so many Westerners marry Asian women. They want real women. Nature will out no matter what you do!'

I laughed, but I was still a little nonplussed. Yesterday morning I had seen Shukri the liberal, sophisticated, educated, urbanized Arab of Bedouin origin. Yesterday afternoon I had seen the Shukri who had messed up his marriage by failing to adhere to Arab tradition. Last night I had met Shukri the superstitious. Today I had Shukri the fundamentalist: we had turned full circle in less than two days. Was it a case of *'in qat veritas'*, I wondered?

'When you chew qat you talk more and more like a fundamentalist,' I said.

Shukri chewed silently for a moment. 'It's not the qat,' he said, 'I think it's being with you. When you meet someone from another culture – especially a strong culture – you either ape their ways and identify with them, or you fall back on your own roots and the things that make you distinct. I have just fallen back on my roots, that's all.'

As an explanation of the origins of fundamentalism in the Arab world this could hardly have been improved upon, I thought.

We halted at another open cabin at Ma'adi, high in the hills, for lunch. A few thin camels snuffled in the stunted bushes outside, and inside an old Bedui in a bright green skirt sat watching a TV set on which Umm Kalthum, the great lady of Egypt and now-deceased icon of Arab music, was warbling dementedly to the heavy brass of her orchestra. We sat on the floor and the landlord brought us roasted goat and rice with bottles of Cola. As we made ready to eat, the old Bedui watching the TV turned and stared at us. 'Don't you know a guest where you come from?' he demanded. I wasn't sure whether he was addressing Shukri or myself – or both – but I felt extremely embarrassed. We had perpetrated the ultimate Bedouin sin: even when eating in a restaurant, it was common politeness to invite others to join you. We had simply forgotten. 'Please,' I said, 'join us!' The old man considered it for a moment, then shuffled over and sat down. He was short but massively built, with enormous hands and feet, a leonine head draped in a rainbow-coloured headcloth with tassels, and a thick silver beard. His name was Hassan and he belonged to the Humum, a large Bedu tribe inhabiting the Jol and the desert beyond. 'Most of us live in mud houses now,' he told me. 'We don't use camels. When they built the road it killed all that. The Bedu used to control all the transport going into the Hadhramaut, because camels and donkeys were the only transport there was, and the Bedu owned them. They started building the road when I was a boy, and the tribes were really furious. We knew that the road would take our carrying-trade away, and we couldn't afford to buy lorries. We used to take pot-shots at them while they were working, not really to kill them, but just to frighten the workers away. Even after they finished building it, we still used to fire at trucks. It used to put the wind up them, by God! Still, it did no good – even the Bedu have lorries now.'

I asked him about the people of the Hadhramaut. 'Some are Bedu and some Hadr,' he said. 'The Hadr are divided into tribesmen and non-tribesmen. The tribesmen carry arms but the non-tribesmen – the "Weak People" – don't. They just work in the fields. In the past they were always under the protection of a tribe.'

'Then what are the Bedu?'

'The Bedu are people of the desert. They have such a hard life that they have agreed between themselves to help each other in trouble. That's what the rules are about. In the Hadhramaut or the mountains you don't need that. Everyone has his own land and his own water and outsiders are sometimes a threat – they aren't needed. Of course, the Bedu don't live such a hard life as in the past. But they are still hospitable to strangers.'

After lunch we descended into the Hadhramaut. It was an entire world hidden in a great groove in the earth, like a fabled Martian canal, its precipitous banks sometimes forty miles apart. Although only occasionally flooded – for there is no rainy season in south Arabia – the Hadhramaut was a fertile channel in the midst of near-sterility, and reminded me of nothing so much as the Nile Valley. As we motored slowly down from the Jol we began to see houses – monoliths of mud with millions of windows – scattered singly across the valley floor, each in its own small hacienda with zebra-stripes of cultivation, clusters of goats browsing on stubble, gloomy-looking camels, men clumping behind sickly donkeys, women whose faces were veiled and shadowed by huge witch-hats of straw, winnowing grain. The scattered fortress-farms became villages built amid explosions of date-palms and ploughed plots along the edges of dry-washes paved with buffed blue pebbles. The mud palazzi – many of them more than four storeys high – were precisely the same russet colour as the wadi's cliffs, as if the builders had been trying to emulate the majesty of the sweeping sandstone. There was a little of Morocco here, a bit of Nubia perhaps, but the place was truly unique. The Hadhrami people were not the scavenging Bedu tribes of the desert, but large, rich families of landowners nurtured on dates and grain and goats' milk, no cowering peasant-farmers, but strong, fierce tribesmen whose character had been moulded by generations of bitter feuding. Their militarized warren-villages reflected the wars, feuds and battles that had ebbed and flowed along the wadi since time immemorial.

Before sunset we arrived at Shibam, a ghetto of mud rearing suddenly out of the evening haze like a gargantuan termites' nest. The town was a defensive structure, ringed with a wall and entered by a single fortified gateway. Because of the restriction of space, the builders of Shibam had been obliged as they multiplied to build upwards so that the houses burgeoned till they reached their limit of stability at seven or eight storeys. The houses had to be built shoulder to shoulder, forming a labyrinth of tower-blocks reached from the rear by tortuous alleys. Some fanciful observers had called it the 'Manhattan of Arabia', though for me it resembled far more a scaled-down version of the old city of Kowloon in Hong Kong – a monstrous warren of tenements supposed to house more than 100,000 people. Kowloon was built of cement and steel, but considering that Shibam was constructed entirely of mud fortified with straw and dung, it was a very formidable accomplishment indeed.

Shukri parked the car in a side-street and we walked through the arched gateway into a small square dominated by the cigar-shaped minaret of a mosque. We wandered through the cool alleys beneath leathery walls in which shallow flutings acted as conduits for the human refuse that dribbled down from on high. The alleys were cluttered with rubble and carpeted with goat droppings. Swarms of children followed us, yelling, 'Where are you from, mister?' Women's faces appeared momentarily at high windows. Donkey-carts laden with clover creaked past. Every nook and broken corner was a roosting-place for scraggly goats, sheep or hobbled donkeys. Chickens and roosters chased each other in clucking confusion. On *mastabas* – raised step-buttresses – men in *futas* and headcloths were clattering out dice on backgammon boards, and old women in black sat silently, taking in the evening savours of goat-musk, animal dung, urine and human sweat. Some of the alleys were shaded with sacking and housed one-room shops where robust men in white dishdashas presided over sacks of grain, and tables heavy with biscuit-tins full of rice, onions, garlic, salt, cumin and red pepper. Flaps of dried shark-meat and tuna were piled up like shards of firewood, the high odours of the fish adding to the matrix of smells. One old greybeard sat contentedly cutting a well-bucket from a section of truck-tyre, the walls of his tiny shop decorated with crafted leather waterskins. Shibam was a world within a world – complete with seven mosques, many schools and several markets. You could have got lost among the twists and turns of its alleys, taken root, adopted local dress and custom, and never found your way out to the light of day. Once, under siege by the Quʿaiti family, the inhabitants had not ventured outside for sixteen years, until they were reduced to eating shoe-leather.

We took tea at a stall in the square. Piratical men sat around it smoking waterpipes made from bean-cans and old coconut shells. Others were humping rubber baskets of squashes and purple aubergines into a store. A weak old gaffer left a trail of onions behind him as he steered his heavy basket towards the gate. Below our *mastaba* men were shouting at each other over a mountain of green and yellow melons shaped like bombs. An emaciated old man with a toothbrush moustache, wearing a white skull-cap, a dirty-white jacket and chequered *futa*, shuffled up for a waterpipe, kicked off his shoes and sat down by the stall on a pad of cloth. He pulled the pipe shakily towards him, then took his own tobacco from his pocket and unwrapped it. He rubbed and rolled the stuff steadily with the ease of long practice, then lifted the pot of his pipe and filled it with unhurried grace. He sat for a moment in contemplation of it. There was all the time in the world to enjoy this pleasure. The tea-boy leaned over with pieces of glowing charcoal on a pincer. The old man planted the stem loosely in a hole drilled in the coconut-shell. He took a deep toke, coughed, spluttered, then toked again. His shrunken face lit up with pleasure as the smoke trickled back out of his mouth and nostrils. 'Where are you from?' he asked me after several more puffs. When I told him I was British, he said, 'Come up to my house when I've finished this smoke.'

The old man's name was Sheikh Moukhtar, and the room he led us to, up several narrow flights of stairs, was huge, cool, bare and spotlessly clean, lit by two brilliant electric bulbs. He opened a window from which we could see directly into the square, and across it to the sandy wadi-bed, and the rust-red cliffs on the opposite side. He had his boy bring more tea, lit another pipe, and talked about the wars between the Kathir and the Yafaʿi tribes that had shattered the peace of the Hadhramaut for generations.

The Kathir, who had spawned many of the Bedu tribes of Oman, were originally a settled people from the region of Sanaʿa, and may have begun moving east as early as AD 800. In 1494 they captured Shibam and made it the capital from which they dominated the Hadhramaut. Only eight years later, they began to import warriors from the Yafaʿi and Zeidi tribes to shore up their tottering strength. Inevitably these fighters had turned against their enfeebled masters, and the two factions had become locked in a deadly struggle which had lasted until recent times.

The Quʿaitis – eventually to become the ruling house of Mukalla – were a dominant branch of the Yafaʿis. The story of their rise began, Sheikh Moukhtar related, from an incident concerning a humble oil-lamp. 'The lamp used to hang in an old mosque in Shibam,' he said, 'and it ran on vegetable oil. Every day when the folk went for their morning prayers they found that the oil was missing. So they set a trap for the thief, filling the lamp with fish-oil instead. Sure enough, the oil was gone the following day, and they caught the head of the Quʿaiti family walking through the market stinking of fish. He was so ashamed that he fled to India, where he became famous working for the Nizam of Hyderabad. He returned from India fabulously rich, and decided to take over the Hadhramaut from the Kathirs. The British supported him, while the Kathirs were backed by the Turks. It was the foreigners who supplied them with modern rifles – and that really wrecked everything. The fighting went on for years, but neither of the families really came out on top. The Quʿaitis controlled Mukalla and the coast, and Shibam was a Quʿaiti town. But in Saiyun and Tarim, the Kathirs ruled the roost. It got so bad in the nineteen-thirties that people couldn't leave their homes – some of them never came out for twenty years! They used to dig long trenches to protect them while they went down to tend their fields. Anyway, in the end it was an Englishman who settled it. I remember him – Igna-ramis – he was the one who made the peace between the tribes.'

I took it that the old man was referring to the almost legendary Harold Ingrams, British Resident in Mukalla in the 1930s. Ingrams had seized on an incident in which a British engineer had been shot at near Tarim, to negotiate more than 1,000 three-year treaties with the autonomous villages, clans and tribes, bringing them under the aegis of the Kathiri Sultan in Saiyun. It was the first time in history that such a settlement had been brought about, though even the ponderous weight of the British Empire had not been sufficient to damp the flames of the age-old conflict for long. 'There was still fighting now and again, of course,' the old man continued, 'but life was a bit more peaceful after Igna-ramis came.'

I asked the Sheikh if there was a difference between the Hadr and the Bedu.

'The Bedu used to move about with their animals,' he said, 'and they were known for their hospitality and generosity. But they were no more courageous as fighters than the settled tribes. Of course, there were the non-tribesmen – the peasants – who didn't carry weapons – but they were always under the protection of a Sultan or a warlike tribe. In those days the Bedu used to depend on the carrying-trade with their camels, but when the Quʿaitis built the road from Mukalla it ended all that. I remember when they brought the very first motor-car here. It was right there in the square. All the people came to see it. Then they brought five aeroplanes to the airstrip, and everyone went to see them. How wonderful we thought them! I've seen everything – aeroplanes, cars, camels and donkeys – but nothing is better than an aeroplane. It used to take five days to Mukalla by camel or donkey. In an aeroplane you can do it in half an hour!'

The following day we drove through Tarim, a town of dark, dusty passageways, and out into the open country beyond. The asphalt road turned to cobble, the valley walls converging closer and closer, as we passed more isolated fortress-farms like mutilated molars, ravaged sleeping-beauty palazzi with roundhouse towers, the skeletons of very ancient villages abandoned on mounds in the wadi. We traversed lapping green water-pools, oblong roods of ploughed earth, a chaparral of mesquites ponderous with flowers, purple bougainvillaeas, pink oleanders, stands of arak whose cheesy odour hung in the air. There were packs of greyhound-slim goats in chess colours tended by witch-hatted women looking as if they belonged more to Mexico than to Arabia.

Not long before sunset we arrived at the first real Bedu camp we had seen. Four canvas marquees of foreign manufacture had been pitched near a few skeleton acacias on the banks of a wadi. Outside stood a Land-Cruiser pick-up with bald tyres, and a row of oil-drums filled with water. A bevy of Bedu women sat in the long shadows of the tents, tending a smoky fire contained in a ring of stones. Nearby, I saw a three-legged cot with a leather awning, in which a two-month-old baby slept peacefully. Behind the tents, a man and some boys were mending a chicken-wire fence that penned in a press of about thirty goats.

When we pulled up, the Arab turned towards the car suspiciously, then left what he was doing and walked over to where a Kalashnikov rifle leaned against a tree. 'I don't like the look of this!' Shukri said. 'He's going to shoot us!' The Bedui seemed menacing as he came towards us, holding his rifle in both hands, with the two boys, aged nine or ten, following at his heels. The boys wore shirts, *futas* and headcloths knotted in the Bedu style, but the man was bareheaded with a frizzle of very curly hair and a thick beard. He wore a dishdasha that was so stained, torn and tattered that it was little more than a rag. He answered our greetings with poker-faced correctness as we shook hands with him. He looked at us long and carefully, considered the car, and then, perhaps deciding that we presented no threat, said, 'Rest here with us. My house is yours!'

The Bedui's name was Suhail and he belonged to the Manahil, a tribe inhabiting the steppes between the Hadhramaut and the sands of the Empty Quarter. He called us over to sit by the fire. One of the women began to make tea, and another brought us a bowl of goats' milk. Suhail sat on his knees, nursing his rifle fondly. 'The communists took all our rifles away,' he said. 'They told us to hand them in and that they would give us new ones. It was a trick, of course. Still, we got new ones on our own. I wouldn't show it in Tarim or Saiyun, but out here in the open country who bothers?' After we had drunk tea, Suhail told his sons to load a plastic barrel into the back of the pick-up – which I noticed was carpeted with moquette – and sent them off to fill it at a local well. One of the boys launched himself happily into the driving-seat and drove the vehicle down the wadi in a slick of dust. 'Isn't he a bit young to drive that car?' Shukri asked.

'In the town he would be,' Suhail said, 'but this is the desert. Our children learn to drive cars as soon as they can touch the pedals. We are Bedu, after all.'

I asked directions to the Mahra region, and he pointed along the cobbled road. 'If you take the left-hand turning ahead you will find the road to Thamud,' he said. 'That's where the tribes live. But you will never make it in that car. You need a four-wheel-drive.'

'What about the right-hand fork?' Shukri asked.

'In that car you could probably reach the shrine of Nabi Hud. It's in a village, but nobody lives there.'

The sun surfed over the rim of the wadi behind us, and the sky turned smoky peach, then rose-pink. There was a hush in the camp. Suddenly a herd of camels peeled out of the dusk – ten or twelve animals of different sizes driven by an old man and a teen-aged boy. The camels seemed to glide across the stones, lowing gently, and Suhail ran off to help the others as they slapped the animals' shoulders to make them kneel, then hobbled their legs with strips of rope. If one forgot the presence of motor-cars here, this scene might look 'authentic', but I had long ago given up trying to decide what 'authentic' really meant. Every culture is dynamic, and the Arabs had merely acquired camel-technology at some point in their history when it suited them, and were now acquiring automotive technology which would suit them until it in turn was rendered out of date.

About 5,000 years ago, indeed, the only camels surviving in the Arabian Peninsula were wild ones grazing here in the semi-arid valleys of the Hadhramaut and the wadis of Mahra to the east. That the aboriginal peoples of south Arabia hunted these animals is clear from bones that have been found in excavated middens. Since the remains of sea-cows were found in greater abundance, though, it seems the hunters were also seafarers, who may already have been familiar with the pattern of the monsoon winds. These early peoples were confined to coastal enclaves by the vast reaches of desert which lay behind them, until they learned how to make use of an animal that could convert useless desert sedges into milk. That animal already wandered wild in the valleys of the interior, and since the aborigines relied on the sea for their main sustenance, they had both the time and the motivation to tame it. Being seamen first and landlubbers only later, it may be that they applied a familiar image to their newly acquired means of survival, naming it 'the ship of the desert'.

These prehistoric hunter-fisherman were not Arabs, nor even Semites. By the time the Semitic peoples first arrived here in 1600 BC, the aborigines had learned first to milk, then to saddle the camel. Locked behind the sand-sea of the Empty Quarter for centuries, they had not only taken their first halting steps into nomadism, but may also have begun to harness the camel's carrying power for the highly lucrative incense trade.

Their spice-caravans had eventually reached the Syrian desert, the homeland of the sheep- and goat-rearing Aribu tribes, which by the time of Shalmaneser III had acquired enough camels to threaten if not defeat the mighty Assyrians. Some of the Arabs may have followed the caravans back to their source in south Arabia and learned the secrets of the camel-trade. In the fullness of time these Arabs overwhelmed and married with the indigenes. So the 'noble camel-breeding tribes of Arabia' were born –

out of adaptability and commercial opportunism, having acquired the superior technology of an alien race.

The two newcomers joined us by the fire. The old man – Suhail's uncle – was called Sayf, and like many of the Bedu he was squat and massive, his features thick and larger than life, with a great anchor nose and an almost unbelievably long chin. The Land-Cruiser clattered back across the wadi, and the boys jumped out. Suhail helped them unload the full drum of water and poured it into one of the iron tanks. After the Bedu had performed their sunset prayer and the darkness was full, Suhail went off and returned dragging a bleating kid. 'You will eat with us!' he said, indicating that he intended to slaughter the goat for dinner. 'Yes,' I said, 'but don't slaughter the goat. It's too much. We will be happy to eat with you but don't kill it!' Shukri joined my protestations, but they fell on deaf ears. When the kid's throat had been slit with a dagger, Suhail slung the carcass from a tree and began to skin it. The boys built up the fire with faggots of acacia wood that gave out a fragrant scent. When it was blazing well they piled smooth round boulders over the flames, to roast the meat in the traditional way. Soon strips of flesh were sizzling on the red-hot stones, the delicious savoury smell of roasting meat blending with the scent of the firewood. The flesh was served on a platter, and we helped ourselves, slicing the joints with knives, stripping the bones and flinging them over our shoulders. Afterwards, tea was brewed on another fire. We sat back and looked at familiar star-patterns while the camels coughed, blubbered, and chewed the cud, occasionally squabbling and tussling heads in the shadows.

'We don't ride camels any more,' Sayf said, looking at them with some pride, 'except over short distances when they're grazing – we just hop on their backs. I don't think we even have any saddles now. I haven't seen one for years. Everything is cars and lorries – they need petrol, and petrol's expensive. Camels don't need petrol and their food is free. A camel will keep going longer than a car. A car just falls to bits in time, but a camel renews itself. You can't milk a car, can you? The Bedu will never give up camels, but I admit it's easier to travel in a car. Perhaps the oil they've found in the Hadhramaut will make us all rich.'

'I doubt it,' Suhail said. 'It will make the government rich, that's all!'

I asked Sayf about the life of the Bedu in the past.

'I'll tell you how it was in the past,' he said. 'I had seven children – three girls, four boys – praise and thanks be to God – but only two are still alive. Three of them died of sickness when they were children. One was bitten by a mating bull-camel and died of the injury, and another – a girl – died in childbirth. A Bedui's family is his life. When I was a young man – still a boy really but old enough to carry a rifle – my elder brother was shot by the Seʿar. In those days the Manahil had no tents like these – we lived in the open. My brother Saʿid was out herding camels with my cousin near Thamud when they saw a raiding-party of about twenty Seʿar racing towards them on camels. My cousin wanted to run away and get help, but my brother – God's mercy upon him – had a rifle and wanted to stay and fight. He put a shot over their heads in warning, but one man jumped from his camel and shot my brother in the hand. My cousin would have killed the Seʿari, but the rifle jammed. So they ran away to our camp, while the Seʿar took our five camels. There was only myself and my younger brother Ahmad in the camp – my father was dead by then and my uncles were away. We wrapped my brother's hand up in a head-cloth as best we could, then I said, "Saʿid, what shall we do? We are only four against them, and we have only two rifles and this useless one. And they have taken all our camels – we only have the broken old she-camel left. Shall we wait till our uncles return?" But Saʿid was angry. "No!" he said. "We shall go after them and get our camels back. God's curse on all Seʿar! Bring the old she-camel and saddle her!" We set off and followed them by moonlight all that night, and the following day, taking turns to ride the camel when we were tired. We couldn't afford to stop for rest. We were very hungry and we met no other Bedu on the way. My brother's hand was painful for him, though he refused to admit it.

We followed the Seʿar for three nights and three days. I wanted to give up, but Saʿid said, "No. We keep going!"

'Then, on the third night we saw their campfire. They didn't dream that we were following them. They had made camp in a wadi and the camels were grazing nearby. We decided to try and take the camels in the darkness, but when we moved down towards them, the Seʿar heard us and started shooting. Saʿid tried to shoot them but his hand was so badly swollen it put off his aim. My cousin had the only other good rifle and he shot at them and thought he'd hit one. Then we had to run away. "What shall we do?" I asked Saʿid. He agreed we should go back for help. I think his hand was really giving him trouble by then. The wound was black and smelt bad. So we started off back to our camp with no food and very little water and an old she-camel that was half dead. On the second day Saʿid fell down from the pain of his hand, and couldn't walk any further. We loaded him on the camel, but before long she collapsed too. We forced her on with sticks, but you could tell she was going to die. It was very hot by day and soon our water ran out. My brother was half mad, talking to himself and moaning, saying his whole arm was on fire and begging for water which we didn't have. Then the she-camel just sat down and refused to go on. Saʿid was far beyond walking, so we made a shelter out of bits of cloth slung on thorn-bushes and put him in the shade. Then we slaughtered the she-camel and slit open her belly – there was about enough liquid in it to fill a bowl – though it was dirty and stank horribly. My brother drank first, then we all had some. I was the next oldest, and I said, "Look. You two stay here with Saʿid and I'll try to get help from our people alone."

'They agreed and I set off alone with one of the rifles. What a walk that was! I saw no Bedu and no animals. After I'd walked for a day I felt I couldn't go on. I was bent over, head first – I couldn't stand upright. There was no saliva on my tongue, and my eyes felt as if they were sinking into my skull. I knew I would die if I didn't find help soon, but I tied my headcloth tight around my stomach and I found this helped a bit and let me stand upright.

'It was heaven when night came. In the distance I saw a fire – at first I thought I'd imagined it – but it was a fire. Thank God! I said. I staggered to the camp and found it was some Manahil. I was so thirsty that I couldn't speak. All I could think about was water, but they wouldn't give me any. "No," they said, "if you drink now it will kill you!"

'They moistened my lips with a wet cloth, then, bit by bit, they allowed me drops of water, until my mouth became less dry. Then, after a while, I was able to drink. I told them that I had to get back to the others. "I must borrow a camel!" I said. "But we haven't got any!" they told me. I had to go with them to a camp nearby and borrow a camel. Then we all went together – everyone who had a camel to ride – as quickly as possible. We followed my tracks to the place where I had left Sa'id and the others. Ahmad and my cousin were all right – they'd been sitting in the shade as I'd advised them to do – but we came too late for my elder brother. Sa'id was dead, may God's mercy be upon him. He died only a short time before we arrived. Ahmad said his last words were, "By God I feel hot!" '

The old man sniffed and turned away for a moment. There was silence but for the rhythmic chewing of the camels, the crackle of wood in the grate. Then Sayf drew himself up. 'You wanted to know what it was like in the Old Days,' he said. 'Well, that's what it was like!'

We stayed with the Manahil that night and in the morning Shukri refused even to attempt the road to Thamud. The wild region of Mahra would have to wait for another journey. Instead we drove to the deserted village of Nabi Hud.

The story of Hud is connected with the pre-Islamic people of 'Ad – the mythical giant race of engineers and builders, fifty cubits high, whose incredible strength enabled them to toss great stone blocks about like bricks, creating the monumental buildings whose ruins are scattered across south Arabia. Hud, himself as tall as a palm-tree, was dispatched by Allah to persuade them to renounce their veneration of the moon, but they sneered at his message and hounded him along the Wadi Hadhramaut. Mounted on his faithful white camel, Hud eluded them by riding straight into the cliff, where he was swallowed up by the rock on the very spot where this shrine was built. As a punishment for rejecting his messenger, Allah destroyed the city of ʿAd, which until now lies buried under drifting sands.

I began to climb up through the warren of blocks to the sweeping staircase that led to Hud's shrine. The eyes of the village leered down at me and the mud walls trembled with heat. On the first level, below the dome, stood an open mosque like a miniature Greek temple – rows of distempered plaster columns supporting Moorish arches, dominated by a wedge of rock which was supposed to be the petrified hump of Hud's mammoth camel. Here was a tale engraved in stone and plaster along the walls of the Wadi Hadhramaut. As I climbed up the next section of stairs, I saw the Peugeot beneath me, a fawn-coloured oblong bejewelled in light.

Inside, the domed building was starkly austere, and the shrine itself came as something of a surprise. If this was truly where Hud was buried – and opinions differ on this fact – then he must really have been as tall as a palm-tree. The shrine was at least ninety feet long.

As I hurried down the steps back to the car, I heard an unexpected noise. It sounded uncannily like a voice calling to me. I suspected at once that 'joker' Shukri was up to some trick. I looked down at the wadi: the car was still in its place. I glanced around me at the blind façades. The sound came again – a ghostly whisper like a faint echo. I strained to catch it, but heard only the creak of an unfastened gate from somewhere below. When I arrived back at the car, Shukri was sitting with his hands already on the wheel. Even before I was settled in the passenger seat, he started the vehicle, and went immediately into a racing reverse, kicking up whoffs of sand from the wadi bed. When he had pointed his bonnet down the track back to Tarim, he sighed. An expression of immense relief passed over his face.

'Anyway,' I said, 'no problem from the Jinns.'

He was quiet for a moment, then he turned his moon-shaped face towards me with a look of utter gravity. 'No?' he said. 'Then who was that old man I saw following you when you were coming down the steps?'

5

The Gulf Stream of Wanderers

Suhail's camp was gone when I passed the spot some months later with a new driver named Faisal. It was spring, and the Manahil had taken to the high prairies of Mahra, pegging out parchment-coloured marquees around man-made lagoons and the dried-up cribs of natural lakes. Mahra was volcanic country: hills and water-basins notched and crinkled, stands of drab camel-thorn and milky-green grass on a landscape of powdered chocolate. All along the track to Thamud we could see tribesmen in luminous shirts and embroidered *futas*, egging on their camels across a surface coal-black with volcanic clinker, or pushing a squash of goats across ivory sand-spills in a glimmer of dust.

Our escorts – two Humumis from the village of Saum – stopped only once, to point out the twisted exclamation-mark of a *gamez*, a wild fig-tree, with its basket of shade. 'Planted by an Englishman, to rest under,' one of them said. 'There are no other trees like it between here and Thamud!'

By late afternoon, Faisal's eyes were bloodshot with thirst, and he was almost panting over the steering-wheel. It was Ramadan, and though in Islam travellers were exempt from fasting, Faisal was determined to waive this right. 'You have to make up the time afterwards,' he told me, 'and it's always harder to fast when you have to do it alone.'

We halted at Hulayya, a strip of deserted buildings with a deep well. I had been hoping to make Thamud by nightfall, but in view of Faisal's weariness, it seemed folly to go on. He protested loudly, and the Bedu sauntered over from their vehicle, Kalashnikovs bristling, to join in. 'We agreed to escort you to Thamud!' one of them – a fierce-looking Samson with African features – said. 'It would be a disgrace for us to leave you here!'

'I'll pay you what we agreed.'

'It's not the money. It's forbidden for us to abandon our travelling-companions. If anything happens to you, we will get the blame!'

I thanked them for this loyalty to tradition, conspicuously absent in my Huwaytat companion in Jordan, and gave them a note exonerating them. Honour seemed satisfied on all sides, and Faisal could rest. After dark, when the Bedu were gone, we were visited by a party of Manahil boys with an ancient, white-haired Sheikh, who joined us at our hearth for tea. The moon soared and deflated smoothly as it rose, flushing out the shadows, and immersing the landscape in satin light. 'Ah, these were the kind of nights we liked in the old days,' the Sheikh said. 'White nights we call them. You can sleep soundly on a night like this, for no enemy can take you by surprise. You can leave the camels unattended and keep your fire burning all night. There are three things the Bedouin herdsman wishes for: eternal moonlit nights, eternal green grazing, and eternal youth!'

'Yes,' Faisal said, 'the moon is a youth, who never grows old, and his wife is the sun, a dried-up old hag who is forever old and who destroys everything. The moon brings the rain, the dew and the green plants, but the sun brings only death.'

Here, wrapped in the soft fibre of Islam, were traces of the moon-worship of the ancient spice-kingdoms, which, more than 2,000 years ago, were the first bloom of civilization upon the barren landscape of Arabia.

It was on an evening a week earlier, in the office of Universal Travel, Sanaʿa, that I had first met Faisal. I had not given up my hope of reaching Mahra country, and this time I had decided to start from the capital of Yemen, where things were altogether more organized than in shell-shocked Aden. Even so, it had not been easy to find a driver with a Land-Cruiser ready to go into Mahra. 'Mahra is too far,' Fuad – manager of Universal – told me, lounging back suavely in his swivel-chair, 'and it is Ramadan, when all the drivers want to stay at home.' After many intense phone calls, however, Fuad had come up with the name of Faisal.

When he clumped into the office to present himself, I was struck by the contrast with the urbane, overweight Shukri. Faisal was a Bedui, proud, disdainful, acute. He wore shiny black shoes, white knee-socks under a *futa* of gilt-embroidered green, and a scarlet headcloth looped gypsy-style. His pinstripe jacket hung askew from the bottle of mineral water stuffed into the pocket, and its breast lay parted to display a hooked dagger. His cheek bulged with qat, and he clutched a bunch of green shoots in his left hand, while cupping a long cigarette in his right. Yes, he would take me to Mahra, no matter how far it was. And no, he didn't give a damn about the Jinns. He spat upon them! He would pick me up at the Taj Sheba hotel at ten, the day after next, and we would head east, first stop, Maʿrib.

I occupied the next evening wandering in Old Sanaʿa – once the Jewish ghetto, but now a crowded market-place. Before sundown, men were already seated at weathered rustic tables outside the gates, waiting impatiently for the time when a black thread could no longer be distinguished from a white one, and the end of another day's fasting. The money-changers were snapping shut their mock-leather briefcases with resignation. The gates were disgorging waves of bearded, kilted, turbaned figures, scuffling homeward in worn-soled shoes, their faces pinched with hunger, carrying qat under their arms in torpedo-shaped bundles. Women looking like red-and-black pears in their concealing sheets were balancing discs of hot bread on their heads as they negotiated the bottleneck of the gate. Motorcycles and scooters buzzed through the crowd like enraged bees. Inside the souq the light was already drowsy along the cobbled alleys between the perpendicular stone-built houses with their ornate glass windows. The shops were shadowy rows of pitchholes and cavities, in which ghost-figures crouched over piles of qat, dates, spices and vegetables, or sat at glass-fronted stalls stuffed with Maria Theresa silver dollars, and paper currency in dense wads of notes.

It was among the bric-à-brac on such a stall that I noticed packets of amber-coloured frankincense resin. I examined them with fascination. Frankincense – one of the gifts presented to the infant Christ by the Magi – was traditionally produced only in part of southern Arabia and the hills of Somalia. In the biblical era it was one of the most precious substances known to man, and on the fabulous profits of its trade the lost civilizations of ancient south Arabia had prospered. To the people of the ancient world the universe was populated by trickster gods and demons, which could be appeased only by the fragrant smoke of incense. Wafting up to the heavens, the sacred smoke symbolized prayer itself – a means of communicating with numinous forces beyond the veil of darkness.

Frankincense and myrrh grew in south Arabia, but it was the camel, tamed by the peoples of the arid steppe – let us call them the 'people of ʿAd' – around 2000 BC, which made the long-distance spice-trade viable. A thousand years earlier the Pharaohs of Egypt had brought back incense seedlings from the 'Land of Punt', which failed dismally to germinate in the valley of the Nile. Naval expeditions were costly and dangerous, however. The Red Sea was full of reefs, unpredictable currents and pirate bands. Beyond the Bab al Mandab – the straits dividing Arabia from Africa – ships were at the mercy of the monsoon winds, whose secrets were known only to the Arabs. The introduction of the camel rendered the overland routes quicker and safer than the troubled sea-lanes. Wonderful cities such as Maʿrib and Shabwa bloomed in the desert along the caravan-roads. The Bedu who remained in the south Arabian deserts profited by breeding the camels essential to the trade, and by pillaging spice-caravans, though unlike their cousins in north Arabia, they were never able to dominate the powerful spice-kingdoms. Instead they learned the protection strategy, and the value of extracting tolls from caravans passing through their territories.

By subtle degrees the shadows lengthened and mingled, and the gush of humanity dwindled: I followed in its wake. Raucous Arab voices grated from hidden recesses, and everywhere men could be seen packing up their wares and slamming the shop doors shut. Soon they were poised in tight circles around their Ramadan breakfast, summoning me to join them with expansive hand-signals as I passed. A moment later the muezzin's voice crashed out of hidden loudspeakers, filling the whole market with sound: 'Allah is most great! Allah is most great! I swear that there is no god but Allah . . . I swear that Mohammad is God's Prophet . . . Allah is most great! . . . There is no god but Allah!'

As soon as we had passed the police checkpoints outside the city the next morning, Faisal halted the Land-Cruiser and pulled up the front seat. There, swaddled in greased plastic, was an airborne-model Kalashnikov AK 47 with a folding butt and a curved magazine. He fitted the magazine with a smack and laid the weapon close to him on the seat. 'Are you expecting trouble?' I asked, grinning.

'If I wasn't expecting trouble, I wouldn't have got it out!' he snapped. 'I might run into someone who has a quarrel with my family. The vendetta still rules in Yemen. When you pass through a village and see everyone carrying rifles, that means a vendetta is still going on.'

It dawned on me then that travelling with the dour Faisal was going to be quite a different story from the previous experience with Shukri. 'I'm forty-five years old,' he told me, 'and, thanks be to Allah, I have five children. When I was a small child my father was shot dead near Bayda by members of another clan. I can still remember hearing the shooting. My mother snatched me out of bed, because they had murdered my father, and she was afraid they would murder me. By God's will we escaped to my uncle's place in Heraz – in the high mountains – where I grew up. It was like a fortress there – right up on the top of the hill – and you could have stayed up there all the time. We had crops on the terraces, goats and cows, and even a dam built across the wadi for water. You were completely self-sufficient and no one could approach you unawares. Anyway, the civil war came and my family fought with the Republicans. I was only a kid but they gave me a rifle and told me to kill people. I got quite good at it. Afterwards, when we had defeated the Imam, I said, "Right. I've killed people I had no grudge against, now, by God, I'm going to avenge my father!" If I hadn't retaliated, the sons of bitches would have crowed over us forever! So my cousins and I drove down there in a jeep and waited near the fields until one of them came with his sheep. Then we just stood up and shot him five or six times. He split open like a water-melon – you should have seen the look on his face, by God! We kept on pumping bullets into him till he lay still. I said, "Thank God! I've done my duty. My father is avenged!" We walked away, and nobody tried to stop us. If they had we'd have dropped the lot of them! I didn't feel bad about it – and I don't now. That was the law – a life for a life. I'd do it again tomorrow, by God! Now, of course, they're still on the lookout for me or anyone of my clan. A vendetta like this never ends. So, yes, I am expecting trouble. Trouble always comes when you expect it least.'

'But was the man you killed one of those who shot your father?'

'No. He was just one of the family – a cousin or something. I doubt if he had anything to do with my father's death. What does that matter? The important thing is that he was part of that family – it's the family, not the individual, that counts.'

'But wouldn't it have been fairer to have given him a chance?'

'Did they give my father a chance? Are you mad? It wasn't a game of cowboys and Indians we were playing! It takes enough courage just to shoot someone, without running the risk of being shot yourself!'

It took only three hours to reach Maʿrib, bowling along a road which cut through arid vineyards and fig orchards, plots of leached earth, hamlets of mud-brick houses in which old and new blended imperceptibly together, over shattered hogsback ridges on which dwellings perched like old men's bad teeth. There were ochre fields full of saplings like miniature Christmas-trees, which Faisal told me were ripening qat. 'It's the most valuable crop now,' he said. 'We used to grow a lot of coffee here. In Turkish times the Yemen was famous for coffee – Mokha, you know. But all that's gone. Qat will grow in more or less the same place as coffee, and it brings more profit these days. Wherever you see a gathering of people in the Yemen, you can be sure there's someone selling qat!'

Soon the marginal cultivation fell away and the landscape swelled into olive-sheen desert country. Maʿrib, a toytown of breeze-block and asphalt, stood in a dustbowl beyond.

In the afternoon we visited the ruins of the great Maʿrib dam, a giant's lair of masonry blocks dressed with flawless precision, stranded on a raw granite irruption, fifty feet above the stagnant pools in the Wadi Dhahna. Faisal guided me along a path that wound behind the magnificent stonework and showed me how the mountain had been shorn away to create sluices that had once carried water into an invisible catch-basin, feeding no fewer than fourteen canals. 'All this land used to be green,' he said, gesturing down the valley, 'There were green fields from here to the Hadhramaut in ancient days. Yemen was great!'

In the soft bed of the wadi below, sand-ghosts dribbled around Sodom's Apple trees with their parchment leaves and poison fruit, snaking across a great plain hazed with heat and scattered with a thousand twisted mushrooms of mud that might once have been houses. Faisal had not exaggerated in saying that Yemen had been great. Here, while Europe was still skulking in the bronze age, the Arabs had mastered the fey floodwaters of the Yemen hills, and brought agriculture to thousands of acres of sterile sands. A great and prosperous kingdom had flourished here – the biblical Sheba

– whose fame had reached the ears of Solomon, in far-off Jerusalem.

From my perch high up on the sluices, I tried to reconstruct the landscape in my imagination. Eighteen hundred feet across the wadi, the remnants of a low wall lay half buried under sand, but the central part of the structure – the pyramid-shaped barrage which had dammed up the floodwaters – was missing. According to one legend, it was torn apart by giant rats which gnawed at its wooden props and pulled away great blocks of stone that could not have been shifted by fifty men. Soon afterwards all that remained was ripped to shreds by raging torrents, and the noble city of Maʿrib flooded. Its population fled to the hills and deserts, splintering into tribes, and resuming the nomadic life they had renounced centuries before. According to Arab tradition, the Maʿrib disaster created havoc among the tribes all over Arabia. The Sultanate of Oman, for example, is supposed to have been created by a man called ʿOman bin Qahtan – the first Arab to settle in the Oman mountains after fleeing the Maʿrib flood. The famous Bedu tribe of Azd, which later occupied the deserts of the Middle East, the Bani Ghassan of the Hauran in Syria, and the Lakhm, who migrated to Egypt in the eighth century AD, are among scores of tribes that trace their origin back to the settled people of Maʿrib. The bursting of the Maʿrib dam is seen in legend as a key event in Bedu history.

No one knows for certain when the dam was built. In 1600 BC, Semitic nomads swept into Yemen from the north, and began to assimilate the natives. One tribe, the Sabaʿi or Shebans – perhaps the same people whose former bloodthirsty reputation as Bedu freebooters is attested in the Book of Job – settled on the plains of Maʿrib. Other tribes took root around the wadis spread across southern Arabia, in which the fabulous city-states of Arabia – Sheba, Maʿin, Qataban, Awsan, Himyar and the Hadhramaut – grew up. If legend is to be credited, though, the monumental water-harvesting technology on which these states were founded may have been developed as early as 1700 BC, by a brilliant engineer called Lukman bin ʿAd, who constructed a system of dams and canals of which Maʿrib was the *pièce de résistance*. 'As a result the arid land of Yemen was transformed into a lush green garden,' the legend goes. 'There were so many trees that travellers were never struck by the fierce sunshine and the air was so fresh . . . that people attained a very advanced age without illness.' By the time of the Greek historian Pliny, the Shebans had become the wealthiest tribe in south Arabia, 'owing to the fertility of their scent-producing forests, their gold mines, their irrigated agricultural lands and their production of honey and beeswax'.

As I pondered the genius of Lukman bin ʿAd, Faisal pointed out the medieval town of Maʿrib, from here a broken claw of buildings balanced on a half-moon-shaped mound above the few remaining patches of cultivation in the valley. Later, when we drove up to the settlement, I saw that it was a crushed shell of a place: a symphony in decay. It was haunted by shadows – faceless, shawled women who trod silently barefoot up steep paths carrying buckets of water, Jinn-faced urchins who raced terrified down rubble-filled alleys and spied on us from behind grilled windows. I wasn't surprised to learn that Fellini had used the old town as the setting for his film *The Arabian Nights*. Everything about the place smacked of some decadent fantasy. There were great tenements built of the stones the Bedu had long ago dragged out of the pre-Islamic ruins, whose walls had cracked into zigzag patterns and settled into unearthly contours and angles. Towers of mud and stone peeled away from the centre like giant dried banana-skins, the spaces between them blocked with dung, dust and debris. A modern water-tank – a decrepit moon-lander on stilts – threatened to topple into the streets on the merest hint of provocation.

At the base of one of the leaning towers a shrivelled man in a loincloth sat in the dust by a doorway whose original level had been so obscured by layers of detritus that one would almost have been obliged to crawl inside on hands and knees. Yet this hovel was his home. He answered my '*as salaam ʿalaykum*' gloomily, and lit a cigarette with blunt fingers. Faisal glared at him. 'Don't you know it's Holy Ramadan?' he demanded. 'Smoking is forbidden before sunset!'

The man puffed out a ring of smoke and ignored him brazenly.

'Where are all the people?' I asked him.

'Gone,' he replied mournfully. 'Gone off to every place. There's just a few of us left now to tend the crops.'

As we walked back to the Land-Cruiser, a multitude of ragged children dogged our heels shrieking, 'Money! Money!' I was about to hand out a twenty-riyal note when Faisal took it sternly, pocketed it, and brought out a wad of smaller denominations in its place. Issuing orders like a drill-sergeant, he arranged the youngsters into family groups and presented a note to the eldest child in each group with a stiff admonition that it must be equally divided. As we pulled out of the old town the children were racing gleefully back across the dung-covered square. 'Poor things!' Faisal said pityingly, as he watched them go. 'Before cars came this place used to be a really important market for the Bedu. Now it's almost dead.' At its apogee, ancient Maʿrib had been 'the Paris of Arabia', a thriving metropolis sited on the junction of the caravan-routes, an emporium of the fabulous riches of India and East Africa as well as of Arabia herself. Three thousand years ago the ancient Shebans enjoyed a standard of living undreamed of by these barefoot urchins. Even in its heyday the medieval town had occupied only a tiny corner of the ancient capital out of whose ruins it had sprung.

In the evening we visited a house in the grounds of the Jamalayn Hotel, to meet the Bedu who were to provide us with an escort for the next stage of our journey – across the Ramlat Sabatayn. It was dark inside the house but for spears of sodium orange that pierced the shutters from the electric lamps outside. As my eyes struggled to adapt, I saw that there were five Bedu tribesmen kneeling on the floor, each one cradling an automatic rifle across his knees. Faisal kept his own Kalashnikov braced loosely against his arm as the Bedu stood up to greet us, their faces shadowy under their tight headcloths. They were lean hawks of men with hawk noses, wearing wraparound kirtles that were weighted with heavy cartridge belts and preposterously large daggers. They moved with an abrupt assertiveness, and their manner was uneasy, suspicious, and unnecessarily forbidding.

Three millennia ago the ancestors of these ʿAbida, who bred camels for the rich spice-caravans that already plodded the length of southern Arabia, realized – like the Nabataeans – that there was more to be gained from guiding and guarding travellers than from pillaging them. It was a lesson which long outlived the caravans themselves. Now, every traveller was advised to engage a Bedu escort with its own four-wheel-drive vehicle when crossing Sabatayn sands, where unguarded foreigners had frequently been held at gunpoint by bandits, robbed of everything down to their underwear, and left stranded in the desert.

We crouched against the hard cushions they proffered, and Faisal accepted a cigarette, smoking it briskly but with dignity, sitting bolt upright with his rifle in his lap. After drawn-out introductions, he announced that we required a Bedu escort for the following day, and that our route would take us through the ruined city of Shabwa – for centuries a sanctuary forbidden to Westerners – to the Wadi Hadhramaut. The Bedu chief, Tom-Thumb-sized with the expression of an enraged penguin, received the request disdainfully. Tea was distributed and quaffed, many cigarettes sucked dry and stubbed out, and conversations yammered with hysterical speed on the flat telephone lying on the floor. Finally, the Sheikh told us: 'We will provide an escort for tomorrow to Shabwa and the Hadhramaut. The fee, non-negotiable, and payable in advance, will be two hundred and fifty American dollars.'

'Two hundred and fifty! That's a bit much isn't it? After all, it's only a day's journey!'

The Sheikh's eyes hardened. 'It's not the length of the journey, it's the danger,' he said. Only a few months ago, it seemed, two Bedu escorts had been murdered. Some bandits had held up a carload of Westerners, intending to rob them, and one of the guards – a young Bedui of the ʿAbida – had opened fire. The bandits had fired back, missing him and killing a foreigner instead. They knew that the government would punish them severely for murdering a foreign visitor, so they had decided to get rid of the witnesses. They had massacred everyone, including the Bedu guards. 'Anyway, that is what we charge,' he said. 'What is two hundred and fifty dollars against your life?'

'What if I decide to go without an escort?'

The Sheikh bared symmetrical rows of sharp teeth. 'In that case,' he said, watching me intently to make sure I caught his drift, 'you will be very unlikely to make it to the Hadhramaut.' I knew that I must either pay or drive miles out of my way, but I still resented this age-old Bedu protection racket. Camel-caravans might have been superseded by cars and spears by Kalashnikovs, I reflected, but in 3,000 years little else had changed.

When we arrived at the Bedu house the following morning, the tribesmen were still snoring under their blankets and sleeping off the Ramadan vigil. The penguin-faced Sheikh scowled at us and ordered us to rendezvous with our escort at a derelict petrol-station on the outskirts of the town in an hour's time. On the way there we passed a row of thirty-foot limestone shafts standing in lapping sands – all that remained visible of the famous Temple of Bilqis – the legendary Queen of Sheba.

The columns actually formed part of a magnificent peristyle hall containing inscriptions, bronzes and statues, now buried under dust. The hall itself was only a small section of a city-within-a-city that was once surrounded by a wall of masonry thirteen feet thick and more than 1,000 feet long. Though the temple is connected by Arab tradition with the biblical Queen of Sheba, it is actually dedicated to the Sheban moon god Ilumquh. Indeed, apart from folk-tales there is little evidence to connect antiquity's most famous queen with the ancient city of Maʿrib, where the earliest inscriptions date from about 800 BC – a century and a half after the reign of Solomon, whom she is supposed to have known.

The legends hold that Bilqis was the daughter of a female Jinn, and her ravishing beauty attracted the eye of Sharabil, King of Sheba, a monarch notorious for his drunkenness and depravity. The girl was betrothed to him, but on their wedding night evaded his amorous advances – arranging for dancing-girls to entertain him, and keeping his wine-cup judiciously filled until he passed out. Bilqis then demonstrated her wild blood by plunging a dagger into his heart, and afterwards assumed the throne in his place. Having become famous as a wise and virtuous ruler, she decided to make the seventy-day camel-trek to Solomon's court, thousands of miles away in Jerusalem, taking with her a retinue of servants, warriors and courtiers, and presents which included 1,000 carpets woven with golden thread, musk, aloe wood and ambergris.

Solomon's jealous pet demons informed him that, being half Jinn, the Queen possessed donkey's feet, and was therefore unsuitable for the marriage-alliance he was considering. The King tricked her into raising her skirts by creating the illusion of a pool of water before his throne, and observed that, far from being donkey-like, her feet and ankles were distinctly appealing. Bilqis accepted the marriage he offered, and after the wedding returned to her palace at Maʿrib, where Solomon, with the aid of a magic carpet, visited her for three days every month.

We waited in the car at the abandoned filling-station, and an hour and a half later the Bedu Land-Cruiser appeared, driven by a middle-aged Arab with a younger boy riding shotgun beside him. The driver wound the window down. 'Come on! Come on!' he shouted.

'Don't dare "come on" me!' Faisal replied like a whiplash. 'We've been waiting for you for hours!'

The cars turned off the road into creamy, jelly-roll dunes that stretched for miles, poling up to top speed, roller-coasting up the faces and bouncing over the crests like police-cars in a film chase. Faisal's face was set in a maniacal grin: 'The only way to take these dunes is at speed,' he grunted, 'otherwise you get bogged down.' On the flat plains between the undulations the Land-Cruisers played around each other like dolphins, racing abreast, circling and overtaking, falling back into file and then overtaking again. There were camel-herds in the sand-folds, grazing on low pepper-and-salt vegetation, and the animals watched us with expressions of faint disdain as we whooshed through the dunes in a frisson of dust.

Then suddenly, the Bedu car was gone.

Faisal cursed under his breath and drove up a dune covered with a billion tiny islets of yellow flowers. He halted on the crest and applied the handbrake, then we climbed out and scanned the desert in every direction. The silence hit me like a shock-wave. Travelling by camel, the desert grew upon your senses organically as you adjusted to its power. After the mad rush in a motor-vehicle, however, it was as if you had been suddenly deposited on an alien planet from space. Faisal shifted his Kalashnikov from hand to hand and cursed again. 'Fools and sons of fools,' he growled. "Escort" indeed! And they don't even know the way! I know the way better than they do!'

We waited for what seemed a very long time, listening intently. Dunes blocked the horizon in every direction. The only movement was the shimmer of heat across the slopes and the silent wave-motion of the frail grasses that covered them. A motion caught my eye in the far distance: sunlight reflected on a dust-mote drifting out of the sand. 'That must be them!' I said. But Faisal's senses were sharper, and suddenly he cocked his rifle with a mechanical 'klack!' 'That's not our car,' he said.

We could hear the purr of the engine now. The vehicle – a black Land-Cruiser – slewed towards us with the cumbrous glide of a boat cutting through surf, and halted some yards away. Inside were two black-faced men with stubbled beards, who peered at us with mocking eyes. Faisal walked slowly towards the driver's open window. The dark man made no move to get out. 'Peace be on you,' Faisal said.

'And on you. What's your business here?'

'We are waiting for our escort. They'll be along in a few minutes' time.'

The black man smiled mockingly again. 'Keep your wits about you. There are a lot of bandits around here!'

As we watched the car slide off into the distance, Faisal relaxed visibly and disengaged his magazine, ejecting a shiny cartridge into the sand. 'Well,' he said, 'we had nothing to fear from them. They were Bureikis. I could tell that by just looking at them.'

I discovered only later that the Bureikis were considered holy Sheikhs. Their role for countless generations had been to guard the sacred places of this part of south Arabia, especially the so-called 'hidden city' of Shabwa, whose ruins stood in the middle of Ramlat Sabatayn. They were probably the descendants of the tribe which had controlled Shabwa when it was an opulent trading city, commanding the caravan-roads across these sands. In the days of Pliny the town was inhabited by 4,000 sacred families, and the name 'Bureiki' itself derives from a root meaning 'sacred'. Like many of the Bedu tribes of south Arabia, they were compelled to give up the life of the town and take to the tent and the camel when the spice-trade declined in the first few centuries of our era.

Within minutes our escort vehicle appeared: 'What happened to you lot?' Faisal demanded dismissively. 'Two hundred and fifty dollars, and you get yourselves lost in the desert!' The tribesmen of the predatory ʿAbida stared back sheepishly, wilting under Faisal's scorn.

The crags of Shabwa crawled slowly into focus – cheese-wedges of rock that had pressed through the organdie-coloured surface. Here, protected on all sides by waterless sands and impenetrable hills, the city had flourished for centuries as the capital of the Hadhramaut, at one period the largest and richest of the incense-states. At its zenith Shabwa was as famous as Maʿrib and, according to Pliny, boasted no fewer than sixty temples.

While it was still cool enough, we walked about the ruins, shadowed by four or five tiny Bedu boys, sent, no doubt, to see that we didn't carry anything off. But little of the glory of the ancient days remained. Shabwa was another Arab honeycomb with the lid shaved off, a dead specimen on a dissecting-table, consisting of hundreds of roofless cells and alleyways leading nowhere. There persisted only the ruined plinths that once supported the pillars of a single temple, and bits of monumental masonry that had been used to shore up the walls of long-ruined Arab houses.

In the time of the south Arabian spice-kingdoms, the bulk of the frankincense was brought to Shabwa from the port of Qana', near modern Bir 'Ali. There were at least two major caravan-routes from the south, and another passing west through the Wadi Qalat, where all openings in the rock wall were sealed, save for a single vast gateway of masonry fifteen feet high. The priest-kings of Shabwa charged a tithe on each measure of incense brought through the town, and made it a capital offence for laden camels to turn aside from the road.

We camped under some acacias in the wadi. Faisal dragged his mattress out of the car and lay down with his Kalashnikov under his head. 'If I fall asleep, wake me up!' he ordered me. 'You have to keep your wits about you in this country!' The ruins loomed down on us, basting in the midday heat. Our escort was nowhere to be seen. Within minutes, Faisal was snoring fitfully. I hadn't the heart to wake him up.

An hour later a youth of about fourteen, with hair curling beneath his furled headcloth, came striding barefoot through the thorns and stones. Quick as a flash, Faisal rolled over, jumped up, and brought his rifle to the ready. The youth stopped abruptly, watching the older man with wide eyes. 'You shouldn't come creeping up on people like that!' Faisal growled.

I called the boy over to sit down and offered him some dates. I asked him where his people's tents and camels were. 'We haven't got any camels left,' he said. 'We are the guardians of the ruins. We get money from the government and we have our goats. I've never ridden a camel, and I don't remember seeing anybody riding one in the last few years. We haven't got any tents either –

we just live in the ruins now.' I inquired what tribe he belonged to, and when he told me 'Kurub', I recognized the name at once. Only fifty years ago, the Kurub had been one of the most feared of all the tribes of south Arabia, and were known to raid as far as Liwa oasis near the Gulf, hundreds of miles away. It seemed that the raiding spirit had departed long since: this boy's family did not even possess camels – reduced from hardy raiders to the caretakers of ruins in a single generation.

For centuries Qahtani tribes such as the Kurub had raided east into Oman, leaving pockets of their descendants scattered across the steppes. These successive waves of movement may have been set in motion by the catastrophe that had overtaken south Arabia in the first few centures AD, symbolized in Arab annals by the bursting of the great Maʿrib dam. Actually the dam was patched up many times throughout its history. By the time it did burst finally in the sixth century – as a reference in the Quran indicates – the grandeur of the spice-kingdoms had long since waned. For centuries the sedentary farmers had been drifting away from the land and taking to the wandering life of the Bedu. Strong tribes may have displaced others and set in motion the kind of chain-reaction imagined by T. E. Lawrence in his book *Seven Pillars of Wisdom*: 'the congestion of Yemen, therefore, becoming extreme, found its only relief . . . by forcing the weaker aggregations of its borders down and down the slopes of the hills . . . Finally . . . the border people . . . were flung out of the furthest crazy oasis into the untrodden wilderness as nomads . . . There was the source of migration, the factory of nomads, the springing of the gulf-stream of desert wanderers.'

But the collapse of the dam was the symptom rather than the root of the decay. If any single event bears the blame for the decline of south Arabia, it was not the ruin of Maʿrib, but the voyage of Hippalus, a Byzantine sea-captain in the service of the Abyssinian navy. Around AD 100, he sailed his ship through the Bab al Mandab, the straits that sever Africa from Arabia, reached India, and brought a laden ship back to the Mediterranean for the first time. The Arabs had grown rich both on their home-grown aromatics, and as middlemen on the trans-shipment of Indian goods, especially cinnamon and cotton cloth. Once Hippalus had grasped the seasonal nature of the monsoon, the Romans were able to deal directly with the source, bypassing the overland routes. Thus the Arabs lost their monopoly, and the power of the caravan-states ebbed. Traders and farmers became nomads, and the elaborate water-harvesting technology that had supported their civilization for generations was no longer maintained. Dams burst and canals were buried under sand. The whole of south Arabia reverted to the desert it largely remains today.

Faisal had hoped to rest until the cool hour of the afternoon prayer, but, by way of revenge for his truculence, perhaps, the ʿAbida turned up at three and churned their engine remorselessly until he clambered scowling from his bed and began to pack up. The strain of driving in the heat without a drop of water or a morsel to eat was already beginning to take its toll, but, since it was purely voluntary in his case, he choked back a bitter rejoinder and started to warm the motor.

Towards sunset we were driving across salt plains with saw-tooth plateaux in the distance – the outriders of the Wadi Hadhramaut. Faisal's eyes were swollen with thirst, hunger and fatigue, and I began to worry that he would faint or fall asleep at the wheel. 'We ought to halt and make camp,' I said.

'Not out here,' he said through cracked lips. 'Too dangerous. I have too many blood-feuds on my hands. If one of my family's enemies came on me while I was asleep, I'd be done for. And you too, probably! No, we must seek the camps of the Bedu.'

This was the age-old dilemma for desert-travellers in Arabia, I reflected. Blood-feuds and bandits made it imperative that they throw themselves on the hospitality of the Bedu.

Not long after, we spied a Bedu place, looking like a circus encampment with its bent jeeps, battle-scarred four-ton lorries, rusting water tanker and cast-off Western-made marquees. Five or six malevolent-looking Bedu with their rifles unslung and ready formed a barrier between ourselves and the camp, and a one-armed man wearing a filthy dishdasha and badly scratched dark glasses sidled up to question our escort. The left sleeve of his dish-dasha had been cut off and sewn up at the elbow, and I noticed with some surprise that he too carried a rifle on a sling. I wondered how on earth he would have been able to use it. He talked with the ʿAbida for a minute, then turned to inspect Faisal. The two Bedu shook hands, and the one-armed man peered at my companion warily.

'Aren't you from Bayda?' he inquired.

'No,' Faisal lied. 'I've never been near Bayda in my life!'

The old man showed us a place to sleep, at some distance from his tents, and after dark brought us freshly baked bread and tea. He ate sparingly, talked little, and gazed disconcertingly at Faisal's face in the moonlight. After he had taken his leave, I asked Faisal why he had lied about coming from Bayda.

'Because I recognized him,' he told me. 'He lost that arm in a gunfight with people from Bayda twenty years ago. I wasn't involved personally, but no doubt he knew me as one of the same people by my dress and accent.'

'Does that mean we're under threat?' I asked him.

'Don't worry,' he said, 'not now we have eaten bread and salt!'

But that night I noticed he kept his rifle and dagger close to him, all the same.

The next morning we parted from the ʿAbida at the first village in the Hadhramaut. As their vehicle wheeled back in its dust-shroud across Sabatayn, Faisal sheathed his rifle into its hiding-place under the front seat. We spent the day driving through the wadi and halted for a while at Shibam. At Saum, the next day, we hired an escort from the Humum to guide us out of the wadi and into Mahra country.

Wilfred Thesiger's *Arabian Sands* was my bible and guidebook on all my journeys in south Arabia. One mystery it contained was a cameo portrait of a handsome Arab with a beard and thickly matted hair. The portrait had always intrigued me, because the caption bore only the legend '*Sulaim, our rabia (companion) from the Mahra*'. My objective here was to meet the Mahra, but a footnote on this journey was to find out if Sulaim was still alive.

In the 1970s, the communist government of what had then been the People's Democratic Republic of Yemen had decreed that the entire rural population should be concentrated in twenty-seven fishing centres and fifty-four agricultural ones. The nomadic Bedu – whom they considered primitive – were to become settled farmers. Thamud had been one of the sites of this failed experiment in social engineering. In earlier days a watering-place for the Manahil and ʿAwamir tribes, it was now a clot of crumbling Stalinist terraces along streets paved with squashed drinks cans and the oxidized rubble of scores of broken motor-cars. There was no sign of the well at which Thesiger and his Bedu had watered their camels on their trek here from Oman in 1946. Instead, life revolved around the petrol-pump, where a young Bedu called ʿAmr was filling up a Land-Cruiser. He studied the photograph of Sulaim from Thesiger's book and said, 'I'm not certain. That picture is very old, but I think it is Sulaim bin Dughshayn – a Mahri who lives near Armah.' He agreed to guide us as far as Armah in place of our escort from the Hadhramaut. First, though, he took us to the house of a very ancient Bedui, who he believed might remember Thesiger's companion.

The old man lay on a vermin-infested mattress in the corner of an airless, lightless room, evidently near to death. His son – himself well past middle-age – helped him to sit up and as he did so an enormous red cockroach scuttled out of the Bedui's ragged robe and dashed through the open door. The old man watched it in horror and let out a whimper of disgust like a child. I shuddered involuntarily. The young man thrust the photo of Sulaim in front of his elder's nose. 'This Englishman has come to ask if this picture is of Sulaim bin Dughshayn of the Mahra!' he shouted, almost in the old man's ear. 'The companion of a Christian who came here with the Bedu years ago. Do you remember?'

The old man stared at the photo with eyes starting out of his head. 'Christian?' he slurred, swaying so heavily to one side that ʿAmr had to catch him and hold him upright, 'I don't remember any Christian.'

'But is this Sulaim bin Dughshayn?' the boy insisted.

The old man's eyes focused on me for a moment. 'Sulaim?' he croaked. 'Why do you want him? What has he done?'

'Nothing. I just want to talk to him.'

He clung desperately to ʿAmr's arms. 'Water!' he sobbed, 'bring me water! I don't know anything about Christians!'

I muttered my apologies and left, and later the man's son came and squatted with us outside the house, where naked children were playing amid flanges of rusted car. 'Do you have any medicine to cure my father?' he asked.

'I'm sorry. It seems that he's had a stroke of some kind.'

'He used to be a very strong man. When I was young we ʿAwamir used to take our camels right into the Sands in the cool season, and stay there perhaps half the year. We used to take the women and children riding in litters. It was a good life. Then the government made us settle here. Living in houses like this gets to be a habit, but to me they have always seemed like a prison. In the old days there were no houses and no cars, but you were free from outside interference. We were better off then in my opinion. Living in houses has reduced my father to this!'

Later we drove towards Armah across a table-land of leopard-skin colours – beige, black and yellow – through stunted hills, past rubble screes and wadis winding through parched acacias. The white trapezoids of Manahil tents stood all around us. In the early afternoon we arrived in a grove of nabak trees, where ʿAmr had pitched his tent. In contrast with the others we had seen, this was a traditional Bedu tent of black goats' hair. We drank tea while his children frolicked around us, and I asked him if his womenfolk had woven the tent in the traditional way. 'No,' he said, 'they wouldn't know how to. We never had tents in the past. We got this one sent ready-made from Abu Dhabi!'

At Armah, another desert eyesore where acres of axles and engine-blocks festered in the sun, we approached a crowd of tribesmen from the Mahra who were repairing a water-tanker. They passed round Thesiger's photograph of Sulaim, squinting at it, alternately shading it with their hands and angling it into the light, bantering in Mahra: 'I know that man!' one of them declared. 'It is bin Dumaysh. He's the Sheikh of the Amerjid section of the Mahra. His tents are pitched not far away.'

'Never,' another cried. 'That is not bin Dumaysh. It is bin Dughshayn!'

'No, by the Prophet!' a third cut in. 'That is nothing like bin Dughshayn!'

I took back the picture, confused. The first Mahri, a weazen-faced man with a pointed beard, said: 'This is Sulaim bin Dumaysh, by God! His tents are nearby. If you pay me money I can take you there!'

We passed out of Armah with the Mahri in the front seat, clutching his AK 47 firmly between his knees. He guided us beneath fractured knolls of metamorphic slag, through copses of *ithil* and *merkh*, across soft-bedded wadis and plains of coarse grass. After we had been driving for an hour and a half, Faisal began to look thirsty and pained. 'Didn't you say the tents were near?' he demanded.

'Not much farther!' the Mahri said.

I began to wonder if we were on a wild goose chase, or worse: this Mahra country was well beyond the reach of any government authority. I started to feel very glad of Faisal and his Kalashnikov. Presently, though, we came to a group of tents oriented along a wall of knotted sandstone, in which a wide cave had been fenced off as a refuge for sheep and goats. A bevy of unveiled Mahra ladies were working around a fire outside, one of them tending a baby in a three-legged cot, and another perched over a sewing-machine.

As we halted, three Bedu men in blood-coloured headcloths, all carrying rifles, came riding up the wadi on magnificent-looking she-camels. These were almost the first camel-riders I had seen in the Yemen, and though they had no proper saddles – only pads behind the hump – the three of them rode with the ease of long practice. They couched the animals in the sand and came to shake hands, genial, self-contained men, whose flint-coloured eyes sparkled through lids made slits from gazing into the sun. The eldest of them showed us a stony shelf across a wadi where we could park the car and spend the night. A hour before sunset, when we had set out our small camp by the vehicle, the men came over to join us, bringing glasses and a pot of tea. I asked after Sulaim, and passed round the black-and-white picture. 'These are the tents of Sulaim bin Dumaysh, my cousin,' the oldest man said. 'But Sulaim has gone off with his goats to the Wadi Mahrat.'

I pressed him over the photograph, and he examined it carefully. 'I couldn't say that it is my cousin,' he said. 'It is a very old picture. I remember stories about an Englishman – Mbarak bin Landan – who travelled with the tribes, but his friends were from the Bayt Imani. The Bayt Imani were neighbours of ours, and used to water their goats not far away at Sanaw, but most of them went to Saudi Arabia or Oman when the communists came. Their territory is Mahra country now. Sulaim will be with his goats in the Mahrat. If you are going that way you might find him.'

Defeated, I put the book away. 'Who are the Mahra?' I asked. 'Are they Bedu?'

'The Mahra are Bedu. There is no distinction between the Mahra and other Bedu, except that we have our own language. This is all Mahra country, from the hills of Dhofar to the Wadi Hadhramaut.'

The Mahra may be the descendants of the Himyarites, who founded the last great spice-kingdom of south Arabia. Bred in the tumbling, terraced hillsides behind the western toe of the Yemen, they conquered Sheba, occupied Maʿrib, took control of the spice-port at Mokha, and became the most powerful and famous people of their time. By then, though, the golden age was past, and the strife between Persia and Byzantium had created a slump in the spice-market. Roman merchant-ships now plied the Indian Ocean, and the Axumites from Abyssinia had secured a major share of the incense-trade. The Maʿrib dam was already tottering through lack of maintenance, and the spice-realms of ancient times had begun to break up. In the third century AD, the Axumites seized much of south-west Yemen, bringing with them their Christian faith. Syrian missionaries, fleeing persecution in their own land, had introduced Christianity to the Yemen long before, though the first Christian embassy was established here by the Byzantine Bishop Theophilos Indus after the Axumite invasion. The power of the old gods – the sun and the moon – had declined as the flow of wealth dwindled, and Theophilos was able to take advantage of this vacuum to establish a church at Aden, and two more in the Himyarite country. Within four years he had received Thaʿran, King of Himyar, into the Faith. Forty years on, though, Thaʿran's grandson turned his back on the church when he visited Yathrib in the Hejaz, and there became a Jew. Afterwards, the Himyarites who remained Christian were systematically hunted down and persecuted. The last King of Himyar, Dhu Huwas, massacred 20,000 of them at Najran. The Christians called on the Byzantine Emperor for help, and he dispatched his proxies, the Christian Axumites – who had withdrawn across the Bab al Mandab decades earlier – to the succour of their religious brethren. They re-invaded the Yemen and remained as rulers until they were defeated by the Persian King, Chosroes, a few years after the birth of the Prophet Mohammad. A century later, elements of the Himyar – by then Muslims and nomadic Bedu – migrated to Egypt, and planted their genes among the Egyptian Fellahin. Writing in the fourteenth century, Ibn Khaldun recorded – with more than a touch of condescension – that the Himyar were one of the tribes which 'lived in the hills and the sources of plentiful living . . . Their lineages were mixed up, and their groups intermingled . . . as a result of intermixture with non-Arabs.'

I asked the Mahra why they were living so far from the government centres in Thamud and Armah. 'The government tried to make us stay in one place,' the old man said. 'They told us that all our children must go to school. If you refused to let your children go, they'd shoot you and take them, people said! They told us that we were backward, and that we ought to become farmers. All right, I said, we have nothing against farming, but you show me some good land that I can cultivate at the same time as I herd camels and goats! They couldn't, of course. If you stay always in one place you can't keep large flocks of goats or herds of camels. Well, why not just move with them, like we've always done? Maybe that's what they call being "backward", but it makes sense to me!'

I reflected again that it was an Arab – Ibn Khaldun – who was ultimately to blame for such folly. It was he who first held that the Bedu were 'more primitive' than sedentary people, not in the sense that they lived materially simpler lives – which was self-evidently true – but meaning that they had been stranded in a 'backward' state, from which the rest of mankind had long since progressed. This view would probably be echoed even today by most sophisticated lay observers – Westerners or Arabs. It was precisely the view that had led governments to condemn the nomadic life as an anachronism from which its victims must be rescued, and made to settle as farmers – that is, to catch up culturally with the rest of the population. Even those who argued against the settlement of the Bedu generally based their case on Ibn Khaldun's premise of Bedu moral purity, as if the Bedu were a rare and exotic species which should be preserved in its natural habitat for the benefit of others.

Archaeological evidence has exploded Ibn Khaldun's argument. We now know that agriculture and pastoral nomadism developed concurrently from hunting and gathering, as a result of the 'Neolithic food-producing revolution'. If both ways of life appeared at the same time, neither can be considered 'the final stage' of human development. In chronological terms, camel-pastoralism, supposedly the 'purest' form of nomadism – with a history that can scarcely be traced back earlier than 2000 BC – developed long after the ancient Egyptians and Mesopotamians had become urbanized in cities. Emanuel Marx has pointed out that, far from being 'primitive', the 'pure' camel-nomads could never have existed other than in connection with a complex urban civilization, because their high degree of specialization rendered them exceptionally dependent on agricultural products, and highly vulnerable to the vagaries of the market.

The following day, when we had dropped our guide back in Armah, we drove towards Sanaw, where Thesiger's favourite tribe, the Bayt Imani, had once watered their flocks. We halted at the Mahra tent to ask directions, and an aggressive-looking Bedui appeared with his rifle. 'Why are you going to Sanaw?' he demanded, nastily.

'Because I want to see it.'

'Have you got your papers?'

'Yes, thanks.'

'Let me see them.'

'No.'

The Bedui scowled at me and showed rotted teeth. 'You shouldn't go to Sanaw. That is near the border with Saudi Arabia. Perhaps you are a spy!'

'Thanks. Let's go, Faisal!'

Before we pulled away, though, the Bedui shouted: 'If you go to Sanaw you will both be killed!'

I brooded over this disturbing incident for several hours as we bounced under blocks of black stone, across rubble floors and long sweeps of valley, past bundles of grass like helmets and scratchy thorn. The day was very hot, and Faisal looked increasingly annoyed as he wrestled with the wheel. Eventually he gave me a look so hard and venomous that I was taken aback. 'Is something wrong?' I inquired.

'That man,' he burst out. 'You should have showed him your

papers. You shouldn't have been rude to him. You foreigners! Coming here and being rude to people. I don't want any trouble!'

'He had no right to ask for my passport. He wasn't the police!'

'How do you know? He could have been a government officer!'

'If he was, he should have said so!'

'Who are you to say that? This is our country!'

'I've got a right to be here. I've got my visa and I have hired you and your car through the most reputable company in the Yemen. That man made me feel I was doing something wrong, which he had absolutely no call to do . . .'

Faisal's reaction was shocking in its suddenness. He screeched to a halt, switched off the engine and instinctively reached for his Kalashnikov with blazing eyes. 'Who are you to say what people have and haven't got the right to do in our country?' he screamed.

I was taken off guard. Faisal had been stern and robust from the beginning, but always reliable and fair. I watched his hand as it tightened around the stock of the rifle, and it occurred to me that I was in the remotest corner of Yemen, alone in the middle of the desert, with a man who had already murdered at least one person in cold blood. I tried to keep my voice calm when I said, 'I'm sorry you feel like this, Faisal, but I think we'd better turn round and go back to Sanaʿa. I'm a stranger in your country; I have hired your car in good faith, and you have your hand on a loaded rifle.'

I kept my gaze steady, staring straight into his eyes. He looked away abruptly and relaxed his hold on the weapon. 'I'm sorry,' he said, suddenly. 'It's the fasting. Driving in this heat without eating and drinking makes you go crazy! It's the first time I've been to Sanaw, and there may be army and police there. I don't want any trouble, that's all.'

'Look, I'm sorry too. We can turn back if you want.'

'No, no! We'll go on!'

When we arrived in Sanaw half an hour later, it was something of an anti-climax: all we found were three wells stinking of sulphur, a deserted police sangar, and a pile of rubble which had once been a British base.

Next day we crossed the switchback pass into the Mahrat – the wadi which formed the heartland of Mahra country. I had never read any detailed description of the Mahrat, and its lushness came as a complete surprise. Here, hidden in the steppe-land beyond the Hadhramaut, was a second great water-system, where cool streams babbled across graded stones, marbled by light strained through the leaves of tangled palm-trees. Here was a tropical forest in the midst of nowhere. There were Bedu tents in the palmeries, but as we moved south, we sighted block-house castles rising from the stepped buttresses of the valley walls, overseeing with multiple eyes the running water, the knots of camels, the cultivated gardens and the date-groves. Evidently the Mahra here were unaccustomed to visitors, for a grown woman carrying firewood pelted away from the car, splashing wildly through the stream, losing both her plastic shoes but retaining the bundle on her head. Further on, two boys eyed us mistrustfully from the branches of a tree and one of them dropped down and rushed towards the nearest tower.

At sunset we made camp in sand on a curve in the wadi between deep groves of arak trees. A thickset old Mahri whose face resembled a weathered granite boulder, with crows' feet puddling in concentric rings from the corners of his eyes, approached us on foot, and willingly partook of our evening pasta. 'This part of the wadi is called the Kidyat,' he said, 'and it's divided between the Bayt Imani and the Mahra. They are mostly farmers. I've lived here and cultivated date-palms all my life.' I suddenly remembered the photo of Sulaim, and showed it to the Mahri, asking if it was indeed Sulaim bin Dumaysh, and whether he knew where to find the man. 'I know bin Dumaysh,' he told me. 'He was here in Kidyat only a few days ago, but he's gone to Oman. The border is closed, but that doesn't bother the Bedu. We put on Omani dishdashas and just walk to Salalah, and say we're from Oman!'

'Do you think I will find bin Dumaysh in Salalah?' I inquired.

The old man beamed. 'God knows, you might,' he said, 'but it won't do you any good!'

'Why?'

'Because the man in the picture is not bin Dumaysh. That is a man called Sulaim bin Mayza. And he's been dead for twenty years!'

6

Another Country, Long Ago

Salalah lies no more than 130 kilometres east of the Mahrat, on the shores of the Indian Ocean. The town is encircled by a hot, pebbled plain, and a little way inland the landscape buckles suddenly into a coronet of hills that, in summer, stand under a perpetual quilt of mist. It is only the mid-section of the range that draws this vital moisture, for the Dhofar mountains are fashioned like a saddle between two pommels, angled in such a way as to channel the monsoon directly to their centre point. The hills are rumpled gently like English downs, dun-coloured, sap-green, verdigris, a-bristle with grass, wrapped in jungle-thick thornbush, from which the trunks of monstrous fig-trees protrude like lengths of plaited cable. Between bights that interlock like soft, giant knuckles, canyons are incised sharply through strata of fluted files.

On a day near the end of the summer wet, a Bedui called Mohammad bin Sa'id and I picked our way down the side of one of these canyons. It was a time of milk and honey for the Bedu, and nomads of the seashores, the mountains, and the deserts had gathered in the gorges to feast their flocks on the last fruits of the monsoon. Below us, the farms of the mountain people, squatting low and flat against the rain, were encompassed by masses of dwarf cattle – dun-and-white, black-and-white, strawberry roan. Mohammad, wearing silver-rimmed spectacles and a studious look, climbed with surprising confidence into the abyss, with the hem of his dishdasha pulled up to reveal muscular legs. He was carrying a bundle of bedsheets tied to the stock of a heavy but beautifully made rifle, yoked across his shoulders like a stick. The track was very narrow – a ladder of boulders on a hillside of thick *macchia*, pitching along the side of the ravine. Where the *macchia* had not penetrated, there were stands of juniper and *tishga* scrub, and mats of mosses and wild yellow flowers. Mellow smells, monsoon smells, cattle smells, drifted up from the humid cleft below. On a clear day you could see the ocean from here, but now the sky was a rinse of vapour, soaking up the last pale fuel of the sun.

Mohammad halted at a flat place and sat down on his bundle. While we shared a cup of water, I inquired why he was carrying his rifle. 'First, because it's a tradition of the Bedu,' he said, 'and second because of the wild animals – leopards, hyenas, wolves, and foxes. Actually, there are hardly any wolves, hyenas, or leopards – it's the foxes I worry about, because they have rabies. We never had rabies here in the past – it arrived recently. When I was a boy I used to look after my family's goats in these valleys, and the thought of wolves and leopards used to frighten me to death. Well, there I was one day, six years old, and a wolf *did* carry off one of our kids. I shouted to my uncle, who was within hearing distance, 'A wolf is carrying off one of the kids!' and he shouted back, 'Chase it! Don't let it get away!' I thought the wolf would eat me, so do you know what I did? I just ran round and round a tree, yelling 'Stop! Stop!' so that my uncle would think I was chasing the wolf! In the end he fired a shot at it and it dropped the goat, which was injured in the throat. Another time, I can clearly remember my father shooting a leopard. He took the skin to the Wali in Salalah and got a reward.'

Mohammad had volunteered to act as my guide in the Dhofar hills, where I was searching not only for the Bedu, but also for the frankincense or *mughur* trees, which had once made Dhofar legendary. He had proved a charming, remarkably intelligent, and unusual companion: 'When things change, something is lost and something is gained,' he was fond of saying. 'Take me, for instance. I am a Bedui born in the desert. I speak both Arabic and the Jabali language as mother-tongues. For the first six years of my life I knew nothing but the desert and herding goats. Then there was the war here in Dhofar and my father was shot dead by the British forces – wrongly, because he wasn't even involved with the guerrillas. Afterwards, my uncle sent me to school. I did well, and ended up going to the University of Arizona to study electronic engineering. Now I'm due to study for my PhD. If the war in Dhofar hadn't happened – if no one had rebelled against Sultan Bin Taimur – then what would I have been? Still illiterate, herding goats in the desert?'

Mohammad's dignity and generosity gave the lie to any misplaced idea that education had somehow 'spoiled' the Bedu. And he himself was under no illusions about the traditional way of life: 'In some ways, perhaps, the lives of our forefathers were happier,' he told me, 'because although they were poor, they knew nothing else. But it was a happiness that came from ignorance, and there is no real nobility in ignorance, or poverty, or disease. Think of the human potential you lose when people can't read or write: when children die as babies, when people's life expectancy is only thirty-eight years!'

'Yes,' I answered, 'but isn't it more important to live those years intensely rather than to live twice as long in boredom?'

I recounted a story I had once heard, in which a pilot had landed his aircraft in the desert to take his lunch. As he was eating, a caravan of nomads had ridden past, and he discovered that both he and they were going to the same place. 'How long will it take you to get there?' he asked them. 'Seven days,' they replied, 'how long will it take you?' 'About half an hour!' 'Great God,' they said, 'but what on earth will you do with all the spare time?'

Mohammad laughed at the story, and then said without animosity, 'That story is nonsense, of course. It implies that the nomads were inferior to the pilot because they would have had less idea of what to do with their leisure than he did.'

'Well, wouldn't they?'

'Do you think we are less intelligent than Westerners? Having more leisure is an important thing because it frees people to use new bits of their mind – to study, to read, to create things, to develop themselves, to see other countries and other peoples. All the great inventions of the past – like cultivation and livestock-rearing – were made because people had the leisure to do it. People who are struggling to survive don't have the time to experiment with new ways. Western technology – the basis of Western supremacy – was only possible because people had the leisure to develop it. Again, it's human potential that is lost when people are condemned to struggle for their entire lives.'

After dark, the humid scents were replaced by the smell of woodsmoke, and campfires were bracelets of light spanning the hillsides. We strayed from the track and approached a fire where a Jehovah of a man with a shaggy grey beard, naked but for his loincloth, sat with his two children by a cattle-fold. The darkness held the odours of sour milk and manure. From some distance away Mohammad called out a greeting in Arabic, and the Jabali shouted back: 'What kind of people are you, that you don't come by the track?'

'We are strangers who don't know the way!' Mohammad said, as we emerged from the shadows. He began to speak in Qara – the ancient mountain language of south Arabia – an ooze of odd sibilants and emphatics. The old man led us on a little way in the darkness, ambling barefoot, and soon after we heard the moan of camels, the glimmer of several campfires, the sound of voices. We broke out of the darkness, and suddenly we were among a crowd of friendly, bearded men, clasping and releasing our hands, and passing us bowls of frothy camels' milk.

They sat us down on fibre mats in the midst of a great circle of camels. A wood fire crackled in the hearth, and the camels' heads bobbed around us like jack-in-the-boxes. The Bedu were wearing loincloths and *ghutras* and all of them had rifles and daggers. They rolled cigarettes of bitter tobacco, constantly replenishing the milk-bowls from milk-skins, everyone talking at the same time. Mohammad's elder brother, Mabruk, a narrow-faced man with a crop of stubble in place of a beard, hailed me in impeccable English: 'I used to work in a helicopter crew,' he said. 'Radio-operator. I was good – very good. I got commended for my work, and they even had me down for training as a pilot. But then I had a row with my boss. I suppose I have hot blood. Anyway, I couldn't see the point in it all. Money – big house, a nice car: what did it mean anyway? So I quit. They were really surprised when I left. "What are you going to do?" they asked me. "I am a Bedui," I said, "I'm going to herd my camels in the hills!" So here I am with my ten camels – this is me!'

'Do you think there's a future in herding camels?'

'Yes, but only if we diversify with sheep and goats and cultivation. In the past you were lucky if you had a camel. Now, everyone has hundreds, and it's a buyer's market, because we are overproducing. Nobody rides camels – except in the races – and people like mutton better than camel's meat. I don't see why the Bedu way of life should die out – I don't think it ever will, while there are animals to be herded. But like everything else, it's bound to change.'

Just then there was a commotion in the bushes, and some of the Bedu jumped up, flashing torches in whose beams, just for a moment, I glimpsed the glittering eyes of foxes. 'Shoot them! Shoot them!' someone yelled, but already the animals had disappeared into the night. Mohammad said that rabid foxes were emboldened by the disease, and had attacked several herders recently. The Bedu kept their eyes peeled and their rifles and torches close as they gathered once again around the fire. There were still a few leopards in these hills, they said, but not enough to pose a threat to their herds. It was difficult to be certain that they were really talking about leopards, though, for while Arabic possesses more than a hundred synonyms for 'lion', most of the lesser species of cat are lumped under the title *nimr* – literally 'leopard', but in practice anything from a cheetah to a caracal. The true leopard, *Panthera pardus*, is certainly to be found in the hills of Yemen and until recently ranged through the whole of western and southern Arabia.

A shy young man called Musallim sat down beside us and announced, to my amusement, that he was Mohammad's uncle, though he was evidently years younger. He added that he had just returned from Britain, where he had graduated in mechanical engineering from the University of Leeds: 'I liked Leeds,' he said, 'I was happy in England. I wouldn't mind going back there. The thing is that the Sultan's Special Forces sponsored me for a degree. The CO promised me that I wouldn't have to do the full selection-course – after all I would only be working in the workshop: I needed to know how to march and salute, perhaps, but not all that special training. Well, when I got back, I found that there was a new CO and the policy had changed. He wants me to do the full thing – running across the desert with a rucksack! I said, "No, by God! I'm not doing that: I'm an engineer! My father was killed in the Dhofar war, as a soldier of the government. He was searching a cave, when a booby-trap went off and blew him up. So much for being a foot-soldier! I don't want any of that, so I thought I'd herd my few camels up here until I find another job. But God, I feel homesick for England!'

It was pondering this totally unexpected expression of sentiment from a Bedui that I retired to my sleeping-bag.

At sunrise on a day two weeks earlier I had awoken on the express bus as it pulled into Salalah, with Muscat lying twelve hours behind me, across a thousand kilometres of desert steppe. A taxi had taken me to the Redan – a hotel on a busy thoroughfare, run by an efficient team of Indian Muslims from the Malabar coast. The town was very different from the ruined village set around a crumbling palace which the explorers Bertram Thomas and Wilfred Thesiger had found here in the 1930s and 40s – a geometry of right-angles in queues of flat-blocks, cinemas, supermarkets, ice-cream parlours and Coca-Cola bars. Yet the old Salalah lay like a phantom among the blocks. At the produce market – an octagon of shade under high arches – men were filling plastic bags with blade-shaped sardines straight out of the net, and bargaining over sharks, dogfish, catfish, squid, mullet and tuna. Women wearing unexpectedly vivid dresses and gold nose-rings were selling bottles of liquid butter, terracotta incense-burners, bags of frankincense, varnished camel-sticks and balls of black goats' hair. Mahra tribesmen were sitting in the sun with headcloths tied around their knees, stroking Lee-Enfield rifles of 1940s vintage, wearing hooked daggers. There had been peace in Salalah since the civil war ended in 1976, but every tribesman still carried a rifle as a matter of course. Around the market there were light trucks full of strangely bald goats, and pick-ups laden with old she-camels bound for the butcher's block.

Despite the roar and honk of gleaming Land-Cruisers, Mitsubishis and BMWs that filled the streets in the afternoon, there remained along the Corniche an almost mesmeric sense of calm: coconut palms with heads like water cascading in the sunlight, cows and bullocks tethered in the shade, waterlogged fishing canoes hauled up out of the surf. As I walked there near sunset I saw whorls of blue cloud over the ocean, pricked by spalls of light igniting volcanic colours across the sky. An ancient Bedui with a beard like steel wire and a scrap of cloth around his head was walking through the wet sand at the sea's edge, balancing a rifle muzzle-forwards on his shoulder, towards a new palace of polished marble walls and Moghul domes, where armed tribesmen in khaki dishdashas guarded the studded doors. The Bedui left a trail of perfect footprints behind him, but soon the old sea lobbed its rollers ever higher up the beach, erasing them for ever.

It was through the intervention of John Crowther – British Council representative in Salalah – that I was introduced to Mohammad bin Sa'id, who, over tea in the Redan, had told me the story of his life. I was concerned to know if he harboured any grudge against the British for the death of his father. 'It wasn't actually the British who murdered him,' he said, 'it was Baluch troops under British command. I still remember the day it happened. Some Baluch stopped my father and told him to leave his rifle and come towards them. As he did so they just shot him in cold blood. My uncle ran to help him and the soldiers ran away. My father was dead, of course. I have never liked the Baluch since then, but after all it was an individual, not a tribe or a people who killed him.'

'Isn't it the tribe that matters?'

'Of course. In the old days there would have been a blood-feud. But that's considered uncivilized now.'

I inquired how he had enjoyed his time in Arizona. 'I liked it,' he said. 'It's desert country similar to Dhofar, so in a way I felt at home. I didn't experience any real prejudice in America. People were friendly. I had more trouble from the Iranian Muslims than anyone else. I remember one Iranian student asking me if I believed in the Ayatollah Khomeini. "What do you mean, 'believe'?" I asked him. "That he is the Imam," he said. I told him that to me an Imam was just someone who led the prayers in any mosque. "Then you are not a Muslim!" he said. Can you imagine how angry that made me?'

Mohammad told me that he admired the West, but pitied Westerners for their spiritual poverty: 'There's no religion, really,' he said, 'there's a big religious gap in people's lives. The West needs something to fill this spiritual vacuum, and I think that Islam will eventually fill it.'

The following day, Mohammad had taken me in his Land-Cruiser to see an agricultural project created by his tribe, the famous Bayt Kathir. All morning we cruised on through the monotonously flat salt-plains of Jiddat al Harasis, a landscape of utter bleakness, unrelieved by trees, rocks or even sand-dunes. Shortly before noon, though, we saw patches of green standing out like an archipelago of islands in the emptiness. Here, at a watering-place known to the Bedu for 400 years, notorious for its remoteness, the wilderness had been turned green by giant water-screws that sprayed acres of wheat and clover and whole fields of water-melons. Pencil-cedars had been planted in interlocking squares as a shelter-belt, and within the perimeter were pens holding spare Dhofari cattle and slim white goats. A covey of hobbled camels moved haltingly through the stubble of a clover-field, and new incense-trees – brought as saplings from the Dhofar hills and carefully nurtured – were in full royal leaf. Pakistani, Egyptian and Indian workers were everywhere, moving amid coils of hose and stand-pipes like strange totems in the desert. A surprisingly tall and stringy Bedui called ʿAli spread a carpet for us by the cattle-pen and brought us buttermilk in enamel mugs, and a plate of fresh water-melon. He wore a ragged dishdasha, smoked cigarettes perpetually, and spoke with an abrupt, abrasive manner. 'You've got better cows than this in your country, I know,' he snapped. 'Yours bring you twenty-five litres of milk a day. These are poor things as far as milk goes, but your great clumping buffaloes would never stand the climate here! I know. I've tried them!'

I asked them if it wasn't something of a come-down for a Bedui to turn settled farmer. 'That's nonsense,' he said, shrugging with exaggerated irritation. 'This is the future for us. Diversification. We've got cattle, goats, camels, cash-crops and fodder. We're not waiting for the rains like they used to in the old days. We're not going to go hungry either – if God wills!'

On the way back to Salalah, we visited the ruin of Khor Ruri. It lay on a bay of black basalt boulders, enclosing mobile turquoise waters and shallow marshland where long-beaked terns and waders were basking in the sun. The ruins appeared to be no more than a formless pile of stones, the same size and colour as the basalt blocks around them, but closer up you could see the remains of standing walls which dated back to the time when this fortress, Sumhuram, guarded the harbour of Moscha, one of the richest and most significant incense-ports on the south Arabian coast.

Samhuram came to prominence late in the history of the spice-trade. An inscription discovered in the ruins reveals that it was built as a colony by King Ilazz of the Hadhramaut – almost 400 miles away – not much earlier than AD 100. Frankincense had flourished in large forests on the northern side of the Dhofar hills, and the settlement had been built as a handling depot for the spice. The spice-mongers of Moscha traded directly with merchant vessels which put in to the harbour, but also floated a large proportion of the crop on rafts made of inflated skins down the coast to Qanaʿ – near modern Bir ʿAli, in Yemen. From there it was shifted overland by camel-caravan to the key distribution-point at Shabwa. Some have surmised that, many centuries earlier, Dhofar was already trading with Solomon's legendary 'navy of Tharshish' – a fleet built for him by Hiram of Tyre – which returned from the fabled 'Land of Ophir' laden with 'gold and silver, ivory, apes and peacocks', after a voyage lasting eighteen months.

In the Redan that night, Mohammad suggested a trek in the Dhofar hills to find what remained of the sacred incense-trees on which the fame of legendary Ophir had been based.

The morning was a tumult of camels grunting and snarling among the trees, a honey-coloured sun rising over the crest of the forested spurs, and Mohammad's brother Mabruk – once a radio-operator – standing on one strut-like leg at the udder of a she-camel, spurting milk into a bowl in time-hallowed Bedu style. He offered the milk to me first: 'We get three litres from each camel morning and evening,' he said. 'Six litres a day. We hardly know what to do with it!'

The day was clear and as Mohammad and I climbed back up the valley we could see camel-herds fanning out across the lush green mountainside – rich mobs of four or five hundred fat beasts tended by walking Bedu, many shoeless, naked but for loincloths. As we crested the escarpment, a Qara tribesman called us over to drink milk. He was very dark, almost Ethiopian-looking, with grey, curled hair that hung in ringlets from beneath a headband of plaited leather. His loincloth was of a deep, rich purple, and he wore a very ornate, filigreed dagger in the folds of a shawl tied around his waist like a cummerbund. He selected a camel-mare with a bulging udder, strapped with cloth, and a calf a couple of weeks old. 'This is my best milker,' he commented. 'She gives me twenty-five litres a day sometimes, but I have to keep the calf near, or she won't let down her milk!' The she-camel squared up aggressively and growled like a male as the Bedui tried to move the calf. When the bowl was full, he presented it to Mohammad, who took it with both hands and crouched down to drink, following Bedouin etiquette.

By mid-morning the monsoon cloud had lifted and sunlight rolled down the valleys, ejecting the lees of mist from the ravines. As we trudged up the steep track we paused often to take in the miracle of this haven in the barren heart of Arabia. Farther on we halted at some corrugated-iron outbuildings, set in a mush of mud. This was a Bayt Kathir place, and we were greeted by yet another of Mohammad's relatives, a young man with a crop of curls and cow-dung behind his toes. An unveiled woman wearing a nose-ring was making buttermilk – shaking a great goatskin to and fro on a wooden tripod. A little boy with goblin features and large ears looked fearfully at my face and began to cry. The man milked a dwarf cow and brought two bowls of cows' milk, then stoked up the fire and placed several large pebbles in the ashes. When the stones were red-hot, he picked them up deftly with a makeshift pincer of sticks, and dropped them one by one into the first bowl of milk. He then poured half of the bubbling milk into the second bowl and beat it with a stick, whipping up a head of froth. He passed the first bowl to us and we drank in turn – the milk tasted slightly toasted, but delicious. The second bowl tasted of vanilla ice-cream – even better than the first. The woman watched us drinking and said something to Mohammad in Qara. He laughed and said in English: 'You know what she said? She asked me how I could drink from the same bowl as a Christian!'

'But surely that's not a problem, is it?'

'No, Muslims are permitted to eat or drink with Christians or Jews – and most of the Bedu wouldn't bother even to ask about religion. But some of these Jabalis – mountain people – are ignorant. I say that, even though they belong to my tribe, the Bayt

Kathir. Most of the Bayt Kathir live in the desert, but a few of them live in the mountains.'

I wondered how the Bayt Kathir would fare in Glubb's paradigm of the Bedu as the 'noble, camel-rearing tribes', for here was a people who reared more goats than camels, who ranged from the sands of the Empty Quarter to the hills of Dhofar, where some of them herded cattle. No one in Oman would dispute that they were 'true' Bedu, though.

Before we left our host made up for the woman's remark by giving us a bag of *janbet* – root-plants which looked like the wizened meat of large walnuts. The tribesman peeled several and handed them to me one by one. They tasted like a rather mature, nutty cheese.

It was already afternoon when we reached the northern side of the mountains where the monsoon-raised vegetation gave way to the raw carapace of the rock. There was no sudden transition from hill to desert: the limestone knolls grew smaller by degrees; deep fissures became shallow washes with frail walls: trees became sparse until there remained only isolated copses of stunted thorn. The Dhofar range began to unhinge in geometrical buttes – pyramids, cusps, and polygons. The *mughur* trees stood on a shallow dry-wash, talons of branches six metres high with tiny scrolled leaves and silvery trunks. Mohammad told me that the Bayt Kathir still culled the incense from them, and that the spice had a small market in Yemen and Oman. 'They only collect from a few of the best trees,' he said, 'and only in the hot season, when the sap flows best.' He ran his hand over the healed wounds on a horny trunk: 'They make an incision here,' he said, 'and peel back a bit of the bark. Then they come back in a week and there is a blob of *luban* (frankincense resin) on the bark, as big as a golf ball. It's still mostly the Bayt Kathir who harvest the *luban*, but the trees are owned by the Qara and a few by the Mahra.'

It was once believed that Dhofar had been the only source of frankincense in south Arabia, though a more careful reading of the classical geographers has revealed that trees of varying quality grew all the way between here and the Hadhramaut. The relatively late foundation of the spice-handling colony of Samhuram may suggest that the Hadhramis were scouring the land farther and farther east as demand outstripped supply. If so, then it may be that they had saved the best until last. The unique geographical conditions of the Dhofar range, with its moist-arid oscillation, its altitude, and its limestone soil, combined to make the frankincense of Dhofar – the so-called 'Sakhalitic incense' – among the most prized of all. In the time of Pliny the incense was produced here by a few families whose members were considered holy. The harvesting of the sacred gum was shrouded in ritual and taboo. While making the incisions, for instance, the harvesters were forbidden either to meet women or to take part in funeral processions. The frankincense was stored in caves in the Qara hills during the rainy season, when the south-west monsoon winds prevented any vessel from leaving the harbours, then shipped by camel down to the coast, where much of it was purchased wholesale by Indian merchants. India remained a substantial market for the spice up until recent times.

Next day we motored to Shisur, a line of neat miniature castles around a spring in a deep cleft in the rock. These bungalows – only recently completed and fitted with globe-lamps, flush toilets and air-coolers – were stranded in the midst of grey stone desert, the homes of the Bayt Musan, a Bedu tribe who drove their camels deep into the Empty Quarter in winter. We were invited to stay by a mischievous-looking man called Salih, who showed us a bed of soft sand outside his house, where we could sleep for the night, and after dark slaughtered two small goats for us.

After we had eaten, we were joined by six or seven Bedu, one of them an old man who recalled meeting Wilfred Thesiger on his first crossing of the Empty Quarter in 1946. 'They watered their camels here,' he told me. 'In those days it was hard work indeed to water your camels at Shisur, but it was necessary, because there was no other good water between here and Mughshin.' In those days the Bedu had been obliged to crawl down between the sand and the overhanging rock, enter a cave, fill their skins and drag them back thirty feet up to the surface. It had undoubtedly been back-breaking work. Now the sandbank had been cleared away, revealing ancient cave-paintings of gazelles and antelopes, and a few years earlier the government had built a flight of steps down to the cave. More recently they had installed an electric pump, which drew the water out at the touch of a button to feed a small but promising garden of date-palms nearby. 'We still move into the Sands,' Salih said, 'but we use motor-vehicles now. There's plenty of grazing in the Sands – much more than there is here.'

I asked about the possibility of hiring some camels to make a trek from here to Mughshin along the Umm al Hayt – the trunk wadi which channelled the washes coming off the Dhofar mountains to the edge of the Sands. 'I'm ready to take you,' Salih said, 'but I will have to get time off from my job.'

'What *is* your job?'

'The *Firgat* – the militia. I don't actually have anything to do, but I'm on call. I have to get permission for time off.'

'How much would you charge?'

'Fifty riyals a day,' Salih said.

'That's more than I'd pay for a motor-car and driver!'

'Well, you need at least three camels, and two Bedu. It's dangerous to make a journey by camel with less than three men.'

'And then there's the camel-feed,' a younger Bedui added. 'You would need a car to bring food and water for the camels.'

'The camels can live off the land, as they did in the old days,' I said.

'That was the old days. The camels aren't used to it any more. They are accustomed to drinking every day and eating properly.'

'Even so, a camel is a camel.'

'But we don't want them to lose condition. We like them fat!'

By now everyone was joining in excitedly. The idea seemed to have whetted their imagination, engaging Bedu rhetoric to the full, if only as a mental exercise. One old man began to take my part, pleading for me like an advocate: 'This is a poor man,' he said. 'He's got nothing. How can you charge so much? Come down a little!'

'No, I can't,' Salih said. 'It's the effort he has to pay for. I mean, we're not used to riding camels any longer. Why go anywhere by camel when you can go by car? We are accustomed to air-conditioning and cool drinks – no one wants to bother with riding camels these days. We don't see the point in it!'

I divined that Salih was not serious about a camel-trek, and even if he had been, what, indeed, would be the point of travelling by camel with a car to bring fodder and water every night?

'But isn't there a challenge in travelling by camel – I mean, without motor-cars?' I asked.

Salih looked at me for an instant with what I took to be incomprehension, then a young, extraordinarily strong-looking Bedui with a thick black beard piped up. 'I know what he means,' he said. 'Remember when three of us set off from Thumrait to ride to Shisur on camels just to see what it was like? That's what he means!'

'Yes, that's exactly what I mean! How was it?'

'Terrible! We took only a small skin of water with us. It was summer and very very hot, and we finished the water quickly. Then we cursed our stupidity. Our fathers would have known, but we didn't. We came to a Bayt Musan tent where they fed us and gave us water and we forgot the problem of thirst. We set off again into the heat and within half an hour we were craving water again. At the tent they had given us a leg of goat, but we were so thirsty we couldn't eat it. We just threw it away into the sand. Then, of course, when we found water, we felt hungry, and we said, "By God, I wish we hadn't thrown that leg of goat away in the sand!" I suppose we thought riding camels would be like driving a car – you'd just get on them and whoooosh – you'd be there! By the time we got to Shisur we were hungry, thirsty and so sore from riding we could hardly stand. I said, "Well, if that's what the lives of our fathers were like, you can keep it! From now on I go by car!"'

I joined the rest of them in their mirth, but I could not suppress a sense of sadness. The passing of old ways, old skills, was inevitably deplorable in hindsight, especially to those, like myself, who did not have to live by them for ever. 'You are no longer Bedu,' I said, laughing. 'You can't ride camels any more!'

'You're right,' the young man said. 'Many of the Bedu live in the city now – in Salalah or Thumrait, or they've gone to Abu Dhabi or Dubai. They get jobs, their children go to school. Already the Bedu are few. Soon they will disappear!'

'Rubbish!' Salih said. 'We are still camel-herders, and besides, it's not going to school or getting a job that makes you what you are.' He placed a hand over his heart. 'Being a Bedui is what you feel here!'

Salih invited me to visit his camels, and we drove out to Umm al Hayt, across grey gypsum flats and salt-licks that stained the smooth desert skin with crystalline white. Sand-coils of orange, several hundred feet high, were levitating above the skyline in platinum wrappers – the outer skirts of the Empty Quarter. The camel-herds were gathering in Umm al Hayt among broken tree-stumps and roots. Two Baluch herdsmen had made their beds inside a wire compound, where two week-old camel-calves – one black, the other white – were tethered to poles. A litter of squashed sardine-cans surrounded the ashes of a fire. One of the Baluch herders – who spoke passable Arabic, and was friendly to the point of obsequiousness – brought us camel's milk. His companion, a dark, silent man, observed us with hostile eyes. The previous night Salih had said, 'We are still herdsmen,' I reflected, but even this was not strictly true: the Bayt Musan had once been camel-herders, but were now camel-owners: the Baluch were, in a sense, the new 'Bedu' of Oman.

Salih insisted on taking us to a Bayt Musan tent, and we followed his Land-Cruiser down the soft wadi bed, passing a procession of camels marching in review order in search of grazing.

There were sand-plants in plenty here, and though the vegetation appeared long dead to me, Salih reported that it was acceptable pasture. Later, he showed us the smudged tracks of a Land-Cruiser straining suicidally to the summit of a sheer dune. 'That was me!' he declared smugly. 'Only the Bedu can drive in sand!'

The tent had been pitched on the salt-flats, outside the wadi. It was almost identical to the black tents of Syria and Jordan, divided by a screen into women's and men's sections, and surrounded by a barbed-wire fence. A small, canvas-covered 'kitchen-tent' stood outside. Inside there were rich carpets, piles of steel trunks, a huge radio/cassette-player, and a TV set attached to two twelve-volt car-batteries. It was occupied only by two women in black robes and purple masks – an old lady, and a plump, chirpy girl, who offered us cans of warm lemonade instead of camels' milk. 'English?' the old lady said, when Salih had introduced me properly. 'I remember the first Englishman who ever came here: Thomas. I was a little girl then. No such things as tents in those days, no, by Allah!' She broke off to ask me the time, then said excitedly to the younger woman: 'Switch the TV on! It's the racing!'

The girl flicked the switch and the screen blinked into life, filling the tent with images of dashing camels ridden by tiny boys in helmets and scarlet livery. The Bedu watched enthralled: 'They tie those boys on with rope,' the old lady said, 'and if the camel falls they often get killed!'

A fire was smouldering outside in the broken lid of a tin box filled with sand. Baluch herdsmen in knee-length shirts were feeding knots of camels, slitting open pink sacks of fodder manufactured in the town. Others were watering camels from a mobile tanker. Despite camel-racing on TV, despite motor-cars, despite affluence, these Bayt Musan were, at the very least, still here in the desert. There was, perhaps, no necessity for them to live this life: for the first time in their history, perhaps, they truly did so out of choice.

The bus to Muscat was full of Indians and Pakistani workers with cardboard suitcases tied up with string. The driver was a Filipino and the conductor Sudanese. An undernourished-looking Pakistani counted out his money into the hand of the Sudanese conductor, blinking hopelessly in the light. The Sudanese shook his head: the money was two riyals short. A tall young Omani in a spotlessly clean dishdasha, sitting next to me, delved into his pocket and handed the two riyals out languidly with scarcely a word. I was deeply touched by this simple act of generosity to a stranger.

The Dhofar hills passed behind us, then Thumrait. The solitary Jiddat al Harasis was a void of desert until we reached Izki, hours later, where the walls of the Akhdar range rose with unexpected grandeur out of the plains like tongues of blazing fire. Muscat was a battalion of halogen lights floating on a pool of darkness. From the bus-station at Qurn, I made my way to the Mina Hotel, near the waterfront at Muttrah.

Muscat is the most beautiful town on the Gulf. Its harbour is an almost perfect crescent under a fraternity of mountains as cold and arid as icebergs. On the Corniche restored Portuguese houses with windtraps and ornate balustrades harmonize with the contemporary architecture: a blend of Arab and Andalusian styles – Moresco arches, *mashrubat* windows, slit openings, white stucco. Everywhere water-wealth is flaunted with conspicuous boldness: water foaming out of giant tilted coffee-pots, tumbling out of water-jars, squirting out of fountain-jets, sizzling out of sprinklers on green lawns. Walking along the waterfront at Muttrah, I saw wooden sailing-vessels like caravels at anchor, and a shattered dhow half drowned in the shallows. Motor-vehicles hummed past, hooting at a Bedui in a shredded dishdasha who was riding a donkey defiantly along the Corniche, his head thrown back in proud disdain, white fingers of beard fluttering against his breast.

At the office of a hire-car company, I met an Anglo-Indian called Gerry, who was to motor me around northern Oman. Like thousands of other Asians, he had come to the Sultanate to make his fortune. He had been a professional musician in India, but had managed to scratch no more than a bare living. When he first arrived in Oman he had known nothing of driving. He had failed his driving test half a dozen times before obtaining his licence. Then he had worked as a van-driver, delivering frozen chickens for a cool-storage company, until – through someone else's perfidy – a load of chickens had gone missing, and he had taken the blame. Nevertheless, I liked Gerry. He was a pleasant man, full of preposterous claims and unexpected sensibilities. I explained that my plan was to cross the small coastal desert called the Wahiba Sands, and inquired if he had had any experience of desert driving. 'Oh yes, Sah,' he assured me, 'I am having plenty of experience of driving in the desert. I am driving many, many people in the desert. Don't you worry, Sah, I am knowing the desert very, very well.'

The next day we motored down to Minterib in the eastern part of the Sultanate, a sleepy town where palms bent the light into dapples, and blue water gurgled along the roadside in shallow troughs. Houses with walls the texture of cheese leaned on each other like exhausted combatants, and a broken water-pitcher lay in the street. A toothless old man was sitting in the dust in the shade of his wall: 'Eh? What's that?' he demanded when I asked him for directions. 'Going to the sands? Yes – just take this track – you'll get into the sands!'

We motored through a half-deserted village of scrapwood cabins, with camels and goats in pens of rusted wire, and women striding about in black robes and hawk masks. A sand-blasted two-seater Toyota pick-up passed us, coming in the opposite direction, driven by a black-bearded Arab who peered at us as he zoomed by. Within half an hour we were enclosed in swales of 100-foot jaguar-coloured dunes, riveted together by a rash of low scrub. A well-defined motor-track wove between the high sands for a while, but no sooner had it petered out than Gerry began to look worried. He edged the speed to 100 kph as if hoping to catch up with the lost track, and the vehicle began to bounce dangerously over ruts and slide unnervingly sideways on the flat.

'Gerry, please slow down!' I told him. 'Shouldn't you let some air out of the tyres?'

'Oh no, Sah! Quite unnecessary!' he said.

Gerry had brought a stock of cassette-tapes with him, and I quickly discovered that his idea of music was hardly sitars and classical Indian fugues: 'Cliff Richard, Engelbert Humperdinck – both Anglo-Indians!' he announced proudly. 'We've got music in the blood!' His tapes were lambada, country-and-western, slow rock. When we halted for an hour or so to investigate an interesting dune, I could hear the car stereo caterwauling at full volume from my place on its summit:

> It's four in the morning and what's more the dawning
> Just woke up a warning in me-eeee . . .

We trawled along for an hour or two until suddenly, ascending a sand-slope, the wheels started to spin. Gerry revved the engine recklessly, but let it stall. He twisted the starter, and the motor spluttered weakly and died. He twisted again: this time there wasn't even a splutter.

For a moment there was complete silence. Finally, he said, 'This should not have happened, Sah! But I'll get it fixed, Sah, I guarantee!'

He jumped out, lit a Gold Flake cigarette, and propped up the bonnet. I watched him tinkering with screws and cables.

'It is the clutch, Sah,' he declared at last. 'Something is wrong with the clutch.'

'Can you fix it?'

'Oh yes, Sah, I can fix it, I guarantee!'

He strode back and forth purposefully from cabin to engine for ten minutes, while I watched, impressed. Finally he paused, leaned on the front wing lighting another cigarette, and said, 'It is not the clutch, Sah.'

'What is it then?'

'It is the dynamo!'

But it wasn't the dynamo, either.

And already the sun was sinking behind the dunes, casting orbs of shadow into the narrow valleys between them. 'Why don't we try to bump-start it?' I suggested, digging into my poor store of strategies for stranded vehicles. 'Where's your shovel? We'll dig out the wheels!'

Gerry wagged his head sadly from side to side. 'I am not having a shovel, Sah,' he said.

'No one goes into the desert without a shovel,' I said. 'Didn't you tell me you'd driven plenty of people in this desert?'

'Not exactly *this* desert, Sah.'

'Which desert, then?'

'Well, actually, I am preferring to stay on the roads.'

'You mean you've never driven in the desert before?'

'Well, not exactly, Sah, no.'

To give Gerry his due, he did volunteer to walk off and look for help, though to me it seemed unwise to leave the vehicle. Instead we made camp, cooked up our supper, and waited for the morning.

Most of the night I lay awake straining for the sound of an engine. This desert might have been no more than a blot on the map of Arabia's Empty Quarter, which itself would have been swallowed whole, many times over, by the immensity of the Sahara. Yet the Wahiba Sands was still as large as Wales, and a dangerous enough wilderness to be stranded in with a useless motor-car. At first light I sat up to see the dune-crests peeking through gossamer mist that eddied around them like liquid. My sleeping-bag was so wet that the sand clung to it in globules. Light sliced through the ground-mist, carving it into smaller and smaller fragments until it disappeared and revealed the true contours of the dunes. For an hour afterwards it remained bitterly cold, then, all at once, the heat throbbed like timpani out of a sky whetted a perfect cobalt-blue.

Suddenly, I was certain I could hear something. At first it was no louder than the whine of a mosquito. I strained my ears again.

The whine was persistent, and it was growing perceptibly louder. I jumped to my feet and scanned the valley. Far in the distance a black comma was clearly visible under a tailback of dust.

The vehicle came directly towards us. When it was a stone's throw away, I recognized it as the same antique, sand-scarred Land-Cruiser pick-up that had passed us the day before, just after we had left Minterib. At the wheel was the same gnarled, black-bearded Bedui. The Toyota creaked to a halt and the Bedui leaned casually out at us. 'All is well, *Inshallah*?' he said.

'Yes, all is well, except our car won't start. Could you help us?'

The man stepped out of his vehicle. He was about my own age, a jaunty figure in a stained mustard-toned dishdasha, with hands and feet that looked over-large for the body, like a Mannerist sculpture. His nose was long and hooked at the end and his eyes were very alert. He shook hands and told us that he was Zaayid of the Wahiba, the largest and most famous Bedu tribe in eastern Oman. He opened up the bonnet of our car, inspected the engine, then leapt into the driver's seat and tried to start it. 'The battery is flat,' he declared. 'Someone must have left the key switched to ignition while the car was at a standstill!'

Within minutes Zaayid had expertly changed his battery for ours, and at the first turn the engine exploded magically into life again. The Bedui trotted around the vehicle letting squits of air out of each tyre. Then he took the wheel while Gerry and I heaved the motor-car out of its pit of sand. Afterwards Zaayid said, 'You have been lucky. Very few cars use this route. And praise be to God you didn't start walking – there is no village in that direction for a hundred and fifty kilometres. My place lies an hour away, over there,' he pointed, using both hands. 'You are welcome to come to my tent, rest, eat and stay with us – just follow me!'

For sixty minutes Zaayid handled his car with the consummate skill of a rally-driver, picking invisible paths through the dunes, vaulting over sand-humps, wrestling with drum-sand. Often he had to wait for us to catch up, and several times he took the wheel from Gerry when our car became bogged down. As he scurried back to his own vehicle, Gerry would gaze after him in admiration.

'This man is Bedu, Sah,' he said. 'They are very famous for their driving in the desert!'

Only a generation ago, I reflected, the Wahiba had known nothing but camels, and for centuries they had been distinguished by their camel-skills. Yet within only a few decades they had adapted to the motor-car and become equally distinguished for their desert driving. One technology had merely given way to another here, but the new technology had not destroyed them: the Bedu continued to be defined by this wild landscape of which they remained the masters.

Soon we halted outside a 'tent' which stood on a sandy stump among a seam of *ghaf* and arak trees. I had been expecting the traditional black tent of the Arabian Bedu: instead, I found a shanty timber shelter with a canvas roof surrounded by a heavy iron fence with a hinged gate. Outside, long-haired goats snuffled among the *ghaf* bushes and there was a single bull-camel, foot-hobbled and tethered to a tree. On a breeze-block platform stood a massive water-tank with a rubber hose, and nearby three or four oil-drums containing petrol. The sand around the camp was littered with the familiar crushed soft-drinks cans, discarded oil-tins, plastic wrappers, bits of engines, perforated cylinders and a rusty giant gas-ring from a cooker.

Under the canvas awning, though, it was cool and pleasant. Light filtered in through coloured cloth that had been stretched across the back of the tent, and we sat on a hand-woven rug against embroidered cushions. A mirror hung on one cloth wall, next to hand-tooled saddlebags of leather. Zaayid introduced us to his wife, a buxom woman, wearing a *burqa* with a curious ridge dividing the face. Two little boys clung to her skirts, staring at us with large brown eyes ringed with kohl. They were dressed in tiny dishdashas, and wore amulets against the evil eye around their necks in cube-shaped pouches.

Zaayid's wife brought in a mass of sticky dates, a giant vacuum flask of tea, and a pot of coffee. Zaayid poured the coffee, a spoonful at a time, in the traditional egg-cup-shaped bowls. It was strong and bitter and spiced with ginger. He continued to refill our cups until we shook them from side to side to signify that we were satisfied. Afterwards he asked if I would like a ride on his camel, and when I agreed he began rummaging about in the recesses of the tent for the necessary gear. 'I'm sure I had an old riding-saddle here,' he said. 'We do ride camels from time to time, but only for short journeys. For any important journey we go by car. When I passed you yesterday I was on my way to Minterib to get some medicine for my wife. That journey would have taken about four days by camel.'

Later, Zaayid couched his bull-camel next to his Land-Cruiser. As he went about strapping the saddle to the camel's rear, I asked him how the Wahiba derived their income.

'The work of the Bedu is rearing goats and camels, just as it was for our fathers and grandfathers,' he said.

'So the Bedu aren't only those who rear camels?'

'Maybe they say that in Saudi Arabia, but not here. Anyway, we could have houses in the town, but we decided to stay in the desert with our goats and a few camels. Now, when you get old, or if you are sick, the government gives you money, but not if you are young and strong. I worked for five years in Dubai as a soldier in the Defence Force, and another five years in Abu Dhabi. They are good countries, but not as good as Oman.'

The work of saddling was over in a moment: the saddle was, in fact, not the double-poled saddle of Jordan and Syria, but the more primitive south Arabian saddle, the *rahl* – the simple pad fixed behind the camel's hump. I sprang aboard and the camel gurgled in annoyance and rose to its feet. It was evidently unaccustomed to being ridden, for it twisted and wormed its head as I took the headrope. Finally, I jumped down into the sand. 'I think I'll walk!' I said.

A sweeping valley opened before us – flat, hard sand rising slowly up to low folds of dunes, pocked with calf-high vegetation and the occasional grove of trees outlined against the sky like parasols. We passed a well, where salty water was being pumped up by an electric motor. Zaayid pointed proudly at the green strips the Bedu had planted with melons and cucumbers.

A little farther on he halted abruptly and called me over to look at a series of sliver-marks in the sand. 'Don't move,' he ordered me. 'Hold the camel!' I watched him as he followed the tracks for a few yards with extreme caution, holding his stick ready. He raised the club slowly, then with incredible speed and force he smashed down at something hidden behind a hump of sand. He took a step closer and whacked down just twice more. Then he looked up triumphantly and beckoned me forward to see the mutilated coils of a puff-adder. 'Very dangerous!' he said. 'You can tell an adder from its tracks, just as you can tell a scorpion.' As we walked on, he drew my attention to some asymmetrical puncture-marks in the sand. 'That is a scorpion,' he said. 'His track is ragged, not clean like a beetle. Scorpions are very dangerous too. Sometimes their sting is fatal, sometimes not.'

Soon we came to another scrapwood and canvas shelter, where an old man with a face like a gargoyle was sitting in the shade of a tree. He was as thin as a cadaver, his features accentuated by their angularity. Pure grey locks fell from beneath his tight headcloth, and a spiral of beard sprang from his chin. He rose to greet us, his eyes glinting almost demonically in the sun, and tattled with laughter as I spoke to him in Arabic. He was wearing thick, ankle-length socks, almost as stiff as boots, woven from layers of black goats' hair. He noticed my interest in them: 'They stop the scorpions and the snakes,' he said, 'and they're good in the hot sand.'

Presently two youths appeared, wearing rust-coloured dishdashas. One of them carried a heavy air-rifle, the other a platter of chicken and rice, which he set before us. 'Come on!' the old man said. 'Eat! Eat!' And we crouched around the platter in the sand. The eating was a serious business, during which conversation was suspended. Afterwards, as the Bedu cleaned their hands in the sand, I asked the old man if times were better before there were cars. 'Ah!' he replied. 'Cars are so good! There's nothing like a car!' He pointed to the steel water-tank that stood next to his tent. 'We have drinking-water now, brought by car. Nothing like that in the old days. We had to bring it by camel, and it was always salty.' He nodded at two youths, busy cleaning the air-rifle. They go to school, now,' he said. 'They can read and write. Not like us. They go to school in Minterib. Couldn't do it if we had no cars. If one of us is sick, we can get medicine from the town. Couldn't do that in the past. All we had to cure sickness was camel's urine or a branding-iron. All nonsense! Children used to die and women used to die in childbirth. Now we can take them to hospital in a car. Camels are fine for riding short distances or for racing or for milk. Cars are wonderful. There is nothing like a car!'

Next morning Zaayid guided us across a sweeping sea of sand washing against purple table-tops, across acres of sand-scoops with thick veins of panicum grass and *ghaf* trees. Wahiba camps were sited on the dune-crests, flat-topped shelters of cotton spaced out one or two kilometres apart, surrounded by oil-drums and parades of sheep and goats. There were about 3,000 of the Wahiba living in these sands, making this tribe a tiny one in comparison with the vast tribes of Syria and the Nejd. In south Arabia, it has probably never been true that the Bedu tribes dominated the settled people, for they were always too small and weak. In north-eastern Oman, power lay in the mountains, which until the Islamic invasions were inhabited by Persians. Soon the dunes merged with hard shoulders of gravel boiling beneath the tyres and smoking behind the vehicle in trails of fine dust. Once, Zaayid waved excitedly and pointed north. Leaping through the low scrub were the lithe outlines of three Dorcas gazelles.

Zaayid parted from us at Hajjar, and for several days we pressed on across the stark Jiddat al Harasis. While the Wahiba had elected to remain in their fertile desert, the Harasis had withdrawn from these raw salt-plains for richer climes. I had searched southern Arabia for the spirit of the Bedu that had once lit the landscape like a flame, and everywhere I had encountered change. In places that spirit still hung on tenaciously, despite everything, but not here in the Jiddat al Harasis. Here the landscape was vacant, naked, meaningless, bereft of the people who had survived upon its scant resources for generations. True, there is no nobility in ignorance, poverty or disease. And yet those people – irrational, and superstitious perhaps – had had a sense of belonging in this unfathomed universe which we rational people will never know. At Marmul, I saw half a hundred steel pumps, like horse-flies, bleeding crude oil from the desert, acrid gas-flares trailing smoke from their chimneys like flags. Once, where these oil-rigs now stood, the Bedu had stayed alive by squeezing the dew out of rags left on bushes overnight. But that was in another country, long ago.

7

Miracles and Wonders

Our caravan departed at first light from a stony place near Mersa Matruh on the sea the ancient Egyptians called the 'Great Green': five camels – three male, two female – a Bedouin called Selmi, and myself, an Englishman. It was a crisp winter morning. The camels shivered as they marched, and their nostrils steamed like steam trains. They picked their way painfully through the stones, occasionally gasping as a sharp one prodded their soft-shod hooves. The smells were of camels, sea-salt, and the chalk and dust scent of the desert. Matruh – Paraetonium to the ancient Greeks – stood like a single whitewashed citadel on the edge of the plain, below a great slice of turquoise sea. The sky was heavy with foam-heads that waltzed across the horizon like dancing dwarfs and anthropomorphic elephants puffing smoke.

The landscape warped into deep gorges, where the local Bedu had built water-terraces to harvest the winter rains. Fig-trees and olives bristled there like green islands in a pastel sea of stone. The Bedu farms were dotted across the plain, flat-roofed dwellings of white gypsum blocks with fluffball sheep in pens of rusty oil-drums, and bony cattle tied to stakes outside. The ground was prickled with calf-high brush, and littered with mother-of-pearl snail-shells. This was the plateau of Marmarica or Al Duffa – a grey isthmus dividing the Great Sand Sea from the Mediterranean. Eight days' march before us lay Siwa oasis, standing at the foot of the plateau, the gateway to an alien world.

It is the very alienness of this desert that thrills me. I might have been born too early to explore Mars or Venus, but travelling on foot in this part of Sahara is an acceptable substitute. It has the loneliness of a primeval planet, where the very remoteness imposes a self-reliance meaningless in our automated landscape. For me, born on an overcrowded island on an overcrowded planet, where most life is sucked into the pullulating cities, the feeling of being able to walk for thirty days – even fifty days – without encountering a soul, a track or even a motor-car is a very special privilege indeed.

The desert may not constitute what northern Europeans have come to regard as beauty. But those who have known it have rarely returned untouched by its magic. Veteran explorer James Wellard wrote of 'An awareness of silence such as is never heard outside the real desert, neither in the mountains nor in the sea; a sense of timelessness that transcends even the sense of mortality; and a glimpse of the mystery of life in its most primeval form.'

To the earth's young civilizations the desert's great silence was awe-ful. The ancient Egyptians feared the Sahara. Their universe was a balance of matching opposites – life and death, night and day, light and darkness, the homely Black Land of the Nile Valley against the sinister Red Land of the desert. The Red Land was Ament – the country of the Dead. Out there lurked the unspeakable evil – the aardvark-headed demon Set, who ripped himself out of the belly of the great Sky-Cow Nut. It was Set who murdered his brother, Osiris, tearing his body into many pieces and scattering them through Egypt. It was Set who raped his nephew, the falcon-headed Horus. Set rode astride the desert's elemental forces, brewing up monstrous typhoons in the earth's bowels, sending the pestilence, drought, famine, the thunder, the lightning, the dust-choked wind.

The ancient Greeks, who made their first landfall in North Africa on Seal Island in 639 BC, regarded the desert as the den of the dreadful gorgon Medusa, whose look turned everything to stone. Perhaps this belief was nurtured by tales of petrified trees and fossilized animals. Medusa was a dark female entity from a lost era – one of a race of stone-age Old Gods that in Greek mythology were to be banished by iron-wielding heroes like Perseus. The Greeks were a sea-roving folk who had little interest in the desert's interior, inhabited as it was by savage tribes they called 'Libyans'.

To these ancient Libyans, Medusa was a symbol of the creative and destructive powers of the earth. She was the Earth Mother, possessing the undying power of the serpent that was able to slough its skin and continually renew itself. Far earlier, in the mists of prehistory, the Libyan tribes had conceived of nature's unifying spirit as a ram or cow holding the sun between its horns. Adopted later by the ancient Egyptians, the solar disc assumed profound significance as an image of the wholeness of life. For the Libyans each feature of the earth, each tree, spring, well, hill, wadi, stone or stream had its hidden spirit – each an aspect of the Earth Mother's power. It is these spirits which linger on in the deserts of the Middle East and North Africa as Jinns. Jinns may enter a man's head and possess him permanently. Their voices may be heard in the howling of the wind, the rumbling of the sands, the rasping of stones. A Jinn may call to you from behind a rock: if you answer you will be dead within a year. A Jinn may properly be seen only in a dream, unless it assumes the form of a ghoul – half human, half animal, with donkey's feet.

The Fellahin of the Nile Valley have inherited their ancestors' fears of the desert and its Jinns. W. S. Blackman has written: 'The vast solitudes of the deserts are terrifying to the country folk, most of whom, up to the present day, cannot be induced to traverse even the lower fringes of these wastes after sunset. Fear of hyenas and still more, fear of ʿAfarit (Jinns), forbids any man to venture beyond the cultivation at night.'

Below us a chasm loomed unexpectedly – steep sides lined with pointed stones like gorgon's teeth. I held the camels while Selmi shimmied among the slabs and pinnacles in search of a way down.

I waited, and my smoky breath mingled with that of the camels which were shifting and nuzzling each other's noses. Soon Selmi reappeared, a slim, graceful figure in his flowing jallabiyya. 'What do you think?' I asked.

'If God wills, we'll get down.'

We manoeuvred the snorting, trembling camels down, and suddenly a bloated sun plopped up miraculously from beneath the skyline, spreading a layer of molten light among the rain-heads. I saw the strange reptile crania of the camels outlined in a sheen of light, and then the sun vaulted into the saddle of my lead camel, Shaylan. For a split second it seemed to balance there, the animal bracing himself against its weight. Ancient Libyan rams had carried it, the Egyptian bull had worn it between its horns. Now it was the camel's turn. Down in the desert's depths, there still resonated the gorgon's song: 'I am the Sun that rose from the Primeval water. My Soul is God. I am creator of the Word.' Selmi followed my eye to the camel's back and for an instant his face was illuminated in wonder as Shaylan carried down his titanic burden.

For eight days Selmi and I marched across an endless flat black plain, where the horizons never flinched or flickered. The camels dragged their feet through crops of angular stones that glittered like rubies in the light of the lowering sun. The sky was leaden with moisture and the clouds furled and billowed like the sails of schooners. Each night we borrowed a piece of the earth – a little bit of Gaia – and furnished it with our familiar surroundings – saddles, jerrycans, panniers and firehearth, and for a few hours it became our own place, a cell of life on the eternal plains. Walking away from this spot at night, it appeared no more than a blemish on the earth's face, and farther away still it was swallowed by the darkness. Then for a moment I could savour the desert's vast silence, truly alone.

In the morning, when we had hoisted our mobile world once more on camel-back, the place reverted to the wilderness it always was. Only a hearth and ashes would tell of our passing.

For the first fresh hours we would walk, leading the camels or letting them wander before us. Walking at camel's pace, occasionally exchanging a few words, more often drinking in the emptiness of the surroundings, we could read the planet's surface like musical notation. Here were the traces of a shepherd's nightly camp: the scuff of sheep-tracks, the shallow depression where the man had lain down, the stumps of the roots he had used for fire. There were the tracks of a renegade she-camel, and there the dog-like prints of a Ruppell's sand fox. There were the tail-slithers of a sand fish, and the crisp nicks of an Anderson's gerbil. There were whole galaxies of the mother-of-pearl shells belonging to the unique edible snail of Marmarica that Bedu children had once collected by the bucketful.

Occasionally we crossed alkali-flats, ovoids of scarlet earth fractured into an intricate tortoiseshell pattern that appeared to glisten with a film of moisture. Once, I reached down to touch the liquid, but like much else in the desert it was an illusion, created by the play of sunbeams on a trillion trillion salt crystals that laminated its surface. Selmi chuckled as he watched me. 'The Devil's mirror!' he said.

To live and survive in the desert, one has to learn the desert's grammar – the syntax of the wind, stones, plants and animals. It is the language of thirst, and all around you see the pressures of moisture conservation. Plants mostly hug the ground and have contrived various tricks for cutting down transpiration. Their leaves are small and sometimes waxy, often able to curl up in the heat to reduce the surface area. They are widely scattered and push down long roots towards the water-table. Some of them – like the desert melon – store up water in succulent organs.

The Great Egyptian jerboa – *Jaculus orientalis* – is an essay in the literature of water-stress. Kangaroo-shaped with huge eyes and ears and sand-coloured fur, it can clear six feet at a bound, reducing contact with the burning sand. It is mostly nocturnal, though, curling up under its long ears during the day in a cool subterranean nest stoppered with sand. *Jaculus* never drinks, but can metabolize liquid from dry plant matter. In 1930, explorer Ralph Bagnold encountered a *Jaculus* colony in the Egyptian Sahara, in a region as lifeless as the moon. 'No vegetation, dead or alive, had been met for the last 220 miles,' he wrote, 'nor was any seen until we reached [ʿUwaynat] 200 miles further on. Yet a colony of jerboa kept us awake by hopping over our faces at night . . . What do they live on? Surely nothing but sand!'

The camel itself is a seminar in the process of water-conservation. It does not store water in its hump, of course, but rather uses its reserves with extreme parsimony. Under normal circumstances – when not being ridden fast or heavily laden – it will not begin to sweat at temperatures less than 40°C. It excretes very concentrated urine – less than a litre per day. Its large body – relatively fatless but for the hump – is a natural radiator that dispels excess body heat without losing water. The Bedu cannot do this, but instead they use the camel's unique qualities to export the water they need into the emptiness in skins or jerrycans. Waterskins are artefacts of great antiquity in the deserts of the Middle East and the Sahara. They have stood the test of time. They keep the water cool by evaporation but lose it by the same process. In this moistureless desert, the advance of the dreaded Ghibli can deplete waterskins with awesome speed. Selmi's Bedu still carried a few skins for the sake of coolness, but several near-encounters with death by thirst had led them to adopt the plastic jerrycan. They used the ten-litre jerrycan, which was easier to carry than larger ones and lost only a trifling amount if smashed by accident. Each of our camels carried four of them and we had our two skins as well. This 200-odd litres would keep us going for at least two weeks.

On the bed of another alkali-flat, Selmi discovered some heavy pieces of red pottery – clumsy sherds that looked as if they had been modelled by hand. He fitted together the two halves of a handle thoughtfully. 'Not the kind of pottery the Bedu use,' he said. 'It probably belonged to the Romans. We find their old houses sometimes.' 'Romans' was Selmi's codeword for the great blank page of the past. For him there was no distant past, only a hodge-podge of tribal legends and stories of raids and heroes. G. W. Murray wrote perceptively that 'The Arab looks at the desert much as the mathematician looks at his space-time continuum.' This is a view with much to be said for it. Often I felt we were not really alone here, but part of a continuing migration of souls across millennia. There were others walking beside us, divided from us only by the flimsy membranes of created time – an invention of civilization. Sometimes, walking silently in desert like this, I actually sensed the presence of someone else. I imagined footfalls behind me, mournful voices aching across the emptiness. Jinns, perhaps, but I was reminded of Eliot's famous lines from *The Waste Land* – the ones about the hooded figure in brown who is always walking alongside.

The Bedu are figures out of myth and folklore for Westerners, but in reality they are no more than ordinary men and women who have learned the lessons of the desert. These lessons are open to anyone with the humility to learn. People of almost every variety of race have adapted to the desert's harsh ministry, and enough adventurous Westerners – ordinary men and women – have survived T. E. Lawrence's 'death in life' to prove his statement mistaken. The Awlad ʿAli – the Bedu of this plateau – for instance, reckon part of their ancestry back to a Greek sailor who was cast up like Robinson Crusoe on the Mediterranean shore. If Selmi and I had walked here only thirty years ago, we would have seen their camels' hair tents pitched in basins around the deep rock cisterns the Romans built. We would have seen whole families on the move – convoys of camels carrying stowed-down tents, bloated waterbags, packs of firewood, braziers and cauldrons, urns and skillets, bedrolls, bundles, scrips and coffers, ropes, hobbles, bridles and halters, and women and infants rolling with the pitch of their litters. We would have seen tailbacks of dust trailing after mobs of loose camels and clowders of goats and sheep, driven by men riding lean stallions, cowled against the dust and carrying spears and antique rifles across their pommels. These were the

Bedu Lawrence Durrell described as 'tall, lean men, made of brown paper, whose voices cracked at the edges of meaning with thirst, and whose laughter was like fury unleashed'.

They hustled their livestock from the green hills of Cyrenaica to the gates of Alexandria – which until 1843 were shut nightly against them – straddling the caravan route that hugged the sea-coast. They scoured a living from the bitter soil, yoking their camels to the plough and sowing barley in the clay hollows in autumn, from which they reaped a good crop once every five or six years. Much of the crop – incidentally – ended up in the breweries of Burton-on-Trent, where it became English ale. They buried their seeds for the following year in secret caches and bartered the remainder for maize, honey, and dried dates in the Delta. In winter they netted quail on the beaches, and tracked down fennecs, jerboas, and sand fish in the desert. Women and children collected snails and sniffed out truffles to vary their diet of cheese, milk and unleavened bread. They also plundered caravans and robbed travellers, and had built up a profitable trade running hashish. Always feared by the Delta Fellahin, they were described in 1929 by G. E. Simpson: 'The presence of these desert wanderers near a village was always a source of anxiety as they may be hostile or more probably robbers . . . They pitch their tents where they choose, and at no time will they submit to any laws except their own.'

Though the Bedu of Marmarica once sneered at those who took up settled farming, 'losing caste among their kind for giving up the free, lawless life of the desert', as Simpson put it, the grandchildren of these same wanderers were now settled in the gypsum-block farms we had seen around Mersa Matruh. The few shepherds we had met marshalling woolly sheep on the edges of the coastal plain were the remnants of a people whose way of life was gone for ever. But their spirits lingered.

One evening, not long before sunset, we sighted a steel skeleton in the far distance, with a winking red eye. It was evidently miles away, yet our gaze was drawn to it. For days, since leaving the coastal plain, we had been entirely alone. Now there was a different focus of life on the bleak landscape, and our perspective was turned inside out. But the desert was too vast to be dwarfed by a steel mosquito, and the surreal, timeless feeling I had acquired on the journey remained. It was as if we were part of a science-fiction scenario. It was an oil-derrick – a tiny colony on a hostile planet, in which there would be crewmen in hard hats drinking beer in a thermostatically controlled environment, with freezers and moisture-seals, and all the paraphernalia of an outstation on Mars. We were the Martians – primitive beings stalking the lifeless peneplains with our pack-animals, suspiciously skirting these visitors from the stars.

The desert here was suddenly churned up by caterpillar tracks that looked as alien as if they had been made by robot-remotes. There were inexplicable impressions of oblongs and squares. Neither Selmi nor I could figure out what had made them. There were roadways marked out by wooden pegs, which with the disregard of barbarians we collected as priceless firewood. The downing sun illuminated a caravan of smoky clouds that migrated across the horizon. We stopped and unloaded the camels, heaving the panniers into a protective wall, setting out our rugs, saddles and jerrycans. Each item had its own prearranged place, and we laboured in silence. A few days had been all it took to work out roles. Selmi doled out grain in the camels' nose-bags, and I stood on guard with my stick as the hobbled animals made grasshopper lurches towards him. With the nose-bags hanging from their snouts they looked like weird Bosch monsters with truncated heads. Selmi lit the fire. I cooked pasta with bully-beef washed down with tea. Afterwards there were our pipes: the comforting gurgle of Selmi's portable hubble-bubble, the scent of honey-tobacco.

It was pitch dark but for that intrusive winking red eye, ruining our sense of aloneness. 'I don't like those things,' I said.

'Why not?'

'They destroy what you feel in the desert.'

'They don't destroy what I feel. They're only doing what my people do. We collect rock-salt. They drill for oil. What's the difference?'

There was justice in his argument. It was only a question of degree. Selmi's Bedu might quarry rock-salt for millennia and not appreciably change the face of the earth. But oil spelt cars and engines, roadways, asphalt and effluent: it meant snarling up the wilderness with human imprints, turning a pristine landscape into a building-site. Roads and engines brought sprawling breeze-block civilization into the last wild lands. But it was futile to argue about change. Change was the only constant in this universe. And the very ground we were sitting on, this desert where the units of history seemed to have no meaning, had been a vital proving-ground for the human race, a veritable laboratory of change.

It is clear now that the ghosts which inhabit this desert landscape are very ancient ones indeed, yet the antiquity of human activity here was hardly even suspected until, in 1930, prehistorian Gertrude Caton-Thompson and her geologist colleague Elinor Gardner began their excavations in Kharja. On the floor of the oasis depression they noticed a number of crater-like mounds with concave tops, packed by three-foot-thick plugs of sand-rock. Neither Caton-Thompson nor Gardner had ever come across their like before.

Slicing into one of the mounds to a depth of twenty-five feet, they were confronted by yet another geological enigma. The intestines of the mound were layered with alternate strata of clay, loam and silver-grey sand that appeared to have been violently disturbed and faulted. Yet the mounds stood high above the oasis bed and still higher above the water-bearing bedrock. 'By degrees,' Caton-Thompson recalled, 'it became clear that the [deposits] had been laid down by a spring of remote age, long ago dead or "fossil".' Slowly, the excavators began to grasp the monumental significance of their discovery. The layers of loam and clay had been built up during periods when the Sahara was far wetter and greener than it is today and the sand deposits marked the hyper-arid eras that had separated them. The Sahara had been green, not just once, but a number of times. In between the wet periods, drifting dunes had covered the valley, and the desert winds had scoured down the surface like an abrasive brush, leaving the spring deposits high and dry. Here, in the bowels of these curious mounds, written in dust and dirt, the biography of a living desert was laid bare.

Between 1930 and 1932, Caton-Thompson and Gardner eviscerated six such fossil springs, making a series of exciting finds. Cemented into the sediments, they discovered very ancient stone tools of the type known as 'Acheulean' – dating back at least 200,000 years. During a rainy period called the 'Abbassia Pluvial', the makers of these stone tools – not yet modern humans but a transitional phase between Neanderthals and *Homo erectus* – had wandered the prairies of the Sahara hunting big game animals such as elephant and buffalo. In the summer months they had retired to the lush verdancy of the oasis, subsisting on wild fruits, roots and berries.

The Acheuleans' art of hand-axe making was a technique that had survived unchanged for more than a million years. When you hold such a hand-axe in your palm, feeling the fine symmetry of its opposing convex faces and the intricacy of its knuckled surface, you suddenly become aware of the sense of beauty, balance and proportion that existed in an almost-human mind perhaps 2,000 centuries ago. Taking a hunk of chert or sandstone, the toolmaker would strike flakes from it with a stone hammer. When the core assumed roughly the right size and shape, he would trim round the edges with a piece of horn or bone, knapping off ever smaller flakes until he had produced a boat-shaped core with a long axis. The hand-axe, also called the biface, represents a combination of several ideas, and is a triumph of technical achievement. The Acheulean peoples of the Sahara also produced fine cleavers, choppers and scrapers; lacking the arrow and the stone-tipped spear, though, they probably drove or lured their prey into game-pits, where they slaughtered it with fire-hardened sticks. That they were efficient hunters is apparent from the vast period over which their tools remained unchanged. In the Sahara, though, about 90,000 years ago, they disappeared.

They were replaced by new men with a new technology which at the time was as superior to theirs as the helicopter gun-ship to the club. While the old Acheuleans had merely sculpted their stone cores into the required shape, these new men – the Aterians – learned to use the flakes struck off the core. This method – a small step in retrospect, but a giant leap for human culture – enabled them to produce light, sharp blades of predictable size. So light and finely tanged were they, the Aterians discovered, that they could be gummed or lashed to a wooden shaft. So the arrow and the stone-tipped spear were born.

It took a million years for the Acheulean hand-axe to become the Aterian spear-point, but technical evolution now seems to rush beyond our understanding at the speed of light, leaving us without anchor in a malevolent cosmos. To deal with this Niagara of change, we must develop a time-sense beyond our immediate perspective – we must be aware that tomorrow's history is today. Our industrial age is nothing, not even a blip on the screen of time – 70,000 million hunter-gatherers walked the earth before our era. And the Acheuleans were late-comers on the scene. There are campsites of *Homo habilis* in the Sahara desert which may be as much as 2 million years old. The great civilizations of the past – the Egyptians, the Persians, the Carthaginians, the Greeks, the Romans, the Arabs, the Turks, the British, the French – are mere flotsam in the tide, of no more significance than an Acheulean hand-axe lying on the desert surface. This oil-well was technology in direct line of descent from that hand-axe. Already there are museums for veteran cars and obsolete aircraft. One day this derrick would be shreds of twisted metal, and oil itself a fossil of a vanished age. And always the landscape remained, the raw fact of the desert before you, as Lawrence Durrell put it, 'the nakedness of space, pure as a theorem, stretching away to a sky drenched in all its own silence and majesty, untenanted except by such figures as the imagination of man has invented to people the landscapes which are inimical to his passions, and whose purity flays the mind'.

Near dawn on the eighth day we came to the place where the world ended. The flat plateau we had been crossing suddenly disappeared over the lip of an abyss in which whalebacks of basalt wallowed in a steam-bath of haze. The landscape shattered like a glacier into icebergs. The rock was sliced into sections to reveal bands of butter and cream, like the layers of a great gâteau. Stone icicles overhung and in places had fallen away, now lying in the chasm beneath like the skulls of tyrannosaurs. There was a subtle change in the air, sea-moisture giving way to the overbearing, spicy scent of sand. This was where the true desert began.

We heard rather than saw the sunrise. Vibrations of light and colour beat bars across the spectrum, a gush of curried gold rose in crescendo then fell away to the low harmonics of the desert. Half a sun, like an upended boat, irradiated in the valley the green promise of palm-groves, olive orchards and vineyards. Siwa oasis, a miniature paradise in the most hostile landscape on earth, sat like an emerald in the silver frame of its salt-lakes. After eight days' march across the wilderness with camels, no sight could have been more refreshing. We led the camels down a sand-slide to the oasis of Amun.

We marched past tilting palms, water gardens, palm-frond fences, soda-encrusted patches, gypsum-block houses, mangy military barracks with models of tanks outside. There was the sound of water purling in the gardens, water spilling out of iron spouts, small fountains playing sparkling colours like diamond prisms across the road. There was the moss smell of rankness, scents of humidity and humus.

Most of us recall childhood illustrations of oases – a few palms in the desert grouped around a neat pool among the dunes. Certainly there are oases in the eastern Sahara almost like that, but Siwa is ten times larger than Manhattan island and contains a quarter of a million palm-trees, over 1,000 springs, and is hemmed in only by salt-lakes that have steadily encroached since classical times on the good earth of the cultivated land. Close up, the oasis resembled an encampment in tropical jungle, chlorophyll-green against the desert pastel, with crusts of hills jutting from its canopy. The Old Town was a derelict tenement – salt-brick masonry being honed down by wind into wolf-fangs bared at the desert sky. To the east was the hill of Aghurmi, where the god Amun's temple had once stood, and in the distance the double plinth of Dakrur hill, where Siwans used to hold their annual orgy of garlic-eating.

The place was dominated, above all, by the bulging dunes of the Great Sand Sea – layer upon layer of carmine and amber sand, seething visibly to the tune of the wind and lazily a-boil with dust-smoke and the wild, shimmering colours of the new sun.

Buildings grew out of the desert and soon we were enclosed in unfamiliar corridors of brick and stone. We passed greasy petrol-pumps, a hotel, flat-blocks, gloomy civic buildings, a flyblown handicraft shop, a market sprawl of shanties, stalls displaying squashy tomatoes and green onions, flaps of bread, pressed squares of Siwan dates. Western tourists freewheeled past on rented bicycles, weaving among flat-bedded donkey-carts, driven by bearded men, and carrying cargoes of women bundled up in grey and black striped sheets from which, cyclops-like, a single eye protruded. Urchins chased behind us, poking at the camels, and a gaping youth drummed on our panniers, babbling in his ancient Berber tongue. 'What's the matter?' Selmi demanded in Arabic. 'Haven't you seen a camel-caravan before?'

'Only in books!' grinned the boy, and I was struck by the unexpected paradox of a Saharan oasis where only a Westerner and his companion would arrive on camels.

We passed gratefully out of the market scramble, into a cool tunnel cut die-straight through palm colonnades. Serrated fronds drooped low enough to touch, intertwining with the silver bladelets of olive trees, the fat fingers of figs, the shiny leaflings of oranges and limes. Sunlight spilt through the gaps and lay in liquid dapples beneath our feet. Green water bubbled along feeder-channels at the forest edge, and if you halted for a moment you could hear again the sacred sound of running water. The smell of it was everywhere. Suddenly, after eight days in desolation, we were assaulted on all sides by life that pressed with vibrant audacity through the palm-fibre fences.

We halted the camels in an abandoned garden, half enclosed by an unkempt mud wall. While Selmi attended to watering our caravan, I hired a donkey-cart, to have a look round the oasis. My guide and driver, a bark-faced old Siwan called Ibrahim, spurred on his bony donkey with judicious kicks from his bare feet, chanting, 'Get on, or I'll sell you to the knacker!' each time the animal paused. As we swayed through the latticework of light and shade among the palmeries, the old man waved his hand expansively at the trees. 'That's the real wealth of Siwa,' he said. 'They talk about tourists – but tourists aren't dependable like dates! When I was a boy the Bedu used to come and help with the date harvest – they would bring their camels and pitch their tents around the gardens, and there was always singing and dancing. I've seen caravans of three or four hundred camels leaving Siwa loaded with dates for Cairo, Alexandria and even Tripoli! That's all gone, of course. They send the dates in lorries now.'

Our first stop was the village of Aghurmi – once the main settlement of Siwa – where mud-brick hovels crouched among the ruins of one of the most famous sanctuaries of the ancient world. Little was left of the temple of Amun but a gateway, a façade and a tangle of blocks and broken pillars standing on an unstable outcrop high above the palms. Yet in the days of ancient Greece and Rome, this place was sought by all the great and noble of the world. Amun was the god of prophecy, and squatting here on his desert promontory, sampling the pure desert wind, he peered across the frontiers of time as a Bedui peers at sand-tracks in the desert: tracks from the past, tracks into the future.

To glimpse the shape of things to come – what fabulous power it implied! So valued was the prescience of the Siwan oracle that the Athenians – a major power of the day – kept a special galley on permanent standby to take their messengers across the sea to Paraetonium – the modern Mersa Matruh. Alexander the Great broke off from his campaign against the Persian king Darius to encounter the oracle personally: Cimon of Athens, laying siege to Cyprus in 445 BC, sent a delegation here to whom the oracle predicted Cimon's own death; Queen Cleopatra came here; Hannibal sent a deputation; the Greek athlete Eubotas was so assured by the oracle's prediction of his success in the 93rd Olympiad that he ordered a victor's statue of himself before the race (and duly won).

The oracle was not a man, but a shapeless peduncle of plaster, probably representing a human body shrouded for burial in the upright manner favoured by the ancient Libyans. Before the consultation a throng of priests would parade it through the palmeries on a silver barque, followed by a procession of maidens singing hymns intended to induce a favourable prophecy. The petitioner would then be called into the secret crypts of the temple, where the god's prophecies were relayed to him by the corps of priests.

The fame of the oracle lasted for almost 1,000 years – suggesting that enough of its prophecies were efficacious to allow it continuing credibility. The last classical traveller of note – the Greek Pausanias, who visited the place in the second century AD – discovered here a stela half buried in the sand, which bore a hymn of praise to the oracle. The poem had been penned by the lyric poet Pindar nearly 600 years before.

Did the oracle predict its own demise, I wonder? A later traveller, in the time of Plutarch, reported that there was nothing left at Siwa of importance but an oil-lamp that was kept burning the whole year – demonstrating, at least, the Siwans' continuing obsession with time. The priests told him that the lamp required less oil from year to year – proving, they said, that the years were becoming shorter.

Ibrahim drove me through tight streets of mud-brick and gypsum-block, looming canyons of buildings in lopsided galleries of pigeon-hole windows and doors like deep throats. Children tumbled in the dust, dogs yapped at us, chickens clucked, geese cackled, men leered out of open windows, women glanced at us slyly from under their shapeless sheets. We arrived back in the bustling market-square, where, leaving the cart, we scrambled up a steep alley. A studded palm-wood door swung open to admit us to the belly of the Old Town – Shali – into which almost the entire population of the oasis had once disappeared like clockwork every sunset. According to the *Anonymous History of Siwa* – a medieval manuscript still held by one of the old Siwan families – the oasis people moved here from Aghurmi in AD 1203. The oasis had fallen into a dark age since the oracle's decline – the Muslims had arrived. 'This famous abode of idolators met with complete destruction at the hands of God,' the manuscript runs, 'in storms and raging tempests of such a force as to overthrow the temples and their statues.' Of more concern to the Siwans of those times were the human tempests – hordes of desert Bedu – who hurled themselves annually on this green haven. The nomads continued to plague the oasis right up until modern times. 'Bedu from Libya used to come here to water their camels,' Ibrahim said. 'No one was safe until they got up into the cliff and locked their doors.' Until 1820, when the Khedive of Egypt took over the oasis and provided a measure of security, few Siwans dared build their houses outside Shali's walls.

The honeycomb of ruined houses resembled a Chinese puzzle of shapes, textures and angles. Floors had collapsed one upon the other, plunging holes had appeared in the centre of the winding streets, frayed and twisted beams hung out of the distorted walls like severed blood vessels. For generations, Siwa families had built upwards inside the girdle-wall of this fortress, each family expanding slowly into the limits of its space, until the hollowed-out hill became a warren of pinched alleys and tilting tunnels, so narrow that two donkeys could not pass. In this almost rainless land, a rare downpour could wreak more havoc than an army of raiders. 'We used to live here when I was young,' Ibrahim told me, 'but then a great shower of rain came that lasted three days. It only rains here once every forty years or so, but when it rains these mud houses fold up like paper. There were even people trapped inside, by God! The government declared it was forbidden to live here after that.'

'It must have been very hot and stuffy in here, anyway.'

'Never! These old mud houses were the coolest houses you could imagine. Not like the concrete ovens they build now. The high windows used to trap the desert air and send it down through the streets. That's why people went on living here even though they knew it was dangerous. Give me the Old Town any time!'

Desirable these close-packed homes might have been, but the claustrophobic conditions bred some dire internal pressures. Within these restricting walls, thick with the musks of men and animals, there festered two cliques of deadly enemies – the 'Easterners' and the 'Westerners' – who slugged out their differences in gun-duels on the wasteland beneath, exchanging shots round by round until one side gave way and the victors rushed into their houses, ravishing their women and stealing their chattels. When the British explorer W. G. Browne arrived here disguised as a Muslim in 1792, he was told, 'on the slightest grounds arms are taken up; and the hostile families fire at each other in the streets and from the houses'.

Later Ibrahim took me to a salt-island, about three miles from the oasis centre, across a slippery causeway through a snow-white lake of shimmering salt. The island was a jungle of palms and olives, where bronze doves crooned in the fronds, and wagtails skittered noisily from branch to branch. Within these groves was a cool glade containing a spring of crystal-clear water, gently shimmering up from about ten feet. Ibrahim showed me how the water was channelled into feeders that gridded the whole island. 'Every piece of land is granted so many hours of water according to its size,' he explained, 'and when each man has had his share, his feeder is closed off with a big stone and another opened.' The crucial distribution of water-flow was supervised by a man holding the ancient office of 'Water Bailiff', who was paid a tree's worth of dates or olives from each garden supervised.

Siwa was dependent for existence on its springs, but traditionally the Siwans had a superstitious fear of these doorways to the unknown. Al Maqrizi, the Arab historian who passed through the oasis in the fourteenth century, remarked that the oasis people were plagued by Jinns, who they believed lived in the springs and emerged each night in the forms of dripping devil-horses, ghost-donkeys and vampire-goats. The Siwans also believed that Jinns floated around in the atmosphere, and held to the supernatural power of the Ghibli – the south wind – which had, they claimed, saved them from invasion on more than one occasion.

As we rattled back towards the oasis proper, I decided to try Ibrahim on the delicate question on the *Zaggalah*. They had been bands of young men working as guards and labourers who were obliged to sleep outside the walls of the Old Town, and who had become notorious for their homosexual practices, including male marriage. 'They were just youths,' Ibrahim told me, 'the younger sons of Siwan families who were forbidden to marry. They lived outside in the hills and gardens and filled the nights drinking palm-spirit, smoking hashish, dancing . . . and you know. Of course, there's none of that left now.'

It was sunset by the time I returned to camp. Selmi had filled all our jerrycans, which stood in files like guardsmen on parade. 'The camels hardly drank anything,' he said. 'No God but God, what an animal! Eight days without water, marching every day, and still they won't drink!' We loaded up and moved out along the tunnels between the groves. The last of the light fell in heavy slats through the greenery and boiled molten on the surface of catch-basins half hidden in the trees. We passed the remains of Umm ʿUbaydhah, Amun's second temple, a nest of stone blocks scattered around a single standing wall inscribed with hieroglyph figures – men with Egyptian crowns, ram-headed gods, serpent-women carrying sun discs. This temple had been discovered by W. G.

Browne on his 1792 visit, but was probably a great deal more interesting in his day. In 1897 an Egyptian administrator had it blown up with gunpowder to provide stones for his office.

Further on, in the grey light of dusk, we came to the glade containing 'Cleopatra's Bath' – a famous spring of bubbling water which had been used as a bath by supplicants to the Siwan oracle – among them Queen Cleopatra, last of the Ptolemies. As we led the camels past, Selmi nudged me urgently, his eyes almost starting from his head. Floating in the water, face-up, was the gently paddling body of a completely naked girl.

'Is that human or Jinn, Omar?' he demanded breathlessly.

'Perhaps it's the ghost of Cleopatra!'

A little further on we discovered a bicycle of the type rented out to tourists, propped up against a palm-fibre fence.

'Omar,' asked Selmi, solemnly, 'did Cleopatra come here on a bike?'

8

The Opposition Stone

We camped for the night beneath the double cone of Dakrur, on the shore of the Great Sand Sea, and awoke in the freezing pre-dawn gloom to find the entire horizon dominated by yellow ochre dunes with domes and crests shadowed in limestone mauve. Yardangs of abraded rock poked through the sand-skin like lone teeth. There was no real sunrise, only a sabre-slash of crimson through the mainsheet of the cloud, then lasers of light cutting a trail of colours across the sand-slides. The low cloud had sealed in the heat, and soon the dunes were steaming with heat-devils. Before leading our camels off, we spared a moment's awe for the majesty of the sands. Here was Gaia's quintessential desert, not the largest sand-sea in the world – that honour belonged to Arabia's Empty Quarter – but certainly the most dangerous. This was a region that was at least partly unexplored. 'The easy bit is over,' Selmi said. 'This is where the journey really starts.'

We marched briskly up towards the towering crests, trying to get the blood circulating in our shivering bodies. Soft slopes folded around us and soon the bights and buttes of sand were manoeuvring like the limbs of giant amoebas to engulf us entirely. Suddenly we were in the zoophage's belly. No human mind could have conceived this fantastic architecture of planes and curves and angles. The dunes were spongy cell walls around us, flowing forwards, bellying out in bays and inlets, building up like globs of amino acids along a double helix. Without warning the camels began to flounder in soft sand, groaning and honking, picking their legs up as if trying to extract them from liquid toffee. Selmi and I rushed to jerk their headropes, plunging up to our knees in sand and wildly shoving them out. We moved up the dune in fits and starts, for the whole windward slope was booby-trapped with these sand-pools, some of them large enough to swallow a tank. You could not distinguish them from the solid going. We were so preoccupied with this drum-sand that we did not see the sharp fall of 200 feet that suddenly gaped at us from below. 'God curse the father of all dunes!' Selmi grunted, pulling back hard on the lead-rope, 'You can't see the drops. It's like walking in the dark!'

As soon we had the animals on the flat sand below, we squatted down for a cup of water. 'I can't believe anyone has crossed these sands by camel,' Selmi said. 'It's impossible going. If the dunes were spaced out with gaps between them it would be easy, but here one dune just opens into another. The camels will be shattered after a day of this, and so will we. And what about the direction? You say you can navigate in a straight line with your compass, but not here. We are wandering all over the place!' This was uncharacteristically pessimistic of Selmi, but I knew what he said was influenced by his experience. All his life he had been trekking through the relatively flat sand-sheets of the desert further south, with only the occasional dune. He had never even imagined dunes like this. And neither had I.

The Sand Sea was like the mythical labyrinth that led to the underworld – a maze of mirrors where every tangent, line and level was out of true. There seemed to be no perceptible pattern to these dunes, no recognizable system from which we could construct a mental map. So strange were the shapes and textures that you could really believe you had entered another dimension. As we trekked, the labyrinth symbolism kept coming into my head. The islanders of the New Hebrides had a myth that after death the soul sought out the gates of the underworld, where a female guardian sat with a labyrinth design in the dust before her. As the spirit approached she would erase half of the design, and the spirit had to restore it accurately to be admitted. Those who failed were summarily torn to pieces.

I knew that if we could not supply the missing half of the labyrinth map, then we too would be torn to pieces by the raw forces of the desert. In the Sand Sea we had no thread to follow but the ordinary human penchant for seeking out patterns. Nothing here was as it seemed. In the high sun the sand burned with a white glare, and there were no shadows to give dimension to the sand-shapes. Instead, our eyes mistook faint colour bands in the sand for non-existent contours. Impossibly acute inclines suddenly became gentle dips when we stepped on them. Bottomless shafts yawned like dragon-maws in apparently continuous sand. Blown sand cannot, in fact, assume an angle of more than 33° before it avalanches, but my eyes were telling me that these gradients were twice as sharp, and I had to force myself down against instinct.

For two days we laboured on through the labyrinth trying to discover its secret rhythms. Locked within the dunes, already as far from the outside world as was Hades, everything seemed larger than life, and I was seeing images of Selmi and the camels blown up as if on a cinema screen. When Selmi spoke, the words came out in big, bright bubbles, like cartoon captions. We crossed drum-sand that boomed like timpani when we broached it, walking on eggshells waiting for the next liquid cave-in. Sand crevasses were hidden behind soft sand-bars. Dunes were joined by narrow necks only knife-blade thick. The entire edifice of the Sand Sea was slowly changing form all day, moving like a rotating stage as the sun waxed and waned, obscuring shapes already familiar and highlighting strange new geometries ahead.

Actually, there *was* a pattern in these sands. The prevailing wind blew from the north-west, and the dunes further south had arranged themselves in chains along its axis. Here around Siwa, though, the pattern had been obscured by the greater depth of the sand and the local vagaries of the wind-currents. Oil company bores show that the sand here is up to 900 feet thick, the dunes overriding an enormous wedge of it that peters out to the south.

No one knows for certain where the dunes came from. For centuries it was believed that they had once been the floor of an ocean which had long since disappeared. In 1981, however, the space-shuttle Columbia, on its second mission, overflew the Egyptian Sahara. On its payload was a radar camera, SIR-A, which produced geological images by bouncing radar signals off the earth. Part of SIR's kilometre-long film was passed to geologist Carol S. Breed of the US Geological Survey, who was astounded to see that the radar had probed sixteen feet below the surface of the sand, to reveal the unmistakable pattern of a very ancient drainage system. A whole network of rivers had flowed in this hyper-arid desert more than 17 million years ago, a few of them passing beneath the dune-chains of the Sand Sea. When these rivers dried up in more arid times, their sandy beds may have been mobilized into the pattern of dunes that exists today.

To the explorer Ralph Bagnold, the dunes seemed to have a secret life of their own: 'some unexplained principle was at work, analagous to life itself,' he wrote, 'capable of doing repetition work on a colossal scale, or organizing innumerable tiny grains of silica into a family of vast creeping forms identical in shape and detail.' The dune-chains are ranks of ancient whaleback plinths, upon the shoulders of which sharp crests form out of the mobile sand blown up the dune face. The crests are the living spirits of the Sand Sea – they may ride forever on their parents' backs or streak across the erg alone, covering 300 feet a year.

We crept up yet another crest and flung ourselves down on a mattress of rippled sand, exhausted. The old camel we called Ghaffir – 'The Caretaker' – promptly slumped down next to us. 'I don't like the look of him,' Selmi said. 'There's something wrong. His eyes are dull, and he's panting too much.' I watched Ghaffir gloomily. We had carefully worked out our requirements in water, food and camel-feed with an ample margin of error – the one thing we could not have allowed for was foundering camels. Unlike Theseus on his search for the Minotaur, we had no unreeling line to follow back out of this maze. We could only go on.

Selmi led the camels off while I drove from behind, through quilts of saffron sand that split open to reveal strawberry sand beneath. Winds stirred ominously in the cauldron of the Sand Sea. The dunes began to quiver and wobble in anger. There was the rasp and buzz of sand-sheets grinding against each other, chattering and rumbling with the voices of the Jinns. We bent double into the surging stream of dust, tightening our headcloths around our heads, stomping on half blind through soft sand up to our knees. Mile after mile we plodded until my calf-muscles screamed with strain from the deep sand. Then suddenly, through a momentary gap in the dust-cloud, we glimpsed an inselberg of black rock winking over the dunes like a mirage – the only suggestion of solidity in the entire landscape. Selmi pointed to it, his motions as slow and ponderous as those of a diver. 'Let's get them over there, Omar!' he bawled. Reluctantly, I gave up all hope of following a compass bearing. Now, getting to that hill became our obsession.

Each time I imagined we had crossed the last barrier dividing us from the plateau there was another waiting, hidden by the phosphorescent skirts of the dunes. The sun grew hotter and hotter and my mouth became gritty and dry. Yet we dared not stop to think. The battle with the sand was sheer will-power, fighting with tortured calf-muscles and straining thighs. This was the hardest day's trek I remembered in almost 15,000 miles by camel. I tried to stop myself wondering what would happen if the camels collapsed. We worked our way up to the top of a candyfloss-pink dune, and the black crag of rock appeared before us. 'This must be the last one,' I told myself. 'We've almost made it!' We began to zigzag the camels down as the wind seethed in our faces. Ghaffir was the last animal on the string. Suddenly he pulled back on the rope and snapped it. He stumbled, hit the steep slope and rolled, twisting madly in a spin of head, feet, panniers and saddle, until he came to rest at the base of the dune and lay there, still.

We brought the rest of the caravan down, then ran over to the motionless Ghaffir. He was still breathing and there was a weak light in his eyes. Selmi pulled off the remains of the saddle and panniers sadly. 'It's over,' he said. 'He will never get up. We can do what we like, but he'll never again move from this spot.' I was tempted to disagree, to try anything, even lighting a fire under him as Arabs were said to do to revive foundered camels. But I realized that Selmi had seen this condition many times. There was no doubt at all in his voice. There was nothing we could do.

'Just leave him,' Selmi said. 'For us he's as good as dead anyway!'

I hesitated, shocked by the suddenness of death in the desert. Already the wind was building up seams of sand against the camel's flanks. This was, I thought, a terribly lonely place to die.

We dragged the remaining camels on, advancing with gritted teeth through the sand-spills and the abrasive wind towards the rocks. Occasionally we turned for a last glimpse of Ghaffir, his useless saddle and panniers piled neatly next to him like a monument. 'See, Omar,' Selmi said, 'camels will do almost anything to keep up with their companions, but he hasn't even moved!'

Soon Ghaffir was out of sight, concealed by the Sand Sea until some other foolhardy traveller – in God knew how many years – might happen on his bones.

The sand-storm had blown itself out on the last embers of sunset. We offloaded the camels and set up our comforting little cell in the emptiness. The camp felt a shade smaller without Ghaffir and we ate silently, nursing our apprehensions about the way ahead. The night sky was clear, but the temperature had dropped near to freezing. The camels were shivering under the old sacks we used to cover their backs. After the meal we smoked our pipes, Selmi wrapped in his home-woven rugs and myself in my sleeping-bag.

'It's my fault,' I said, breaking the silence. 'I could have stopped the fall. I was too slow.'

'It wasn't the fall that killed him, Omar,' Selmi said. 'It wasn't fatigue, either. This sand is hard going, but the camels have only been travelling for ten days, which is nothing for trained animals. The beast had something inside him – you could tell that from his eyes and his rotten breath. I think it was the sleeping-sickness.'

The words exploded in my head: sleeping-sickness – tripanosomiasis – trips – a flyborne disease prevalent in the Nile Valley and the Delta, that sometimes infected large numbers among the camel-herds being brought to Egypt from the Sudan. Its presence didn't matter to the merchants as long as they got the camels to market, for most of the camels at Imbaba were sold for meat.

'It comes so quickly,' Selmi went on, 'and you can't tell if the animal's got it before it comes.'

'Then the others might have it too?'

'Yes. They might.'

For the first time, Selmi looked really worried. 'I've seen it happen in the caravans,' he said. 'You can have five or six camels with the sleeping-sickness and they all go down. But on the salt-run we know every inch of the way because we've done it since we were children, and we leave caches of food and water for the way back. Here we're in strange country – we have no secret caches and no camels to spare. These dunes make my head spin. You said that you could find the way with your compass – but now you have no idea where we are!'

I had to admit that Selmi was right – indeed, had been right all the time. I *had* boasted about my ability to navigate using the compass, but I had never expected the dunes to be so incredibly dense and irregular. All the reports I had read suggested that they were arranged in 'avenues' and that one could easily travel between them. I knew that for two days we had not been travelling on a direct bearing, but wandering in a series of squiggles. I looked around desperately, and felt panic welling up inside me.

We were trapped in the labyrinth with a caravan of potentially sick and dying camels, completely lost.

Later I managed to get the panic under control, and examined the map carefully by torchlight. I picked up Bahrein, a small oasis somewhere to the east of us, where at least there would be water. The problem was that, since I didn't know exactly where we were, I should have to guess our position, with the possibility of missing the oasis entirely and ending up even more lost than before. 'I can find the way to Bahrein with the compass,' I told Selmi, with much more confidence than I felt. 'We'll be all right as long as the camels keep going.'

Selmi looked at me doubtfully. 'What's Written cannot be unwritten anyhow,' he said. 'All of us die – men and camels – when it's time for us to die. The name of every human being is written on a leaf that grows on the Tree of Life. When your time comes, the leaf with your name on it withers and falls. Then you die.'

I thought of a story told by Professor C. Vance Haynes, the leading authority on the eastern Sahara. Motoring in the desert west of Dakhla, Haynes had come across the heat-mummified remains of a camel. There was nothing particularly odd about this, except, he noted, that one of the camel's legs had been cut off, and was missing. A little further east he discovered the missing leg, and further on still he found the corpse of a man. The cadaver's skin was intact enough for Haynes to identify him as a Tubu or Tuareg rather than an Arab, and even the man's tattered clothes still clung to his bones. Since the man had been heading east, he had probably been fleeing from Libya or northern Chad, across unknown country, when his camel died. He had cut off and taken the camel's leg as food, but had soon succumbed to thirst. In the pocket of his rags, Haynes found a leather purse containing silver coins used in Libya during Turkish times – perhaps 100 years ago. The man had died a miserable death in country so hostile that even the vultures scorned it – no one had even laid eyes on his corpse until Haynes and his team had happened by, decades later.

Next morning Selmi told me he had been dreaming. 'I dreamed there were no more dunes,' he said. We marched along the edge of the rock wall, leading the four camels beneath crooked crags and pinnacles of ebony stone that seemed to have been stained by generations of soot. Soon, we found a tapering pass that led us straight up into the dunes. 'So much for your dream!' I commented drily. We plunged into the sand, which stung like freezing water. Gasping, we struggled up to the crest, to see an endless grey-black plain covered in sharp particles. The pinkish coxcombs of the dunes curved far to the south. Selmi regarded me with silent triumph. 'All right,' I admitted at last. 'Your dream was right after all.'

Things were looking up. For the first time since leaving Siwa we were able to mount our camels. As the sun seamed through the clouds, roasting the black spall beneath us, we slipped into the saddle by mutual consent. 'Aaah!' grunted Selmi. 'How good to ride after walking so far! Like water to a thirsty man!' We settled down to the pounding rhythms of the camels. The day was utterly still, and there was no sound but the slapping of water in our jerrycans, the creak of saddle-frames and the crunch of camels' feet on the stones. The percussion of their pace lulled me into a trance. I was absorbed into the timeless continuum of the desert.

Selmi hooted suddenly, snapping me out of my daydream. The plain had ruptured into a moonscape of black ridges, and on one of them, standing out distinctly, was a tooth-shaped mound – a pile of stones, the first sign of human existence we had seen for days. After being lost in the ageless dunes of the Sand Sea, it was almost like finding traces of human presence on the moon. For generations Arabs had left these road signs all over the Sahara. A pile of rocks maybe, but a cairn could give directions, warn, advise and even tell jokes. Coming across it like this you felt no time-barrier between yourselves and those who had made it: they were merely ahead of you – an hour, a year, 100 years.

Half a mile away was another cairn, then a whole parade of them, attracting the attention like a deafening shout in the silence.

Soon we came across camel-grooves, shallow, straggling curves that meandered gracefully between the ridges. Camels never travel in straight lines, but oscillate left and right, giving their grooves a serpentine beauty that bears no relation to the stark symmetry of a road. 'These tracks were made by many, many camels,' Selmi said, 'and not in a day or a year – in many years. They were probably made by the date-caravans from Siwa in the old days.'

Further on we found flat places where camels had knelt down on the sooty ground – the shape of their folded legs and chest-pads deeply engraved in the earth. On gravel serir centuries of desert winds could not erase a single track. Even the grooves made by Roman chariots were – until they were destroyed recently by rally-drivers – clearly visible in parts of the Egyptian desert. The minutiae of history were scratched in the desert surface as on a vinyl gramophone record. Each step of the way was imprinted with memories, and man was the needle that played them. The camel might have been superseded, but for us these camel-tracks were as significant as they were for the Arabs who made them long ago. The grooves sometimes passed through double cairns – stones piled four feet high, standing several yards apart. 'We call them "doorways",' Selmi said. 'They mark the edge of the way.' We both burst out laughing at this Bedu joke: doorways in an infinity of space – doorways into nowhere.

We arrived at the head of an abyss, where a camel-skeleton lay, a bag of barbed-wire bones and hard leather ligaments. A clear alphabet of signs led us down on to the valley floor, into a boxed arroyo whose walls had been weathered into bell-jar shapes. The valley opened out slowly, and our grooves drifted along the line of the scarp until they were absorbed by the sand. Selmi trod a wide crescent around us but came back crestfallen. 'Only God knows which way now,' he said.

'Look. These caravan tracks behind us – thousands of camels over hundreds of years – *must* have been going somewhere, and it can only have been Bahrein oasis. There's no other place the caravans could have found water and grazing!'

'How do you know? There *may* be other watering-places. The caravans may not have watered at all! And even if it's true, we can't follow the tracks. They've been eaten up by the sand.'

'Yes, but if I set my compass in the same direction, we are bound to see Bahrein sooner or later.'

Selmi gulped. He knew how questionable my decision was. 'You're the guide, Omar!' he said, at last.

We spent a restless night, both silently nursing our fears. The caravan-tracks had seemed a boon, but had they really been leading us towards Bahrein? If not, then my solution of setting a compass bearing on the direction of the tracks would only take us deeper into unmapped desert, where we would eventually flounder madly around in circles until our water ran out or the camels died, and we expired on the sand. I thought of the mummified corpse Haynes had found east of Dakhla, of Selmi's relative who had been so sure he knew the way, but had never returned, of Selmi's companion who had dropped dead while cooking a meal. I shivered. Once again, I felt panic hovering on the edge of my consciousness. I knew that in a totally alien landscape like this, the worst danger could come from inside oneself. Not only Westerners, but Arabs too, had succumbed to the terrors of this void. Even the seasoned Bagnold had described how easily one could be seized by the impulse to rush in any direction in a frenzied effort to escape from the soul-flaying nothingness, like a drowning man gasping for air. The most horrific story I had heard of the power of such terrors concerned three British soldiers in the 1914–18 war, who had strayed from their column in the desert south of Mersa Matruh when their light car had broken down. Having fixed the fault, they drove very fast in the wake of the convoy, only to find after several hours that they were without water and hopelessly lost. Then the terror had struck. Accelerating in panic, the sergeant-driver had crashed the car into a rock. The three men had begun the long walk back to the coast, but depressed by his failure or demented by a combination of sun, thirst, shock, and the terrifying sterility around him, the sergeant had drawn his pistol and shot himself in the head. Unfortunately, he had only succeeded in maiming himself, leaving the two privates to finish him off with their bayonets. Some time later the two soldiers were discovered by a British patrol, half dead and ranting, crawling on their hands and knees towards Mersa Matruh. Their water-bottles had been filled with the sergeant's blood.

Next morning was still and clear. We marched for four hours without a break, until we sighted grey cliffs on the horizon, and beneath them upright totem-pole figures wrapped in cocoons of shadow. We stared and squinted and shaded our eyes, thinking we could see palm-trees and even the outline of houses. 'Are those real, or just an illusion?' Selmi asked. It took more hours of agonized marching before the vertical shadows resolved clearly into palm-trees. This might or might not be Bahrein, but it was certainly an oasis. As we drew nearer still, Selmi observed that there were no signs of human beings – no litter, no power-lines, no sound of engines – just a ragged mess of trees, pieces of palm-fronds, old trunks, fibrous ribs scattered in velveteen sand. What we had thought were houses, indeed, were no more than the reflection of the sun on sandstone crags.

The final 100 feet seemed to last a lifetime, and then suddenly we were into the trees and leaping from our camels. We shuffled up a sand-ridge among the jungle of palms. There below us was a stunning sight – a lake of bluer-than-blue rippling water surrounded by reeds and palms and tamarisk-trees. On the surface of the lake, there were flocks of pink roosting flamingos. Selmi gasped, then held up his stick with two hands, as if it was a rifle, pointing it at them. 'We could have had one of those for dinner!' he said.

Later we hobbled the camels in thick *ʿagul* bush, and Selmi smashed his way enthusiastically through reeds to get at the lake. He hurled himself in, jallabiyya and all, and found suddenly that the water was only up to his ankles. Recovering from this surprise, he lifted a handful of the liquid to his lips with an expression of rapture – open water in the desert was a Bedui's dream. At once an intense look of disgust crossed his features. He spat the water out with a long 'Yuuuuuk!' looking at me with wide eyes. 'God's curse on it!' he said. 'This water is brackish!'

Afterwards we spread our rugs beneath the palms, unwrapping our pipes and settling down to enjoy this respite from the terrible Sand Sea. Watching the camels shuffling happily from bush to bush, I felt as if I was gazing back into history. Although date-caravans had not been here for thirty years, it was still possible to maintain the illusion that nothing had changed for centuries. 'You can tell from the state of the palm-trees that nobody lives here,' Selmi commented. 'There are still old dates on the trees. Nobody has harvested them for ages. Are you sure this is Bahrein oasis?'

'Where else could it be?'

'God knows, Omar,' he said, laughing. 'It could be Zerzura!'

I laughed with him, thinking of the abortive journey I had once made with a Bedui companion years ago, in search of Zerzura – the legendary lost oasis of the eastern Sahara. Supposed by the Arabs to contain fabulous treasures, Zerzura was a myth that reflected the peculiar Bedouin view of the desert. While ancient Egyptians, Greeks and Romans had feared those wastes, the Bedu always believed that wealth awaited them in the wilderness for the picking of the wise. There was wealth in the form of rich grazing at the desert's edges for their goats and camels, wealth in the form of trans-Saharan trade of which they became the masters, wealth in the form of salt which cost nothing, yet which in the heyday of the old caravans could be bartered weight for weight in gold. And if precious salt could be found lying in the sands, a bequest of some forgotten age, then why not treasure itself? Tales of lost oases and treasure-cities in the desert can be traced in the *Arabian Nights* and even in the Holy Quran.

'What do you know about Zerzura?' I asked Selmi.

'My father told me about it. A Bedui from Dakhla once tracked a lost camel-calf into the desert and found it in a green valley full of palm-trees and lakes, just like this. He roped the camel, and before he left he cut down a bunch of dates from one of the palms and tasted them. They were the best dates he had ever eaten in his life. He drove the animal back to Dakhla, eating the dates and dropping the stones on the sand, so that he'd be able to follow them back. He got all his brothers and cousins together and they saddled their camels and set off to find the place again. They never found the oasis or even one of the date-stones he'd scattered. My father said that Zerzura only opens up at certain times, which is why it can never be found twice, but if you know the right spells and if you make a sacrifice – preferably human – it will open up to you!'

The idea of a lost city in the desert that can never be found twice is a very ancient one in North Africa, and probably even predates the arrival of the Arabs. Writing in the first century AD, Strabo repeats a legend common in ancient Libya of a city of Dionysus lost in the desert sands that might be happened upon by travellers, yet which they could never find again. The *Anonymous History of Siwa* elaborates on this theme, recounting the tale of a group of men who fled from the Nile Valley and who were led by a wild ram to an oasis blooming with orchards and vines. The fugitives remained there happily for years, but yearned to make a last visit to their homes on the Nile before returning to live out the rest of their lives in the oasis. After visiting the river, they set out once again into the desert, but found no trace of the fabulous valley.

The lost oasis might have remained no more than an eccentric reflection of Bedu culture had it not been for the interference of foreigners. The story of the quest for Zerzura really began with a British traveller, Sir J. Gardiner Wilkinson, who visited Dakhla oasis in the 1830s and inquired of the natives what places lay in the unexplored desert to the west. Surprisingly, they listed two places called 'Wadee Zerzoora' – one of them five days' journey away, the other three. The latter was the first of a trinity of wadis in one

18. Husn al Ghuwayzi, Mukalla, Yemen. Constructed on a perilously overhanging rock, this fortress dates from 1884, when the Hadhramaut and its coast were in the throes of a struggle between the Kathir and Qu'aiti families for control of the region.

19. Sultan's Palace, Saiyun. Built in Indonesian style, the palace was the hub of Kathiri power in the Hadhramaut until 1967.

20. Ruins of old Maʿrib. This medieval town was built on the ruins of a much older and larger city which flourished in the time of the legendary Queen of Sheba. Once a flourishing caravan centre for the Bedu, Maʿrib is now all but abandoned.

28. Jibrin wad ʽAli. Jibrin, my Kababish companion on the journey to Selima oasis, works on his saddle-pad as we camp with a camel-herd bound for Egypt.

29. Old man of the Bishariyyin, Sudan. Occupying the Red Sea hills in the eastern Sudan, the Bishariyyin are of mixed Bedouin and Beja ancestry. They still live in palm-fibre tents and wooden huts like this one.

30. Bishariyyin woman serving coffee, Sudan.

of which grazed many cattle. Beyond these three wadis, farther west still, lay oases called 'Gebabo', 'Tazerbo', 'Wadi Rebiana' and 'Aujela'.

Of these four places listed by Wilkinson, only Aujela was then known to exist – a major caravan-centre in Libya's Jalo oasis, which had been visited by Friedrich Horneman in 1789. Almost a century later, though, in 1878, Gerhard Rohlfs discovered that Gebabo and Tazerbo were parts of the vast Libyan oasis of Kufra. In 1922, Ahmad Hassanein Bey and Rosita Forbes confirmed that a group of oases called Rebiana stood beyond Kufra to the west. Zerzura remained the only missing part of the puzzle. If all the other oases mentioned to Wilkinson by the Dakhla people existed, why not Zerzura?

The hunt for the lost oasis fired Western imagination. *Murray's Guide to Egypt* of 1896 mentioned four different possible locations for Zerzura, all of them elicited from the statements of Bedu. One story, reported by the explorer H. W. Harding-King, was that buried in a secret place near Dakhla were a mirror and a manuscript. The manuscript gave directions to Zerzura, and when one looked in the mirror the oasis would appear. In fact, there *was* a book containing directions to Zerzura which required no secret directions or digging. This was a fifteenth-century guide to Egyptian treasure-troves called *The Book of Hidden Pearls*, published in French, but originally written in Arabic. The book listed 400 sites in Egypt that could be discovered by spells and incantations, many of them believed to be mines of precious metals and minerals once used by the ancient Egyptians or the Romans, but long since forgotten. The book's reference to Zerzura as a white city with the effigy of a bird on its gate, in which a king and queen were asleep on a hoard of treasure, was to provide a tantalizing image to later explorers.

The quest gathered momentum between the wars, when Egypt became the backdrop for a cast of wealthy colonial dreamers, adventurers, scholars, surveyors, diplomats and royal princes which would not have been ill at home in the pages of Hergé's

Adventures of Tin-Tin. For this desert-venturing jet-set, Zerzura had become the *raison d'être* of their sometimes frivolous endeavours. Even the level-headed Ralph Bagnold was caught up in the romance. In 1930, over a few cold beers in a Greek bar in old Wadi Halfa – a town now lost under the waters of Lake Nasser – he and his colleagues founded the 'Zerzura Club' – an association that would flourish mainly over good dinners in exclusive London clubs during the Indian summer of that decade.

One of the most intriguing of the Hergé-esque characters of the 'Zerzura Club' was the self-styled 'Count' Ladislas Almasy, a Hungarian pilot who turned up in Egypt in the entourage of the Crown Prince of Liechtenstein. In 1932, Almasy re-examined Wilkinson's original account of the Zerzura story. Four of the oases mentioned there had been discovered since Wilkinson's day – only Zerzura itself remained an enigma. He perused the map with a pilot's attention to detail. If one were setting off in a straight line from Dakhla to the oases in Libya named by Wilkinson, he reasoned, one would almost certainly have to pass through or round the massif of Jilf Kebir – an island-sized inselberg in lifeless desert where archaeologists had found rock-paintings and pottery belonging to the forgotten peoples of the Sahara. The Jilf was not an oasis of the artesian type – it was not near the water-table – but Almasy learned that there were fertile wadis inside the massif, fed by the occasional rains. A reconnaissance flight over the plateau confirmed that there *was* rich vegetation there, and later he managed to enter the massif on foot, discovering two wadis full of blossoming acacia trees. Wilkinson's account had mentioned three wadis, however, and Almasy's conclusions looked doubtful until an old Tubu guide told him that a third wadi did indeed exist, and that the Tubu – black Saharan nomads – had grazed their cattle there for centuries. Since the wadis were rain-fed, rather than depending on groundwater, Almasy thought, the vegetation would persist for only a few years after a big rain and then, perhaps, die out. This would explain the disappearance and appearance of the Zerzura legend – the 'lost and found' motif.

It was on this uncertain note that the affair ended. Almasy assured himself that he had found the lost oasis – albeit a far cry from the white city and treasure-hoard of *The Book of Hidden Pearls*. Ralph Bagnold, master of the 'Zerzura Club', was less convinced, however. 'Assuming that Zerzura does not now exist,' he wrote, 'it may have done so once . . . at a time when rain fell more frequently than it does now, or it may have a foundation in reality, being the exaggeration of some small inconspicuous water-hole, difficult to find, but still existing; or again it may exist entirely in the Bedouin mind.'

Ironically for Bagnold, perhaps, the 'Bedouin mind' proved the cryptic clue which brought about the revival of the Zerzura question, long after he himself had left the Sahara forever. In his day it was well known that Bedu from Egypt – Selmi's people – hauled rock-salt from the Sudan. As early as 1909 customs officer Andre von Dumreicher had noticed the tracks of salt-caravans entering Kharja from the south, and had proposed to stop the salt-smuggling by reporting the Bedu to the Salt Monopoly. Dumreicher, like most of those after him, assumed that the salt came from 'Bir as Sultan' – one of the wells in Al ʿAtrun, which was the Sudan's major source of the mineral. Yet he was wrong. The Bedu had kept the whereabouts of the salt-oasis a closely guarded secret for generations.

In 1980, when Bagnold was in his eighties and most of the old 'Zerzura Club' long dead, C. Vance Haynes, Professor of Earth Sciences at the University of Arizona, made a surprising discovery. Exploring the desert north of Merga, in the Sudan, he picked up some unexpected camel-tracks. Following them for several miles, he and his Bedouin guide found themselves in a deep depression, whose floor sparkled with rock-salt crystals. In the depression they saw a well, and a caravan of black nomads digging rock-salt. The nomads told them that the depression was called 'Oyo'. Haynes realized quickly that this was where the Egyptian Bedu had quarried their salt, undiscovered for so long. The only vegetation to be found there was some coarse esparto grass, though a number of toppled and sand-blasted palm-trunks revealed to Haynes that the oasis had been more fertile in times past. Was Oyo – the last oasis to be discovered in the eastern Sahara – also Zerzura? Or were there other Zerzuras left to be found, one of them containing a white city with a king and queen asleep on a mass of gold, as the legend specified?

Haynes, one of a new generation of explorers for whom science and legend were merely data to be used to the same end, gathered up the scattered clues of the Zerzura story to create an overview that in its way was far more fascinating than the dream of a white city in the sands. Oases, Haynes said, were no more static than any other living structure – no more fixed than the desert itself. Like stars, bacteria, oysters and human beings, they had a life-cycle of their own. The oases of the eastern Sahara, he explained, were the remnants of an age in which this desert was a rich savannah roamed by giraffes, elephants, buffaloes, and many other creatures of the open veldt. The animals had watered at shallow lakes and water-bearing depressions, which had become the last centres of life as the Sahara unravelled into sand. 'As these [lakes] began to dry up with the expansion of the Sahara,' Haynes wrote, 'they passed through stages of lakes or open pools to marshes, to places where water could only be had by digging shallow wells, finally to complete dessication. After the final stage is reached the depression becomes a lost oasis, known only to tribal elders until it becomes lost altogether to human memory and is relegated to legend. Thus between 3000 BC and AD 1500 there were many potential Zerzuras in the eastern Sahara.'

Later, Selmi knocked some dates down from the trees above us, and we sat down to taste them. They looked dry and desiccated and dissolved into sawdust at the first bite. Selmi spat out the lees noisily. 'No, this can't be Zerzura,' he said. 'The dates there were supposed to be wonderful, but these are the most horrible dates I've ever tasted in my life!'

In the morning we led the camels up a red sand-hill to a sky skeined in salmon-pink wisps of cloud. All the way along the sand-folds, there were souvenirs left by previous visitors – shreds of camel-bone like polished teeth, an old tin trunk full of sand, a dead quail, and even the tracks of a gazelle. From the crests we looked over a landscape of luxuriant curves, tumbling in every direction. Gazing back down the dunes we could see now that there were two distinct lakes at Bahrein – two separate circlets of vegetation like dark scuffs on the virgin plain. Within the haloes of the trees, water flashed electric-blue in the sun. What we were seeing was almost a miracle, for in this desert-of-deserts the sun is so merciless that liquid is transformed into vapour at a phenomenal rate. The relative humidity in this part of the Sahara is reckoned at less than 2.5 per cent – which gave human water-pots like me and Selmi about forty-eight hours without recharge to be burned to a frazzle. How, then, could such lakes exist? The answer lay in the Great Invisible River – the water-bearing aquifers that underlie the vast area of the eastern Sahara, which are almost everywhere the same height above sea-level. Bahrein, like Siwa, is one of a string of oases sprawling along the northern rim of the Great Sand Sea on a fault-line where the aquifers surface. Qattara – the Sahara's greatest depression – is also part of this feature. Once a vast lake, it is now a salt-marsh in the process of maturing into a desert *sebkha*. Open water could exist at Bahrein, despite the terrific evaporation rate, because of the awesome volume of underground water recharging it.

The going remained too soft and steep for riding, but as we trawled steadily along the dunes, we were able to talk. I asked Selmi what he would do with the money I was paying him. 'I'm going to buy the concessions on some land,' he answered. 'I'm going to become a landowner – there's profit and security in land. There's profit in salt too, of course, but I've tired myself out with salt-caravans and camels. My family came from Sohaj in Upper Egypt. My forefathers lived in black tents and herded goats and sheep and a few camels on the edges of the desert, outside the cultivation in the Nile Valley. In the old days, before I was born, the Bedu used to move up and down the river. They didn't stay in one place, so they weren't subject to taxes or military service. Then the government said, "Fine. You want to keep moving, then keep moving!" and they refused to let the Bedu pitch their tents anywhere. They had to keep wandering all the time. The women and children slept in litters on the move, and they used a special brazier so that they could cook food on the camels' backs – that's my father's story, anyway. In the end, of course, they had to settle in one place. The government was able to grab them for military service and taxes. In those days, a lot of the land on the Nile was owned by a few rich families. Jamal Abdal Nasser ended all that by putting a limit on the number of *feddans* any one person could own, and that made land available for the poor. He started a big agricultural project at Kharja and Dakhla, which he called 'The New Valley', and the concessions on the land were going cheap. My father bought some and we moved to Kharja when I was still a baby. At first we lived in some mud houses right out in the desert, but when they built the new road from Kharja, they moved us to Baghdad.'

I had heard about the 'New Valley' Project. Dreamed up by Nasser in 1958, its prodigious aim was literally to create a second river Nile across the Western Desert, branching out from Lake Nasser and flowing into the Qattara Depression. The scheme had probably been inspired by the myth of the Bahr Bela Ma – the 'River without Water' – which since Persian times was rumoured to exist out here in the western wastes.

Herodotus had called Egypt 'the gift of the Nile', and only by traversing the vast empty landscape of the Western Desert, perhaps, is it possible fully to appreciate that fact. A mere 11 per cent of Egypt's total area is agricultural land, most of it situated along the Nile Valley. Nasser's vision was simply a new incarnation of an obsession with which all recent Egyptian leaders had been concerned – how to increase the agricultural potential of a country that was 89 per cent desert.

Nasser did not succeed in creating 'The New Valley' – the geographical obstacles proved insurmountable, and the visionary project had to be abandoned. Though large numbers of settlers – among them Selmi's family – were moved to the oases of Kharja and Dakhla, and new areas cultivated there, the pioneers had to depend on the faithful water-table that had sustained the population since the Acheulean hand-axe makers had moved into the oasis 200,000 years ago.

'Now, of course, the land in Kharja has become expensive,' Selmi told me, 'and a lot of the springs have given out, because there are too many people using the water. I'm not looking for land at Kharja, but at the new project at ʿUwaynat, where it's much cheaper.'

I gaped at my companion as I digested the irony of this fact. ʿUwaynat, an oasis lying 400 miles south-south-west of Kharja, had been abandoned by cattle-nomads of the C-Group 5,000 years ago, when the Sahara's latest arid spell matured. Now Selmi, the settled Bedui whose family were among the hopeful pioneers of Nasser's 'New Valley' Project, would play a part in reclaiming that long-isolated corner of the Sahara. The wheel turned once more.

ʿUwaynat remained unknown to history until 1923. It was in that year that Ahmad (later Sir Ahmad) Mohammad Hassanein Bey, with four Bedu companions, left the Mediterranean coast at Solloum to begin a journey that would take him 2,000 miles through unexplored territory, and turn into one of the epic camel-treks of all time.

Hassanein, an Anglophone Egyptian, graduate of Balliol, Oxford, fencing blue, boxer, friend and tutor of Egyptian monarchs, a 'gentleman of quality by the highest standards of any nation or time' – as one obituarist put it – might have come out of the pages of Lawrence Durrell's *Justine*. Before discovering ʿUwaynat in 1923, he had already won distinction as an explorer by reaching Kufra with Mrs Rosita Forbes two years earlier. On that journey he had come across the remains of a caravan that had perished, half buried in sand. A human hand, the colour of parchment, had stuck out of the sand, and as Hassanein's caravan passed, one of his men had reverently hidden it again. It had been a grisly reminder of the hazards of desert travel, and – like Selmi – Hassanein had sworn that this first desert trek would be his last. But the call of the unknown had proved too strong. Within a year he had been planning a journey into the *terra ignota* beyond Kufra.

The region through which he intended to march was a blank in space as well as time. It had been unknown to the classical geographers – Strabo, Heredotus and Pliny – and largely avoided by earlier explorers. No motor-car had ever penetrated it and no aeroplane flown over it. He had had little more to guide him than the assertions of his Bedu camel-men and a collection of folk memories. Hassanein was aware of the vague but persistent rumours of fertile lands hidden in the great desert west of the Nile, of the legends of Zerzura and the mythical Bahr Bela Ma. On his first visit to Kufra he had heard tales of 'lost oases' in the desert beyond – places which the local people knew only by tradition and hearsay. Two unnamed and apparently uninhabitable oases had been placed on the map – from the same hearsay evidence – by Justus Perthes of Gotha in 1892.

Hassanein sighted the hills of Arkenu – the first of these two oases – in the early hours of 23 April. Racked by exhaustion after an almost sleepless eight-day march from Kufra, his Bedu were driving the camels through a warren of plunging dunes when the mountains suddenly sprang up before them out of the dust-haze like a vision of enchanted Gothic castles. For Hassanein, this was the outstanding moment of the journey: 'I let the caravan go on,' he wrote, 'and for half an hour I sat on a sand-dune and let the sight of these legendary mountains do its will on my mind and heart. I had found what I came to seek.'

Within the rock walls he found a lush green valley, where his men made camp. As they sat down to eat, a party of Tubu nomads slipped out from among the boulders. Far from being hostile, they gave the explorer ample information on the second oasis – ʿUwaynat – where, they said, Jinns had left strange animal drawings on the rocks – 'Writings and drawings of all the animals living,' they told him, 'and nobody knows what sort of pens they used for they wrote very deeply on the stones, and Time has not been able to efface the writings.' Hassanein could hardly contain his excitement. After a crippling all-night march his caravan reached the hills of ʿUwaynat, and within forty-eight hours he had located the unique rock-pictures.

At this time no other explorer in history had laid eyes on such pictures in the Egyptian desert. There, careening over the rocks, like a shower of stars, were the shapes of wild animals no longer found within hundreds of miles of ʿUwaynat. There were troupes of giraffe with shimmering reticulate coats, prides of lion, scuttling ostrich, phlegmatic cattle, gambolling gazelle of many species. Skilfully etched on to the stone, a quarter to half an inch deep, the animals were so weathered in places that Hassanein could easily scratch off their lines with a fingernail. As he studied them, he was struck by two things. First, whoever had made these engravings had had no interest in – and therefore probably no knowledge of – the camel. Second, an animal which could not today survive in this hyper-arid country – the giraffe – was the creature most commonly depicted there, suggesting that it had once been plentiful. The only date which Hassanein had to work with was that of the camel's supposed introduction into northern Africa by the Persians in 524 BC. He concluded that not only must these pictures be at least 2,500 years old, but the environment here had been dramatically different before that time. Hassanein's discovery was startling. It was to be another ten years before Caton-Thompson and Gardner would investigate their fossil springs at Kharja, and give scale to the breathtaking antiquity of the Sahara's past. Hassanein had unearthed something of more lasting consequence than a lost oasis or a hoard of treasure – incontrovertible evidence that the most sterile desert on earth had once been green.

And if it had been green once, surely it could be made green again. The Suez Canal and the Aswan Dam had already begun to impress upon the Egyptians the regenerative power of twentieth-century technology. Unfortunately, it was soon realized that ʿUwaynat was not an artesian oasis like Siwa, but merely a hump of mountain high enough to trap the Sahara's rain-bearing winds. It was not until decades after Hassanein's death – in a motor accident in Cairo – that space-shuttle Columbia's state-of-the-art radar photography revealed reservoirs of groundwater in the desert to the east of ʿUwaynat. The water was of the 'fossil' type – the harvest of rains that had fallen here in prehistoric times – and was not subject to recharge from the water-table. This meant that, like Arabia's oil, it was a finite resource – if tapped, it would possibly last 100 years. Against the advice of some geologists, the Egyptian government – desperate for land as always – decided to go ahead with the plan to turn the desert into a new agricultural scheme.

'When I get my concessions at ʿUwaynat, I'm going to get married again,' Selmi said. 'My wife isn't interested in having any more children. She was very upset when one of our children died, but it didn't bother me. I said, "Don't worry, I can easily just ride you again and get another one!" I want to marry a girl like one of those we saw in Cairo. I've already told my wife that I want to marry again. It's good to have two wives – one working in the house and one always pregnant – that's how it should be!'

'Wasn't she angry when you told her?'

'No. I think she was pleased. We didn't get married for love, you see. We got married out of duty to the family. It didn't seem to bother her at all when I told her – but it's true that some women really go crazy with jealousy when their husbands remarry. There was a Fellah in Baghdad whose second wife died only a few weeks after he married – everyone said the first wife had poisoned her. I don't know if it's true, but women are perfectly capable of it. They haven't got the sense that men have, that's why they need to be kept in their place. There was a girl-relative of mine, for instance, who did very well at school and wanted to study at the university as a teacher. Then she would have lorded it over us, because we can't even read and write. Her cousin, who had first refusal on marrying her, was a tough man, and decided to take her for a wife. "I'll soon put a stop to this studying nonsense!" he said – and he did. Now she's a good wife with three children.'

'Why do you always marry your cousins?'

'Well, for one thing, the girl inherits some of the land and animals of her father – so if she married outside, the wealth would go to another family. Our women are very special to us. They are Bedu women – they wear the veil, dress in black, and can dance like Bedu. The women are ours – our property. I don't say I love my wife strongly, but if she did it with anyone else, by God I'd kill her, then I'd lure whoever it was out into the desert and slit his throat! The women are our honour. There are Bedu who take Fellah women as wives – usually second wives – but we would never, never give away one of our girls to a Fellah!'

I reflected that it was the Bedu passion for blood-lines, the endogamy which gave every man the right to marry his first cousin, the preservation of 'pure' genetic strains – which had so endeared them to Western aristocracies, for whom they represented the 'purest race on earth'. The *crème de la crème* of the Bedu were those tribes which were dominant, and whose members could recite their genealogies back in a direct line to a noble ancestor. That line had, they claimed, been preserved by continual interbreeding between first cousins. In fact, the genealogies themselves were in essence fictitious, and would be altered frequently to admit individuals and groups who had no blood-ties at all with the rest of the tribe – just as Selmi's people married Fellahin women. These groups and individuals would, of course, eventually intermarry with members of other households and so introduce new strains into the genetic pool.

The tribal genealogies were actually a political weapon. They were supposed to define the relationships between tribes – that is, which were 'superior' and which 'inferior' according to purity of blood – but were in fact constantly reconstructed to suit the power-relationships that existed at any given time. As one tribe or lineage grew more powerful, for example, the genealogy might be altered to show that it was in direct line of descent. If it grew weaker it would be moved to a peripheral place on the tree, and might eventually be dropped from it altogether.

A classic example of the process of rewriting genealogies can be seen in the Quda'a, an Ishmaelite tribe who fought with the Qahtanis in the civil war in Arabia in AD 680–84. As a result of their alliance with the Qahtan, they were magically switched from the Ishmaeli to the Qahtani side of the tree.

Far from displaying actual genetic purity, the genealogy was a diagram of those who acted together and felt themselves close, no matter what backgrounds they might originally have come from – it was a metaphor for the *de facto* situation. Glubb's edifice of Bedouin 'nobility' comes crashing down on this point. Such a quality can be assigned neither to 'pure' breeding, nor even to morally superior behaviour. It is simply an acknowledgement of wealth, prestige and political power.

'The family comes before everything to the Bedu,' Selmi continued. 'Whatever we earn – whether from the land or from the caravans – we give to my father, and he gives us back according to our needs. He'd be very angry if we held on to it. Only my brother Mohammad is outside the family, because he's such a spendthrift and he does no work. With this money you're paying me, though, I want to get the concessions on my own land, so that I can set myself up. I don't want to go on giving my father money for ever. The only time I did anything that wasn't for the family was during my military service. My father didn't like it, of course. He said my duty was to the family, not to the government, but there was nothing he could do. It was quite a good life – I got about a bit, saw different places, and we ate well. I was in the Border Police, so a lot of the time I was on guard duty in the desert. When the officers – university boys from Cairo – used to lord it over us and treat us as if we were complete fools, I used to pretend to be a bumpkin and half-wit who knew nothing – so as not to attract attention. They don't like Bedu – they know we look down on them – so I kept quiet. I smiled and nodded, and said, 'Yes, Sir!' but I knew there wasn't a single one of them I couldn't have left behind in the desert if I'd wanted to!'

I asked him if he really meant to give up the salt-caravans that had been part of his life for so long. He considered the question for a moment, then said, 'Only God knows, Omar. It's good to have land, but I doubt if the Bedu will ever give up camels. It's a question of balance. The Bedu in the eastern Sudan – our relations – have a great many more camels than us, but when there's a drought and famine, they might lose them all. It's better to have a balance between livestock and land, then you are more secure. The same applies with everything else. It's good to have motor-vehicles when you need them. They aren't good for everything, of course, but you'd look a bit silly going to the shops in Cairo on a camel. I admire modern things, but it doesn't mean I despise camels. Those Saudis we talked to in Cairo had all the money in the world, but they still love their camels. All my children will go to school – even the girls – because, while we are proud of our customs, there has to be a balance between the old and the new. The future belongs to the children. It's not my job to make a life for them, but it is my job to make sure they have a chance. It would be wrong to tell them, "No need for reading and writing," when every poor Fellah's kid can read and write. Only God knows what the world will be like tomorrow. Perhaps we'll be going to the moon, or perhaps all the oil will run out, and we'll be going back to camels again! Everything that has been or will be is Fate. I don't even know if I'll survive to get the concessions I'm after. Only Allah knows that!'

All morning we trudged, and the streaks of cloud that had decorated the cold dawn were licked down into a sink-hole hidden in the sands. The sun was left unshrouded and its fire blazed along the crests, shaking out heat-devils that smouldered all around us. Selmi was tirelessly magnificent, always jogging ahead, undeterred by sinking sand, ferreting out the safe ground, gauging the steepness of the slopes, tracing an easier path down the sand-slides. In the valleys between the dunes there were limestone blocks lying smashed like giant crabs scuttled on a beach. Along the dunes there were milk-white streaks – deposits of calcium flakes the size and shape of penny coins There were trillions of them, some lying flat on the ground, others arranged in groups with their edges uppermost like strange razor-blade plants. I picked up one of the larger plaques. On its upper side was etched the perfect four-petalled pattern of a flower. 'Beautiful!' Selmi commented.

They were fossilized spatangid sea-urchins. In a sea that ceased to exist here long before these dunes were formed – the Tethys Sea – this tiny creature had filtered limestone out of the water to construct its shell. Somewhere on neighbouring land, the roots of a tree had dissolved the limestone in the rock beneath it, and the rain had washed the solution down to the sea. Sunlight to plant to sea-urchin to ocean to desert floor. The spirit of Gaia wandered its unceasing migration between life and non-life and back again. 'A question of balance,' Selmi had said, and, handling this shred of the planet's history, who could doubt it? Life is a cybernetic system, a process of feedback, a question of balance. No one knows exactly why this desert has switched back and forth from green to arid over the ages, but the frequency of the change suggests that some vast regulating system is at work. Milutin Milankovich, a Serbian mathematician, believes that every 40,000 years or so the earth wobbles on its axis, changing the amount of heat the planet absorbs from the sun. The change is small, but enough to trigger off an expansion of the ice-caps: a new ice-age is born. Glaciers begin to move south, their glittering spines reflecting the sun's heat back into space like giant mirrors. This reflection continues the cooling process, and the colder it becomes, the further south the glaciers push. So much water is locked up in the ice that the sea-levels fall, reducing rainfall in some areas. The Sahara reverts to desert. Only after the feedback switch is tripped – perhaps by concentrations of carbon dioxide in the atmosphere, which tends to heat the earth – does the ice melt, and, for a time, rain falls afresh on the desert plains.

This happened last in about 10,000 BC, when the great Wurm glaciers that had covered Europe for millennia began finally to recede. Rain fell again on the sizzling plains west of the Nile, and enterprising pioneers – Selmi's spiritual if not genetic forebears – moved out to colonize the new lands. The shapes of these men and the world they knew – changing, always changing – appear on the rocks like Chinese shadow-puppets. For thousands of years pluvial periods alternated with arid ones. Somewhere, lost in the tempest of these fluctuations, hunter-gatherers became cattle-nomads. The Sahara's great lakes expanded and contracted as the warm-weather regime stabilized in other parts of the world. Finally, by about the third millennium before Christ, it was all over.

The anvil on which the most adaptive of creatures – man – had beaten out his skills of cultivation and pastoralism was lost, its ancient tracks forgotten. The tribes and cultures which once mingled in the desert were scattered and divided, the old contacts severed. The Sahara became a sea of stone and sand, its inhabitants stranded across it on islands called oases. Where elephants and giraffes had browsed in green forests, the Ghibli wind now spun drifts of sand. Where hippos had basked in mud, families of barchan dunes took root. Where cattle had mooched across grasslands, men now measured out their water cup by cup. Millennia later, paper-dry, wind-gnarled men with hawkish eyes and wizened faces would come dashing across the sands on strange beasts called camels. Robed and muffled, obsessed by the need for water, they would know nothing of the green world that had once teemed beneath their feet. The strange pictures they would find on the rocks – messages from a forgotten time – would always remain for them the work of Jinns.

Selmi and I were perhaps among the last of these sand-riders, as we kicked up plumes of dust down the dune-slopes. We halted between them to eat our midday meal – tins of sardines, hunks of dried bread green with harmless mould – and afterwards Selmi broke out his pipe. He was about to light it when he stopped, sniffed, put down the mouthpiece, and hopped to his feet. 'Look at that!' he cried, gesturing to the horizon. Pillars of dark smoke were moving across our flank like a forest fire. Pricks of grit struck our faces. The desert trembled as if a vast cart was rolling over its surface. 'This could kill us!' Selmi shouted. 'Let's get the camels moving!' Before we had finished packing, sand was screeching down on us like waves of harpies. We wrapped up our faces. Both of us were wearing three jallabiyyas apiece and woollen jerseys, but still we shivered from the cold. We stalked out into the clouds of sand like a jungle of reeds around us. Visibility was down to a few metres already. The whole desert was alive with a malevolent force. We dropped down from the dunes on to a flat serir, but still the dust-demons chased us, hacking at our heads, searing at the camels, rasping into our eyes, noses and ears. Underfoot the sand-billows were thicker and in places they moved in particles like huge armies of ants. We stumbled into soft sand and stumbled out, tripped over sharp rocks, cursing and shouting. Swell upon swell of middle-sand slapped against our heads. The wind was so strong that even the camels turned their heads away. For hours, all afternoon, we pressed through the storm. Suddenly Selmi yelled to me to stop. I looked round to see that the male camel we called ʿUmda – 'The Mayor' – was sitting down.

'It's the sickness!' Selmi shouted. 'He won't budge!'

We kicked and pummelled to no avail. The earth belly-growled, the sand slashed at our ears.

'Either we stop here, or we leave him!' Selmi croaked through his muffling headcloth. 'There's no way he's going on while the storm lasts.'

'All right. We'll stay here until the morning.'

Tonight there was no shelter behind our panniers. The wind whipped through them and around them, and we had to sling a rug from the backs of two camels to keep the sand out of our eyes. For almost an hour we struggled to light the fire before giving up.

As we scrambled into our covers and went to earth hungry, Selmi said, 'This is really the work of men, isn't it, Omar? Just think, if we'd stayed at home we'd have missed all this!'

The raw energy of this wind was terrifying, and I began to understand the power it had exerted on the minds of those who lived around this desert. For the ancient Egyptians it was pure evil – the spawn of Set – but the people of Siwa believed that the south wind had been their saviour several times, spectacularly in the case of Cambyses' army.

Cambyses II of Persia conquered Egypt in 524 BC, and in the same year sent an army of 50,000 soldiers across the Western Desert, on what was probably the first Saharan expedition ever to be equipped with camels. The force had been detached from the main column at Thebes, near modern Luxor, with orders to attack the Siwans, reduce them to slavery, and burn the oracle: 'The force can be traced as far as the town of Oasis, seven days' journey across the sand from Thebes,' the historian Herodotus wrote. 'General report has it that the army got as far as this, but of its subsequent fate there is no news whatever.'

The 'town of Oasis' – a week's trek across the desert from Thebes–Luxor – can only have been Kharja. From there, the troops might have marched straight across the desert to Siwa, or chosen the more logical route through the chain of oases that spans the Western Desert – from Dakhla to Farafra and into Siwan territory. 'When the men had left Oasis, and in their march across the desert had reached a point about mid-way between the town and the Ammonian border,' Herodotus noted, 'a southerly wind of extreme violence drove the sand over them in heaps as they were taking their mid-day meal, so that they disappeared for ever.'

In the morning we awoke to a cold, eerie silence. The sky was still glowering grey, but the storm had passed over, leaving its legacy of dust in everything. 'Umda was still alive, and after we had reduced his load to nothing, he stood up groaning. We strung the camels together and advanced over pasteboard-blue rock and pockets of soft sand. We lurched into another range of dunes washed clean by the storm, and Selmi pointed out something glowing brilliantly in the middle of the valley. From a distance it looked almost like a concrete bollard – but how could such an object have come to be in the sands? Selmi walked up to investigate it. He turned it over easily and then lifted it up for me to see. 'A pot!' he said in surprise. 'Who would bring a pot out here?'

I hobbled the camels and walked over to examine the object. It was a perfect amphora, pale cream in colour, standing almost a metre high with a narrow neck and side-handles – a water-jar, but certainly not a modern one. Its base was pitted and scored by wind, sand and time. It could quite easily have been here for millennia. Could it have been dropped by Cambyses' army, I wondered, when it passed here in 524 BC? Could the bones of Cambyses' soldiers lie under these dunes? The geography seemed about right. Assuming that the Persians took the logical route, it is likely that they met their fate somewhere between Farafra and Bahrein – somewhere around here.

Selmi called to me excitedly and pointed out the flash of white bones – hundreds upon hundreds of them – lying half buried in sand under a nearby ridge. The bones were clearly very old, for they were no more than slivers of polished enamel scattered for a great distance along the valley floor. It was impossible to tell whether they belonged to humans or animals. Selmi began digging in the sand with his stick, however, and soon pulled up a thigh-bone like a giant's clenched fist. 'Camel!' he declared. We hunted among the sands further, finding skulls, leg-bones and rib-cages that were clearly those of camels. Selmi pointed mutely to another nest of finds further on still – a galaxy of blackened hearthstones arranged in the triangular pattern used by the Bedu, and scattered around them the butt-ends of sooty sticks, a bent enamel drinking-mug with a hole in it, a pair of sun-browned sardine-cans, a twisted oil-can, even the heat-crushed corner of an old waterskin, and a fibre camel-hobble that fell to pieces at the touch. 'This is Bedu stuff!' he said.

On the way back to the camels, I examined the almost intact

amphora once more. Clearly, the Bedu camel-men had not brought such a thing with them. How old was this vessel? And again – how did it get here? Dumps containing pottery ranging in age from modern to classical have been found in other places in the Western Desert. In 1917 the geologist John Ball, on a military reconnaissance about 120 miles west of Dakhla, sighted a fin-shaped hill, around which he found dozens and dozens of earthenware pots, all but a few of them smashed. Some were of the style still used in the oases, while others were of ancient Greek origin. Why should so many water-pots be lying here in open desert, he wondered? Inquiring about this place at Dakhla, he was given an answer.

Ever since the dawn of history, Dakhla and her sister oases had been plagued by attacks from scavenging black nomads out of the desert to the west. One such raid had taken place on Farafra around 1770, when the bandits had carried off women and children. Another one had occurred around 1850, and on this occasion the Dakhla people had chased the raiders far out into the desert, tracking them to the place Bell named 'Pottery Hill', and discovering the cache of water-jars. They had smashed most of the pots, believing that they were used by the raiders for storing water. Since the presence of Greek amphorae suggested great antiquity, Ball was inclined to think that this water-store had been used by raiders since ancient times, and was itself the origin of the Zerzura legend.

I wanted to take the amphora with me, but, knowing that I would inevitably be accused of 'grave-robbing', and considering the state of our camels, I reluctantly settled for a photograph. Then we quickly roused the caravan and stepped out into the desert. Our stopping-place soon blended into the background as if it had never existed. Had we found a souvenir of Cambyses' army? Was there ever an army in the first place? Why should Cambyses, one of the world's most powerful kings, have concerned himself with an unimportant desert oasis such as Siwa, which posed not the slightest military threat to his forces? The

Victorian traveller Vivian St Martin suggested that Herodotus or his informants had been mistaken. He believed that Cambyses' real objective had been not Siwa, but rather the oasis of Dakhla, a reasonable ten days' direct march across the desert from Thebes. Dakhla had also had a temple of Amun, he explained, so the 'Ammonites' mentioned by Herodotus could equally have been the people of Dakhla. Other scholars quickly pointed out that, even if Dakhla had been a town of any importance in Cambyses' day – which it had not – its Ammonian temple dated only from the later, Roman, period.

Fifty thousand men with camels and all the panoply of war would have been a difficult skeleton even for desert as lonely as this to conceal over two and a half millennia, always supposing that there had ever existed a sandstorm powerful enough to bury an army, as Herodotus described. Historian Oric Bates suggested that an ordinary sandstorm had blown up and the Persians had panicked, killing their local guides and wandering around aimlessly until they died of thirst. Others have surmised that the guides were local partisans who had deliberately lured the column into the desert in order to abandon it there. Perhaps the whole story was concocted by the Siwans themselves as a warning to anyone who threatened their oracle. We shall never know for certain, until bones, armour and weapons are recovered from their putative resting-place under the desert sands.

For a while we trekked through a region where table-top plateaux succeeded one another in serried ranks, their walls in places gnawed out by erosion into fantastic pillars and dolmens like the relics of grotesque stonehenge temples, built by a race of giants. Soon, though, the plateaux fell away and we found ourselves in infinite black plains, unchanging mile after mile, hour after hour, day after day, inducing the familiar feeling that we were not travelling through space at all, but merely marking time on the same spot. On these plains there was not a single snail-shell, leaf or blade of grass. There was nothing to indicate that we were in Egypt or, indeed, on planet earth at all. Not only was there no life here, there was no indication that life had ever existed – no camel-grooves, no hearth-bricks, no droppings, no car-tracks. Instead there were stones, stones and more stones – stones like old apples with the cores cut out; stones like squids and sponges; stones like cast-off bits of iron in a welder's yard; stones laid out in patterns as if by children; stones like black and red billiard balls lying on mats of velvet sand. Then, abruptly one evening, a week after the storm, we were dropping down through carved and moulded sugar-loaves, beneath hills like wine-pitchers without handles, to another flat valley floor. In the morning we saw the wall of Jabal Quss Abu Sa'id, a forbidding 1,000-foot high amalgam of sheer rock and sand-slope, arching out of the newborn light. This was the landmark we had been searching for – the only recognizable feature in the whole lifeless desert.

It was at precisely this moment that 'Umda collapsed. Selmi managed to coax him up, but after a few minutes of staggering he went down again. This time, even I could observe the ragged panting and the glazed eyes that were symptoms of the disease. We settled him in a patch of sand, and Selmi doled out some grain and – as a desperate emergency measure – a little water in our cooking-pot. Finally we induced him to march again, and reached the base of the inselberg, turning east and trekking along its shadow.

For the first time in days we saw the evidence of rain – channels the water had carved out of the rock and patches of sand with sparse *khurayt* bushes. Selmi told me that it often rained in this area – once every few years at least! The sand turned to brown chalky soil, and there were low plinths of white plaster scattered across the valley like fungi. Unexpectedly, there were camel-tracks – not the grooves of ancient caravans, but fresh tracks and droppings made only a few hours ago. Selmi squeezed a black ball of dung between finger and thumb. 'Eating greens, these camels,' he said. 'Must be camels from Farafra!'

The ground underfoot became softer and softer. In the distance we sighted lines of pencil-cedars like smoke. Then there was the flash and sparkle of light on a stream of liquid coiling across the brown silt. I stopped and peered at it with shaded eyes, thinking that it must be a mirage. But further on there were knots of tamarisk-bush, and a great tract of marshland in a tangle of phragmites reeds. It was no mirage, I realized, but water, running in the desert. No sooner had the camels sniffed it than their heads jerked up and they were pounding towards it, pulling against the headropes for the first time since we had started. We had to run to keep up with them. 'Slowly! Slowly!' Selmi roared. 'Be careful here!' But it was too late. Already the camels were floundering up to their hocks in mud, slipping and sliding in the undreamed-of wetness. Three of them managed to romp through it to a drier patch, but 'Umda's strength deserted him. He lost his footing and plumped over, up to his armpits in the squishy soil. Selmi and I rushed to help him. 'Umda turned on to his side, struggled ineffectually, then lay still, whimpering. We began frantically to dig out the buried limbs which his struggles had only embedded more deeply in the mud. We dug down, and heaved on his back. 'Umda made one last tremendous rally and we heaved again. In a moment he had dragged his legs clear and half-leapt, half-slithered out of the quagmire to join the others on the solid ground. He looked a sorry sight, caked in sulphur-yellow mud up to his shoulders. 'It's criminal!' Selmi said. 'They make a bore and they're supposed to keep the water in a tank with mud walls, but the walls burst and they just leave the water running in the desert like that! There was a Bedui in Baghdad who got twenty-five camels bogged down in the mud in one day. He had to get a tractor to pull them out, but two of them died. Mud is worse than anything for camels, by God! Even the dunes weren't as bad as that!'

Soon we found a pool of open water with more stable banks, where the camels could drink with ease. The water, pumped from another deep bore, was clean and good, lapping around tamarisk and phragmites reeds, from which came the cries of water-birds. The camels lowered their great heads like cranes and drank – for the first time since we had left Imbaba, twenty-three days before.

Selmi filled a bowl and, as we took turns to drink, I watched a black moorhen gliding serenely across the pellucid surface.

Not long before sunset we came to a spin-off from Nasser's 'New Valley' scheme. It was an agro-project outlying the village of Farafra – a huge tract of whiffling green wheat contained in a basin like a giant bathtub, surrounded by a rampart of earth on top which an asphalt road had been laid. All around its rim soft limestone hills had been bulldozed and flattened. Inside the tub, jets of water foamed into the wheat from stand-pipes like huge maggots, and there was the constant burr of tractor-engines. As we led the camels along the base of the earth wall, a man came along the road above us, riding a bicycle. He did not wave or acknowledge our presence in any way. We had not seen a living soul since leaving Siwa, twelve days before, yet the first human being we encountered ignored us completely – it was almost as if we had become invisible.

We reached the corner of the agro-basin, where a gothic-looking pipe protruded from above, decorated with taps and stop-cocks from which water, dripping into the desert beneath, had produced a miniature salt-lick edged with reeds and a few stunted tamarisk-bushes. 'Umda chose this damp place for his demise. His eyes, inflamed now, were almost closed. He slumped down into the salty sand. Both Selmi and I knew this was the end. The sleeping-sickness, the cold, the heat, the hunger and the thirst, had finally finished him. He had already made a heroic effort. 'Pity,' Selmi said. 'It's only one more day to Abu Mingar. If he could just have made it there, he might have been saved!'

On the morning after the following day, we arrived at Abu Mingar, the settlement near Farafra oasis where Selmi's family owned houses and land. Ahmad, Selmi's elder brother, a slight man with an irrepressible smile, stood outside the house watching us descend from the plateau with our three surviving camels. He waited, grinning but composed, as we marched along the dusty track through squares of green wheat and *fuul*-beans, basking suddenly in the smell of rich earth, the trill of birds, the scent of water. Girls in brilliant red and yellow dresses came racing across the cultivation towards us. A Massey-Ferguson tractor, magnificent in scarlet livery, thudded to a halt, and the driver leaned out of the cab to shout a welcome. An escort of youths trailed after us on white donkeys. At Ahmad's house seven or eight Arabs were waiting to greet us. They helped us to couch and unload the camels, gathering close around us, shaking hands, greeting us with the double cheek kiss, exuding relief and palpable warmth. From the background, invisible women loo-loolooed shrilly and small, peanut-faced children peered around doors with saucer-eyes, crying, 'Selmi! Selmi is back with the foreigner!'

'I dreamed Selmi would come today,' said Hiroun, Selmi's uncle, a Bedui with a maudlin face and gold teeth. 'You are heroes, by God!' Selmi swelled with barely contained pride at this compliment, and I felt happy for him. 'But tell me,' Ahmad said, as he ushered us into the shade, and brought water, 'where are the other two camels?'

'How did you know there were two more camels?'

Ahmad grinned again, showing gleaming teeth. 'I got all the news at Imbaba. I arrived there the day after you left and ʿAlaysh told me you'd taken five camels. Now I see only three!'

We sank gratefully on to the rugs he had spread for us, and watched Selmi's younger brother, Salim, leading the weary camels off towards some mesquite bushes. Later Salim returned with a cartload of clover which the animals fell on ravenously – the first fresh fodder they had found for many days. Another Arab brought us glasses of scalding tea. As we sipped, Selmi explained how we had left Ghaffir in the Sand Sea, and how, only a day and two nights ago, at sunset, ʿUmda's strength had finally given out.

Abu Mingar was the end of the first stage of our journey. From here, we would trek across the open desert to Kharja, and then traverse the limestone plateau that divided the Western Desert oases from the Nile. Ahmad examined Zamzam, our grey she-camel, and announced, 'She's mangy. If you take her much farther, she'll flounder too!' Luckily there was a vet in the village, a young man called Salama who sported Levi jeans and a mock-leather jacket like a city tough but who was nevertheless politely deferent to the Bedu and their knowledge of camels. He puffed Cleopatras from the side of his mouth cowboy-style as he inspected the animal. 'Don't worry,' he said. 'It's not trips in her case. It's just a blood-parasite – oh, and quite a serious attack of mange as well!'

He produced a doctor's black bag and brought out of it a colossal hypodermic like something bought in a joke-shop. While Selmi, Ahmad and I held Zamzam's head, he speared her in the neck, puffing his cigarette and talking: 'Mange isn't a fatal disease. It's really a skin parasite – a sort of fungus that exists in the air and can strike at any time. It causes very bad irritation, though, and can drive the camel so crazy that it can't go on. Then it will die of thirst.' Afterwards he brought out three paper sachets marked 'Naganol', for the blood-parasite. 'I'll have to inject them all,' he said, 'because the parasite is highly contagious.' He asked for three tea-glasses, dissolved a packet of white powder in each, then filled the mammoth syringe and injected the camels in the jugular. Afterwards, as we relaxed over tea, Selmi and the doctor got into a heated argument about camel-ticks, which Salama said developed from eggs laid in the camel's hair, but Selmi asserted formed spontaneously from the camel's blood when it was exhausted.

Selmi's uncle Hiroun slaughtered a sheep for lunch, and we sat in the shade of the *mejlis* on rope-beds as we waited for the women to prepare it, smoking, talking and drinking tea. Mohammad, Selmi's eldest brother – the most experienced caravaneer of the family – was a mildly spoken, almost apologetic man, who seemed fascinated by Zerzura and *The Book of Hidden Pearls*. 'Yes, by God,' he said, 'the treasure of the Romans and the Pharaohs is still there. You only have to know where to look. I've heard about a well near Kharja, for example, in which, if you descend right into its depths, you will find a door. If you open the door you will find yourself in an old town, full of treasure. I know where the well is, but it's very deep and I've never been able to go down it.'

After lunch, he asked me to walk a little way into the desert with him and we sat on rocks warming ourselves with cigarettes in the freezing wind. He was a charming companion, and I wondered why Selmi had said that he was 'outside the family'. When I asked him about this, he was not at all abashed. 'I don't share with the rest of the family, because I found that I was doing all the work – I've been to the salt-place far more than anyone, for example – and I was getting no benefit. I'm hard up. Next time, you should take me on a camel-journey instead of Selmi. Do you know, I've got six daughters and no sons? It's all Fate, of course. I did have a son, but he died when he was four years old.'

'That's hard!'

To my surprise, he actually laughed. I could not make out whether it was to cover his deep anguish, or genuine amusement at my concern.

'It's not hard,' he said, 'it's the Will of God. It's no good getting upset about it. You've got to accept it. It's Fate. It's best just to say, "God have mercy," and accept it rather than crying and beating the wall like some do. We're all going to be dead as doornails soon enough – none of us knows when!'

We sat in silence for a few moments, then finally Mohammad came up with the subject that I suspected had been on his mind from the beginning. 'Omar,' he said, 'next time you come, could you bring me a copy of that book about buried treasure, *The Book of Hidden Pearls*? I'd really appreciate it.'

From Abu Mingar, we made a wide loop through the southern part of the sand-sea, skirting Dakhla oasis, far out in the desert. We trekked through the very heart of Set's country – through Daliesque rocks shaped like sharks and flying swans, fragments of human limbs, butchers-block leftovers, scraps of rusted steel, wafer biscuits, Henry Moore sculptures, wet-look leather coats. It was as if some great and terrible holocaust had swept through this place aeons ago. Were these stones the crashed fallout of some fantastic galactic star-wars; or dragon-bones; or the relics of dinosaurs, I wondered?

The cold never let up now. The days were the coldest I had ever known in the desert, so cold that my hands would tremble as I laced up my saddle, and Selmi would stand quaking helplessly for minutes after getting up, as if paralysed, holding a sack over his hands, moaning, 'It burns! It burns!' until I shouted, 'Get moving, for God's sake or you'll freeze to death!' We learned later that this had been the coldest winter in the Middle East for forty years.

We passed through a region of petrified trees – great gnarled and fluted trunks lying where they had fallen in the sand ages ago, looking precisely like sun-pickled wood, until you ran your fingers along their grain and felt the polished wood surface of old stone. As we walked among them I closed my eyes for a moment and imagined a forest in this lifeless spot. Trees with green canopies quivering above me, humidity, wet ground, insects, animals – it was all here but a moment ago, a heartbeat ago on the scale of the universe. The desert is a space-time continuum – time present and time past, present in time future, and time future in time past. There is no real difference between 1,000 years and 10,000 years, between a million years and a second. I imagined a hunter stalking in a forest here, my ancestor, carrying my seed in his loins. I opened my eyes and saw trees become rock, lying toppled in the sand. What would this place be like tomorrow, in a million years' time? Would there still be a creature called man, or would all his sound and fury have been burned out at the flick of a finger? If I closed my eyes again I could feel the planet's engines rumbling under me, feel the reflexes in my legs tense and relax, feel the earth's electric pulse moving in them, and the universe sizzling in and out of my head like magnetic power. I staggered on with these images spurling through my mind like water, aware of the desert and the camels' pounding feet, but at the same time only dimly aware. Slowly the vision faded and was carried off, leaving imperfect shadows on the shores of my consciousness. The desert did this. The desert restored equilibrium. For the 'Black Land' of the Nile to exist, it was also necessary to have the 'Red Land' of the desert. The existence of the wilderness is essential to the human sense of balance, for only in the wilderness can we truly appreciate who we are, how far we have come and how far we have yet to go. Red Land and Black Land – Horus and Set – desert and sown – wilderness and civilization – each was inconceivable without the other. 'We have long been ill-disposed towards deserts and expanses of tundra and ice,' Barry Lopez has written. 'They have been wastelands for us; historically we have not cared at all what happened in them or to them. I am inclined to think, however, that their value will one day prove inestimable to us.'

As for the Bedu, they are the supreme example of man's ability to adapt to a hostile environment without destroying himself. They are not separate, but merely ourselves in another guise. By living and travelling with them, we urban men can see ourselves more clearly – what we have gained, what we have lost, what we have yet to gain. No longer to be able to do so may be a tragedy for us, but not necessarily for the Bedu. They too must have the knowledge that there exists the possibility of an alternative life. The idea that development provides the answer to all problems – the myth of progress – is as inadequate as all other myths, but a ceaseless trend towards greater and greater technical sophistication is the hominid way. 'Nearly all of us have been told more than once by our tribal elders that things were better in the "good old days",' James Lovelock has written. 'So ingrained is this habit of thought that it is almost automatic to assume that early man was in total harmony with the rest of Gaia . . . [in fact w]hen primates . . . first formed an intelligent nest, its potential for changing the face of the Earth was as revolutionary as that of the photosynthetic oxygen producers when they first appeared aeons before. From the very beginning this organization had the capacity to modify the environment on a global scale.' To yearn for the past is futile, for the past is an illusion – no one knows in which direction it lies. And besides, while the desert exists, and while people herd livestock within it, there will always be Bedu. They may not ride camels or live in tents, they may not even be related to the Bedu of the past, but they will still be Bedu. For the Bedu are not ideal beings, noble people, elves or fairies. The Bedu are people of the desert.

After many days' march we turned due east, and, slugging on through the wastes south of Kharja, we climbed up into the limestone plateau at the pass of Dush. Old ʿEid, Selmi's father, who had made this part of the journey many times, had described the route to us: 'Beyond the pass of Dush, you will find two dead calves,' he had told us. 'Then you will find, next to the camel-tracks, a great stone, called the "Opposition Stone". In the old days caravaneers had to move the stone from one side of the tracks to the opposite side to show that they had passed. It was a kind of test of strength, because the stone is a very heavy one, and shaped so that only one man can lift it. After that you will come to a cairn that divides the way, left to Isna, right to Idfu.' We followed ʿEid's directions exactly, tramping past the skeletons of the two dead calves, and coming shortly afterwards to a single pumpkin-sized stone standing by the side of age-old camel-grooves – the Opposition Stone. I slipped down from my camel and lifted the thing, grunting with effort as I just managed to shift it from the northern side of the grooves to the southern side. Not to be outdone, Selmi jumped down and shifted it back. 'I wonder how long it has been since anyone moved it!' Selmi said, jogging back to his camel. And I realized that this was yet another time-capsule the Bedu employed to communicate across the hidden dimension. I wondered how long it would be till someone moved it again.

After almost a week's marching we descended a steep defile into a sheer-sided gorge axed out by water, aeons ago, which widened gradually into the rocky hammada that verged on the Nile Valley. One morning, just as we were leading the camels off from our camp in sight of the plateau, we heard the sound of engines. Selmi hesitated and stared south. I followed his gaze, and saw, racing across the hard gravel, the shapes of Land-Cruisers –

eight or nine of them – black and silver in the new sun, buzzing towards us in the heat, like flies. 'Those aren't army or police,' Selmi said, his eyes searching wildly around for non-existent cover. 'I don't like the look of it, Omar. They're coming straight towards us.' The drone of the engines was nearer now, and with an ominous appearance of purpose the vehicles sluiced out of the desert in their shrouds of dust, coming to rest in a rough semicircle around us. There were ten Land-Cruisers, new-looking, each containing one or two hatchet-faced men in long jalabbiyyas, tight turbans or woolly hats and sunglasses. Doors creaked open, and the men began to get out. As they did so, I saw that several of them were armed with Kalashnikov rifles. They watched us with the forbidding countenances of hawks. For a second no one spoke, then Selmi said, without any noticeable nervousness, 'Peace be on you!' The men replied in a grumble with a telling lack of enthusiasm, then one of them, a robust man with a dark face, like a Sudanese, waddled towards us, balancing his Kalashnikov. The others remained where they were.

'Where are you coming from?' the fat man demanded.

'From Kharja,' Selmi replied.

'What is your tribe?'

''Awazim.'

'And that man there,' he nodded towards me. 'Who is he?'

'He's an Englishman and he doesn't speak Arabic.'

'I see. What are you carrying?'

'Nothing, only camel-food. The Englishman is on a journey. The *Mukhabaraat* – the Intelligence Service – have given him permission. These are his camels.'

The dark man tensed at the mention of the Intelligence Service. He rubbed his chin with a bulbous paw. For a moment the tension was palpable. Then he snapped, 'Move on, and don't look at the cars. If anyone asks, you haven't seen us!'

'Of course,' Selmi replied, as we started the camels moving. 'It's not our business. Come on, Omar!'

We marched way from the semicircle of cars briskly but not as briskly as to suggest fear, putting a hundred, two hundred, three hundred yards between ourselves and them. 'Don't look back!' Selmi whispered urgently. At last we heard the sound of engines gunning and gears grating. Only after another interval did we glance behind to see the cars searing off into the haze of the desert. 'Who on earth were they?' I asked.

'They were ʿAbabda, Arabs from the eastern desert,' Selmi said. 'I know them. I could tell by their accent. Thank God you were with me, Omar! Only the fact that you were a foreigner and had the permission of the *Mukhabaraat* saved us. That's why I said you didn't know Arabic. Thank God, you didn't speak! If I'd been on my own, they would probably have shot me! The only people who drive through the desert like that are smugglers, and they think nothing of silencing witnesses. Who would ever know out here, so far from the Nile? Pray God they don't change their minds and come back!'

Selmi looked genuinely frightened, and I felt a thrill of adrenalin, followed by the sinking sensation that came with the knowledge that we had no weapons, and not the least chance of defending ourselves if they happened to change their minds. I thought again of the corpse found by Vance Haynes – so many secrets concealed in the desert.

'What do you think they were smuggling?' I asked.

'I reckon it was fish.'

Despite my apprehension, I burst into loud giggles, at which Selmi looked seriously offended. 'Good God!' I said. 'Tell me it was rifles or heroin or opium or anything, but don't tell me we stood to lose our lives for a few smelly boxes of fish!'

The minutes passed, the hours passed, and we heard no growl of engines. By afternoon we had drifted under great electricity lines crackling with power generated by the Nile in Aswan, on its way to light up Cairo. The camels mounted hard gravel shoals from which the earth opened to reveal the Nile Valley below us. 'There it is, Omar!' Selmi said. 'God is generous. When those cars pulled up this morning I thought we'd never make it!'

There were acres of green such as we had not seen in the two months of our journey, peat-brown mud villages, factories belching smoke, and, to the south, the river was a snake of quicksilver meandering around a leaf-shaped island. From this height, with the weight of 1,000 camel-miles of Red Land behind us, I could see the valley as it really was – a fragile strip of fertility in the most sterile desert on earth.

We passed out of the Red Land, following car-tracks, bulldozer-tracks, camel-tracks down towards the asphalt road that outlay the Nile, but before we had come within a few hundred yards of it, a decrepit pick-up screeched to a halt, and out dived five or six soldiers in battledress, led by an officer. They lined up outside the jalopy, rifles at the ready, with what seemed exaggerated drama. But I could see triumph on their faces – they had caught us red-handed, they were thinking, two ragged Bedouin smugglers with laden camels in the very act of reaching the Nile. The soldiers advanced on us. '*As salaam 'alaykum*!' I said. No one replied.

One of them – a heavy man with eyes of Afrangi green and a gingery complexion rarely seen in Egyptians – halted impertinently close to me, and shook a hairy, freckled fist under my chin, eyes flaming with righteousness. 'What have you got in those panniers?' he wanted to know.

'Listen,' I said, fixing my eyes on his, 'I am an Englishman and a guest in your country. I have permission from the *Mukhabaraat* for this journey, so I will thank you to speak to me with a little more respect!' The soldier's eyes registered disappointment. The fire slowly died within them. It had all seemed so obvious. The officer gave him a scowl and shoved him away. 'Your permission, please?' he said. I produced my carefully preserved piece of paper and he scrutinized it, then handed it ruefully back. 'There are a lot of smugglers about,' he said, half in apology, half in explanation for the rough treatment. 'Did you see any cars out there?'

'No,' Selmi cut in. 'We saw nothing.'

The officer directed us grudgingly towards Bimban, the

famous ferry-point on the west bank where camel-herds were transported across the Nile after their forty-five-day journey from the Sudan, to the camel-market at Daraw. We were in Upper Egypt, where the Nile Valley was wilder and less populated than further north, and where the river meandered through narrows dominated by palmeries, acacia-woods, and terraced limestone cliffs. We hauled the camels across the asphalt road, past a field where a phalanx of Fellahin with troglodyte faces and flowerpot hats were slashing down sugar-cane with bush-knives that glittered and brilled like swords as they advanced. Other men were hefting loads of cane on to the back of a four-ton truck. 'Where are you coming from?' someone shouted. 'From the Oases!' Selmi shouted back.

The men looked blankly. 'Where's that?' one asked. 'Is it in the Sudan?'

'No, no!' someone else answered him. 'The Oases are a long way. Near Libya. Libya itself, really!'

Selmi smirked. 'These Nile Fellahs only know the Sudan,' he said. 'They don't even know where the Oases are!' We followed the crags along the river, where a path had been beaten in the dust by the tracks of scores of camels going to the ferry-point at Bimban. Below us the sunlight formed a million gold dewdrops that rode like stars on the deep, sombre stream. We descended to a road that wound through more green fields – banana trees with their leaves burned copper-brown – trenches full of stagnant green water – palms with rustling feather heads.

We found a deserted place close to the riverbank to make camp. The acacias here were in bloom, and their caramel perfume mingled with the smells of humidity, dust and sweet earth. 'Every time I smell that smell – the scent of the Nile Valley – I feel drunk!' Selmi said. We unloaded near some trees on a shelf from which we could see the river scything east around the hull of the island. After we had hobbled the camels so that they could browse leisurely, we sat by the phragmites reeds that shrouded the shore, smoking our pipes, and listening to the glugging of water against the banks, like music. The sunlight fell in silk bars across the ripples. A felucca glided past under sail, like a floating flower. A bumboat breasted the current, laden with stones, shirts flapping like signal-flags from a line across its deck. Squads of cormorants with sheeny black feathers preened themselves on limestone steeples high above the trees. A black and white kingfisher, perched on an overhanging branch, made a headlong dive, splashing into the stream, and reappeared carrying a small silver fish. Suddenly a great pleasure-boat chugged into view, a floating white tourist-palace on whose decks sprawled men in shorts and women in bikinis. They saw us sitting there and waved and pointed cameras at the camels. Selmi and I shouted and waved back, rolling with laughter.

As the sun sank into an aurora behind us, the phragmites reeds were inflamed. The river sucked and lapped at the shore. From somewhere upstream came the poignant fugue of the Call to Prayers. To know fully the beauty of the Black Land, one must also know the hardship of the Red – it had been worth marching 1,000 miles across the most arid part of the earth, just to absorb that fact. The sun-disc was a delicate hyacinth-coloured ball spinning on the edge of eternity, its day's journey done. For a moment the great theatre of the world halted to watch its fall into Ament, the Country of the Dead.

9

Voyage into Nubia

Souq sounds washed through the window of my room in Aswan like a dawn chorus – the braying of a donkey, the rumble of carts wheeling down the narrow street, the constant gurning of voices. I awoke with the rags of a dream in my head, and for a moment I was disoriented. I recalled the streets of the bazaar the previous evening, the light slumping along them like liquid lead, the drift of blown sand in the gutters, the skirl of Arab music, baskets of dates, rolls of carpet, the smells of coffee and spices, a boy riding pell-mell on a donkey, yelling '*Baalak*!', an angular Sudanese camel-man still wearing the desert's dust, shouting at a shopkeeper.

I had to crank my memory backwards, pausing at each significant node – yesterday afternoon I had parted with Selmi at Daraw; yesterday morning we had sold the camels; the night before, we had slept in the palm-groves outside the market, and the night before that, on the riverbank. While waiting for the pick-up to take him back to Kharja, I remembered, Selmi had asked me a question, that, he said, had puzzled him for some time. 'How was it,' he asked, 'that you knew where to find us? I mean, we were the only people in Egypt who could have helped you on that journey, and yet you knew exactly where to come. How did you know?' There had been no time to tell him the full story then, but now, as I lay in bed, drinking in the sounds of the street, my thoughts returned to the Sudan, the country that, over a period of almost ten years, had become my home. I recalled that last journey I had made with Jibrin to Selima oasis, a journey that, in a sense, had begun here in Aswan, on a crisp winter morning like this one, when I had boarded the Lake Nasser ferry, bound for Wadi Halfa.

After breakfast I took the train to the High Dam. The morning sun was already burning the colours out of the sallow sky, purging the dam's long shelf of shrinking shadows. Seagulls were riding the thermals above the smoke-blue waters, and the wakes of giant catfish were circling along the hull of the steamer *Sinai*. The ferry was already at the quay with its barges lashed alongside, looking as if they might have graced a gunboat in the days of General Gordon. The Sudanese were massed to take occupation, a wild army of tall, dark men in gleaming white robes and turbans, standing amid humps of luggage. Egyptian officers in tight uniforms and peaked caps were strutting about with hands on hips, or posing to tilt bottles of 7-Up to their mouths with self-conscious nonchalance. The ramp crashed down on the quayside, and the signal to embark was given. The Sudanese struggled, twisted, elbowed, cursed, and thrust themselves into a crazy dogs-leg of a line, as if gathering for an assault. Already you could taste the wildness of the Sudan, a thrilling, otherwordly sense of the exotic that belonged to no other country.

By the time I reached the third class quarters – the deck – the passengers had already crammed themselves into almost every available nook and cranny, and many were already crouching around white enamel bowls, dipping their hands into Egyptian *fuul* and white cheese. I made my way up to the roof of the crew's cabins where an incredibly weedy, bronze-skinned young man in European clothes was already sitting. I took him to be Sudanese, but he introduced himself as Abdu, a Somali with Kenyan citizenship. 'It will be cold up here at night,' he told me in English, 'but for now it is better than being stuck down on deck!' Abdu's only baggage was a blanket and a black briefcase, which he opened to reveal, among other papers, a neat wad of air-tickets – perhaps eight or ten of them. My curiosity was engaged. It was impossible to say whether or not the tickets were used, but if they were not, why was this young Somali travelling third class on the Lake Nasser ferry? If they were used, why was he carrying them, neatly banded, in his briefcase? He plucked a address-card from the case and snapped it shut. The card read: '*Abdal Gadir: Khadija Islamic University of Angola*'. 'That is my work,' he said, 'I am founding an Islamic University in Angola.'

'But why Angola? It's hardly an Islamic country!'

'That's the reason I chose it. It is a communist country. There are no Muslims, but I hope we will make converts. We will teach all subjects, especially Islamic subjects, and all students will be welcome. I have been working on this project for four years, with only God's backing. I made a request for 150 million dollars from the Islamic Development Bank in Saudi Arabia, and from the Al Saud. They have promised to help. I am also expecting support from the Gulf countries – Kuwait, Bahrein, Qatar, and the others!'

I wasn't quite sure what to make of this. There was a fanatic, almost hypnotic gleam in Abdu's eyes which made me feel slightly uneasy. Were these delusions of grandeur, or a calculated confidence trick on the grand scale?

We watched the final passengers picking their way through the crowds on deck: two colossal women in pink *taubs*, their faces deeply etched with vertical Nubian tribal scars, exuding the fragrance of smoked sandalwood; some stick-dry camel-men from the Red Sea coast, who had just driven camels all the way from the Sudan; a tribe of dark-faced Nubians, carrying canteens of aluminium vessels fitting neatly inside each other like Russian dolls; a trickle of waxen-faced farmers wearing woollen hats, yakking incessantly over the price of dates.

At last the ramp was shut with a bang. The screw churned. A wet breeze snaked amid the tight-wedged passengers. A youth began to play an accordion, pumping out base tones – and a hum of repetitive bars spiralled around the deck in a swelling vortex. *Sinai* shook and rocked like an old motor-wagon out into the lake.

This lake – 'Nasser' to the Egyptians and 'Nubia' to the Sudanese – had grown out of the eternal Egyptian dream of controlling the restless waters of the Nile, on which the country's life depended. The ancient Egyptians had never discovered the source of the Nile, nor understood why the inundations came during the hottest part of the summer. They knew only that in the years when the floods did not arrive they faced starvation, and if the waters failed for successive years the entire edifice of their civilization might topple. From time immemorial they had sought to appease the Nile gods, but in the industrial era their successors aspired to conquer them through the miracles of technology. By the turn of this century, the demography of Egypt had altered little since Pharaonic times – its population stable at about 10 million. By mid century, however, the population had doubled, and would very soon be trebling. Egypt ceased to be the exporter of foodstuffs it had been for millennia: it needed desperately to cultivate new land. The solution was the High Dam at Aswan. Completed in 1960, the dam created a reservoir – the lake – which extends 500 kilometres south, covers an area of 5,000 square kilometres, and has brought 2 million acres of new land under tillage.

Abdu and I arranged our baggage, and looked at the baked-crust edges of the hills with their shaded terraces and flat tops, almost fluorescent in the high sun. The waters were curls of steel-blue, creamed along the surface with runnels of spume. Abdu told me he was on his way back from Saudi Arabia. 'When I got there the Saudis arrested me because I didn't have a visa,' he said. 'I told them I had come to perform the ʿUmra – the Minor Pilgrimage – not to try and get a job. They sent me to Riyadh, but they gave my passport to an air-stewardess with instructions to see that I reported to the authorities there. I managed to give her the slip at Riyadh airport and got away.'

'How did you manage that?'

'Easy. I have the power to make myself invisible.'

'Really!'

'Yes. When you reach such a high level of Quranic study as I have, you develop special powers. You see that this life and all the world are nothing. You should not fear any government – they are nothing. Only God is Great!'

'So you escaped by becoming invisible?'

'Yes, but after a while it wore off. I was arrested by the police and held in prison for nine days. I decided then that if God did not help me perform the Minor Pilgrimage I would resign from Islam. Then the Prophet sent me a message – it was brought by some pigeons which I saw from the window. The message said that I would be taken to Jeddah, and once I arrived I should say, "I'm going to Mecca. Goodbye!" and walk out. Well, the next day they took me to Jeddah in a prison-bus – it was a long journey, I was handcuffed, and the bus had no air-conditioning. But we had hardly got out of Riyadh when it broke down – this was a sign that invisible forces were working for me. At Jeddah prison I was surrounded by soldiers, but the moment they unlocked the cuffs, I said: "I'm going to Mecca. Goodbye!" and I simply walked out. No one lifted a finger to stop me! In the end I had an interview with the Sharif of Medina, who promised to supply me with twenty thousand copies of the Holy Quran!'

All this was related with a dead-pan face, burning eyes, and the perfect appearance of sincerity. Abdu fumbled in his briefcase again, and came up with another address-card. This time it read: '*Abdal Gadir: President: The World Security Council of Islam*'. Delusions of grandeur indeed!

By now it was midday, and the sun was a savage overlord in a sky unblunted with cloud. The heat reverberated back from the steel decks. I suggested a trip to the first class saloon – the only place where decent meals were served. We sat at a square wooden table covered in a plastic tablecloth bearing poor reproductions of Pharaonic tomb-paintings. The steward brought us omelettes,

Egyptian *fuul*, cheese, jam, fresh bread and coffee. As we were tucking in, Abdu asked: 'Why are you travelling to the Sudan?'

I explained that my interest was principally in the Bedu.

'That's interesting,' he said. 'I am a Bedui myself – almost every Somali is a Bedui!'

There was truth in this: though the Somalis were not Arab, and did not speak Arabic as their mother-tongue, they did fit into at least one definition of the Bedu – as nomads who lived in the desert. Even in south Arabia, Somalis were considered tribesmen and counted as being on a par with the noble Bedu tribes. And Somalia was the world's leading producer of camels – with 3 million head, it outstripped even the Sudan. 'I was a camel-boy until I was eleven years old,' Abdu went on. 'I was born the last child of a woman called Halima. She had produced four children before me – three boys and a girl – but the boys all died, so my father divorced her while she was pregnant with me, and married a woman called Hawa. When I was small my sister and I were sent to live with Hawa, who had children of her own. They were younger than us, but bigger and stronger, so they used to beat us. Hawa used to water down our camel's milk so that we would always be weak. When I was about seven, I rebelled, and of course Hawa had been waiting for this excuse to attack me. She choked me until I wet myself and fainted. But my sister ran to call a neighbour – an old man – who stopped her going further, otherwise she would surely have killed me! Later, my mother, Halima, arrived at our camp, and heard the story, but said nothing. The same day we were moving pasture, and she packed her camels and moved out with us. Out in the bush, mother stopped and tied her camels to a tree. Then she thrashed the living daylights out of Hawa with her fists and feet. "That's a lesson to you for beating my children!" she said. Hawa couldn't resist her, because my mother was big and very strong, and Hawa was afraid of getting a worse beating. Mother just laid her on the back of one of the camels and led them to a new camp, where my father was to be found. She told him what had happened and that she was taking my sister and me with her: "If you want to fight, I'm ready to take you on," she told him, but my father was aware of her strength and of the shame of being beaten by a woman, and let us go. After that we went to live with my grandfather at Al Wak.'

Later, we were invited to the crew's quarters below decks by a galley-mate with one blind eye, who claimed to have served with the British army. He brought us tea, while five men in sneakers and torn trousers, crammed around a tiny table, played dominoes, shuffling and reshuffling the plastic pieces, creating ever new configurations on the table, slapping them down with terrific force as if trying to intimidate each other into submission, keeping up an endless current of banter as they played. Near sunset we were back on our perch, as the steamer approached Abu Simbel – a great protrusion of rock from which the famous temple of Amun-Ra emerged, its vast statues of Ramses II staring with blind eyes and self-satisfied expressions through the sea-damp aura. Centuries after these colossi had first been hauled into place by the Pharaoh's slaves, parties of men whose tribes and tongues had not even existed in Ramses' day had sawed the old temple to pieces, moved the pieces with machines, and glued the entire structure together only 200 feet from where it had always stood.

Before the 1960s, the long stretch of river between Aswan and Wadi Halfa, now uninhabited, had been a living, flourishing land of palm-groves and mud-built villages, the homeland of more than 100,000 Nubian Fellahin. Half of them were officially Egyptian, half Sudanese, but they shared languages and a culture which had survived the ragbag of races – including the Arabs – they had absorbed from the outside world. The villages and palm-groves had been drowned by the waters of the lake and the tribesmen transplanted, the Egyptians to Kom Ombo, north of Aswan, and the Sudanese to New Halfa, in the semi-arid plains of the eastern Sudan.

The sky was painted suddenly with clouds like bats' wings, and a thousand little rivulets of fire slipped along the darkening waters. As the day melted into methyl orange along the banks, I reflected that it was on this route that Bedu warriors first entered the Sudan, soon after they had conquered Egypt in AD 642. In Nubia they encountered a very different enemy from the enfeebled Byzantine regiments they had so recently defeated in the Delta. In Egypt, the Byzantine rulers had lacked the vital support of the Christian natives, some of whom welcomed the Arabs as their deliverers. The Christian kingdoms of Nubia, however, were indigenous and well organized, accustomed to defending their borders against Egyptian incursions. Their bowmen – the famed 'Nubian archers' – proved doughty foes, as the Arab historian Al Baladhuri recalled: 'I saw one of them [a Nubian] saying to a Muslim, "where would you like me to place my arrow in you?" and when the Muslim replied "in such-and-such a place," he would not miss.' As a result of such haughty skill, the Arabs returned 'with many injured and blinded eyes, so that the Nubians were called "the pupil smiters".'

In time, the Arabs had abandoned the idea of conquering the *Bilad as Sudan* – the 'Land of the Blacks' – and instead concluded a treaty with the Christian king whose capital lay at Old Dongola, on the east bank of the Nile. The Nubians agreed to pay a number of slaves annually to the Arabs, and to allow Muslim traders access to their markets without hindrance, in return for immunity from attack, and quantities of grain, wine and horses. This treaty – *al Baqt* – defined relations between Muslim Egypt and Christian Nubia for 600 years.

During those centuries the Bedu achieved by infiltration what they had failed to achieve by military conquest. Following the Muslim invasion of Egypt, each new governor brought his own private contingent of Bedu troops, swelling the numbers of restless warriors moving up the Valley of the Nile. In 834 all Bedu fighters in Egypt had their salaries and pensions struck off. Many returned to the life of pastoralists, driving their herds ever farther year by year, until they reached the rich ranges of the Sudan. By the fourteenth century, the Juhayna – a tribe which had migrated to Egypt in 732 – were established on the Butana plain between the Atbara and the Blue Nile. Bedu families also drifted down the west bank of the Nile, and by 1300 they had formed a rough confederation across the desert marches of Kordofan and Darfur. This assortment of nomads raised camels and sheep, and since they were of both Qahtanite and Ishmaelite origin, they named themselves *Kababish*, after the Arabic word *kabsh* – meaning a ram. Today, the Kababish remain the largest group of camel-herding Bedu in the Sudan.

After dark, Abdu continued with his autobiography, holding me spellbound with his mesmeric tale. 'When I was eleven, I went to school in Nairobi,' he said. 'I didn't distinguish myself there. But my uncle, who was working in America, arranged for me to go to Newark County College in Washington State. At first the USA amazed me, but the shine soon wore off. I found the Americans uncivilized and racist, and I was glad to get back to Kenya at the end of the year. My uncle had a transport business, shipping coffee from Uganda – a very profitable business – and he gave me a lorry. In a few years I had a fleet of lorries of my own and I was making more money than my uncle. The trouble was that I was living a wild life – spending too much on women and qat and entertaining – and soon I had no money to pay any hire-purchase debts. The finance company repossessed my vehicles and I was indicted on a charge of forgery and corruption. I never maintained that I was innocent – I admitted I was guilty – but I told the judge that I had no fear of the government, because my government was God, and I only feared Him. This made a great impression on the Muslims and was reported in the press. I received a message from the Prophet that I would not be punished severely. Everyone was saying I would get thirty years in prison, but as it turned out I only got two years' probation. No one could believe it! I still had the problem of bankruptcy, though. My uncle told me that no one in the family would help me, because I had rejected the advice of my elders and lived a wild life. I told him I didn't need his help: I needed only the help of God. Well, the next day I got the bus to Nairobi and I found a sack on the seat next to me. Inside it there was almost one million Kenyan shillings! I went to the finance company and got one of my lorries out of hock, and I was soon in business again!'

I felt like commenting that I wished all *my* problems could be answered with such prompt manna from Heaven, but Abdu told his stories with a 'disbelieve-it-if-you-dare' attitude that defied mockery. These might be delusions, but if so they were tales constructed with loving detail. Instead, I asked why God should have rewarded him for such evident wrong-doing. 'Faith in God will always be rewarded,' he answered, without a moment's hesitation. 'We should not fear anyone or anything but God.'

The steamer docked at Wadi Halfa at about ten in the morning, and the crowds erupted into a frenetic madness, screaming and tearing their way to the ramp. Abdu and I waited, leaning on the rails and watching a troop of Sudanese longshoremen unloading sacks of onions and sheafs of aluminium buckets from the vessel's hold. Before the creation of the Nubian Lake, Wadi Halfa had been a fine old river-town of noble buildings, housing more than 40,000 people. The new Wadi Halfa, which stood several kilometres from the docks, though, was a shanty railhead of buildings constructed partly of mud and partly of sleepers and rails taken from the railway which Kitchener's army had built along the Nile in 1898. The shacks were spreadeagled over a treeless yellow plain, whose pale foundations fell into the dazzling blue and silver waters of the lake. On two sides the town was contained in an amphitheatre of weathered sandstone crags sculpted by the chafing sands of the Nubian desert.

We joined the queue of Sudanese being marshalled by immigration officials in uniforms of grey dacron. A hollow-cheeked old sergeant examined my passport and said: 'Your visa has expired!'

I looked at him in astonishment and began to protest, when he held up the document with a languid expression. 'Expired yesterday!'

'What can I do?'

'We can do it here, but for a price – let's say fifty Sudanese pounds?'

'That seems a bit stiff!'

'You think that's stiff? I'll tell you, fifty is nothing! I have been working here for thirty-three years, and I still don't have the price of my own coffin!'

Afterwards we made for the station, where the Khartoum train was standing ready. Donkey-powered carts were creaking into the yard carrying loads of custard-powder and Chinese lamps, and traders were setting out piles of Egyptian goods on fibre sheets to tempt the passing travellers: monstrous platform-soled shoes, synthetic textiles in the most sickeningly gaudy colours, aluminium cooking-pots and woollen shawls. On the platform I parted with Abdu, whose destination was Khartoum, and set off to find a lorry heading down the Nile.

There was no proper road along the east bank of the Nile, only a crude track that alternately followed the river or threaded out between the sandstone buttes of the Nubian desert. Along the alluvial terraces big, spare men with faces of acacia bark, as brown as the soil, were at work on the rich earth, following the wizened haunches of oxen trundling ploughs. We bounced through strings of villages, glimpsing the flash of the Nile through acacia-jungles, sleeping at night on the floor of one-roomed inns, eating bread still warm from the baker, and drinking many glasses of tea. We passed through Akasha, Abri, Delgo, Kerma and Seleim. On the fourth day from Wadi Halfa, I was stepping off a lorry at the town of Ed Debba.

10

To the Last Oasis

Ed Debba was a rural market which for generations had served the desert nomads. It was here that the Wadi al Milik, a seasonal watercourse, in places thickly forested, in others a stagger of thorn-trees across sterile desert, drained into the Nile. The Wadi al Milik was the watering-place for almost four-fifths of the Kababish, yet in prehistoric times, when the Sahara was greener than it is today, it was a perennial river and an important artery of movement. It was probably along Milik that the mysterious cattle-people known to archaeologists simply as the C-Group colonized the Nile, migrating from the plains of the Sahara, as it turned barren year by year. In time, these cattle-people would be succeeded by camel-rearing men.

I had come to Ed Debba to find a companion for a long camel journey. Ever since my first visit to the Sudan, years ago, it had been an ambition of mine to reach Selima, a tiny oasis near the Sudanese–Egyptian border, once a station on the ancient caravan-route known as the Forty Days Road.

In the souq I was introduced to a Bedui from the Kababish, called Jibrin. About thirty-five years old, he was small and lean as a gazelle, beardless except for a toothbrush fuzz of whisker on his firm chin, his eyes the smoke-grey shade that some Kababish had, his features hard and angular like interlocking blades. His body might have belonged to an athlete or a swimmer – broad shoulders, rope-like pectorals, muscular thighs, clearly defined calves. He moved with a curious spring-like quality that I had only seen among nomads. Jibrin was modest, reserved, and mindful of his dignity. He was a man who saw all and said little: his speech clipped, gruff, considered, and to the point.

Jibrin had pitched his camels'-hair tent squarely in the middle of the market-place, as if in protest against the terrible drought that had shorn his family of their animals and their livelihood. 'All my life I've lived in the desert,' he told me, 'and I've seen plenty of bad years, but never one as bad as this. In the desert, if it doesn't rain in one place you can pack your tent on your camels and move to the place where it has rained. But this year we had nowhere to move to. The rains usually come during the hot season, and as soon as the news breaks we move south. Then we follow the clouds – women, children, tents and everything, halting for a few days wherever there's pasture. In a good year we would go right into the Great ʿAtmur and the men and boys would stay there for weeks sleeping on the ground and drinking only camel's milk. When the grazing is over, and the days get hotter, we retire to the wells in the Wadi al Milik with our families.'

This year, as they sweltered out the summer in the wadi, news of the rains had never come. Jibrin's family, like many others, had decided that they had no alternative but to trust themselves to the safekeeping of God and move to the Nile. Though Jibrin had visited Ed Debba once or twice before to sell animals, the river remained for him a foreign land. 'We always dislike the towns and villages, and always distrusted the townspeople,' he said. 'Some of them are good and some bad, of course, but most of them are out to take your money or cheat you in one way or another. In the desert we were free. Our law was the law of the tribe. It's true that the tribes were always fighting, and there were camel-raids and blood-feuds, but at least you knew who the enemy was. In the towns we are subject to the police and the government, who always demand money and treat us badly. The government is just a trick to steal money from poor people. The merchants, the police, the army – they're all in on it! And if they are the government, why didn't they help us in the drought? Why did they leave us to starve, when they've got plenty?'

Now, stranded in the town without his animals, Jibrin had begun to wonder if he would ever escape. 'The towns are dirty places,' he commented. 'Even the air is full of fevers. We hadn't been in Debba for more than a week when my nephew and my wife went down with the sickness.' He had been obliged to take on work for a wealthy townsman, watering the trees in his palm-groves. This was better than starving, though it was demanding work for a Bedui. If the palms had been his own, he would have had no such reservations, but the work was hard and the man paid him a pittance, because he knew Jibrin had no choice. 'How I hate the town!' Jibrin said. 'You can't see the sky there like you can in the desert. You feel shut in. You can't read the tracks because there are so many, all crossing each other and fouling each other up. You can't trust your senses because there are so many smells and noises and sights to contend with. In the desert you know every tribe, and even if you don't know the individual by sight, you can soon tell who he is and where he belongs. In the towns people are all mixed up and you don't know who is who.'

Despite the suspicion the Bedu reserved for the settled places along the river, there had always been an intimate relationship between the desert and the sown. They were not separate but like a pair of scales constantly shifting in balance. Since the earliest times nomads had been spilling out of the Sahara as its climate fluctuated from fertile to arid, finding a niche among the villagers and eventually merging with them. It was interesting to note that in times of hardship the Kababish automatically moved east to the Nile rather than west to the hills of Chad, almost as if they had a traditional memory of the safe havens to be found there. Their dialect words for 'north' and 'south' mean 'down' and 'up' respectively, which suggested a long-standing orientation along the direction of the river. Among the original population of the river-banks – the Nubians – who had retained their own languages, there were pockets of Arabs who had kept their old tribal names and spoke Arabic, yet who had been farmers for generations. Obversely, there were fully nomadic Kababish clans who had almost certainly, at one time or another, been settled along the Nile. Bedu to Hadr to Bedu – nomad to farmer to nomad – it was a reversible system in ceaseless motion, and as Jibrin and I rode north along the Nile's banks from Ed Debba, I found striking evidence of it.

Along the stark gravel shoulders of the desert, outside the palm-groves and farthest from the river, stood the tents of new arrivals – Bedu displaced by the recent drought, as Jibrin's family had been. They were shelters of the most temporary nature – often no more than a ragged piece of woven camels' hair draped over a frame of sticks – that could be loaded on a camel within moments. The Bedu had not bothered to take pains over pitching their tents properly, as if to say, 'We're not staying long!' Further in, on the plain between the cliffs and the palm-groves, were straw dwellings, extended with bits of tent, sometimes surrounded by wire pens containing knots of goats or a brace of hobbled camels. These were more permanent, but could still be packed up and moved if circumstances changed. In the next rank of houses, though, straw walls were being replaced by mud-brick, and further in still were Arab huts built entirely of mud. Their owners were in transition from Bedu to Fellahin – they had come to stay. Beyond them, among the verdant foliage of the palm-groves, stood only the mud forts of the Nubians and the tribes who claimed Kababish ancestry, but were no longer counted among the nineteen sections of the desert Kababish.

I recalled how, on my last journey in the Sudanese desert, I had picked up a small, blue stone shaped like a bivalve, polished on both sides, with a keen cutting edge. I had known at once, having seen many like it, that it was a stone celt or hand-axe of the type made by nomads of the C-Group perhaps 5,000 years ago. I handled the smooth stone, feeling how perfectly it fitted into my palm, how painstakingly it had been shaped and sharpened all those centuries ago. Primitive beside a smart bomb, perhaps, but in its time the ultimate state-of-the-art precision engineering. Who were the engineers, I had wondered, whose humanity was hidden under the remorseless term 'C-Group'? What was their story?

Between 1929 and 1934, a prehistorian called Oliver Myers, who was excavating at Armant, in Upper Egypt, had unearthed some curious potsherds. Quite unlike any other ancient Egyptian pottery, they proved to be identical to sherds found in several sites across the Sahara – the nearest at the oasis of Bilma, 1,500 miles away. Myers realized with mounting excitement that he had happened on the remains of a lost Saharan culture that had once stretched from the Atlantic to the Nile.

Myers's first objective was to establish the age of this pottery. Sifting through the dust in the excavation-site, his team found evidence that suggested a connection with the VIth Dynasty, beginning with the Pharaoh Unas in 2400 BC. Myers began a careful study of ancient Pharaonic texts from the period, and came across a reference to a tribe of cattle-breeding nomads – the Temehu – who had first been sighted in Egyptian territory at this time. Could the Armant pottery-makers and the Temehu be one and the same? As Myers reconstructed some almost complete vessels, he noticed that they were strikingly similar to others belonging to the people prehistorians already knew as the C-Group – named after their C-shaped hieroglyph – who had arrived on the Nile in Nubia around the same time. He divined that C-Group and Temehu were branches of a related culture, a cattle-herding people which had migrated out of the desert in mass exodus in the third millennium BC. In that era, quite suddenly, the once-fertile Sahara had become inhospitable to cattle-rearing men.

For the story of the C-Group, I realized, I had no further to look than to Jibrin, to his people the Kababish, to the changing texture of the Bedu dwellings along the hard shoulder of the Nile. The time had been different, the details varied, but the story was essentially the same. A nomadic people, whose appearance and language we do not know, had been driven out of the desert by climatic changes still not fully understood. Their cattle-culture had eventually been replaced by one more adapted to the severe conditions of the desert – the camel-culture. Now, 5,000 years on, the wheel turned again, and those same camel-breeders, once the 'new men' of the desert, were being driven out by precisely the same inexorable forces.

On our first evening, near Al Ghaba, we halted at one of the mud-brick houses built outside the palm-groves, occupied by the family of Hamid, a cousin of Jibrin's. Lean and lithe like Jibrin, Hamid was dressed in a long, townsman's jallabiyya and a white skull-cap. He welcomed us with the profuse, lingering greeting of the Bedu, clasping our hands over and over again, repeating, 'God greet you! God's blessing upon you! Your coming is blessed! God give you peace!' Hamid and his son unsaddled our camels with their own hands and laid our equipment neatly along the wall of their house. Later, they dragged out their own *angarebs* – beds of heavy wood upholstered with string, like Indian charpoys – and insisted that we slept on them, though I knew that this meant they themselves would be sleeping on the ground.

They brought armfuls of sorghum-stalks for our camels and adamantly refused to take money for it, though I guessed that Hamid had had to buy it himself. After dark our host laid before us a bowl of goat stew with fresh salad and quarters of home-made bread, apologizing repeatedly that there was no fresh goats' milk. 'What could we wish for more than this?' Jibrin countered. 'God requite you! May your bounty increase!'

Hamid had been living on the Nile for a couple of years, and his talk was of date-farming, crop-growing and the price of cattle. 'It's not a bad life in the village,' he said. 'In the desert it's so precarious – you live close to the margin, and if a bad year comes you go over and everything you have is gone. Here things are more reliable, because we've got the one thing that the Sons of Adam must have to survive – water. That makes all the difference. The people of the Nile are more "civilized" than those of the desert. They wear clean clothes, they wash, they have decent food to eat. A lot of them can read and write. I want my children to go to school, and maybe – God is all-knowing – to university and to become important people. Here, everything is possible.' Jibrin remained unconvinced, however. 'It's green here, I'll grant you,' he said, 'and there's water. You have to say it's more fertile than the desert. But you feel confined here by walls, and houses and people. It's like being in prison. Give me the open country any time!'

After we had eaten and drunk several glasses of very sweet tea, Hamid fetched his prize possession – a Japanese radio/cassette-player – something I had never seen among the desert Kababish. 'Listen to this!' he said, proudly, as he snapped into place a cassette of modern Sudanese music and turned up the volume. Jibrin smiled appreciatively, but my heart sank. I knew that Hamid had brought out the cassette-player for our entertainment, but as the singer's voice squawked and trembled to the crash of the band, I longed for the silence of the desert.

The next morning Hamid walked us out of the village, as Bedu politeness demanded. Then we trekked along the desert road. On our left the Sahara stretched away west, flat and sparkling like a sheet of white ice. To our right we saw the fluffed heads of date- and dom-palms, as dense as rainforest along the river, punctuated by Nile acacias in winter bloom, their saffron-petalled flowers giving out a heady perfume. There were squares of cultivation – green wheat and clover – fed by thumping irrigation-pumps which sent clear, cool water down narrow channels. Villagers in shirts and tight white turbans laboured in the fields with hoes and curved knives. Women in *taubs* of pink, saffron and lime-green rode side-saddle on muscular white donkeys.

The sand was soft and deep and the going hard. Once, a Fiat lorry rumbled past, startling the camels, and the two black lorry-boys perched on the cab jeered at us. Later, though, we found the lorry stuck in the sand, its engine screaming in rage, its great wheels spinning impotently, lashing the lorry-boys with dust as they toiled with shovels and sand-boards. Jibrin chuckled. 'That's what you get when you go by lorry!' he commented as we rode past. 'A camel is better any day!' The youths scowled at him and turned away. However, we soon had a problem of our own to contend with: there was no clover to be had for our camels. Each time we halted to ask the villagers working in clover-fields, they answered rudely, 'It's not for sale!'

By sunset that evening we had found neither clover for our camels, nor the firewood we needed to cook our evening meal. Firewood was at a premium along the Nile, and most of the villagers cooked with charcoal, which was of little use without a brazier. The sun was firing the desert with pumpkin-toned streaks, and the first electric lights, powered by private generators, came up among the palm-groves like baubles hung on their fronds. Cicadas began their rasping sunset chorus in the cultivation, and from the direction of the river came the honk of frogs. Just before dark we heard the grumble of an engine and saw an immensely broad-shouldered man in an elaborate turban at the wheel of a Massey-Ferguson tractor, with a fitted disc-plough. This was a rare sight, even for the affluent Nile, and Jibrin and I stopped to watch as he shunted back and forth, turning over the sod in a wide field. Beyond the field, sheltered by *nim* trees, stood a rambling house of mud with buttressed walls and moulded steps, partly encircled by high walls, from which time and the occasional rain had bitten substantial chunks. Through one such breach I spotted a cluster of big-boned cows tucking into a bale of clover.

'We can't go on in darkness, anyway,' Jibrin said, following my eyes. 'This is a good place to stop. Perhaps these people would sell us some clover. As for dinner,' he nodded towards the tractor, 'they won't turn away a guest.' We did just as we would have done had we come to a Bedu tent. We couched the camels at a respectable distance from the house, and began unloading, expecting our host to come and greet us warmly. As we laid out our saddlery, the man driving the tractor cut the engine, jumped down and walked over to us. Compared with the diminutive Jibrin he was a giant – six feet three if an inch, and towering over us in his dung-splattered jallabiyya. His face was dark, bullish and broad, with low brow-ridges. Before we could wish peace upon him, he said: 'You can't stop there!'

'Why not?' Jibrin inquired. 'Is it your land?'

'No,' the giant replied. 'It's the graveyard!'

Only then did I notice the dozens of shaped stones underfoot, some of them scrawled with Arabic writing. We muttered apologies and moved camels and equipment to the edge of the plot. The big man disappeared inside the house, without, we both noticed, inviting us to dinner. 'I've never seen anything like that in my life!' Jibrin fumed. 'They talk about the meanness of the village people. That man must be rolling in money, but he didn't even invite us to spend the night in his yard. By God, what a miser! If anyone did that among the Bedu he'd never live it down!'

'Well. Perhaps he'll invite us to dinner later. Anyway, we'll have to go and ask him to sell us some clover.'

We climbed the shallow steps and battered on the door, shouting out a greeting. After a while the tractor-driver appeared, scowling, and answered our '*as salaam ʿalaykum*' with a grunt. I explained that we had no clover for our camels and concluded, 'I thought we could buy some from you.' The man's eyes bulged at me. 'We have no clover here.'

Jibrin and I exchanged glances. I was about to protest, when the giant was abruptly replaced by another man, clad in the same kind of dirty jallabiyya, and if anything even taller and broader than the first. 'What is it?' he asked. I repeated my request to buy fodder. The second giant, older and more weathered-looking, shifted uneasily and then, looking at me pointedly, said, 'Come inside. Just you, not the Arab.'

Jibrin's eyes flared with anger at this incredible rudeness. 'We go everywhere together,' I said.

'No, that's all right, Omar,' Jibrin said. 'You go in. One of us should keep an eye on the camels.'

The room was oddly shaped and full of shadows from the thick mud columns whose presence made it surprisingly small. Two string-beds with mattresses stood side by side at one end, next to a chair with a hole in the seat. A oil-lamp, smoking in an embrasure in the stucco wall, had left soot-coloured streaks on the plaster. A faded old mirror and an assortment of shirts hung precariously from nails. A palm-fibre mat had been spread on the floor, and the men sat down heavily on it. I kicked off my sandals and joined them. They asked questions about who I was, where I was going, and why. 'What's your name?' the younger one inquired.

'Omar.'

'No, I mean your *real* name. That's an Arab name. What's your English name?'

'All right. Michael.'

The big man's eyes lit up in recognition. 'Oh!' he said, see-sawing his massive arms in a parody of dancing. 'Like Michael Jackson!'

'Yes,' I said, determined to get the conversation back to clover. When I mentioned it again, the old man said, 'We haven't got any clover for sale, but there are some old melon shoots you could have. We don't need those. Cows won't eat them. I'll let you have them for five pounds! I'll come over and sort it out later.'

'Thanks,' I said, and, thinking that it would be too much to mention the firewood, I rose to my feet. 'Wait,' the older giant said. 'Surely we can offer you something before you go!' He had been wrestling with a deep pocket, from which he brought out a small brown chemist's bottle. He unscrewed the top and held it out to me. The bottle contained small white pills. '*Valium*,' the man said, smiling. 'Have one!'

I muttered no thanks, slipped on my sandals and walked out, but not before I had seen both giants swallow a small white pill each, with evident satisfaction.

'Animals, not people!' Jibrin said later, as we lay on the hard ground with rumbling bellies. 'They are . . . they are blacksmiths – that's what they are!' This was about the most withering insult an Arab could think of – blacksmiths being universally detested as uncouth and untrustworthy in the Sudan, as in most Arab countries. These men had flunked the absolute Bedouin litmus test of humanity – they were worthy only of disdain. 'Curse their fathers!' Jibrin continued. 'To let us go to sleep on empty stomachs! The worst thing one can ever say about a man is that he did not know a guest!' We slept fitfully, and in the morning awoke to find that while we had lain there starving, the local termites had made a great feast on chunks of our blankets and saddle-gear.

For days we wandered north through Nubian villages of houses like cream-cake slices – cubes and rhomboids of painted alabaster with oval doorways, elaborate stairways and stepped *mastabas.* Often we discovered earthenware pots of ice-cool water on iron stands nestled in the shade of *nim* trees, each with its own steel cup on a chain – an offering to passing travellers like ourselves. 'They always keep the pots full,' Jibrin said, 'because they believe that if they run dry then the river will dry up too.'

Sometimes we were able to follow the Nile itself. Its waters were either serene and beryl-blue, a-glitter with stars, or, when the wind whipped up from the desert, swelling sea-green, furious with waves and seamed with froth. In places the stream was cleft by blade-shaped islands top-heavy with jungles of date-palms. The islands could be reached only by barges under crackling butterfly-wing sails, steered by old men with melting ceramic faces, heaving on rudders like giant halberds. We wandered in and out of palm-groves, hearing the wind soughing in the palm-heads, and emerged again into the pack-ice infinity of the desert, where dunes had piled over broken walls and wormed their substance to the very water's edge. Chattering children played on donkeys at the well-heads, and Nubian ladies, giggling under soft *taubs*, called us to eat bread and tomatoes in the shade of tamarisk-trees. Often we met wayfarers coming in the opposite direction – a file of walking men, perspiring under heavy sacks, who answered our greeting with grimaces; an Arab in a greatcoat leading a camel-caravan laden with firewood for sale in the town; two Nubians clicking along on donkeys behind a drove of mottled sheep; two riders on swift dromedaries, their faces white-bandaged and inscrutable, who waved to us and were gone. Nowhere did we encounter the lack of hospitality we had met at the 'House of the Giants': almost every time we halted someone would scurry out from the nearest house to welcome us, and return later with fresh bread and stew, or a plate of griddle-cakes.

On the outskirts of Dongola al Urdi, the capital of the Sudan's Northern Province, some boys, their jallabiyyas tucked into baggy trousers, were playing football in a square. As we passed through them we met some Arabs whom Jibrin knew by sight. We halted to greet them with the drawn-out greeting of the desert, our camels shifting nervously as the boys hooted, shrieked and scuffled around us, chasing their plastic ball through the dust, oblivious of all but their game. The Arabs advised us to spend the night in the local mosque, for, in the Sudan as in many Islamic countries, mosques also doubled as inns for poor travellers.

We found the mosque nearby. It was small and square, enclosed by a low wall in which a row of taps for ritual ablutions were shaded under a narrow roof. The Imam, a stocky man as fair as an Egyptian, with a neatly cropped silver beard, welcomed us at the gate, and helped us to unload and hobble our camels outside. He allotted us a place to sleep, in the shelter of the wall, and later we were joined by some displaced Kababish who were looking for work along the Nile. After sunset, local villagers arrived with a tray laden with dishes – Egyptian *fuul* in a sauce of onions, crumbled white cheese, beef stew, sardines, fresh radishes and tomatoes, flat griddle-cakes and loaves of leavened brown bread still warm from the oven. The Kababish, small, bird-like men with bearded faces and sand-coloured shirts, wearing their rosary beads around their necks in Bedu style, told us that they, like Jibrin, had lost all their animals in the drought. 'Those who still have their camels have moved far south to places no Arabs have ever been before,' one of them explained. 'Right up to the Jonglei river. But we heard that some of them had been attacked by blacks and shot dead. Those infidels are scoundrels, by God! The Arabs went to their country in time of need and that was the kind of welcome they were given!'

It was tragic, but easy to forget that in the old days the Arabs had built up a profitable trade, burning the villages of those same southerners, killing the old and useless and leading off the rest in chains. 'The blacks should be taught a lesson,' the Imam cut in. 'The government should send the army down there and wipe them out!' This seemed a singularly uncharitable opinion for an elder whose God was deemed 'The Compassionate, The Merciful', yet certainly if a southerner should walk in here and now, he would have been made comfortable just as I had been. Later, as the wind blustered against the mosque wall and our camels rumbled contentedly outside, I basked happily in the glow of Muslim hospitality. Whatever the savage sentiments expressed, I thought, where else at the end of the twentieth century but in the Sudan could an Englishman dressed as an Arab and riding a camel find welcome in a mosque, and be treated as just another human being in need of food and shelter?

One morning, as we awoke on a sandy shelf by the river, Jibrin told me that a camel-herd had passed our camp during the night. 'Must be a herd going to Egypt,' he went on. 'If we catch up, we might be able to travel with them for a while.' By mid-morning we had sighted them, about 100 animals as tightly packed as a school of fish streaming along in a current. Balanced upon the humps of several camels were white Nile egrets, their heads and beaks buried in their breast-feathers, looking like miniature hitch-hikers cadging an easy passage to Egypt. The camels were being driven by four Arab drovers dressed in overcoats, turbans and woollen shawls, who chanted camel-cries as they wheeled their riding-beasts and cracked their hippo-hide whips to keep the herd in line. At midday, the drovers pushed the beasts into a grove of tattered tamarisk and unloaded their saddles and firewood. The guide was an oldish man named Shawish, whose parched face was a long tale of wind, sun and deprivation, and who was wearing around his neck a pair of antediluvian motorcycle goggles. He invited us to share their lunch – a half-football of polenta, served with spiced gravy.

Afterwards, when we had scrubbed our scorched fingers in the sand and drunk tea, Shawish began to fill a biscuit-tin with the moist black tobacco that the Bedu used orally and only very occasionally smoked. He took a pinch of tobacco and placed it tenderly between his teeth and lower lip. He spat out the excess and arranged himself comfortably in the sand, his chin bulging. 'Good stuff,' he sighed happily. 'The good tobacco can only be found on the Nile!'

He told us that there were scores of camel-herds moving downriver behind them, and dozens more in front. 'Like an invasion!' he said. 'The Bedu are selling their camels in thousands because of the drought. It's either that or let them die, or move south to the Jonglei, where the blacks are waiting. They're going dirt cheap and all the merchants are trying to make a few pounds. Even the settled people of the Nile are taking herds to Egypt now!' When he discovered I was British, he gave me a grin restrained by his wad of tobacco. 'I know the British!' he said. 'I was a gunner in the Sudan Defence Force during the war – a sergeant, that's why they call me 'Shawish'. It was an air-defence battery, with Bofors guns. I fought at Jalo in Libya. What a fight! Shot down a lot of Italian planes.' He grinned twistedly again, and added in tortured English, '*Bloody fools! Bloody stupid fools! Bloody man!*'

I suppose it was only the English he knew.

We travelled north with the herd for several days, passing from the teeming Dongola reach and into the wilder, more remote region known as the 'Belly of Stone', where the broad swaths of cultivation were replaced by blue volcanic magma, crushed and pounded and layered into strange formations. At the village of

Oki, a clot of square buildings on a rocky shelf which overlooked a plunging ravine, the drovers ran their camels into a copse of acacia-trees. I walked to the edge of the ravine to see the Nile, glinting metallic-blue below. Suddenly there was a shout, and I looked up to see a little old lady in a pure black *taub*, her witch face a mask of hatred, hurtling towards me flailing a flexible palm-rib and shrieking, 'Eeeh! You dogs! Eeeh! You sons of the forbidden!' Only at the last moment did I realize that she was on a collision course, and take evasive action, dodging a slashing blow from the palm-rib. The old woman was no higher than my shoulder, as thin and frail-looking as brown paper, yet she was astonishingly agile. She gave me a whack on the shin before I managed to get hold of the stick, and as I tried to wrest it away she clung on with surprising tenacity, her face knotted with effort. 'Get your camels off our land!' she spat. 'These trees are for our donkeys! We've had enough of the likes of you Egyptians stealing our browse!'

We were doing a sort of precarious tango around the edge of the ravine, with the old lady cursing and myself laughing and protesting: 'These camels aren't mine! They're nothing to do with me!' and trying to prevent any more blows from connecting, when Jibrin and Shawish appeared and managed to pull her away.

'These aren't his camels!' the guide said. 'Only one of them is his!'

'Whose are they then?'

'I'm the guide,' Shawish said, and he was obliged to leap ungracefully sideways to avoid a swipe of the palm-rib. 'You stupid woman!' he gasped. 'You'll be lucky if we don't beat you black and blue!' I guessed it was pride more than intention talking. The old woman backed away among the camels and began to belabour left and right with the rib, still crying, 'Eeeh! Eeeh! Drive them out!' as the animals bucked and snorted in their rush to get away.

Shawish made a move towards her, but as he stepped out a sharp stone hit him squarely on the cheek with an audible crump. He rubbed his cheek, examined a trace of blood on his fingers, laughed to maintain face, and then noticed, as we all did, that dozens of other villagers, men, women and children, were pouring out of the houses, waving sticks, picking up stones and shaking home-made rattles of pebble-filled steel jugs, which were extraordinarily effective in scaring the camels. Another volley of sharp stones spattered in the sand near us, and as I jumped back quickly to get out of range, I tripped over a boulder and twisted my ankle. 'All right! All right!' Shawish was shouting to the villagers. 'That's enough, by God! Drive them out, boys!' As we slunk away in the wake of the camels, I turned to see the little old lady standing on the rock platform outside the village, swinging the palm-rib in ferocious triumph, with her family gathered around her.

In the morning my ankle was badly swollen, and I had to lean on my stick as I walked. To my relief no one commented. Trailing behind the herd, I came alongside one of the camels which was, like me, hobbling painfully and lurching from side to side. An Arab ran back and walloped the beast once or twice with his whip, with no appreciable effect. There was a dull glaze in its eyes, I noticed. The herder stopped his walloping and said, 'It's no good. His nerves are completely shot. Hunger has pierced his heart!' Soon after, Shawish halted the herd and the animal was led off to its execution. The Bedu couched the camel and hobbled it, then one of them doubled its head backwards and down into the sand. Shawish took out his razor-sharp dagger from its arm-sheath and plunged it into the beast's carotid artery, just below the neck. Blood sparged the sand. The camel gave one pathetic snort, and the light in its eyes was switched off for ever. The Arabs hustled around with their daggers ready, excited by the prospect of meat. They skinned it expertly, severing the neck, ripping out the entrails, slicing off the muscle. Within minutes, two leather saddle-bags were brimming with wet meat, and we were crouching around a bowlful of raw liver that was still warm. 'Eat!' Shawish shouted. 'You don't get liver as fresh as this every day!'

The hollow carcass of the camel still knelt among the rocks in precisely the position in which it had met its death, a giant blood-spattered insect, already surrounded at a respectable distance by a gang of black Nubian vultures, roosting truculently on the teeth of the rocks, waiting patiently for our departure. The herd was one camel less, but the deficit was made up – if only momentarily – before we had even got the camels moving again, when a pregnant she-camel gave birth to a foal. The foal lay in the sand, a whimpering, wriggling rag-doll wearing a slimy membrane like a jacket. The she-camel stood over her baby, directing a deep-throated warning roar towards the vultures, which turned their gaze on the foal with malevolent interest. Another pair came gliding in with a snap of wing-feathers, and on the opposite side there gathered a back-up shift of smaller Egyptian vultures with white feathers and sulphur-yellow heads. A third contingent was made up of piebald crows which croaked, cawed and fluttered with an impatience that seemed vulgar beside the massive imperturbability of the vulture tribe. I knew that as soon as we moved away the scavengers would tear the living foal to shreds, eyes first. 'We can't take it with us,' Shawish said, 'and we can't wait for it to walk. It'll be dead soon anyway. Tonight Hassan the Jackal will be out to do his work!'

As the Bedu moved the herd off, the mother howled pitifully. More than once she turned back to the helpless foal, but the herders caught her and forced her on, keening. Before we had gone 300 feet, the big vultures were hopping clumsily towards the rag-doll in the sand, circling it like a death-squad. The last time I looked, one of them was pecking out its eye.

In the evening we made camp under a rocky overhang. The drovers piled their equipment along the base of the rocks and laid out their blankets. Someone made a fire and began cooking camel-meat. Others twisted hobbles out of fibre they had brought with them, and the guide, sucking tobacco, occupied himself in cutting out leather patches from a cow-skin and dunking them in a bowl of water. Afterwards he stitched the patches to the camels' hooves with a packing-needle and leather thread. 'These camels are accustomed to the soft sand of Kordofan,' he said. 'They're not used to rocky ground and sometimes the skin wears right off their hooves. We have to stitch these patches on like shoes, or they'll never make it to Egypt.' Thinking of the beast slaughtered that morning, I asked him how many camels he generally expected to lose on the forty-five-day trek. 'Only God is all-knowing,' he answered. 'Perhaps five, maybe ten. It depends on the state of the camels to start with and what you find to eat on the way. I once lost forty-three camels from a single herd – almost half of it – on the way to Egypt.'

After we had eaten roast camel-meat and drunk tea, the Bedu sat up, talking and telling stories. Nursing my swollen ankle, I retired to my bed in the shelter of a rock. Venus came up like a fireball gleaming yellow, and shortly a full moon rose over the desert, so bright and personal that I was immediately transported beyond myself, beyond the individual units of life, beyond birth, death and predation, into a vision of a vast, eternal process in which everything, both organic and inorganic, played a part.

Jibrin left the company and settled down next to me, staring at the moon. 'You know,' he said, 'the Arabs say that the moon is the husband of the sun, and twice a month they have intercourse. She is so insatiable that the moon is weakened and grows thin. Once, when he refused to sleep with her, they had a fight and each knocked out the other's eye – that's why there is that dark patch on the moon – you can see it – where his lost eye should be.'

'Some people – Christians – have already walked on the moon, but they didn't find a blind eye!'

'Walked on the moon! That's just nonsense!'

'All right. Perhaps it is.'

The she-camel was still howling, bemoaning her lost foal. Later, in the moonlight, Hassan the Jackal came out to do his work on the leftovers of our dinner. He passed so close to my bed that I could almost touch him.

It was in the desert west of the Nile, several days after we had parted from Shawish and his herd, that we sighted the mysterious footprints. A seething wind had seared our bodies all morning as we drifted on behind our camels, hoping their bulky frames would give us some protection from the cold. Jibrin shivered as he marched. Both of us had snuffling colds, and I was limping from my sprained ankle. Jibrin's camel – already weak when we had started the trek thirteen days before – was now exhausted, its eyes glazed with a sinister mist whose meaning Jibrin knew only too well. 'Look at him,' he said fretfully. 'Look at the way he holds his head!' He was obliged to walk to preserve his camel's strength, and I felt obliged to walk too, out of solidarity. The pain in my ankle was excruciating and I would have given almost anything for a few moments in the saddle, but pride prevented me from mounting up. Each time Jibrin prompted me to 'Ride! Ride!' I always answered, 'No. Not until you do!' And of course he never did.

By midday the wind had mercifully blown itself out and the desert was still and featureless except for the crags which lay directly in our path. Though Jibrin had never been in this region before, he had made inquiries from the caravaneers at Saqiyyat al ʿAbd, and told me that these crags marked the second of three stages in the journey from the Nile. Once a year a caravan would set out from Saqiyya to collect salt from the oasis of Selima, taking three days each way. The caravaneers, who had once been nomads but were now settled on the Nile, halted in precisely the same places on each journey. As we approached, the crags gradually solidifed into crusty basalt blocks, growing like alien fungi on the pale sand-and-gravel desert floor. It was here that Jibrin spied the footprints weaving drunkenly from side to side as they approached the rocks. He knelt down to examine them and looked up, mystified. 'These tracks are only a few hours old,' he said. 'They've been made since the wind dropped, which means that whoever made them is not far ahead. But there is no sign of a camel! No God but God, this is strange! Who would travel in this wilderness without a camel?'

'Perhaps his camel has been stolen.'

'No. There are no thieves in empty desert. The camel-raiders live on the fringes of the desert where there's plenty of movement. Here, a bandit would have to wait weeks – maybe months – without water to come across a single camel. It wouldn't be worth his while. No, this is strange, very strange indeed!'

We followed the tracks for a while until they disappeared into a patch of hard gravel almost surrounded by a wide circus of rock. On one side the basalt had been eaten away to form a perfect overhang. Beneath it were the remains of old cooking-fires. Spread out at the base of the rock wall lay a carpet of dried grass – the remnants of bales of hay the caravaneers had carried months ago from the Nile to feed their camels. Jibrin brightened visibly. We had been feeding our camels on sorghum-grain, but his mount was constantly jibbing – it pined for grass.

While the camels grazed, however, I looked around the circle of rock, and felt suddenly depressed. In the basalt I saw the grotesque figures of dragons and griffins. The sky was momentarily dark. The rock overhangs and the remains of old fires produced an inexplicable sense of gloom. Panic oozed up inside me, and then something happened that I have never experienced before or since. Suddenly, it was as if a voice was screaming inside my head, sobbing, *'Oh God! There's a dead man here!'*

At sunrise we saw a broken hill scarring the horizon, which I took to be Selima mountain. Jibrin reserved judgement. We packed up and set out grimly into a polar wind that rendered the desert ghostly and insubstantial. The sun hovered reluctantly above the fuzzy skyline, colouring the sands raw sienna and salmon-pink. Jibrin's camel still wobbled unsteadily, but no more unsteadily than myself – my ankle was softball-size after the previous day's hard trek, and it was all I could do to limp. To cap it all, my snuffle had worked itself up into full-blown fever. My temperature was 39.5. 'I can't understand it,' I told Jibrin. 'This is the worst I've ever been in my years of travelling by camel!'

'I don't know why you do it! You could have got here in a day by car. Why go through all this when you have the choice?'

As we shuffled along in silence behind the camels, I wondered what answer I should give. I might have said that it took a Western genius like Einstein to formulate a simple truth that should have been obvious to any traveller – namely, that the speed of the observer changes his perception, squashing and distorting the landscape. When Westerners first began to explore this desert with motor-cars in the 1920s, they found their Bedu guides useless. 'They have no idea of distance in a car,' wrote Ralph Bagnold, '. . . accustomed to reckoning distances by the time of camels' movement . . . they are many miles past a landmark before they think of looking for it.' If I had travelled here by car, my experience would have been a blurred confusion of images with only highpoints standing out, like a videotape on fast-rewind. Walking along at camel's pace allows you to perceive the environment as it unfurls in its full royal glory. James Lovelock has written: 'the simplest way to explore Gaia is on foot. How else can you easily be part of her ambience? How else can you reach out to her with all your senses?'

This drifted through my mind as I limped on feverishly, but by the time I had thought it out, Jibrin had long ago given up waiting for my answer, if indeed he had ever wanted one. We climbed the spur, dragging the camels by their headropes across a surface littered with flat shards of basalt which chinked like steel under their feet. The ascent was agonizing, but I was driven on by the thought that from the summit we were certain to see Selima below us. From the top, though, we saw nothing but sand-devils playing over empty desert and another ridge of rock in the distance. We inched painfully down the perilous slope into a gully where the stones were gnarled and twisted. Beneath them were a few red sherds of broken pottery, decorated with rough but intricate striations. I picked up one of the sherds. It was a relic, perhaps, of Oliver Myers's C-Group nomads, whose cows had tramped through the golden savannahs that covered this desert 5,000 years ago.

In 1938 Myers joined the motor-explorer Ralph Bagnold on

an expedition deep into the *terra ignota* of the eastern Sahara. Rattling out of Kharja oasis in their 'flying bedsteads' – Model 'T' Fords – his team's objectives were the remote oasis of ʿUwaynat and the plateau of Jilf Kebir, standing near the Libyan border, where earlier explorers had found fascinating drawings etched into the rock. It was Myers's hope that these rock-pictures could be connected in some way with his Armant pottery – that they would provide a direct window into the world of the C-Group nomads.

At Jilf Kebir – a sandstone massif almost as large as Sicily – he investigated two wadis where there was evidence that prehistoric lakes had formed behind sand-bars that blocked their upper reaches from wall to wall. Stone-age peoples had camped around the lakes, and the presence of grinders and milling-stones suggested that these nomads had planted barley in the wadis. Myers also found pottery, stone tools and ostrich-shell beads, and stone rings that had probably been laid around nomads' tents of hide or straw. The pottery was different from that of his Armant invaders, but further south, at ʿUwaynat, he found sherds that were identical.

While Myers had been searching for potsherds, his colleague, Hans Winkler, a Swiss art-historian, had spent two weeks wandering the arid valleys of ʿUwaynat and Jilf Kebir, examining boulders, scrambling over screes, and peering into dim caves, recording the mass of rock-art to be found there. He discovered an entire literature of engravings and paintings that told the saga of Saharan prehistory from as far back as Paleolithic times. The pictures showed human figures – some of them lumpen matchstick men who lassoed dinosaur-necked giraffes or swayed hand in hand around some sinister masked shaman in a hypnotic dervish-dance. Others were more finely drawn figures painted yellow, white and red: men with triangular trunks and waspish waists, loping off with bows and arrows in pursuit of gazelles: figures in penis-sheaths jerking with skirt-clad women in a rhythmic mazurka. There were globe-skulled warriors with devils' horns and feathers guarding herds of mottled cattle, and couples lounging like pashas in caves and grass huts with milk-pots suspended from the roofs. Among the animals Winkler found, there were plump ostriches, stumpy elephants, pooch-like lions, cows with swollen udders and bent horns, dogs on leashes, spider-legged camels, skeletal horses, and antelopes with comb-like limbs. There were abstract shapes that might have been filched from surrealist art – Catherine-wheel spirals, rippling serpentine strings, fishbone trees, blots and blips on legs, the outlines of hands, clusters of toadstools, clumps of interlocking honeycombs and lizards with human heads.

The story these pictures told was of far greater import than that of a single exodus of cattle-people out of the Sahara. The displacement of the C-Group was but one chapter in a vast cycle of change – of successive waves of peoples that moved back and forth across the Sahara as it expanded and contracted, now rich and fertile, now dissolving into sand. The earliest pictures, Winkler thought, had been made by hunter-gatherers: 'Animals, footprints of game, geometrical designs, occupy the mind of these men. They had little interest in the portrayal of human beings. In the moment of first discovery of these drawings and again after having studied them week after week, I feel they are expressions of quite a foreign mentality . . . the same genius which inspired artists of other primitive hunters – in Australia and North America . . .'

The waspy-waisted men in penis-sheaths, more numerous than the matchstick hunters, were always found in association with herds of cattle. It was among them, Winkler surmised, that the C-Group belonged. Cattle were everything to these men, and their beasts were often decorated with amulets, suggesting a cult significance. Carefully drawn udders denoted the importance they had attached to milk. Here, he felt, was something extraordinary. These men had somehow discovered the secret of taming wild cattle, and probably plant cultivation too. They had 'broken the eternal flow of Paleolithic times and started the explosion of a new era in humanity's life'.

In more recent pictures, the cattle-people had disappeared. Their vivacious portraits of men and cattle had given way to poorly drawn horses and riders, then to pipe-cleaner camels with over-large humps. Evidently, these pictures belonged to a later period when conditions in the Sahara had changed. One final picture that intrigued the metaphysically inclined Winkler was of a British soldier seated in a tent, with an eccentric-looking locomotive puffing by. He wrote: 'We may look at our material from the desert, a material beginning with hunters and with an early mentality which is to us incomprehensible, and ending with our day of railways and guns. The main acquisitions not only of these desert peoples, but of humanity, have appeared beneath our eyes: the domestication of cattle, the discovery of plant cultivation, and the taming of horses and camels.'

As we moved, four tiny living creatures in the vast cathedral of the desert, I felt humbled by the knowledge of this breathtaking epic that had lasted hundreds of thousands of years. Beside that, the wails of Western romantics – myself included – over the Bedu becoming settled, or adopting motor-cars and machines, seemed as insignificant as a whirling dust-devil on the desert sands. The saga on the rocks was the saga of endless diversity – of humanity thirsting and thrusting to adapt and to improve. The machine-age – represented in Winkler's rock-art by a single picture – was simply the latest stage in a journey that had begun with the crudest stone tools, and has never ceased. On the stage of eternity it would be over in the winking of an eye, and something yet undreamed-of would take its place.

Suddenly Jibrin pointed to a long shadow on the desert floor. It was made by a rough cairn, and no sooner had we come abreast of it than a wonderful sight met our eyes. There, in a saucer-shaped depression, invisible from afar, lay a garden of palm-trees, tamarisk and esparto grass, like a vision in a fairy-tale picture book. Selima was the perfect oasis of myth and legend – a small, compact, bloom of palms heavy with unpicked dates, its greener-than-green grasses blossoming around pools of open water. It seemed incredible to find it here.

We drove the camels into the luxury of its dappled shade, unsaddled them and sent them off into the tamarisk and the esparto grass. We laid out our blankets under the palms, and while Jibrin sauntered off gleefully to knock down the ripe dates with stones, I lay back, resting my swollen ankle, and enjoying the immaculate peace and harmony of this tiny paradise that seemed to belong to a different age – far beyond roads and cars and aircraft. My movements were heavy, my eyelids weighted with lead. My eyes closed. I drifted off on a gently undulating wave of tranquillity.

And then an engine growled.

It was so totally unexpected that I jerked up in fright. Jibrin stopped his date-bashing and stared into the desert beyond the trees. About 300 metres away, a heavy truck that had been converted into a bus had just materialized out of the dust-sheen, and was grinding to a halt. Even before it stopped, something told me it was a tourist vehicle. And this was unbelievable, because in my time in the Sudan I had only occasionally met a tourist, and never an organized group. Sure enough, the doors snapped open, and out came a score of pale-faced Europeans, elderly men and women in safari pants, T-shirts and sun-hats, who lurched across the sand towards us with the determination of disturbed bees. Almost all of them were carrying cameras or camcorders with microphones, and they jostled each other to get at us, jabbering in French. They surrounded us, pointing their cameras, poking microphones and zoom lenses into our faces. Jibrin, who had never seen a camera before – or a European other than myself – blanched with fear and looked around for escape. 'These are hyenas!' he said. I could smell the sun-screen, the deodorant and the insect-repellent, and as they pushed nearer, I found myself thinking: 'So this is what it's like to be photographed by tourists!'

I flattered myself that they had taken me for an Arab, and when the initial excitement had worn off, I began to explain who I was in English to the tour-guide, a dark, confident-looking Frenchman called Jean-Yves. 'I know who you are,' he said, deflatingly, 'because the police on the river told us you had left for Selima. Actually we have been following your tracks. The reason these people are so excited is because they think you might have had something to do with the dead man.'

'Dead man!'

'Yes. This morning we found a dead body only a few metres from the place with the rock overhang. We found your tracks there. You must have seen it, surely! One of these men is a doctor. He said the man hadn't been dead for more than a day. Probably died of thirst, because he had with him an empty gallon jerrycan with a missing top.'

I thought of the mysterious tracks we had found in the desert the previous day, the place with the rock overhang, the feeling of depression, the momentary panic I had felt – the voice that had screamed inside my head: *There's a dead man here!* I had never believed in premonition or any kind of ESP, and I had to rack my brains to be certain I actually heard that voice: there was absolutely no doubt in my mind.

I had hardly recovered from my surprise when Jean-Yves hit me with another: 'Did you see the salt-caravan?' he asked.

'Salt-caravan? But the caravans from the Nile only come once a year.'

'This one wasn't coming from the Nile. It was coming from the south – from the desert!'

He had hardly finished speaking when a train of about forty camels suddenly uncoiled out of the desert, led by four walking men in jallabiyyas with unfamiliar wide sleeves and white turbans. One of the men was limping badly, I noticed. Each camel carried two cylinder-shaped baskets packed with rock-salt. Jibrin stared at them as they couched the camels some distance away. They unloaded quickly, and turned their camels out to join ours among the tamarisk. Suddenly this remote spot in the desert, only a few minutes ago the most tranquil haven imaginable, was as busy as Piccadilly Circus.

'Those aren't Kababish,' Jibrin said. 'I never saw any Bedu who used baskets. From their dress you'd say they were villagers. I thought I knew all the tribes in the desert, but they don't belong to any tribe that I know!'

The French tourists immediately lost interest in us and scurried off to photograph the newcomers. We hung back until the tourists had gone off to make camp, then we approached the caravaneers. They had stripped off their jallabiyyas and turbans, and were wearing only woollen long-johns and singlets. They were certainly Arabs, not Sudanese townsmen, but their features were different from those of the Kababish. As we sat down among them, though, I could hear the accent of southern Egypt. They were Egyptian caravaneers on Sudanese territory – one of the most unexpected sights I had met with in all my travels in the Sudan. One of them, a shrivelled old man, told us: 'We are ʿAwazim – Bedu from the Kharja oasis in Egypt. We travel into the Sudan to get rock-salt from Al ʿAtrun.'

'I've been to Al ʿAtrun, but I've never seen or heard about Bedu from Egypt!'

'Ah, you've been to the Sudanese ʿAtrun. Our ʿAtrun is in a different place. No Sudanese know about it. It's beyond the oasis of Laqiyya, and beyond Merga, but its exact location is our secret. From Laqiyya we follow the old route called the Forty Days Road.'

The situation grew more intriguing by the minute. For years I had been searching for Bedouin who knew the Forty Days Road, the ancient caravan road that for millennia had joined Egypt to the Sudan. I had believed that the route was disused and forgotten since the British had halted the slave-trade along it a century ago. Even the veteran Ralph Bagnold – doyen of motor-explorers in the eastern Sahara – wrote: 'There is probably no one left alive who remembers the old trade along the "Forty Days Road".' Now, quite unexpectedly, I had discovered that the secret of the old route had been kept alive by the Egyptians. I did not dream then that in due course I would come to know some of these Egyptian Bedu almost as intimately as I knew the Kababish.

The ʿAwazim brought us tea in large enamel mugs and offered us packets of Cleopatra cigarettes, of which they had enormous quantities in their saddlebags. Cigarette-smoking was almost unknown among the Kababish, and Jibrin raised an eyebrow at their obvious affluence. He ran his practised desert eye over their camel-gear – their cylindrical baskets, now standing in ranks on flat bases, and their curious saddles – no more than a V-shaped wooden frame on a huge pad of sacking and palm-fibre. The old man showed us how the ensemble worked – the baskets were so tall that they stood higher than the camel's back, and were held in place by two pegs. As the camel rose it took the strain of the baskets, and when it was couched their flat bases simply rested on the ground. 'No lifting or lowering,' the old man said proudly. 'No ropes. Not a single knot to tie. One man can load and unload fifty camels without any trouble. We have these baskets made to our pattern by artisans, but we make the saddles ourselves!'

I asked if the ʿAwazim were still nomads.

'A generation ago there were those among us who lived in tents,' the old man said, 'but now the government has settled us into houses. We grow our own crops as well as having goats and cattle. We don't breed camels because there is little grazing in Kharja – we usually buy them in the market at Daraw. We are still Bedu, though.'

By now, the French had erected a line of two-man bivouac tents in the belly of the oasis, and Jibrin, never having seen such things before, was intrigued. He inspected one of them, felt the lightness of the material, and as a professional tent-dweller pronounced them 'suitable'. I was wondering what scathing remarks he would make about Christian meanness if they failed to offer us hospitality, but to my relief Jean-Yves invited us both to dinner after dark.

As we walked back to our camp afterwards, the normally silent Jibrin was full of talk: 'Did you see that, Omar? Every one of them had his own stool that could be folded up and put away. No sitting in the sand for them! Men and women eating together, but instead of eating with their hands out of a dish, everyone had his own plate – made of paper! And they changed the plate every time they changed the food. They ate with tools that I've never seen before – forks or whatever you call them. What that stuff was we ate only God knows – it looked like a lot of worms – it was quite disgusting, and I had to force myself to eat it. But that horrible yellow thing they gave us afterwards, with the bad smell, was too much. I just couldn't eat that.' He was referring to a very expensive variety of French cheese.

'At least you can't say they didn't know a guest!'

'No, they didn't fall short. But I've never seen women like those, showing their hair and their legs. Don't they feel ashamed?'

'What did you think of them?'

'Well, some of the women were quite nice, but the men looked like hyenas. So ugly! I can't understand how the women can sleep with them!'

The Bedu caravan set out at first light, and the tourists soon after, both heading for the Eyptian border. We let our camels graze while Jibrin filled half a sack with dates from the palm-trees, then began to saddle up. Before we left, Jibrin inspected the tourists' campsite and called me over, chuckling, to look at something they had left in the sand. It was a very large, black, leathery turd, smothered in ream upon ream of supersoft toilet paper. Jibrin was staring at it in wonder. 'Paper! No God but God, now I've seen everything!' he said.

As we tramped back across the lonely desert in our own footsteps, heading for the Nile, Jibrin told me, 'I think one day soon the Kababish will be like those Egyptian Bedu. Perhaps we'll start to grow crops and live in houses, and just keep a few camels to bring salt and water, and a handful of goats. Did you see how rich they were? They had everything, by God!' I could hear the envy in his voice. 'Perhaps we will go back to our lands if the rains come. Perhaps we will remain in the towns. Only God is all-knowing, but for the Bedu nothing will ever be the same again.'

It was tragic to witness the end of an era, I thought. But the wheel of change turned ineluctably, crushing all who would stand in its path. Man is an adaptive animal – he had adapted to this most extreme of environments. With his technical ingenuity even the elderly Westerners we had met at Selima, who knew virtually nothing about the desert, could survive here. The true threat to existence lies not in change, but in becoming entrenched in a rigid response to a universe which is itself always changing. No matter how successful such a response may be, time and change will ultimately render it worthless. The Bedu are perhaps history's most brilliant example of man's ability to adapt. They have endured precisely because their ways were not immutable – because they have always been able to ride and roll with the waves of change. In shifting to cultivation and motor-cars they were merely doing what they had always done, using the same penchant for adaptation they had employed for 4,000 years.

The dead man lay precisely where Jean-Yves had said, his skin parchment-yellow and stretched tight over his skull, lying in a foetal crouch under his ragged jallabiyya. He was partially covered with stones from the half-hearted effort the French had made to bury him on the hard ground. Jibrin took a long look at the taut, lifeless face and exclaimed, 'By God, I know that man! That is Falih of the Kababish! God have mercy upon him!' This far from the Nile there were no vultures, and his eyes were mercifully intact, but I shall never forget the rictus of suffering on his features as a terrible warning of the agonies of death by thirst. Near to him we found an empty plastic can that had once held motor-oil, and an army-surplus haversack containing some sorghum-flour and a pair of new leather shoes. Knowing we should have to report his death to the police on the river, we searched his pockets, hoping for some documents. Instead, we found them stuffed with refuse – a page of algebra torn from a child's exercise-book, a piece of a cigarette packet, part of a plastic bag, a sweet-wrapper, a ragged ribbon, a bit of newspaper. Jibrin grasped all these trifles in his hand and shook his head sadly as he examined them. 'I remember seeing him in Ed Debba,' he said. 'He was crazy even then. They say he was once a Sheikh, a rich man with fifty camels and a huge flock of sheep, famous for his hospitality. Then the drought came, and most of his animals died. He gave away the rest out of compassion for the suffering of others. Then he moved to the town, where his four children and his wife were taken by the sickness. He was left a beggar. I suppose his mind couldn't stand it. He took to wandering up and down the Nile as a madman, talking to himself and collecting this kind of rubbish. Falih was a Bedui. None knew better than him the dangers of walking out here without a camel. He must have realized his time was finished, and returned to the desert to die!'

We left Falih buried under a cairn of stones, another monument to the history of a landscape. Here, I thought, lay the last of the Bedu. Yet I knew deep down that I was mistaken: that in my search for the last of the Bedu, I had been hunting the snark. There are no last things. Individuals die, cultures change, life evolves, flowing always against the direction of time. In several billion years our sun, whose heat had flayed Falih to death, will burn out, and this planet will be no more. Yet those billions of years give life an almost infinite chance of survival. The adventure is only just beginning. Time present and time past are present in time future – the lessons life has learned through the Bedu will never be lost. As entities we wither, but as a process we continue. We shall change, but we shall survive. We shall survive.

BIBLIOGRAPHY

Abu Lughod, Lila, *Veiled Sentiments: Honor and Poetry in a Bedouin Society*, California, 1986.

Adams, William, *Nubia – Corridor to Africa*, London, 1977.

Al Baz, Farouk, and Maxwell, Ted, *Desert Landforms of SW Egypt: a Basis for Comparison with Mars*, Washington, 1982.

Al Faruqi, Ismael, and Lamya, Lois, *The Cultural Atlas of Islam*, 1986.

Armour, Robert, *Gods and Myths of Ancient Egypt*, Cairo, 1986.

Asad, Talal, *The Kababish Arabs – Authority and Consent in a Nomadic Tribe*, London, 1969.

Asher, Michael, *In Search of the Forty Days Road*, London, 1984.

Asher, Michael, *A Desert Dies*, London, 1986.

Asher, Michael, *Impossible Journey*, London, 1988.

Bagnold, Raph, 'Journeys in the Libyan Desert in 1929 and 1931', *Geographical Journal*, 1930.

Bagnold, Ralph, 'A Further Journey through the Libyan Desert', *Geographical Journal*, 1935.

Bagnold, Ralph, *Libyan Sands*, London, 1935.

Bagnold, Ralph, 'An Expedition to Gilf Kebir and Uwainat in 1938', *Geographical Journal*, 1938.

Bailey, Clinton, *Bedouin Poetry from Sinai and the Negev*, Oxford, 1991.

Barakat, Halim, *The Arab World – Society, Culture and State*, London, 1993.

Bates, Oric, *The Eastern Libyans*, London, 1914.
Beadnell, H., *An Egyptian Oasis: Kharga*, London, 1909.
Blackman, W. S., *The Fellahin of Upper Egypt*, London, 1927.
Browne, W. G., *Travels in Africa*, London, 1797.
Browning, Iain, *Palmyra*, London, 1979.
Browning, Iain, *Petra*, London, 1982.
Bulliet, Richard, *The Camel and the Wheel*, Cambridge, Mass., 1977.
Burckhardt, J. L., *Notes on Bedouins and Wahabys*, London, 1831.
Campbell, Joseph, *The Masks of God: Primitive Mythology*, London, 1959.
Caton-Thompson, G., and Gardner, E., 'The Prehistoric Geography of Kharja Oasis', *Geographical Journal*, 80, 1932.
Clark, J. Desmond (ed.), *Cambridge History of Africa: Volume 1*, Cambridge, 1982.
Cole, Donald Powell, *Nomads of the Nomads. The Al Murrah Bedouin of the Empty Quarter*, Chicago, 1979.
Cribb, Roger, *Nomads in Archaeology*, London, 1991.
Deledale-Rhodes, Janice, 'The True Nature of Doughty's Relationship with the Arabs', in *Explorations in Doughty's 'Arabia Deserta'*, ed. Steven E. Tabachnick, Georgia, 1987.
Dickson, H. R. P., *The Arab of the Desert*, London, 1948.
Doe, Brian, *Southern Arabia*, London, 1971.
Donner, Fred M., *The Early Islamic Conquests*, New York, 1981.
Doughty, Charles, *Travels in Arabia Deserta*, London, 1885.
Durrell, Lawrence, *The Alexandria Quartet*, London, 1968.
Eliot, T. S., *Collected Poems 1909*, London, 1966.
Fakhry, Ahmed, *Siwa Oasis*, Cairo, 1974.
Fedden, Robin, *Lebanon and Syria*, London, 1946.
Fiennes, Ranulph, *Atlantis of the Sands*, London, 1992.
Gabrieli, Francesco, *Mohammad and the Conquests of Islam*, 1968.
Glubb, John Bagot, 'The Bedouins of Northern Iraq', *Journal of the Royal Central Asian Society*, 1935.
Glubb, John Bagot, 'Arab Chivalry', *Journal of the Royal Central Asian Society*, 1937.

Groom, Nigel, *Frankincense and Myrrh*, London, 1983.
Harding-King, H. W., *Mysteries of the Libyan Desert*, London, 1925.
Hassanein, A. M., *Lost Oases*, London, 1925.
Haynes, C. Vance, *et al.*, 'Holocene Palaeontology of the Eastern Sahara: Selima Oasis', *Quaternary Science Review*, 1989.
Haynes, C. Vance, 'Oyo: a "Lost Oasis" of the Southern Libyan Desert', *Geographical Journal*, 155, 1989.
Helms, I., *Early Islamic Architecture of the Desert*, London, 1990.
Herodotus, *The Histories*, trans. A. de Selincourt, London, 1954.
Hitti, Philip, *History of the Arabs*, London, 1937.
Holt, P. M., Lambton, A. K. S., and Lewis, B. (eds.), *Cambridge History of Islam: Volume 1*, Cambridge, 1970.
Hourani, Albert, *A History of the Arab Peoples*, London, 1991.
Ingrams, Harold, *Arabia and the Isles*, London, 1952.
Janzen, Jorg, *Nomads of the Sultanate of Oman: Tradition and Development in Dhofar*, London, 1980.
Jarvis, Claude S., *Yesterday and Today in Sinai*, London, 1931.
Jarvis, Claude S., *Three Deserts*, London, 1936.
Johnson, Douglas L., *The Nature of Nomadism*, Chicago, 1974.
Kabbani, Rana, *Imperial Fictions*, London, 1986.
Kay, Shirley, *The Bedouin*, London, 1978.
Lancaster, William, *The Rwala Bedouin Today*, Cambridge, 1981.
Lawrence, T. E., *Seven Pillars of Wisdom*, London, 1935.
Lopez, Barry, *Arctic Dreams*, London, 1986.
Marx, Emanuel, *Bedouin of the Negev*, Manchester, 1967.
Marx, Emanuel, 'Are There Pastoral Nomads in the Middle East?', in *Pastoralism in the Levant*, 1992.
Murray, G. W., *The Sons of Ishmael*, London, 1935.
Musil, Alois, *The Manners and Customs of the Rwala Bedouin*, New York, 1928.
Palmer, E. H., *The Desert of the Exodus*, London, 1871.
Rodinson, Maxine, *The Arabs*, London, 1981.
Russell, Kenneth, W., *Ethnohistory of the Bedul Bedouin of Petra, Jordan*, Amman, 1993.

Shoup, J. A., *The Bedouin of Jordan: History and Sedentarisation*, MA thesis, unpublished, Utah, 1980.
Simpson, G. E., *The Heart of Libya: The Siwa Oasis, Its People, Customs and Sport*, London, 1929.
Sitwell, N. H. H., *The World the Romans Knew*, London, 1984.
Stookey, Robert W., *South Yemen: A Marxist Republic in Arabia*, London, 1982.
Sweet, Louise E., 'Camel Raiding of North Arabian Bedouin: a Mechanism of Ecological Evolution', *American Anthropologist*, 1965.
Thesiger, Wilfred, *Arabian Sands*, London, 1959.
Thomas, Bertram, *Arabia Felix*, London, 1932.
Thurman, Sybil, *Rivers of Sand*, 1984.
Tidrick, Kathryn, *Heart-Beguiling Araby: The English Romance with Arabia* (revised edition), London, 1989.
Vatikiotis, P. J., *The History of Egypt*, London, 1969.
Weir, Shelagh, *The Bedouin*, London, 1990.
Wellard, James, *The Great Sahara*, London, 1964.

INDEX

Proper names are indexed alphabetically according to the commonly used element in the names, and where they are prefixed with al, Ibn or bin, these words remain as prefixes but are ignored for purposes of alphabeticization, thus Ibn Khaldun is indexed under K.

INDEX

INDEX